D1107351

Calculus and Analytic Geometry

Calculus and analytic geometry

John A. Tierney

United States Naval Academy

Boston: Allyn and Bacon, Inc.

QA
303
T54

Copyright © 1968 by
Allyn and Bacon, Inc.
470 Atlantic Avenue
Boston, Mass. 02210

*All rights reserved. No part
of this book may be reproduced
in any form, or by any means,
without permission in writing
from the publisher.*

Printed in the United
States of America

*Library of Congress
Catalog Card Number:
68–13728*

Preface

The objective of this text is to present the underlying concepts of calculus and analytic geometry in a manner that the average student can understand and appreciate. Prerequisites are high school algebra, geometry, and trigonometry.

The analytic geometry of straight lines and very simple curves is presented in Chapter 2. Differential and integral calculus are developed in Chapters 3 and 4 and in later chapters the powerful methods of the calculus are applied to more advanced topics of analytic geometry. Thus the student is not confronted simultaneously with new concepts of both disciplines, and yet the two subjects are truly integrated. Chapter 4 contains a detailed development of the two fundamental theorems of the calculus. The first establishes the fact that differentiation and integration are inverse processes; the second applies the differential calculus to the evaluation of definite integrals.

Vectors are treated extensively and are employed throughout Chapter 15 in the study of three dimensional geometry. The important concept of limit of a sequence is introduced in Chapter 1 and utilized in the remainder of the book. Logical reasoning is stressed and several applications of the law of contraposition are included. The function concept, the major theme of modern mathematics, is developed in detail by means of numerous illustrative examples. Similar treatment is accorded the concepts of limit and continuity while more advanced concepts such as uniform continuity and uniform convergence are omitted. Considerable attention is given to the historical development of the subjects.

The problem lists are graded, beginning with many simple exercises, progressing to problems of moderate difficulty, and concluding with a few problems which will challenge the best students.

Set terminology is employed although set notation and logical quantifiers are omitted. This is due to the fact that many students are confused by an excessively concise notation. Since the language is modern, instructors who wish to do so can easily employ a more sophisticated notation.

Although ϵ-δ definitions are carefully stated and discussed, manipulations of formal epsilonics are kept to a minimum. Many important theorems are stated and illustrated but not proved; references to proofs are given. This approach is consistent with the recommendations of the CUPM (Committee on the Undergraduate Program in Mathematics). The 1965 Committee Report to the Mathematical Association of America states that "it is the level of rigor in the student's

29827

understanding which counts and not only the rigor of the text or lecture presented to him," and that "mathematical understanding is a matter of degree, and some kinds of informal understandings can be adequate for a long time."

This is an attempt to produce a book which has a mathematical flavor but which is not at the same time a text on real analysis. A formula-type, cookbook approach to the calculus can be very boring, while an overly sophisticated approach can be terrifying. It is my hope that the readers of this book will find their study of man's outstanding intellectual achievement a richly rewarding educational experience.

John A. Tierney

Contents

Chapter
1

Preliminary concepts

1.1   The Real Number System

The principal elements employed in analytic geometry and calculus are the real numbers. Although we will not give a precise mathematical definition of a real number, it will be sufficient for the student to regard these numbers as elements satisfying the usual laws of operation employed in elementary algebra. For example, if a, b, c, and d denote arbitrary real numbers, the following laws hold:

(i) Commutative laws for addition and multiplication:

$$a + b = b + a, \qquad ab = ba.$$

(ii) Associative laws for addition and multiplication:

$$a + (b + c) = (a + b) + c, \qquad a(bc) = (ab)c.$$

(iii) Distributive law:

$$a(b + c) = ab + ac.$$

The real numbers also satisfy the usual laws applying to inequalities. For example:

(i) If $a < b$ and $b < c$, then $a < c$.
(ii) If $a < b$, then $a + c < b + c$.
(iii) If $a < c$ and $b < d$, then $a + b < c + d$; etc.

It is also convenient to think of the set of real numbers as the totality of numbers representable by infinite decimals (repeating and nonrepeating). The real number 2/3 is represented by $0.666 \cdots$, the real number π is represented by $3.14159 \cdots$, etc. The number 3/2 is represented either by $1.500 \cdots$ or by $1.499 \cdots$.

The student is already familiar with the following members of the real number system:

$$0, \ \pm 1, \ \pm 2, \ \pm 3, \ \cdots.$$

These might be termed integral real numbers, but we will call them integers. Although there is a logical distinction between the set of integers and that subset of the real numbers which corresponds to the integers, this distinction need not concern us. The integers include the positive integers, the negative integers, and zero.

A convenient geometric interpretation of the integers is obtained by drawing a straight line and associating an arbitrary point on this line with the integer zero. A second point on the line is chosen, also arbitrary except that it is distinct from the first point, and this second point is associated with the integer one. The arbitrary choice of the distance between the two points establishes a number scale on the line. The point associated with the number 2 is the point which is the same distance from number 1 as 1 is from zero, and which is in the same direction from 1 as 1 is from zero. The point associated with the number negative 1 is the point that is the same distance from zero as 1 is from zero, but which is in the opposite direction. Continuing in this fashion, a correspondence is obtained between the integers and a subset of the points on the line. Although not essential, it is customary to draw the line in horizontal position and to locate the points corresponding to the positive integers on the right half of the line, as shown in Fig. 1.1. The line is called the x-axis, the point corresponding to zero the origin, the right half of the line the positive x-axis, and the left half the negative x-axis.

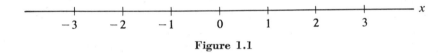

Figure 1.1

We next form the quotient p/q, where p and q are arbitrary integers except that q must be different from zero. Numbers of this form are rational real numbers, but we will find it convenient to refer to them as rational numbers. We now associate points of the x-axis with the rational numbers. If $q = 1$ we use the same correspondence we used in Fig. 1.1. The manner of locating points corresponding to rational numbers when $q \neq 1$ will be illustrated by two examples.

Example 1.   Locate the point corresponding to 3/4.

The portion of the x-axis from 0 to 1 is divided into four equal parts by inserting three points as shown in Fig. 1.2. The right-most point of these three points corresponds to 3/4, the others to 1/4 and 2/4 = 1/2 as shown.

Example 2.   Locate the point corresponding to $-5/3$.

Since $-5/3$ in Fig. 1.2 is between -2 and -1, the portion of the x-axis from -2 to -1 is divided into three equal parts by inserting two points as shown in Fig. 1.2. The left-most of these points corresponds to $-5/3$, the other to $-4/3$, as shown.

It is easy to see that the scheme described will locate one and only one point on the x-axis corresponding to a given rational number p/q. One might easily

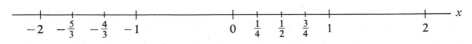

Figure 1.2

conclude that every point on the x-axis corresponds (by the same scheme) to some rational number p/q. This seems reasonable, since the arithmetic mean or average $\frac{1}{2}(x_1 + x_2)$ of two distinct rational numbers x_1 and x_2 is also a rational number and, furthermore, lies between x_1 and x_2. (See Problem 13 of Problem List 2.) This makes it appear that if one could locate all the points corresponding to the rational numbers, he would use up or exhaust all the points on the x-axis. It is a remarkable fact that there exist points on the x-axis which do not correspond to rational numbers. We shall locate one such point. In Fig. 1.3, $ABCD$ is a unit square, A and D coincide with the points 0 and 1 on the x-axis, and diagonal $AC = AE$. By the Pythagorean theorem

$$(AC)^2 = (AD)^2 + (DC)^2 = 1 + 1 = 2,$$

and hence if point E corresponds to a rational number x, it follows that

$$x^2 = 2.$$

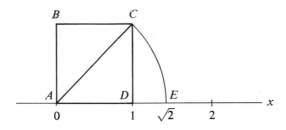

Figure 1.3

But if x is a rational number, it is possible to write x in the form $x = p/q$, where p and q are integers. We assume that p and q are not both even integers, since p and q can be so chosen. Then, since

$$x^2 = \frac{p^2}{q^2} = 2,$$

$$p^2 = 2q^2$$

and p^2 is even. Thus p is even; otherwise its square would not be even. Since p is even, p^2 is divisible by 4. Therefore $q^2 = p^2/2$ is divisible by 2 and q^2 is even, from which it follows that q is even. This is impossible, since we originally chose p and q not both even. It follows that there is no rational number whose square is 2; that is, the square root of 2 is irrational.

Another example of an irrational number is furnished by the number π, the ratio of the circumference of a circle to its diameter.

The existence of irrational numbers was discovered by the Greeks during the

Fifth Century B.C. This discovery precipitated the first great crisis in mathematics, since it invalidated much of Greek geometry. The crisis was resolved when the Greek mathematician Eudoxus (408–355 B.C.) devised the first logically satisfactory method for treating irrational numbers. His "Theory of Proportion," which parallels closely the modern theory of irrational numbers, was reproduced in Book V of Euclid's *Elements*.

More advanced courses include a logical development of the number system of algebra. It will be sufficient for our purposes to assume that the real numbers are in one-to-one correspondence with the points of the x-axis. This means that to every real number there corresponds one and only one point on the x-axis, and that to every point on the x-axis there corresponds one and only one real number.

We will have occasion later to deal with complex numbers, which are numbers of the form $a + bi$, where a and b are real numbers and $i^2 = -1$. We will also deal with elements called vectors, to be defined in Chapter 15. But unless we state otherwise, whenever we refer to a number we will mean a real number.

PROBLEM LIST 1

1. Locate on the x-axis the points corresponding to (a) 3, (b) −2, (c) 4/5, (d) 13/4, (e) −8/3.

2. Locate on the x-axis the points corresponding to (a) 2, (b) −4, (c) 3/5, (d) 15/4, (e) −7/3.

3. Locate approximately on the x-axis the points corresponding to (a) $\sqrt{5}$, (b) $\sqrt{6}$, (c) $\sqrt[3]{-9}$, (d) $\pi/3$, (e) $\sqrt{2} + \pi$.

4. Locate approximately on the x-axis the points corresponding to (a) $\sqrt{3}$, (b) $\sqrt{10}$, (c) $\sqrt[3]{-10}$, (d) π, (e) $\sqrt{3} + \sqrt{2}$.

5. Let a/b and c/d be rational numbers. Show that their sum, difference, and product are also rational. Is their quotient $a/b \div c/d$ also rational?

6. Prove that the following numbers are irrational: (a) $\sqrt{3}$, (b) $\sqrt{6}$, (c) $\sqrt[3]{3}$, (d) $1 - \sqrt{2}$, (e) $\sqrt{2} + \sqrt{3}$.

7. Let a square have diagonal d and side x. Show that there is no real number k such that $d = mk$ and $x = nk$, where m and n are positive integers. Thus, no matter how short a length k a line segment may have, it will never be contained an integral number of times in both d and x. The diagonal d and the side x are said to be incommensurable, meaning that they have no common measure.

1.2   *The Square Root of a Real Number*

The square root of a real number x is a number y such that $y^2 = x$. If x is positive, it has two real square roots. For example, the square root of 4 is either $+2$ or -2. We use the sign $\sqrt{}$ to denote the positive square root of a positive real number. This is called the principal square root.

Example. $\sqrt{4} = 2$.

The student is familiar with this convention from his study of algebra. The quadratic formula gives the roots of $x^2 - 6x + 8 = 0$ as $3 \pm \sqrt{1}$. If $\sqrt{1}$ denoted both ± 1, it would be redundant to give the roots as $3 \pm \sqrt{1}$. We would write instead $3 + \sqrt{1}$. The convention is employed so that we will know which square root we are denoting.

The real number zero has only one square root, which is the real number zero. $\sqrt{0} = 0$.

A negative number does not have a real square root, since the square of a real number is never negative.

1.3   *The Absolute Value of a Real Number*

The absolute value of a real number x, written $|x|$, is equal to x if $x \geqslant 0$, and is equal to $-x$ if $x < 0$.

The absolute value of a real number indicates how far the number is from the origin on the x-axis, but does not indicate whether the number is positive or negative.

Examples. $|5| = 5, |0| = 0, |-3| = 3$.

Similarly, $|b - a|$ indicates how far b is from a on the x-axis, but does not indicate whether b is to the left or right of a.

Examples. $|7 - 5| = 2, |3 - 5| = 2$.

Another way to obtain the absolute value of a real number is to square it and then take the nonnegative square root. That is,

$$|x| = \sqrt{x^2}.$$

Thus we could define the absolute value of a real number as the nonnegative square root of its square.

We now prove two useful theorems.

Theorem 1-I.   The absolute value of a product is equal to the product of the absolute values of the factors.

   Proof. $|xy| = \sqrt{(xy)^2} = \sqrt{x^2 y^2} = \sqrt{x^2}\sqrt{y^2} = |x||y|$.

Theorem 1-II.   The absolute value of a sum is less than or equal to the sum of the absolute values of the terms.

   Proof.   Let x and y be arbitrary real numbers. It is simple to verify that

$$-|x| \leqslant x \leqslant |x|$$

and

$$-|y| \leqslant y \leqslant |y|.$$

   Adding, we obtain

$$-(|x| + |y|) \leqslant x + y \leqslant |x| + |y|.$$

Since $-k \leqslant u \leqslant k$ implies $|u| \leqslant k$ (see Problem 3 of Problem List 2) we conclude that

$$|x + y| \leqslant |x| + |y|.$$

Theorem 1-II is called the triangle inequality. We will learn why this designation is appropriate when we study vectors.

1.4　*Operations Involving Zero*

The following relations hold where a is an arbitrary real number:

$$0 + a = a + 0 = a - 0 = a,$$
$$a + (-a) = a - a = a \cdot 0 = 0 \cdot a = 0 \cdot 0$$
$$= 0 + 0 = 0,$$
$$0 - a = -a.$$

The quotient a/b of two real numbers is defined as the unique real number c, if it exists, such that $bc = a$. When we apply this definition we always get a unique answer except when $b = 0$. For example, $6/2 = 3$, since $2 \cdot 3 = 6$. Or $0/5 = 0$, since $5 \cdot 0 = 0$.

If we apply the definition of division to $4/0$ we see that there is no real number c such that $0 \cdot c = 4$. If we apply the definition of division to $0/0$ we see that there is no unique real number c such that $0 \cdot c = 0$. Thus it is impossible to divide any real number by 0, since the application of the definition of division does not yield an answer. We say that *division by zero is undefined*.

Example.　The expression x/x has the value 1 when $x \neq 0$. We could write $x/x \equiv 1$ for $x \neq 0$.

When $x = 0$ we sometimes say that x/x assumes the indeterminate form $0/0$. It is preferable to say that x/x has no value or is undefined when $x = 0$.

1.5　*Inequalities*

Since inequalities play an important role in our subject, we now review the definition of the symbol $>$.

If $a - b$ is positive, we say that a is greater than b and we write

$$a > b.$$

This defines the symbol $>$. The statement

$$c < d$$

means that $d > c$ and hence that $d - c$ is positive. The statement $a \geqslant b$ means that either $a > b$ or $a = b$. Similarly, $c \leqslant d$ means that either $c < d$ or $c = d$. Geometrically, $a > b$ means that a is to the right of b on the x-axis. Any number on the x-axis is greater than every number to its left and less than every number to its right.

Examples. $3 > 2, 0 < 4, 0 > -3, -2 < 1, -4 < -3.$

1.6   Intervals

The set of all real numbers that are greater than or equal to a and less than or equal to b is called a closed interval and is denoted by

$$a \leqslant x \leqslant b.$$

If a and b are excluded, the set is called an open interval and is denoted by

$$a < x < b.$$

The set of real numbers x satisfying

$$a \leqslant x < b$$

is a half-open interval which includes a but not b. Similarly, $a < x \leqslant b$ is half-open and includes b but not a.

The set of real numbers greater than or equal to a is denoted by

$$a \leqslant x < \infty,$$

read as "x greater than or equal to a and less than infinity." Infinity is not a number; we merely use the symbol ∞ because it often enables us to write statements concisely. The symbol ∞ is discussed more fully in Sec. 1.7.

Example 1.   The set of all real numbers is denoted by

$$-\infty < x < \infty.$$

Example 2.   The set of negative real numbers is denoted by

$$-\infty < x < 0.$$

Example 3.   The set of points on the x-axis from $x = 1$ to $x = 2$, including 1 and 2, is denoted by

$$1 \leqslant x \leqslant 2.$$

Due to the correspondence between sets of real numbers and sets of points on the x-axis, we can always regard a set of real numbers as a set of points on the x-axis, and vice versa.

Example 4.   The interval $-a \leqslant x \leqslant a$, where $a > 0$, is often denoted by

$$|x| \leqslant a.$$

The complement of this interval, meaning the set of all real numbers not contained in $|x| \leqslant a$, is denoted by $|x| > a$. This is a concise way of denoting the set of all real numbers satisfying either

$$-\infty < x < -a \qquad \text{or} \qquad a < x < \infty.$$

PROBLEM LIST 2

1. What is the square root of 9? What is the value of $\sqrt{9}$?

2. Evaluate **(a)** $\sqrt{4}$, **(b)** $-\sqrt{9}$, **(c)** $\sqrt{(-3)^2}$, **(d)** $\sqrt{0}$.

3. Prove that $-k \leqslant u \leqslant k$ implies $|u| \leqslant k$.

4. Evaluate **(a)** $|-3|$, **(b)** $|3|$, **(c)** $|0|$, **(d)** $|-3+4|$, **(e)** $|-4-5|$, **(f)** $|-x|-|x|$, **(g)** $|x|^2 + x^2$.

5. Prove that $|x-y| \leqslant |x| + |y|$.

6. Prove that $|x| - |y| \leqslant |x-y|$.

7. Evaluate **(a)** $0+0$, **(b)** $0 \cdot 0$, **(c)** $6/0$, **(d)** $0/7$, **(e)** $0/0$.

8. What is the value of
$$\frac{(x-1)(x+2)}{(x-3)(x+4)}$$
when x equals **(a)** 1, **(b)** 2, **(c)** 3, **(d)** -2, **(e)** -4?

9. What is the value of $(x^2 - 4)/(x-2)$ when x equals **(a)** 1, **(b)** 2, **(c)** 3, **(d)** 4, **(e)** -2?

10. Which of the following are true?
    (a) $3 < 2$, **(b)** $-3 > -5$, **(c)** $0 < -4$, **(d)** $2 > -3$, **(e)** $|x| > x$, **(f)** $-3 \geqslant -3$.

11. Identify the following sets of points on the x-axis by making a separate sketch for each set:

    (a) $-1 < x < 3$.   **(g)** $|x-2| < 1$.
    (b) $x \geqslant 2$.   **(h)** $|x-3| > 2$.
    (c) $x \leqslant -1$.   **(i)** $-\infty < x < 0$.
    (d) $x \geqslant 0$.   **(j)** $1 < |x-2| < 5$.
    (e) $|\dot{x}| \leqslant 2$.   **(k)** $2 < |x+3| < 4$.
    (f) $|x| \geqslant 3$.   **(l)** $x < x^2$.

12. Prove that $|x+y+z| \leqslant |x| + |y| + |z|$.

13. If rational number a/b is greater than rational number c/d, show that their arithmetic mean m is rational and that $c/d < m < a/b$.

1.7 *Sequences*

A sequence is a set of real numbers in one-to-one correspondence with the positive integers. The sequence whose elements are
$$x_1, x_2, x_3, \cdots, x_n, \cdots$$
is denoted by the symbol $\{x_n\}$.

The sequence
$$\frac{1}{1}, \quad \frac{1}{2}, \quad \frac{1}{3}, \quad \frac{1}{4}, \quad \cdots, \quad \frac{1}{n}, \quad \cdots$$
is denoted by $\{1/n\}$.

A variable is a symbol, such as x, that may take any value in a given set of elements. If the set of elements consists of real numbers, x is called a real variable. We are frequently interested in what happens when a real variable x assumes values that are elements of a sequence $\{x_n\}$, in the order

$$x_1, x_2, x_3, \cdots, x_n, \cdots.$$

Example 1.   If x takes on the values

$$\frac{1}{1}, \frac{1}{2}, \frac{1}{3}, \cdots, \frac{1}{n}, \cdots,$$

it is clear that x gets arbitrarily close to zero. We say "arbitrarily close" because we can make $1/n$ as close to zero as we please merely by taking n sufficiently large. We write

$$\lim_{n \to \infty} \frac{1}{n} = 0,$$

read as "the limit as n becomes infinite of $1/n$ is zero," and we say that the sequence $\{1/n\}$ has limit zero or converges to zero.

We now state a formal definition of what we mean when we say that a sequence has a limit.

Definition.   A sequence $\{x_n\}$ has a limit L if for every positive number ϵ there exists a positive integer N such that

$$|x_n - L| < \epsilon \qquad \text{for all } n \geqslant N.$$

This is a precise way of saying that we can get arbitrarily close (within ϵ) to L and remain arbitrarily close by going sufficiently far in the sequence. It is only by employing precise definitions of this type that we are able to know what we are talking about in analysis, the branch of mathematics which deals with limits and infinite processes.

Geometrically, the sequence $\{x_n\}$ of points converges to L if, after omitting the first $N - 1$ points of the sequence, all remaining points of the sequence lie in the interval

$$L - \epsilon < x < L + \epsilon.$$

It should be emphasized that the value of N is determined in general by the size of ϵ. If a smaller ϵ is assigned, the corresponding value of N will in general be larger. The important fact is that a suitable N exists.

In our example, $|(1/n) - 0| = 1/n$ will be less than ϵ whenever $n > 1/\epsilon$. If $\epsilon = 0.001$ is specified, $N = 1001$ makes $1/n < 0.001$ for all $n \geqslant 1001$.

If a sequence does not have a limit, we say that it diverges.

Example 2.   The sequence

$$2.1, 2.01, 2.001, \cdots, 2 + (0.1)^n, \cdots$$

converges to 2, since

$$|2 + (0.1)^n - 2| = (0.1)^n$$

is clearly less than any $\epsilon > 0$ for all n sufficiently large.

Example 3.   If x assumes the values

$$2, 4, 8, 16, \cdots, 2^n, \cdots,$$

it is clear that x eventually becomes larger than any preassigned number M, however large M may be. It is essentially a question of what happens to the nth term 2^n as n increases indefinitely through positive integral values. We express this by writing

$$\lim_{n \to \infty} 2^n = \infty,$$

read as "the limit as n becomes infinite of 2^n is infinity." Infinity is not a number and the statement merely means that if an arbitrary number M is specified, then there exists a value of $n = N$ such that $2^n > M$ for all values of $n \geqslant N$. For example, if $M = 1000$, an acceptable N is $N = 10$, since $2^n > 1000$ for all $n \geqslant 10$.

Geometrically, the statement

$$\lim_{n \to \infty} x_n = \infty$$

means that if we choose a point M on the x-axis, regardless of how far M is to the right of the origin, there will exist an $n = N$ such that all the points

$$x_N, x_{N+1}, x_{N+2}, x_{N+3}, \cdots$$

will lie to the right of M.

The sequence $\{2^n\}$ is but one of many sequences along which x may become infinite. Examples of other such sequences are

$$\{n\}, \quad \{n^2\}, \quad \{10n\}.$$

Although these sequences do not possess limits and hence diverge, we find it more descriptive to say that they have limit $+\infty$.

Example 4.   If x takes on the values

$$-1, -4, -9, \cdots, -n^2, \cdots$$

we write

$$\lim_{n \to \infty} (-n^2) = -\infty.$$

All members of the sequence $\{-n^2\}$, after a certain point, lie to the left of an arbitrarily chosen point on the x-axis. Sequences of this type are divergent, but we find it convenient to say that they have limit $-\infty$.

Example 5.   The sequence $\{2\}$, whose elements are

$$2, 2, 2, \cdots, 2, \cdots,$$

has limit $L = 2$. Hence it is possible for some or all elements of $\{x_n\}$ to assume the limit L approached by $\{x_n\}$.

A more complicated example is afforded by the sequence $\{\sin(n\pi/2)/n\}$, in which x_n assumes the limit $L = 0$ of $\{x_n\}$ an infinite number of times and also assumes an infinite number of nonzero values.

Example 6.   The sequence

$$-1, 2, -3, 4, \cdots, (-1)^n n, \cdots$$

does not approach ∞, $-\infty$, or converge to a limit L. We merely say that it diverges.

Example 7.   As n increases, the nth term of the sequence

$$1, 0, 1, 0, 1, 0, 1, \cdots, \frac{1 - (-1)^n}{2}, \cdots$$

oscillates between 1 and 0, and hence this sequence diverges.

Example 8.   The sequence

$$\left(1 + \frac{1}{1}\right)^1, \left(1 + \frac{1}{2}\right)^2, \left(1 + \frac{1}{3}\right)^3, \cdots, \left(1 + \frac{1}{n}\right)^n, \cdots$$

converges to a limit L. One cannot guess the value of L by inspection; moreover, it is far from obvious that L exists. At this time we state only that $L \neq 1$. This sequence will play an important role in our later work.

Example 9.   A prime number p is an integer greater than 1 whose only divisors are 1 and p. Euclid (about 300 B.C.) demonstrated that infinitely many primes exist. The sequence

$$\frac{1}{2}, \frac{1}{3}, \frac{1}{5}, \frac{1}{7}, \cdots, \frac{1}{p_n}, \cdots,$$

where p_n denotes the nth prime, converges to 0. In the present state of our knowledge about primes, it is impossible to write the nth term in terms of n, since no known formula for p_n exists. We cite this example to emphasize that a sequence is determined if it has a first element x_1 and if each element has a unique successor.

PROBLEM LIST 3

1. Write the first four elements of each of the following sequences:

(a) $\{n^2\}$.   (e) $\{\pi\}$.

(b) $\{(-1)^n n^2\}$.   (f) $\left\{\frac{(-1)^n}{n}\right\}$.

(c) $\left\{\frac{n-1}{n}\right\}$.   (g) $\left\{\frac{2^{n-1}}{n}\right\}$.

(d) $\{(1 + n)^{1/n}\}$.   (h) $\left\{\frac{\cos (n\pi/2)}{n}\right\}$.

2. Prove that the following sequences converge. State the limit of each sequence.

(a) $\left\{\frac{1}{2n}\right\}$.   (e) $\{3 - (0.01)^n\}$.

(b) $\left\{\frac{n+1}{n}\right\}$.   (f) $\{5 + (0.1)^n\}$.

(c) $\left\{\frac{n-2}{n}\right\}$.   (g) $\left\{\frac{1}{n^2}\right\}$.

(d) $\left\{\frac{n}{n+1}\right\}$.   (h) $\left\{\frac{n}{2n+1}\right\}$.

3. Investigate the convergence or divergence of the following sequences:

(a) $\{n^3\}$.

(f) $\left\{\dfrac{2n+1}{n}\right\}$.

(b) $\{(-1)^n n^2\}$.

(g) $\left\{2 - \left(\dfrac{1}{3^n}\right)\right\}$.

(c) $\{3\}$.

(h) $\left\{\left(\dfrac{2}{3}\right)^n\right\}$.

(d) $\{1 - (-1)^n\}$.

(i) $\left\{n \sin\left(\dfrac{n\pi}{2}\right)\right\}$.

(e) $\left\{\dfrac{1-(-1)^n}{n}\right\}$.

(j) $\left\{\dfrac{n}{3n-1}\right\}$.

4. The sequence $\{3 - (1/2^n)\}$ converges to 3. Find the smallest value of N such that $|3 - (1/2^n) - 3| < \epsilon$ for all $n \geqslant N$ if (a) $\epsilon = 0.01$, (b) $\epsilon = 0.001$, (c) $\epsilon = 0.0001$.

5. The sequence $\{3^n\}$ has limit $+\infty$. Find the smallest value of N such that $3^n > M$ for all $n \geqslant N$ if (a) $M = 100$, (b) $M = 1000$, (c) $M = 10,000$.

6. The sequence $\{-n^2\}$ has limit $-\infty$. Find the smallest value of N such that $-n^2 < M$ for all $n \geqslant N$ if (a) $M = -100$, (b) $M = -1000$, (c) $M = -10,000$.

7. Prove that a sequence cannot converge to two different limits.

8. Prove that $\{1/\sqrt{n}\}$ converges.

9. Prove that $\{(-1)^n (n+1)/n\}$ diverges.

10. Prove that $\{\sin(n\pi/2)/n\}$ converges.

11. (a) Write the first five terms of the sequence $\{x_n\}$ defined by

$$\begin{cases} x_1 = 3, \\ x_n = x_{n-1}^2 + \dfrac{1}{x_{n-1}} & \text{for } n \geqslant 2. \end{cases}$$

(A sequence defined by giving the first term and the nth term in terms of its predecessors is said to be defined recursively.)

(b) Write the first ten terms of the sequence $\{x_n\}$ defined recursively by

$$\begin{cases} x_1 = 0, \\ x_2 = 1, \\ x_n = x_{n-1} + x_{n-2} & \text{for } n \geqslant 3. \end{cases}$$

This is the Fibonacci sequence which was first encountered by Fibonacci (1175–1250), also known as Leonardo of Pisa, in a problem involving the offspring of rabbits. The Fibonacci numbers have an extensive literature.

1.8 Functions

A mathematical function is a correspondence between two sets of elements D and R such that each element in D corresponds to one and only one element in R. The function concept, first introduced by the German mathematician and philosopher Gottfried Wilhelm Leibniz (1646–1716), one of the discoverers of the calculus, plays a major role in mathematics. In fact, it is the central concept of modern mathematics.

If D and R are sets of real numbers, the function is called a real-valued function of a real variable, and it is such functions with which we concern ourselves. D is called the domain of the function and R the range of the function. Let f be a function, x an arbitrary element of the domain D of f, and y the element of R which f associates with x. Then we write

$$y = f(x),$$

read as "y equals f of x."

This notation is due to the Swiss mathematician Leonard Euler (1707–1783), a textbook writer as well as a brilliant mathematician of first rank. It is a tribute to Euler that his notation for a function has persisted to this day. However, his notation is slightly misleading because it implies that y is the function, whereas the function is actually the correspondence f while $y = f(x)$ is the functional value corresponding to x. We say that $f(x)$ denotes the value of f at x. A function f is also called a mapping or transformation of the set D into the set R.

The following equivalent definition of a function f is often employed:

A function f is a set of ordered pairs (x, y) no two of which have the same first element x.

In this definition, x denotes an element of the domain D and $y = f(x)$ denotes an element of the range R. We say the pairs are "ordered" because it matters that we write x (the element of D) first, and y (the corresponding element of R) last. The pairs $(2, 3)$ and $(3, 2)$ are *different* ordered pairs.

Example 1.   Let f be defined by $y = f(x) = c$, where c is a constant.

This is called the constant function, since y is constant for all values of x. D is the entire set of real numbers and R consists of c alone.

Example 2.   Let f be defined by $y = f(x) = x$.

This is called the identity function, since y is the same as x for all x. D is the set of all real numbers, and R coincides with D.

Example 3.   Let f be defined by $y = f(x) = x^2$.

This is a special case of the more general set of algebraic functions called polynomials. D is the set of real numbers and R is the set of nonnegative real numbers. The following illustrate that $f(u)$ is the value of $f(x)$ with x replaced by u:

$$f(3) = 3^2 = 9$$
$$f(0) = 0^2 = 0$$
$$f(a) = a^2$$
$$f(a^2) = (a^2)^2 = a^4$$
$$f(t + 1) = (t + 1)^2$$
$$f(t + h) - f(t) = (t + h)^2 - t^2 = 2th + h^2$$
$$f^3(2t) = [f(2t)]^3 = [(2t)^2]^3 = 64t^6.$$

Example 4.   Let f be defined by $y = f(x) = \sqrt{x}$.

Then D is the set of nonnegative real numbers and R coincides with D. We do not allow x to be negative because we are interested in real functions only.

Whenever a function f is given by an algebraic formula, it is understood that the domain D is the set of all real numbers x for which $f(x)$ is real unless the domain D is otherwise specified. It should be emphasized, however, that a function is never determined before its domain is specified. This convention merely specifies the domain by implication.

Example 5.   Let f be defined by $y = f(x) = \sin x$. D is the set of all real numbers while R is the set $-1 \leqslant y \leqslant 1$. This is an example of a trigonometric function.

Example 6.   Let f be defined by $V = f(r) = \pi r^2 h$.

This function exhibits the correspondence between the volume V of a right-circular cylinder and its radius r. The height h must be regarded as fixed, although later we will remove this restriction by considering real functions of two variables.

We might wish to regard r as fixed and study the correspondence between V and h. We could then write

$$V = g(h) = \pi r^2 h$$

where the function is denoted by the letter g to distinguish it from the function f. Observe that $f(3) = 9\pi h$, whereas $g(3) = 3\pi r^2$.

Example 7.   Let f be defined by $y = f(x) = |x| = \sqrt{x^2}$.

This is the absolute value function. D is the set of real numbers and R is the set of nonnegative real numbers.

This function can also be defined as follows:

$$f(x) = \begin{cases} x & \text{if} & x \geqslant 0 \\ -x & \text{if} & x < 0 \end{cases}.$$

Thus we see that a function need not be given by a single algebraic formula. Examples of functions defined by more than one expression abound in both pure and applied mathematics. The following is another such example.

Example 8.   A uniform sphere of radius a and mass m exerts a force of F pounds, directed toward the center of the sphere, on a unit mass which is r feet from the center of the sphere. The function f denoting the correspondence between F and r is given by

$$F = f(r) = \begin{cases} \dfrac{mr}{a^3} & \text{for} & 0 \leqslant r < a \\ \dfrac{m}{r^2} & \text{for} & r \geqslant a \end{cases}$$

If the unit mass is inside the sphere, F is found from mr/a^3; otherwise it is found from m/r^2.

The correspondence between F and r is a consequence of Newton's law of universal gravitation. Sir Isaac Newton (1642–1727), generally considered one of the outstanding mathematicians of all time, developed the calculus while formulating his system of Newtonian mechanics.

Example 9.   Let p_n denote the nth prime number. Then $p_n = f(n)$ defines a function f even though no known formula exists for $f(n)$. It is only necessary that there exist a unique prime number corresponding to each positive integer n. The prime 2 corresponds to 1, the prime 3 corresponds to 2, etc. D is the set of positive integers and R is the set of primes.

This example makes it clear that a sequence is a function whose domain is the set of positive integers.

Example 10.   Let f be defined by $y = f(x) = x/x$.

This function has the value 1 for all values of x except $x = 0$. When $x = 0$, there is no corresponding value of y and we say that the function is undefined for $x = 0$. The domain D is the set of all real numbers, excluding 0, and the range R contains but one element, the number 1. The function f is not identical with the function g defined by

$$y = g(x) \equiv 1.$$

The following function h, however, is identical with the function g. Let h be defined by

$$y = h(x) = \begin{cases} \dfrac{x}{x} & \text{for} \quad x \neq 0 \\ 1 & \text{for} \quad x = 0 \end{cases}.$$

It is now correct to write $g(x) \equiv h(x)$.

PROBLEM LIST 4

1. If $f(x) = x^2 + 1$, find

    (a) $f(0)$,
    (b) $f(1)$,
    (c) $f(a)$,
    (d) $f(b)$,
    (e) $f(a + b)$,
    (f) $f(ab)$,
    (g) $f(-3)$,
    (h) $f(x + h)$,
    (i) $f(x + h) - f(x)$,
    (j) $f(2x)$,
    (k) $f(\sqrt{x})$,
    (l) $f(t^2 + 1)$.

2. If $f(x) = (x^2 - 4)/(x - 2)$, find

    (a) $(f(1)$,
    (b) $f(0)$,
    (c) $f(2)$,
    (d) $f(-2)$,
    (e) $f(-x)$,
    (f) $f(2/3)$,
    (g) $f(2 + \epsilon)$,
    (h) $f(x + h)$,
    (i) $f(x - h)$,
    (j) $f(x) + f(-x)$.

3. Describe the domain D and range R of the function defined by

    (a) $y = x^2 + 1$,   (b) $y = \sqrt{x - 1}$,

(c) $y = 5$,   **(h)** $y = \sqrt{1 - x^2}$,

(d) $y = \dfrac{1}{x}$,   **(i)** $y = (\sqrt{x})^2$,

(e) $y = \dfrac{2x}{x}$,   **(j)** $y = 4 - x^2$,

(f) $\{n^2\}$,   **(k)** $y = |\sin x|$,

(g) $y = \cos x$,   **(l)** $\left\{\dfrac{1}{n}\right\}$.

4. Describe the domain D and range R of the function defined by

    (a) $y = x^2 - 1$,   **(g)** $y = 1 - \cos x$,

    (b) $y = 3x - 5$,   **(h)** $y = \dfrac{1}{x - 1}$,

    (c) $y = x - |x|$,   **(i)** $y = \dfrac{1}{x^2 + 1}$,

    (d) $y = \dfrac{x}{|x|}$,   **(j)** $y = x + |x|$,

    (e) $y = \sqrt{4 - x^2}$,   **(k)** $y = x^2 + 2x + 2$,

    (f) $y = \dfrac{x}{x - 1}$,   **(l)** $\left\{\sin\left(\dfrac{n\pi}{2}\right)\right\}$.

5. For the function f defined by $f(x) = \sqrt{x}$, show that

$$\frac{f(x + h) - f(x)}{h} = \frac{1}{\sqrt{x + h} + \sqrt{x}},$$

provided $h \neq 0$.

6. A function f satisfies the following relationship, known as a functional equation:

$$f(xy) = f(x) + f(y).$$

Show that $f(1) = 0$, providing $f(1)$ is defined.

7. If $f(x) = x^2$ and $x = g(t) = t + 2$, find $f[g(3)]$.

8. A sphere of radius r has its volume V given by $V = f(r) = 4\pi r^3/3$ and its surface area S by $S = g(r) = 4\pi r^2$. Show that $3f(r) = rg(r)$.

9. Does the expression $y = \sqrt{x} + \sqrt{-x}$ define a function? If so, describe D and R.

10. Explain why $y = \sqrt{-1 - x^2}$ does not define a real function.

11. Describe the domain D and range R of the function f defined by

$$y = f(x) = \begin{cases} \sin x & \text{for} \quad x \geqslant 0 \\ |x| & \text{for} \quad x < 0 \end{cases}$$

12. A rectangle has perimeter 20 in. Find a function f denoted by $A = f(x)$ which gives the area of the rectangle in terms of one of its sides. What is the domain D of this function?

REFERENCES

1.1 E. T. BELL, *Men of Mathematics*, Simon and Schuster, New York, 1937.

1.2 T. L. HEATH, *The Thirteen Books of Euclid's Elements*, Cambridge University Press, New York, 1926.

1.3 H. P. THIELMAN, "On the Definition of Functions," *American Mathematical Monthly*, Vol. 60 (1953), p. 259.

Chapter

2

Elements of plane
analytic geometry

2.1 Rectangular Coordinates

In Chapter 1 we represented the real numbers geometrically as points of the *x*-axis. We also introduced functions as correspondences involving ordered pairs of real numbers. We now present a method for representing ordered pairs geometrically.

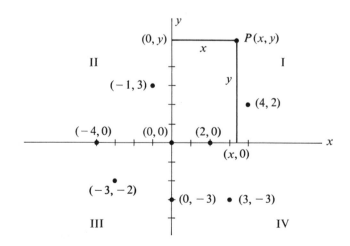

Figure 2.1

In Fig. 2.1 we erect a perpendicular to the *x*-axis at the origin and label this line the *y*-axis. We associate the points on the *y*-axis with the real numbers in the same manner that we associated the points on the x-axis with the real numbers. It is customary to take the positive y-axis upward, although this is not essential. It is also customary to use the same scale on both axes and we will do so unless we state otherwise. Thus, if the x-axis were rotated about the origin counterclockwise through 90 deg it would coincide with the y-axis. The plane determined by the x- and y-axes is called the xy-plane. The x- and y-axes divide the xy-plane into four quadrants, labeled I, II, III, and IV as shown in Fig. 2.1.

Given an ordered pair of real numbers (x, y) we associate this pair with a point P in the xy-plane as follows:

The point P is x units to the right of the y-axis if $x \geqslant 0$, and x units to the left of the y-axis if $x < 0$. It is y units above the x-axis if $y \geqslant 0$, and y units below the x-axis if $y < 0$. The numbers x and y are called the coordinates of the point P; x is termed the abscissa of P and y is termed the ordinate of P. Points are often denoted by capital letters, the origin $(0, 0)$ usually being denoted by the letter O. The point $P(x, y)$ (read as "the point Pxy") refers to an arbitrary point in the xy-plane.

It is clear that if an ordered pair (x, y) of real numbers is specified, the scheme outlined will produce one and only one point P in the xy-plane corresponding to this pair. It is also evident that if a point P in the xy-plane is selected arbitrarily, there will exist one and only one ordered pair of real numbers corresponding to P. Thus we have established a one-to-one correspondence between the set of ordered pairs of real numbers and the set of points in the xy-plane. "Ordered pair of real numbers" and "point in the xy-plane" will be used interchangeably in the same fashion that we used "real number" and "point on the x-axis" interchangeably.

Locating a point in the xy-plane corresponding to an ordered pair of real numbers is called "plotting the point." A few points are plotted in Fig. 2.1.

The system we have described for locating points is known as the cartesian system of rectangular coordinates. This is in honor of René Descartes (1596–1650), the French mathematician and philosopher who was one of the founders of analytic geometry. His *La Géométrie*, published in 1637, was a landmark in the history of the subject.

2.2 Distance Between Two Points

Let $P_1(x_1, y_1)$ and $P_2(x_2, y_2)$ be points of the xy-plane. If $x_1 = x_2$ and $y_1 = y_2$, the distance $d = P_1P_2 = 0$.

If $y_1 = y_2$ and $x_1 \neq x_2$, the distance $d = P_1P_2$ from P_1 to P_2 is $x_2 - x_1$. This distance is said to be directed, since it can be either positive or negative. It is positive if P_2 is to the right of P_1 and negative if P_2 is to the left of P_1. Thus, if two points lie on the same horizontal line, the absolute value of the distance between them is obtained by subtracting the abscissa of the leftmost point from the abscissa of the rightmost point.

If $x_1 = x_2$ and $y_1 \neq y_2$, the distance $d = P_1P_2$ from P_1 to P_2 is $y_2 - y_1$, and is positive or negative according to whether P_2 is above or below P_1. Thus, if two points lie on the same vertical line, the absolute value of the distance between them is obtained by subtracting the ordinate of the lower point from the ordinate of the upper point.

Examples.   The directed distance from (3, 3) to (3, 3) is 0.
The directed distance from (−4, 1) to (6,1) is 10.
The directed distance from (2, 3) to (−5, 3) is −7.
The directed distance from (2, −3) to (2, −7) is −4.
The directed distance from (−5, −3) to (−5, −1) is 2.
The directed distance from (−5, −1) to (−5, −3) is −2.

The abscissa x of $P(x, y)$ can now be described as the directed distance from the y-axis to P. Similarly, the ordinate y of P is the directed distance from the x-axis to P.

If $x_1 \neq x_2$ and $y_1 \neq y_2$, we find the distance $d = P_1 P_2$ by applying the Pythagorean theorem to the right triangle having vertices P_1, P_2, and $P_3(x_2, y_1)$, shown in Fig. 2.2.

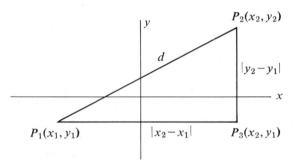

Figure 2.2

Since $P_1 P_3 = x_2 - x_1$ and $P_3 P_2 = y_2 - y_1$, we have
$$d = \sqrt{|x_2 - x_1|^2 + |y_2 - y_1|^2}$$
or
$$d = \sqrt{(x_2 - x_1)^2 + (y_2 - y_1)^2}. \qquad (2.1)$$

The important relationship (2.1) is called the distance formula. Observe that the distance between two points A and B is nonnegative and is not a directed distance when A and B do not both lie on the same horizontal (or vertical) line.

If A and B do lie on the same horizontal (or vertical) line, the distance formula yields the absolute value of the distance rather than the distance, which may be negative.

Example 1. The distance from (2, 3) to (5, 7) is $\sqrt{(5 - 2)^2 + (7 - 3)^2} = 5$. The distance from (5,7) to (2, 3) is also 5.

Example 2.   The distance from (−3, −7) to (−6, −2) is $\sqrt{(-6+3)^2+(-2+7)^2}$ $= \sqrt{34}$.

Example 3.   Show that the points $A(5, 4)$, $B(4, 1)$, and $C(3, 2)$ are vertices of a right triangle.

By the distance formula

$$c = AB = \sqrt{(4-5)^2 + (1-4)^2} = \sqrt{10},$$

$$a = BC = \sqrt{(3-4)^2 + (2-1)^2} = \sqrt{2},$$

and $\qquad b = AC = \sqrt{(3-5)^2 + (2-4)^2} = \sqrt{8}.$

Since $c^2 = 10 = a^2 + b^2 = 2 + 8$, ABC is a right triangle. The conclusion follows from the converse of the Pythagorean theorem.

The Pythagorean theorem states that:

If ABC is a right triangle ($C = 90°$), then $c^2 = a^2 + b^2$.

The converse states that:

If $c^2 = a^2 + b^2$, then ABC is a right triangle ($C = 90°$).

Example 4.   The point $P(x, y)$ is on the x-axis and is five units from $A(5, 2)$. Find x and y.

Since P is on the x-axis, y must be 0. Since $AP = 5$, it follows from the distance formula that

$$5 = \sqrt{(x-5)^2 + (0-2)^2}.$$

Simplifying, we find that x must satisfy

$$x^2 - 10x + 4 = 0,$$

and hence the only possible values of x are $5 + \sqrt{21}$ and $5 - \sqrt{21}$ It is easy to verify that $(5 + \sqrt{21}, 0)$ and $(5 - \sqrt{21}, 0)$ are both five units from $(5, 2)$.

PROBLEM LIST 5

1. Plot the following points: $(0, 0)$, $(1, 2)$, $(3, -2)$, $(5, -6)$, $(-4, 0)$, $(0, -3)$.

2. Plot the following points: $(1, 1)$, $(2, 3)$, $(-4, -3)$, $(-2, 3)$, $(3, -1)$, $(0, 5)$, $(4, 0)$.

3. Plot the points $(3, 4)$, $(3, -4)$, $(-3, 4)$, and $(-3, -4)$.

4. Plot the points $(5, 2)$, $(5, -2)$, $(-5, 2)$, $(-5, -2)$, $(-2, 5)$, $(-2, -5)$, $(2, 5)$, and $(2, -5)$.

5. Plot (approximately) the points $(\sqrt{2}, \sqrt{3})$, $(-\pi, \sqrt{3})$, $(1 + \sqrt{2}, -3)$, $(\pi - 1, \sqrt[3]{6})$.

6. Describe the location in the xy-plane of the points $P(x, y)$ for which

    (a) $x > 0$,

    (b) $x > 0$ and $y < 0$,

    (c) $x = 0$,

    (d) $x = y$,

    (e) x and y have the same sign,

    (f) $x < 0$ and $y \geqslant 0$,

    (g) $|y| = -|x|$,

    (h) $y > x$,

    (i) $x = 2$ and $y = 3$,

    (j) $x = \sqrt{x^2}$.

7. Describe the location in the xy-plane of the points $P(x, y)$ for which

    (a) $y > 0$,

    (b) $y = 0$,

    (c) $y = 2$ and $x \geqslant 0$,

    (d) $|x| \geqslant 2$,

    (e) x and y have opposite signs,

    (f) $x = 3$ and $y = -2$,

    (g) $x > 3$ and $y = -2$,

    (h) $y > |x|$,

    (i) $-|x| \leqslant y \leqslant |x|$,

    (j) $xy = 0$.

8. Find the distance from A to B:
   (a) $A(0, 0)$, $B(-5, 2)$.
   (b) $A(-2, 3)$, $B(-2, -6)$.
   (c) $A(-3, 4)$, $B(6, -5)$.
   (d) $A(-3, 5)$, $B(-6, 5)$.
   (e) $A(7, -3)$, $B(4, -1)$.
   (f) $A(-3, -4)$, $B(6, 0)$.
   (g) $A(3, 2)$, $B(3, -5)$.
   (h) $A(3, 3)$, $B(-3, -3)$.

9. Find the distance from P to Q:
   (a) $P(-3, 4)$, $Q(0, 0)$.
   (b) $P(0, -5)$, $Q(0, 3)$.
   (c) $P(5, -2)$, $Q(-1, -6)$.
   (d) $P(4, -3)$, $Q(-5, -3)$.
   (e) $P(-4, -4)$, $Q(-4, -4)$.
   (f) $P(-4, 4)$, $Q(-4, -4)$.
   (g) $P(4, -4)$, $Q(-4, -4)$.
   (h) $P(4, 4)$, $Q(-4, -4)$.

10. Find the distance from B to A for each pair of points in Problem 8.

11. Find the distance from Q to P for each pair of points in Problem 9.

12. Show that $A(-1, 2)$, $B(7, 5)$, and $C(2, -6)$ are vertices of a right triangle. State the geometric theorem upon which the conclusion is based.

13. Find the perimeter and area of the triangle in Problem 12.

14. The distance from $(x, 1)$ to $(2, -1)$ is 5. Find x.

15. The point $P(x, y)$ is on the x-axis and is six units from $(1, -4)$. Find x and y.

16. Show that $(3, -4)$ is farther from $(-7, -1)$ than from $(5, 6)$.

17. Show that the points $(3, 2)$, $(4, 1)$, $(5, 4)$, and $(6, 3)$ are vertices of a rectangle. Show that the diagonals of the rectangle have the same length.

18. Prove that $(6, 0)$, $(-4, 3)$, $(-7, -7)$, and $(3, -10)$ are vertices of a square.

19. Find the perimeter and area of the triangle having vertices $(-3, 1)$, $(2, 3)$, and $(5, -2)$.

20. Find the perimeter and area of the quadrilateral $ABCD$ having vertices $A(-7, -1)$, $B(2, 5)$, $C(6, 4)$, and $D(3, -3)$.

21. Let $A(0, 0)$, $B(c, 0)$ and $C(b \cos A, b \sin A)$ denote the vertices of triangle ABC. Employ the distance formula to derive the law of cosines ($a^2 = b^2 + c^2 - 2bc \cos A$).

2.3 Graph of a Function

A function consists of a set of ordered pairs (x, y) of real numbers (no two pairs having the same first element x). The set of corresponding points (x, y) in the xy-plane is called the graph of the function. We draw the graph of the function by exhibiting a sufficient number of these points in the xy-plane to enable us to determine by inspection the principal properties of the function.

Example 1.   The graph of the absolute value function is shown in Fig. 2.3.

Only the portion of the graph in the neighborhood of the origin is shown. It would be impractical to show the point $(1000, 1000)$ or the point $(-6825, 6825)$. It is necessary only that the graph provide a visual interpretation of the functional relationship.

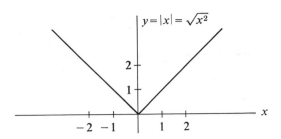

Figure 2.3

Example 2.   The graph of the sequence $\{4/n\}$ is shown in Fig. 2.4.

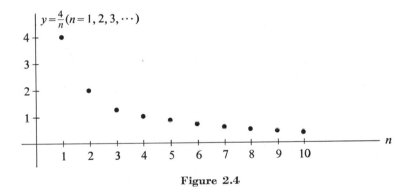

Figure 2.4

Only ten points are shown even though the graph consists of an infinite number of points. It is clear that as n increases, the points of the graph get closer and closer to the n-axis.

Example 3.   The graph of the function defined by $y = f(x) = 2$ is shown in Fig. 2.5.

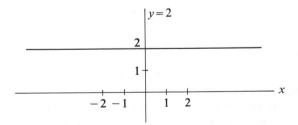

Figure 2.5

Example 4.   The graph of the function defined by $y = g(x) = 2x/x$ is shown in Fig. 2.6.

The graph of f is identical with the graph of g except that the point $(0, 2)$ is not part of the graph of g. This is indicated in Fig. 2.6 by drawing a small circle about the point $(0, 2)$.

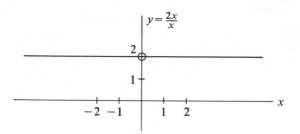

Figure 2.6

Example 5. To draw the graph of the function defined by $y = x^2/4$, it is helpful to assign values to x, compute the corresponding values of y, list these pairs (x, y) in a table, and plot the points corresponding to these pairs. See Fig. 2.7.

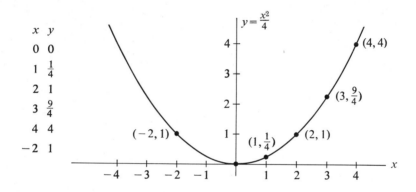

Figure 2.7

After a sufficient number of points have been plotted to reveal the essential nature of the graph, a smooth curve is drawn through the points. This is called plotting the graph, but we prefer to say "drawing the graph," since one of our major objectives is to develop techniques which will enable us to draw graphs without having to plot a large number of points. Observe that in Fig. 2.7 it is unnecessary to plot any points in quadrant II. If $(a, a^2/4)$ is a first-quadrant point on the graph, it is clear that $(-a, a^2/4)$ is a second-quadrant point on the graph, since $(-a)^2/4 = a^2/4$.

If for every point (a, b) of a graph the point $(-a, b)$ is also a point of the graph, we say that the graph is symmetric with respect to the y-axis. Various types of symmetry exist, and we will consider this topic in a later section.

Whenever a function is given by an equation, the graph of the function is called the graph of the equation. The graph of the equation $y = x^2/4$ is shown in Fig. 2.7.

Example 6. Draw the graph of the function defined by $y = 3x + 2$.

The student is undoubtedly familiar with the fact, which we will later prove, that the graph of a linear equation is a straight line. It is because of this that the equation is called "linear." The simplest way to draw the graph of a straight line is to plot the points where the line intersects the x- and y-axes.

Setting $x = 0$ we obtain $y = 2$, and setting $y = 0$ we obtain $x = -2/3$. We call 2 the y-intercept of the line and $-2/3$ the x-intercept of the line. After plotting the points $(0, 2)$ and $(-2/3, 0)$ we draw the graph as shown in Fig. 2.8.

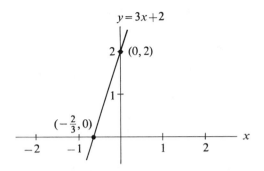

Figure 2.8

One or more additional points on the line can be plotted as a check. If the origin is on the line one or more other points should be plotted.

Example 7. The graph of the equation $y = \sqrt{-x^2}$ consists of the single point $(0, 0)$.

2.4   Inverse of a Function

If a function f has the property that to every element y of its range R there corresponds one and only one element x of its domain D, we can obtain a second function by using the same set of ordered pairs and interchanging the roles played by D and R. The new function is called the inverse of f and is denoted by f^{-1}, read as "f inverse." The "-1" is not an exponent, although the notation is suggested by the familiar law of exponents

$$a^1 a^{-1} = a^0 = 1 \qquad \text{for} \qquad a \neq 0.$$

(See Problem 23.)

Example 1. Let f be the function consisting of the three pairs $(1, 2)$, $(3, 4)$, and $(5, -7)$. The domain D of f is the set $\{1, 3, 5\}$ and the range R of f is the set $\{2, 4, -7\}$.

The inverse f^{-1} is the function consisting of the pairs $(2, 1)$, $(4, 3)$, and $(-7, 5)$. The domain D of f^{-1} is the set $\{2, 4, -7\}$ and the range R of f^{-1} is the set $\{1, 3, 5\}$.

Example 2. Let the function f defined by $y = f(x) = 3x$ have domain D given by

$$0 \leqslant x \leqslant 1.$$

The range R of f is given by

$$0 \leqslant y \leqslant 3.$$

The inverse f^{-1} of f is given by $y = f^{-1}(x) = x/3$. The domain D of f^{-1} is the set $0 \leqslant x \leqslant 3$, while the range R of f^{-1} is the set $0 \leqslant y \leqslant 1$. The graphs of these functions are shown in Fig. 2.9.

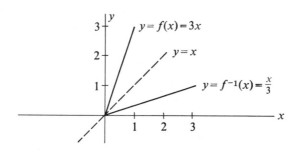

Figure 2.9

If $P(a, b)$ is a point of the graph of f, then $Q(b, a)$ is a point of the graph of f^{-1}. Consequently, the line $y = x$ is the perpendicular bisector of the line segment PQ. (See Problem 24.) If P and Q are identical, the point P is on the line $y = x$. We say that the graphs of f and f^{-1} are symmetric with respect to the line $y = x$. We also say that the graph of f is the reflection of the graph of f^{-1} in the line $y = x$.

Example 3.   Consider the function f defined by $y = f(x) = 2x + 1$. To find the value of an element of the range, we multiply the value of the corresponding element of the domain by 2 and add 1 to the result. If we solve for x in terms of y we obtain the function g defined by $x = g(y) = y/2 - 1/2$. The function g is the inverse of f and is denoted by $g = f^{-1}$. To find the value of an element of the range of $g = f^{-1}$, we divide the value of the corresponding element of the domain of $g = f^{-1}$ by 2 and subtract 1/2 from the result. To graph the function $g = f^{-1}$, we denote an element of the domain of g by x and the corresponding element of the range of g by y. We then write $y = g(x) = x/2 - 1/2 = f^{-1}(x)$. The symbol employed to denote an element of the domain is immaterial; it is merely customary to use the letter x. The function g could

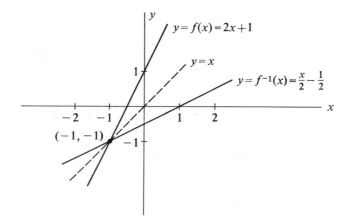

Figure 2.10

just as well be given by $g(t) = t/2 - 1/2 = f^{-1}(t)$. The graphs of f and g are shown in Fig. 2.10.

Example 4.   The inverse of the function f defined by $y = f(x) = \sqrt{x}$ is obtained by solving for x in terms of y

$$x = y^2$$

and then interchanging x and y to obtain

$$y = f^{-1}(x) = x^2, \qquad 0 \leqslant x.$$

Observe that the domain D of f^{-1} does not include negative numbers, since the range of f does not. The graphs of f and f^{-1} are shown in Fig. 2.11.

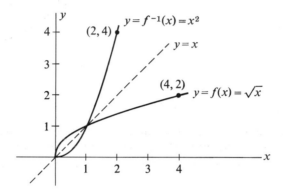

Figure 2.11

Example 5.   Consider the function f defined by $y = f(x) = x^2$.

If we solve for x in terms of y we obtain

$$x = \pm\sqrt{y}$$

and if we interchange x and y we have

$$y = \pm\sqrt{x}.$$

This expression does not determine a function, since two values of y are determined for each $x > 0$.

For convenience we separate the function f into the two functions g and h defined by

$$y = g(x) = x^2 \qquad \text{for} \qquad x \geqslant 0,$$

and

$$y = h(x) = x^2 \qquad \text{for} \qquad x < 0.$$

Then g and h have inverses given by

$$g^{-1}(x) = \sqrt{x} \qquad \text{for} \qquad x \geqslant 0,$$

and

$$h^{-1}(x) = -\sqrt{x} \qquad \text{for} \qquad x > 0.$$

The graphs of g and g^{-1} are shown in Fig. 2.12(a) and those of h and h^{-1} in Fig. 2.12(b).

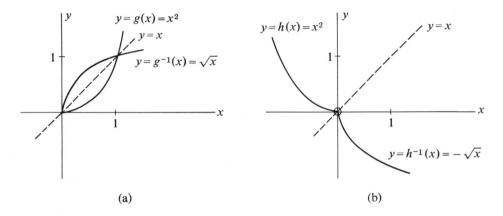

(a)   (b)

Figure 2.12

This method of constructing two or more functions from a function f is employed when a horizontal line meets the graph of f in two or more distinct points. The purpose is to restrict attention to functions that possess inverses.

2.5 Implicit Functions

A relation is defined as a set of ordered pairs (x, y) of elements. We are interested in the case in which the elements x and y are real numbers. A function is a particular kind of relation. A relation is an arbitrary set of ordered pairs, and a function is a set of ordered pairs, no two of which have the same first element. The pairs $(2, 3)$ and $(2, 4)$ could be pairs of a relation but not pairs of a function. A function is a relation but a relation is not necessarily a function.

A relation may be given by an equation of the form

$$f(x, y) = 0. \tag{2.2}$$

The symbol f denotes a real function of two real variables x and y. The domain of such a function consists of a set of ordered pairs (x, y) of real numbers and the range consists of a set of real numbers. However, if (2.2) is to hold; that is, if $f(x, y)$ is to have the constant value zero, it is clear that x and y are no longer independent. If x is fixed, one or more values of y may be determined and if y is fixed, one or more values of x may be determined. Thus, an equation of the form (2.2) may determine a relation that in turn may determine one or more functions. Such a function is called an implicit function.

Any ordered pair of real numbers (x, y) for which $f(x, y) = 0$ is called a solution of $f(x, y) = 0$, and the set of all solutions of $f(x, y) = 0$ is called the solution set of the equation.

Example 1.   The equation $2x + 3y - 12 = 0$ determines the function f given by $y = f(x) = -2x/3 + 4$, obtained by solving for y in terms of x. We say that $2x + 3y - 12 = 0$ determines the implicit function denoted by $y = f(x)$ because $2x + 3y - 12 = 0$ implies the possible existence of one or more functions whose ordered pairs (x, y) have elements x and y satisfying $2x + 3y - 12 = 0$. When the correspondence between y and x is written $y = -(2x/3) + 4$, it is in explicit rather than implicit form, since the equation $y = -(2x/3) + 4$ tells us explicitly how to find y when x is assigned.

The equation $2x + 3y - 12 = 0$ also determines the function g given by $x = g(y) = -(3y/2) + 6$, obtained by solving for x in terms of y. The function g, which we could also denote by $g(x) = -(3x/2) + 6$, is the inverse of f.

Example 2.   The equation $x^2 + y^2 - 1 = 0$ determines the two functions f and g given by

$$y = f(x) = \sqrt{1 - x^2} \qquad \text{and} \qquad y = g(x) = -\sqrt{1 - x^2},$$

both having domain $-1 \leqslant x \leqslant 1$. The range of f is the set $0 \leqslant y \leqslant 1$, and the range of g is the set $-1 \leqslant y \leqslant 0$.

The graphs of f and g are shown in Figs. 2.13 and 2.14. Neither f nor g possesses an inverse.

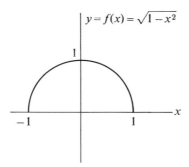

$$y = f(x) = \sqrt{1 - x^2}$$

Figure 2.13

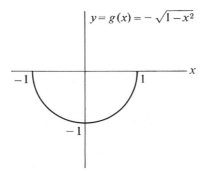

$$y = g(x) = -\sqrt{1 - x^2}$$

Figure 2.14

Example 3.   The equation $x^2 + 2y^2 + 1 = 0$ does not determine any real function of a real variable. If x is a real number there is no real number y such that $x^2 + 2y^2 + 1 = 0$. Similarly, if y is real, there is no corresponding real x such that $x^2 + 2y^2 + 1 = 0$.

The theory of implicit functions, considered in books on advanced calculus and analysis, is by no means a simple one. (See Ref. 2.3.)

PROBLEM LIST 6

1. Draw the graphs of the functions defined by

    (a) $y = 2|x|$,

    (b) $y = -3$,

    (c) $y = \dfrac{x}{x}$,

    (d) $y = \dfrac{x^2}{2}$,

    (e) $y = 4x$,

    (f) $y = 3x + 5$,

    (g) $y = -2x - 3$,

    (h) $y = \dfrac{1}{x}$,

    (i) $y = x^2 - x$,

    (j) $y = \dfrac{1}{x^2}$.

2. Draw the graphs of the functions defined by

    (a) $y = \dfrac{|x|}{2}$,

    (b) $y = 2$,

    (c) $y = x^2 - 1$,

    (d) $y = -\dfrac{x}{2}$,

    (e) $y = x^3$,

    (f) $y = \sqrt{x - 1}$,

    (g) $y = \sqrt[3]{x}$,

    (h) $y = \dfrac{|x|}{x}$,

    (i) $y = \sqrt{-x}$,

    (j) $y = |x| + x$,

    (k) $y = x - |x|$.

3. Draw the graphs of the functions defined by

    (a) $y = \dfrac{x}{|x|}$,

    (b) $y = \dfrac{x^2 + 1}{4}$,

    (c) $y = x|x|$,

    (d) $y = \sqrt{x^2 - 1}$,

    (e) $y = 1/(1 + x)^2$,

    (f) $y = -\sqrt{4 - x}$,

    (g) $y = x^3 - x$,

    (h) $y = \sqrt{4 - x^2}$,

    (i) $y = (x - 2)/(x - 2)$,

    (j) $y = \dfrac{2(x - 1)(x + 3)}{(x - 1)(x + 3)}$.

4. Draw the graph of the sequence $\{6/n\}$. Find the inverse of this function and draw its graph.

5. Draw the graph of the sequence $\{2 + (1/n)\}$. Find the inverse of this function and draw its graph.

6. Draw the graphs of the functions defined by the following equations. Also draw the graph of the inverse of each function:

    (a) $y = 2x$.

    (b) $y = -x + 5$.

    (c) $y = \sqrt{2x}$.

    (d) $y = x^3$.

    (e) $y = \sqrt{2 - x}$.

    (f) $y = 4x - 2$.

    (g) $y = \sqrt{-2x}$.

    (h) $y = x^5$.

7. Draw graphs of functions determined by each of the following equations:

    (a) $2x + 4y - 5 = 0$.   (e) $x^2 + y^2 - 9 = 0$.

    (b) $x + 3y - 6 = 0$.   (f) $y^2 - 4x = 0$.

    (c) $y - x^2 = 0$.   (g) $x^2 - y^2 = 0$.

    (d) $x - y^2 = 0$.   (h) $y^2 - x^2 - 1 = 0$.

8. A force (F pounds) that stretches or compresses a spiral spring is proportional to the resulting change (s inches) in the axial length of the spring. This relationship determines the function given by

    $$F = f(s) = ks$$

    where k, the constant of proportionality, is known as the spring constant. This is a form of Hooke's law, named after the English experimental physicist Robert Hooke (1635–1703).

    Draw graphs of the function f for (a) $k = 10$, (b) $k = 20$, (c) $k = 30$, (d) $k = 40$. Use convenient scales on the s- and F-axes and restrict s to the interval $0 \leqslant s \leqslant 5$.

9. The period of a simple pendulum of length l undergoing small oscillations is given by

    $$T = f(l) = 2\pi\sqrt{\frac{l}{g}}$$

    where l is in feet, T is in seconds, and g is the acceleration due to gravity. Assume that $g = 32$ and draw the graph of the function f.

10. A function f consists of the ordered pairs $(1, 3)$, $(2, 4)$, $(-1, 6)$, and $(4, 2)$. Draw the graph of this function. On a separate set of axes draw the graph of the function f^{-1}.

11. Draw the graph of the equation

    $$y = n\pi \qquad (n = 0, 1, 2, \ldots).$$

12. Draw the graph of the equation

    $$y = \frac{\pi}{2} + n\pi \qquad (n = 0, 1, 2, \ldots).$$

13. The volume of a sphere is given by $V = f(r) = 4\pi r^3/3$; the surface area by $S = g(r) = 4\pi r^2$. Draw the graphs of the functions (a) f, (b) f^{-1}, (c) g, (d) g^{-1}.

14. In Problem 13 find the function given by $V = h(S)$. Graph this function together with its inverse.

15. Let x be an arbitrary real number and let y be the greatest integer in x, meaning the largest integer which is less than or equal to x. This determines a function f which is customarily denoted by

    $$y = f(x) = [x].$$

    For example, $[3] = 3$, $[0] = 0$, $[2.4] = 2$, $[-7/3] = -3$. Draw the graph of f.

16. Let y denote the number of primes $\leqslant x$. Then $y = f(x)$. Draw the graph of f for $-3 \leqslant x \leqslant 17$.

17. Draw the graph of the function defined by $y = |x|/3$. Separate this function into two functions denoted by $y = f(x)$ and $y = g(x)$ such that f and g possess inverses. On one set of axes draw the graphs of f and f^{-1}, and on another set of axes, those of g and g^{-1}.

18. In Example 8, Sec. 1.8, draw the graph of the function denoted by $F = f(r)$ for $m = 2$ and $a = 1$.

19. Under certain conditions the cost of sending a parcel not exceeding 20 lb in weight is 5 cents per ounce or fraction of an ounce. If x denotes the weight in ounces, the cost $y = f(x)$ is given by

$$y = f(x) = 5r \qquad \text{if } n - 1 < x \leqslant n,$$

where $n = 1, 2, \cdots, 320$.

Using convenient scales on the x- and y-axes, draw the graph of f for $0 < x \leqslant 6$.

This "postage" function is an example of a set of functions known as step functions. The name "step function" is suggested by the appearance of the graph of such a function.

20. The unit step function denoted by $y = u(x)$ is defined by

$$y = \begin{cases} 0 & \text{for} & x < 0 \\ 1 & \text{for} & x > 0 \end{cases}.$$

Draw the graphs of **(a)** $y = u(x)$, **(b)** $y = u(x - 1)$, **(c)** $y - u(x + 2)$.

21. The function given by $y = F(x) = u(x - a) - u(x - b)$, where u is the unit step function, is sometimes referred to as the filter function. The graph of $y = F(x)\,G(x)$ looks like the graph of the function defined by $y = G(x)$ for $a < x < b$, but consists of the x-axis for $x < a$ and $x > b$. The unit step function and the filter function are useful in both pure and applied mathematics.

Draw the graphs of

(a) $y = x^2 u(x)$,

(b) $y = x^2 u(x - 1)$,

(c) $y = x^2[u(x - 1) - u(x - 3)]$,

(d) $y = 2x[u(x - 2) - u(x)] + (-x + 6)[u(x - 2) - u(x - 6)]$.

22. If a function f possesses an inverse f^{-1}, then the function g given by $g(x) = f[f^{-1}(x)] = 1x = x$ is the identity function. It is this property that suggests the notation for an inverse function, due to the analogy with the familiar law of exponents:

$$aa^{-1} = a^0 = 1 \qquad \text{for} \qquad a \neq 0.$$

For each of the following functions given by $y = f(x)$, find $f^{-1}(x)$ and verify that $f[f^{-1}(x)] = x$:

(a) $y = 2x - 1$.   (c) $y = x^3$.

(b) $y = 3x + 2$.   (d) $y = \sqrt{x}$.

23. For each of the functions in Problem 22, show that

$$f^{-1}[f(x)] = x.$$

24. If $a \neq b$, show that the line $y = x$ is the perpendicular bisector of the line segment joining (a, b) and (b, a).

25. Draw the graph of

(a) the signum function defined by

$$y = \operatorname{sgn} x = \begin{cases} 1 & \text{for} & x > 0 \\ 0 & \text{for} & x = 0; \\ -1 & \text{for} & x < 0 \end{cases}$$

(b) the Heaviside unit function defined by

$$y = H(x) = \frac{1 + \text{sgn } x}{2};$$

(c) the function f defined by

$$y = f(x) = x^2 \text{ sgn } x.$$

2.6   *Inclination and Slope of a Line*

In Fig. 2.15, l is an arbitrary line intersecting the x-axis at $A(a, 0)$. Let $P(p, 0)$ be any point on the x-axis such that $p > a$ and let $Q(c, d)$ be any point on l such that $d > 0$. Then the measure of $\theta = \angle PAQ$ is called the inclination of l.

If a line does not intersect the x-axis, its inclination is defined to be 0 radians (or 0 degrees). The x-axis itself has inclination 0.

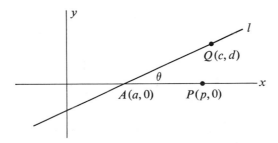

Figure 2.15

The slope of a line is usually denoted by the letter m and is defined by

$$m = \tan \theta. \tag{2.3}$$

Equation (2.3) defines a function whose domain D is the set $0 \leqslant \theta < \pi$, with $\theta = \pi/2$ excluded, and whose range R is the set of all real numbers.

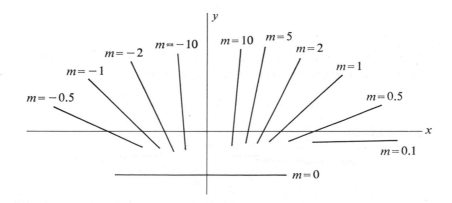

Figure 2.16

If the inclination is measured in degrees rather than radians, θ satisfies

$$0° \leqslant \theta < 180°, \qquad (\theta \neq 90°).$$

Figure 2.16 makes it evident that the slope of a line is a precise measure of its steepness.

A vertical line has inclination $\pi/2 = 90°$, but does not have a slope because the function given by $m = \tan\theta$ is undefined for $\theta = \pi/2$. The slope of the y-axis is undefined.

2.7 The Slope Formula

In Fig. 2.17, l is a line with inclination θ and $P_1(x_1, y_1)$ and $P_2(x_2, y_2)$ are two distinct points of l. Assume that $x_1 \neq x_2$ and that $y_2 > y_1$.

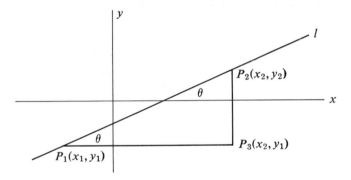

Figure 2.17

From triangle $P_1P_2P_3$ we have

$$m = \tan\theta = \frac{P_3P_2}{P_1P_3} = \frac{y_2 - y_1}{x_2 - x_1}.$$

The formula

$$m = \frac{y_2 - y_1}{x_2 - x_1} \tag{2.4}$$

is known as the slope formula.

The slope of the line l in Fig. 2.17 is positive, since $y_2 - y_1$ and $x_2 - x_1$ are both positive. If the figure is drawn with $x_1 > x_2$, then $x_2 - x_1 < 0, \theta > \pi/2$, and

$$m = \tan\theta = -\frac{y_2 - y_1}{|x_2 - x_1|} = \frac{y_2 - y_1}{x_2 - x_1},$$

so (2.4) still holds.

Finally, since

$$\frac{y_1 - y_2}{x_1 - x_2} = \frac{y_2 - y_1}{x_2 - x_1},$$

it is immaterial which point is regarded as P_1 and which as P_2. We need only remember that the slope is the difference of the ordinates divided by the difference of the abscissas, the differences being taken in the same order.

If $y_2 = y_1$, l is horizontal and (2.4) still holds, since $m = 0$.

Example 1.   The slope of the line through $(3, -4)$ and $(-2, 5)$ is given by

$$m = \frac{5 - (-4)}{-2 - 3} = \frac{-4 - 5}{3 - (-2)} = \frac{-9}{5}.$$

Example 2.   The slope of the line through $(-2, 3)$ and $(7, 3)$ is given by

$$m = \frac{3 - 3}{7 - (-2)} = \frac{0}{9} = 0.$$

The line is horizontal.

Example 3.   The line through $(2, -3)$ and $(2, 5)$ has no slope, since $x_1 = x_2$. The line is vertical.

2.8   Parallel Lines

If two lines are parallel they have the same inclination and hence have the same slope or are both vertical. If two lines have the same slope they have the same inclination and hence are parallel. Vertical lines are also parallel.

2.9   Angle Between Two Lines

In Fig. 2.18, l_1 and l_2 are lines having inclinations

$$0 < \theta_1 < \theta_2.$$

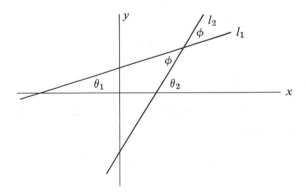

Figure 2.18

We define the angle ϕ between l_1 and l_2 as the angle between their upward directions when the x- and y-axes are drawn in their usual positions.

Since $\phi = \theta_2 - \theta_1$, we have

$$\tan \phi = \tan(\theta_2 - \theta_1) = \frac{\tan \theta_2 - \tan \theta_1}{1 + \tan \theta_2 \tan \theta_1}$$

or

$$\tan \phi = \frac{m_2 - m_1}{1 + m_2 m_1}, \qquad (2.5)$$

provided neither l_1 nor l_2 is vertical and $1 + m_2 m_1 \neq 0$.

Although θ_1 and θ_2 are drawn as acute angles in Fig. 2.18, it is easily verified that (2.5) holds if $\theta_2 > \pi/2$ or both $\theta_1 > \pi/2$ and $\theta_2 > \pi/2$.

If $\theta_1 = 0$ and $\theta_2 \neq \pi/2$, (2.5) still holds and reduces to $\tan \phi = m_2$.

If either l_1 or l_2 is vertical, ϕ is easily found from a geometric figure.

After $\tan \phi$ is computed from (2.5), ϕ can be found from a table of trigonometric functions or by slide rule.

2.10   Perpendicular Lines

If lines l_1 and l_2, having slopes m_1 and m_2, are perpendicular, $\phi = \pi/2$ in (2.5) and hence $1 + m_2 m_1 = 0$. Otherwise, $\tan \phi$ would be a real number and ϕ would be different from $\pi/2$. Therefore

$$m_2 = \frac{-1}{m_1} \quad \text{and} \quad m_1 = \frac{-1}{m_2}. \qquad (2.6)$$

That is, if $l_1 \perp l_2$, and m_1 and m_2 are defined, then the slope of either line is the negative reciprocal of the slope of the other.

Conversely, if $m_2 = -1/m_1$, $1 + m_2 m_1 = 0$, $\tan \phi$ is undefined, and hence $\phi = \pi/2$. Otherwise, $\tan \phi$ would be a real number.

Example 1.   Show that the line l_1 through $(4, -1)$ and $(5, 1)$ is perpendicular to the line l_2 through $(3, 1)$ and $(9, -2)$.

$$\text{Slope } m_1 \text{ of } l_1 = \frac{1 - (-1)}{5 - 4} = 2.$$

$$\text{Slope } m_2 \text{ of } l_2 = \frac{-2 - 1}{9 - 3} = \frac{-3}{6} = -\frac{1}{2}.$$

Since $m_1 = -1/m_2$, $l_1 \perp l_2$.

Example 2.   Find the angle between two lines having slopes $1/2$ and 3.

In (2.5) we take $m_2 = 3$ and $m_1 = 1/2$. Then

$$\tan \phi = \frac{3 - (1/2)}{1 + (3/2)} = 1,$$

and hence

$$\phi = \frac{\pi}{4} \quad \text{or} \quad 45°.$$

Example 3.   Points $A(2, -5)$, $B(-4, -3)$, and $C(-1, 5)$ are vertices of a triangle. Determine whether angle B is acute or obtuse.

Triangle *ABC* is shown in Fig. 2.19.

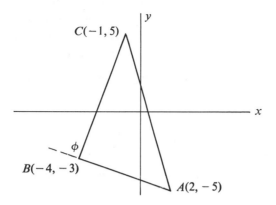

Figure 2.19

Formula (2.5) will yield tan ϕ where ϕ, shown in Fig. 2.19, is the angle between the upward directions of lines *AB* and *BC*, provided m_2 is the slope of *AB*, the line of greater inclination. We now compute

$$m_2 = \text{slope of line } AB = \frac{-3 - (-5)}{-4 - 2} = \frac{-1}{3},$$

$$m_1 = \text{slope of line } BC = \frac{5 - (-3)}{-1 - (-4)} = \frac{8}{3},$$

and

$$\tan \phi = \frac{(-1/3) - (8/3)}{1 + (-1/3)(8/3)} = -27.$$

Since $\tan \phi < 0$, $\pi/2 < \phi < \pi$, and hence angle *B*, the supplement of ϕ, is an acute angle.

PROBLEM LIST 7

1. Find the inclination of
   (a) the *x*-axis;
   (b) the *y*-axis;
   (c) the line bisecting the second and fourth quadrants;
   (d) the line through $(0, 0)$ and $(\sqrt{3}, 1)$;
   (e) the line through $(-2, 1)$ and $(-3, 1 + \sqrt{3})$;
   (f) a line having equal nonzero *x*- and *y*-intercepts.
2. Find the slope of
   (a) the *x*-axis;
   (b) the *y*-axis;
   (c) the line whose equation is $y + 3x = 0$;
   (d) the line through $(-1, 1)$ and $(1, -1)$.

3. Find the slope of the line through the following points:
   - (a) $(0, 0)$ and $(-1, 2)$.
   - (b) $(1, 3)$ and $(4, 5)$.
   - (c) $(4, 2)$ and $(-4, 2)$.
   - (d) $(3, -1)$ and $(3, 5)$.
   - (e) $(6, -5)$ and $(-3, -7)$.
   - (f) $(-4, 8)$ and $(0, -2)$.
   - (g) $(9, 1)$ and $(6, -4)$.
   - (h) $(\pi, 3)$ and $(-3, 2)$.

4. On the same set of axes draw lines having the following slopes:
   - (a) 3.
   - (b) -3.
   - (c) 0.2.
   - (d) -10.
   - (e) $-3/5$.
   - (f) $\sqrt{2}$.

5. Which of the following sets of points are collinear?
   - (a) $(2, -3), (6, 3), (-2, -9)$.
   - (b) $(5, 1), (-3, 2), (11, -1)$.
   - (c) $(1, -2), (-2, 10), (2, -6)$.
   - (d) $(0, 0), (3, 4), (9, 11)$.
   - (e) $(-2, 3), (1, -1), (5, -7)$.
   - (f) $(1, 1), (-1, 1), (-1, -1)$.

6. Each of the following pairs of points determines a line. Which lines are (i) parallel (ii) perpendicular?
   - (a) $(-3, 4), (5, -6)$.
   - (b) $(2, -7), (4, -2)$.
   - (c) $(3, -5), (0, 4)$.
   - (d) $(0, 4), (5, 2)$.
   - (e) $(1, 10), (-2, 1)$.
   - (f) $(0, 1), (1, -2)$.
   - (g) $(5, 4), (2, -5)$.
   - (h) $(5, 4), (10, 8)$.

7. Each of the following pairs of points determines a line. Which lines are (i) parallel (ii) perpendicular?
   - (a) $(-3, 4), (6, 2)$.
   - (b) $(4, 0), (6, -1)$.
   - (c) $(1, 0), (0, -1)$.
   - (d) $(4, 17), (-4, -19)$.
   - (e) $(-5, 3), (6, -2)$.
   - (f) $(-3, -2), (2, -5)$.
   - (g) $(2, 8), (-2, -10)$.
   - (h) $(4, 5), (-2, -7)$.

8. A line of slope 3 goes through $(2, 1)$. Find two other points on the line, one with ordinate $y > 1$ and one with $y < 1$.

9. A line with slope $-(3/4)$ goes through $(-4, 2)$. Find two other points on the line, one with abscissa $x > -4$ and one with $x < -4$.

10. Find x if the points $(-3, 4)$, $(2, -1)$, and $(x, 5)$ are collinear.

11. Find y if the line through $(-4, 3)$ and $(-1, 5)$ is parallel to the line through $(6, -1)$ and $(4, y)$.

12. Find x if the line through $(-3, 4)$ and $(5, 1)$ is perpendicular to the line through $(7, 3)$ and $(x, -2)$.

13. Find x if the line through $(x, 2x)$ and $(-2, 3)$ is parallel to the line through $(-1, -2)$ and $(3, -1)$.

14. Show that each of the following sets of points determines a right triangle.
    - (a) $(-3, 2), (4, 1), (5, 8)$.
    - (b) $(3, 5), (-1, 2), (6, 1)$.
    - (c) $(8, 2), (-3, -2), (1, -13)$.
    - (d) $(1, 0), (0, 1), (-1, 0)$.

15. Show that the points $(0, 3), (3, 4), (4, 1)$, and $(1, 0)$ are vertices of a rectangle.

16. Points $A(-3, 2)$, $B(6, -5)$, and $C(1, 7)$ are vertices of a triangle. Find **(a)** the slopes of the sides, **(b)** the slopes of the altitudes.

17. Points $A(-2, 4)$, $B(5, -1)$, and $C(x, 2)$ are vertices of a right triangle. Find x.

18. Find the angle between the lines having the following slopes:

   (a) 3 and -1.   **(d)** -3 and -5.

   (b) -4 and 3.   **(e)** 0 and -2.

   (c) 2 and 3.   **(f)** -3 and -8.

19. Find the angles of triangle ABC, given

   (a) $A(3, -4)$, $B(1, 5)$, $C(2, -4)$;

   (b) $A(-4, 1)$, $B(-1, 6)$, $C(2, -3)$;

   (c) $A(-3, 7)$, $B(1, 4)$, $C(0, 0)$;

   (d) $A(-1, 5)$, $B(0, -2)$, $C(5, 0)$.

20. Verify that $A(-3, 1)$, $B(-1, 7)$, $C(2, 8)$, and $D(0, 2)$ are vertices of a parallelogram. Show that the opposite angles of the parallelogram are equal.

21. Given points $A(0, 3)$, $B(2, -1)$, $C(6, 3)$, and $P(x, 3)$, where $0 \leqslant x \leqslant 6$, let ϕ = angle CBP and ψ = angle PBA. Find

   (a) $\phi + \psi$,

   (b) x if $\phi = \pi/4$,

   (c) x if $\psi = \pi/4$,

   (d) x if $\phi = \psi$,

   (e) ϕ and ψ if $x = 3$.

2.11   Midpoint Formulas

In Fig. 2.20, $P(x, y)$ on line P_1P_2 is between $P_1(x_1, y_1)$ and $P_2(x_2, y_2)$, $x_2 > x_1$, $y_2 > y_1$, and r is the ratio of distance P_1P to distance P_1P_2.

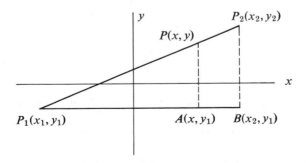

Figure 2.20

The abscissa x is clearly equal to

$$x_1 + P_1A = x_1 + \left[\frac{P_1A}{P_1B}\right]P_1B.$$

Since triangle $P_1AP \sim$ triangle P_1BP_2,

$$\frac{P_1A}{P_1B} = \frac{P_1P}{P_1P_2} = r$$

and hence

$$x = x_1 + r(x_2 - x_1). \tag{2.7}$$

Similarly,

$$y = y_1 + r(y_2 - y_1) \tag{2.8}$$

and it is easy to verify that both (2.7) and (2.8) hold if $y_2 = y_1$.

By drawing a figure similar to Fig. 2.20 it can be verified that when $y_1 > y_2$,

$$y = y_2 + (1 - r)(y_1 - y_2). \tag{2.9}$$

The use of (2.8) and (2.9) will be clarified by the following example.

Example 1.   Find the point $P(x, y)$ which is two-thirds of the way from $(-5, 2)$ to $(4, -4)$. See Fig. 2.21.

From (2.7) we have

$$x = -5 + \frac{2}{3}[4 - (-5)] = 1,$$

and from (2.9), since $2 > -4$, we have

$$y = -4 + \frac{1}{3}[2 - (-4)] = -2.$$

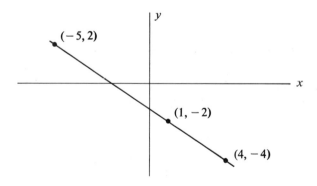

Figure 2.21

If we set $r = 1/2$ in (2.7) and (2.8)—or in (2.7) and (2.9)—we obtain

$$x = \frac{x_1 + x_2}{2}; \qquad y = \frac{y_1 + y_2}{2}. \tag{2.10}$$

Equations (2.10) are known as the midpoint formulas.

Since x_1 and x_2 (or y_1 and y_2) can be interchanged without affecting (2.10), it is immaterial which point is regarded as P_1 and which as P_2. The midpoint formulas state that the coordinates of the midpoint of a line segment are the averages of the corresponding coordinates of the endpoints of the segment.

Example 2.   Find the midpoint of the line segment from $(-3, 2)$ to $(6, -4)$.

From (2.10),
$$x = \frac{-3 + 6}{2} = \frac{3}{2}$$

and
$$y = \frac{2 - 4}{2} = -1.$$

Example 3.   On line AB find point $P(x, y)$ which is twice as far from $A(-2, 3)$ as it is from $B(4, 0)$ if $y < 0$.

Since B is the midpoint of line segment AP, we have, from (2.10),

$$4 = \frac{x + (-2)}{2} \qquad \text{and} \qquad 0 = \frac{y + 3}{2}$$

from which $x = 10$ and $y = -3$.

PROBLEM LIST 8

1. Find the midpoint of the line segment determined by each pair of points:
    (a) $(-3, 5)$, $(6, -4)$.   (c) $(-7, 3)$, $(0, -6)$.
    (b) $(4, -2)$, $(-7, -3)$.   (d) $(5, 2)$, $(-7, 2)$.

2. Find the midpoint of the line segment determined by each pair of points:
    (a) $(5, 1)$, $(11, 3)$.   (c) $(-3, -7)$, $(-3, 4)$.
    (b) $(6, -4)$, $(-1, 0)$.   (d) (a, b), (b, a).

3. The point $(6, -3)$ is the midpoint of the line segment determined by $(4, 2)$ and (x, y). Find x and y.

4. The point $(x, 4)$ is the midpoint of the line segment determined by $(7, y)$ and $(-1, 6)$. Find x and y.

5. Points $(4, -2)$ and $(3, 6)$ are endpoints of a diameter of a circle. Find the center and radius.

6. Points $A(6, -4)$, $B(-2, 6)$, and $C(8, 0)$ are vertices of a triangle. Find the lengths of the medians. Show that the line segment joining the midpoints of AB and AC is parallel to BC and is half the length of BC.

7. In Problem 6 replace A, B, C by $A(-3, -5)$, $B(-1, 3)$, and $C(7, 1)$.

8. Points $A(-4, -2)$, $B(-2, 5)$, $C(5, 3)$, and $D(-2, -6)$ are vertices of a quadrilateral. Show that the midpoints of the sides are vertices of a parallelogram.

9. Points $A(-3, 1)$, $B(-1, 7)$, $C(2, 8)$, and $D(0, 2)$ are vertices of a parallelogram. Show that the diagonals bisect each other.

10. Find the point which is three-fourths of the way from $(-4, 3)$ to $(8, -13)$.

11. Find the point which is four-fifths of the way from $(8, -1)$ to $(-2, 4)$.

12. Find the point on line AB which is three times as far from $A(-4, -1)$ as it is from $B(3, 2)$ and which is (a) between A and B, (b) not between A and B.

13. Find the point on line AB which is twice as far from $B(-4, 7)$ as it is from $A(2, -3)$ and which is (a) between A and B, (b) not between A and B.

14. Points $A(-4, 2)$, $B(8, 6)$, and $C(2, -10)$ are vertices of a triangle. Show that the medians intersect in a point which is two-thirds of the way from each vertex to the opposite side.

15. In Problem 14 replace A, B, C by $A(-5, 3)$, $B(1, 11)$, and $C(5, -7)$.

16. Points $(0, 1)$, $(4, 2)$, and $(2, -2)$ are the midpoints of the sides of a triangle. Find the vertices of the triangle.

2.12   Graph of an Equation

The graph of an equation $f(x, y) = 0$ is the set of all points whose coordinates satisfy the equation. This is consistent with the definition, given in Sec. 2.3, of the graph of a function. However, it is more general, since in Sec. 2.3 we considered only equations which defined functions.

Example.   Draw the graph of the equation $y^2 - x^2 = 0$.

Solving for y in terms of x, we obtain $y = \pm x$, from which we readily draw the graph shown in Fig. 2.22.

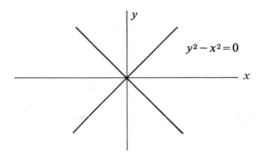

$$y^2 - x^2 = 0$$

Figure 2.22

Drawing the graph of an equation is one of the two major problems of analytic geometry. As stated previously, we intend to study this problem in detail as we progress.

2.13   Equation of a Graph

Let S denote a set of points or graph in the xy-plane. We say that $f(x, y) = 0$ is an equation of the graph, providing:

(i) If $P(x, y)$ is a point of S, then the coordinates of P satisfy $f(x, y) = 0$.
(ii) If the coordinates of $P(x, y)$ satisfy $f(x, y) = 0$, then P is a point of S.

To verify that $f(x, y) = 0$ is an equation of a graph, we must show that both **(i)** and **(ii)** hold. Instead of verifying **(ii)** we may establish

(iii) If $P(x, y)$ is not a point of S, then the coordinates of P do not satisfy $f(x, y) = 0$.

Statement **(iii)** is called the contrapositive of statement **(ii)**. It is obtained by negating both the hypothesis and the conclusion of **(ii)**, and then interchanging them. In logic it is shown that a statement and its contrapositive are equivalent; that is, either they are both true or they are both false. (See Ref. 2. 2.)

If $f(x, y) = 0$ is an equation of a graph S, the equation is the algebraic analog of the graph, and the graph is the geometric analog of the equation. The power of analytic geometry derives from its ability to study graphs analytically by considering their equations. The fundamental principle of analytic geometry is that a point lies on a graph if and only if its coordinates satisfy every equation of the graph.

The set S may be characterized by giving some condition or conditions satisfied by the points of S. Or, if the points of S lie on a curve, some defining property of the curve may be stated. The second major problem of analytic geometry is to find an equation of a curve or graph. We will also study this problem in detail.

Example.   Find an equation of the set S of points, each of which is three units from the origin.

Since we are dealing with plane analytic geometry, we do not bother to state that the points of S lie in a plane; this is always understood.

In Fig. 2.23 we denote by $P(x, y)$ an arbitrary point of the graph, namely, any point three units (in absolute value) from $(0, 0)$.

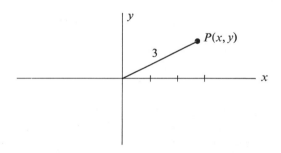

Figure 2.23

Employing the distance formula to translate the condition on P into an equation, we have

$$3 = \sqrt{x^2 + y^2}. \tag{2.11}$$

Simplifying (2.11), we obtain

$$x^2 + y^2 - 9 = 0. \tag{2.12}$$

It is easy to show that (2.11) and (2.12) are equivalent equations, meaning that they are both satisfied by the same ordered pairs of real numbers. Although (2.12) is merely another form of (2.11), we prefer (2.12) because it is simpler.

Thus far we have shown that **(i)** is true, namely, that if P is a point of the graph, then the coordinates of P satisfy $x^2 + y^2 - 9 = 0$.

To show that **(ii)** holds, assume that x_0 and y_0 are real numbers such that

$$x_0^2 + y_0^2 - 9 = 0.$$

Then

$$x_0^2 + y_0^2 = 9,$$

and

$$3 = \sqrt{x_0^2 + y_0^2}.$$ **(2.13)**

Note that it would be impossible for $\sqrt{x_0^2 + y_0^2}$ to equal -3.

But (2.13) states that $P_0(x_0, y_0)$ is three units from $(0, 0)$, and P_0 is therefore a point of S. Hence, since we have shown that **(i)** and **(ii)** both hold, we conclude that $x^2 + y^2 - 9 = 0$ is an equation of the given set S of points.

We say "an" equation rather than "the" equation, since S has more than one equation. Equation (2.11) is also an equation of S. For that matter, it is easy to see that $g(x, y) = (x^2 + y^2 + 1)(x^2 + y^2 - 9) = 0$ is also an equation of S. In general, we try to find equations that are as simple as possible.

After we have derived an equation of a set S of points, it is natural that we try to draw the graph of the equation. In our example we know that the graph of $x^2 + y^2 - 9 = 0$ is a circle with center at the origin and radius 3. We know this only because we know the definition of a circle from plane geometry. Later we will study circles in more detail.

2.14   *Equation of a Straight Line*

A straight line l is characterized by specifying its inclination θ and by giving a point $P_0(x_0, y_0)$ on l. If $\theta = \pi/2$, l is vertical and has equation

$$x - x_0 = 0$$ **(2.14)**

since (2.14) is satisfied by (and only by) the coordinates of all points $P(x, y)$ on l.

If $\theta \neq \pi/2$, the line has slope $m = \tan\theta$. Let $P(x, y)$ denote an arbitrary point on l other than P_0. Then we have, from Fig. 2.24,

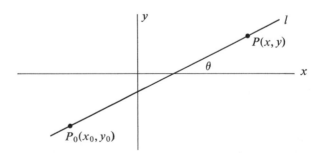

Figure 2.24

$$\frac{y - y_0}{x - x_0} = m$$

or

$$y - y_0 = m(x - x_0).$$ **(2.15)**

Equation (2.15) is satisfied by the coordinates of all points on l, since the coordinates of P_0 satisfy (2.15) by inspection.

If $Q(a, b)$ is any point not on l, then

$$\frac{b - y_0}{a - x_0} \neq m$$

and hence

$$b - y_0 \neq m(a - x_0).$$

We have verified (i) and (iii) of Sec. 2.13 and have therefore shown that (2.15) is an equation of l. Equation (2.15) is called the point-slope form of l.

We have also shown that every straight line has a linear equation.

Example 1.   An equation of the vertical line through $(5, -2)$ is $x - 5 = 0$.

Example 2.   An equation of the line of slope 3 through $(-7, 2)$ is

$$y - 2 = 3[x - (-7)]$$

or

$$3x - y + 23 = 0.$$

Example 3.   An equation of the line through $(4, 1)$ and $(-2, 1)$ is

$$y - 1 = 0(x - 4)$$

or

$$y - 1 = 0.$$

Example 4.   Find an equation of the perpendicular bisector of the line segment joining $(-2, 3)$ and $(4, -7)$.

The given line segment has slope

$$\frac{3 - (-7)}{-2 - 4} = \frac{-5}{3}$$

and midpoint $(1, -2)$. Hence we seek an equation of the line through $(1, -2)$ having slope 3/5. By (2.15) we obtain

$$y + 2 = \frac{3}{5}(x - 1)$$

or

$$3x - 5y - 13 = 0.$$

PROBLEM LIST 9

1. Find an equation of
    (a) the x-axis;
    (b) the y-axis;
    (c) the line bisecting the first and third quadrants;
    (d) the vertical line through $(-4, 5)$;
    (e) the horizontal line through $(6, -1)$.

2. Find an equation of the line
   (a) through $(-6, 3)$ having slope 4;
   (b) through $(-1, 5)$ having slope 5;
   (c) through $(7, -2)$ having slope -3;
   (d) through $(6, 2)$ having slope 0;
   (e) through $(4, -3)$ and $(5, -2)$;
   (f) through $(-5, 2)$ and $(-4, 3)$;
   (g) through $(-1, 2)$ and $(4, 0)$;
   (h) through $(6, 0)$ and $(-10, 2)$.

3. Find an equation of the line
   (a) through $(-5, 7)$ having slope 6;
   (b) through $(-3, 4)$ having slope -5;
   (c) through $(5, -3)$ having slope 2;
   (d) through $(-2, 2)$ having slope 0;
   (e) through $(-4, -2)$ and $(11, 1)$;
   (f) through $(-3, 3)$ and $(-2, 13)$;
   (g) through $(6, 5)$ and $(-3, 8)$;
   (h) through $(5, 7)$ and $(7, -1)$.

4. Find an equation of the line
   (a) through $(-2, 0)$ and having inclination $45°$;
   (b) through $(2, -1)$ and having inclination $90°$;
   (c) through $(-4, 3)$ and having inclination $135°$;
   (d) through $(-3, 5)$ and having inclination $60°$;
   (e) through $(-3, 2)$ and having inclination $0°$.

5. Find an equation of the perpendicular bisector of the line segment joining
   (a) $(3, -2)$ and $(5, 4)$;   (d) $(4, -3)$ and $(3, -4)$;
   (b) $(2, 5)$ and $(7, -3)$;   (e) $(-2, 5)$ and $(-2, -1)$;
   (c) $(6, 4)$ and $(-3, 4)$;   (f) $(2, 1)$ and $(8, -9)$.

6. Find an equation of the perpendicular bisector of the line segment joining
   (a) $(-3, 2)$ and $(4, 6)$;   (d) $(6, -4)$ and $(5, -2)$;
   (b) $(-1, 0)$ and $(6, -8)$;   (e) $(8, -3)$ and $(-1, 5)$;
   (c) $(-3, -2)$ and $(-3, 7)$;   (f) $(-2, 5)$ and $(-1, 5)$.

7. Show that an equation of the line of slope m passing through $(0, b)$ is $y = mx + b$. This is called the slope-intercept form.

8. Find an equation of the line through $(-4, 2)$ which is perpendicular to a line having slope -3.

9. Find an equation of the line through $(2, -5)$ which is perpendicular to a line having slope $3/4$.

10. Show that if a and b are both different from zero, an equation of the line through $(a, 0)$ and $(0, b)$ is $(x/a) + (y/b) = 1$. This is called the intercept form.

11. Find equations of the sides, altitudes, and medians of the triangle having vertices $A(6, 2)$, $B(2, 4)$, and $C(-4, -6)$.

12. Find equations of the sides, altitudes, and medians of the triangle having vertices $A(-8, 3)$, $B(-2, 6)$, and $C(4, -6)$.

13. Is $x^2 + y^2 - 1 = 0$ an equation of the semicircle through $(-1, 0)$, $(0, 1)$ and $(1, 0)$? Explain.

14. Is $y - \sqrt{1 - x^2} = 0$ an equation of the unit circle with center at the origin? Explain.

2.15   Graph of a Linear Equation

The relationship

$$ax + by + c = 0, \qquad\qquad (2.16)$$

in which a and b are not both zero, is called the general linear equation in two variables. The word "general" is used because (2.16) includes all possible equations of this type.

   If $b = 0$, then $a \neq 0$ and (2.16) can be written $x + (c/a) = 0$. Thus, in this case, the graph of (2.16) is a vertical line through $(-c/a, 0)$.

   If $b \neq 0$, and $a = 0$, (2.16) can be written as

$$y + \frac{c}{b} = 0,$$

in which case the graph of (2.16) is a horizontal line through $(0, -c/b)$.

   If $b \neq 0$, and $a \neq 0$, (2.16) can be written as

$$y - 0 = -\frac{a}{b}\left(x + \frac{c}{a}\right),$$

in which case the graph of (2.16) is a straight line through $(-c/a, 0)$ having slope $-a/b$.

   (It is useful to remember that the slope of $ax + by + c = 0$ is equal to minus the coefficient of x divided by the coefficient of y.)

   We have established the following theorem.

Theorem 2-I.   A linear equation in two variables represents a straight line.

2.16   Intersection of Two Graphs

Let us assume that $f_1(x, y) = 0$ has graph S_1 and $f_2(x, y) = 0$ has graph S_2. If a point $P(a, b)$ is on both S_1 and S_2, then $f_1(a, b) = 0$ and $f_2(a, b) = 0$. Conversely, if $f_1(a, b) = 0$ and $f_2(a, b) = 0$ then, providing a and b are both real, the point whose coordinates are $x = a$ and $y = b$ is a point of both S_1 and S_2.

   Thus, to find the intersections of S_1 and S_2, we solve the equations $f_1(x, y) = 0$ and $f_2(x, y) = 0$ simultaneously. The real solutions are the ordered pairs which correspond to the points common to S_1 and S_2.

Example 1.　Find the intersection of the lines $2x - 3y + 5 = 0$ and $4x + y - 4 = 0$.

Solving the equations simultaneously we find that $x = 1/2$ and $y = 2$. Hence the lines intersect in $(\frac{1}{2}, 2)$.

Example 2.　Find the intersections of $x^2 + y^2 - 25 = 0$ and $3x - 4y = 0$.

Solving the equations simultaneously we find $x = \pm 4$ and $y = \pm 3$. The graphs and their intersections are shown in Fig. 2.25.

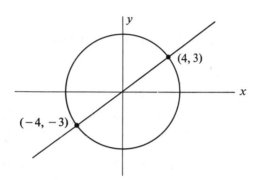

Figure 2.25

PROBLEM LIST 10

1.　Find the slope of each of the following lines and sketch its graph:

(a) $3x + 2y - 6 = 0$.　　　　　　(g) $9x - 11y + 4 = 0$.

(b) $4x - 3y + 7 = 0$.　　　　　　(h) $4x + 3y = 0$.

(c) $-2x + 4y - 9 = 0$.　　　　　(i) $6x - 5y = 0$.

(d) $3x - 2 = 0$.　　　　　　　　(j) $5x + 6y - 10 = 0$.

(e) $2y + 3 = 0$.　　　　　　　　(k) $4x + 6y + 1 = 0$.

(f) $x + y + 1 = 0$.　　　　　　　(l) $(2x/3) + (3y/2) - (2/3) = 0$.

2.　Find the intercepts and sketch the graph of each of the following lines:

(a) $3x - 4y + 24 = 0$.　　　　　(e) $5x - 2y + 1 = 0$.

(b) $x - 6y + 11 = 0$.　　　　　　(f) $2x + 2y - 3 = 0$.

(c) $9x + 4y - 3 = 0$.　　　　　　(g) $2x - 2y - 3 = 0$.

(d) $x + 7y - 2 = 0$.　　　　　　(h) $x + y - 1 = 0$.

3.　Find the points of intersection of the graphs of the following pairs of equations. Draw the graphs showing both the curves and their intersections.

(a) $2x - 3y + 4 = 0$ and $4x + y - 1 = 0$.

(b) $8x + 3y - 1 = 0$ and $6x - y + 4 = 0$.

(c) $x + y - 3 = 0$ and $3x + 4y = 0$.

(d) $x^2 + y^2 - 169 = 0$ and $12x + 5y = 0$.

(e) $x^2 + y^2 - 1 = 0$ and $y = 3x$.

(f) $y = x^3$ and $y = x^2$.

(g) $y = 1/x$ and $3x - 2y + 1 = 0$.

(h) $y^2 - x = 0$ and $2x - 4y + 5 = 0$.

(i) $x^2 + y = 0$ and $2x - 3y + 6 = 0$.

(j) $y = 4/(1 + x^2)$ and $y = 2x$.

(k) $y = |x|$ and $x - 5y + 10 = 0$.

4. Find the length of the chord of $x^2 + y^2 = 25$ determined by $x + y + 1 = 0$.

5. Find the length of the chord of $x^2 + y^2 = 16$ determined by $x + y - 1 = 0$.

6. Find an equation of the line through the intersection of $2x - 3y + 4 = 0$ and $3x + 4y - 1 = 0$ and through $(2, 3)$.

7. Find an equation of the line through the intersection of $4x + 3y - 1 = 0$ and $2x - 6y + 5 = 0$ and through $(-2, 1)$.

8. Fahrenheit and centigrade temperatures are related by the equation $9\,C - 5\,F + 160 = 0$. Draw the graph of the equation.

   Find F when $C = 0$ and when $C = 100$. Also find C when $F = 0$ and when $F = 100$. All values are given in degrees.

9. Points $A(0, 0)$, $B(8, 6)$, and $C(12, 0)$ are vertices of a triangle.

   (a) Write equations of the altitudes and show that they meet in a point.

   (b) Write equations of the medians and show that they meet in a point.

   (c) Write equations of the perpendicular bisectors of the sides and show that they meet in a point.

10. In Problem 9 replace A, B, and C by $A(-5, -1)$, $B(2, 4)$, and $C(5, -3)$.

11. Show that an equation of the line through (x_1, y_1) parallel to $ax + by + c = 0$ is $ax + by = ax_1 + by_1$.

12. Show that an equation of the line through (x_1, y_1) perpendicular to $ax + by + c = 0$ is $bx - ay = bx_1 - ay_1$.

2.17   One-Parameter Family of Curves

An equation of the form $f(x, y, a) = 0$ (read as "f of xya equals zero") may be regarded as a relationship between x and y for each possible value of a. When we adopt this viewpoint we refer to the auxiliary variable a as a parameter. The set of curves obtained by allowing a to take on all possible values is called a one-parameter family of curves.

Example 1.   The equation $x^2 + y^2 - a^2 = 0$ represents a one-parameter family of circles. If we replace a by any real number other than zero, we obtain a circle with center at the origin and radius a. When $a = 0$, the graph of $x^2 + y^2 = a^2$ is the point $(0, 0)$, which for convenience we regard as a point circle or circle of radius zero. It is instructive to think of $x^2 + y^2 - a^2 = 0$ as representing all possible circles having center at the origin.

Example 2.   The equation $y = 2x + b$ represents a one-parameter family of lines, each having slope 2, the parameter b representing the y-intercept. The family includes all lines of slope 2.

Example 3.   The equation $y - 2 = m(x - 3)$ represents a one-parameter family of lines, each passing through the point $(3, 2)$. The family includes all lines through $(3, 2)$ with the exception of the vertical line $x = 3$.

There is no value of the parameter m which reduces $y - 2 = m(x - 3)$ to $x = 3$. The graphs of a few one-parameter families are displayed in Fig. 2.26.

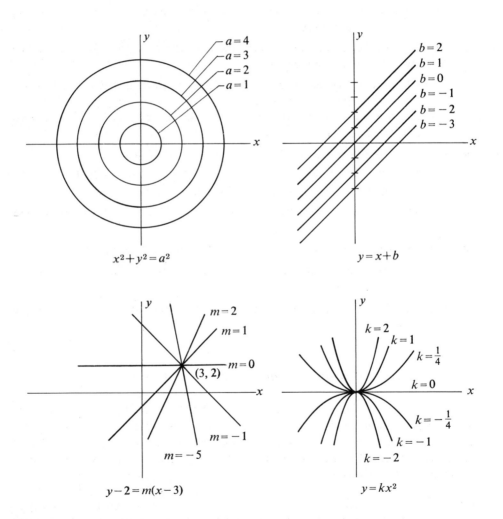

Figure 2.26

Example 4.   The equation

$$(x - y - 2) + k(2x + y - 7) = 0 \tag{2.17}$$

represents a one-parameter family of lines passing through the intersection (a, b) of the lines $x - y - 2 = 0$ and $2x + y - 7 = 0$. For every real k, (2.17) is a linear equation and hence represents a line. Also, since (a, b) is on both lines,

$$(a - b - 2) + k(2a + b - 7) = 0$$

reduces to $\qquad\qquad 0 + k(0) = 0.$

Thus, every member of the family (2.17) passes through (a, b) regardless of the value assigned to k.

To find the member of (2.17) which passes through $(2, 4)$ we substitute $x = 2$ and $y = 4$ in (2.17) and solve for k:

$$(2 - 4 - 2) + k(4 + 4 - 7) = 0,$$

from which $k = 4$.

Substituting $k = 4$ in (2.17) we obtain the required line

$$(x - y - 2) + 4(2x + y - 7) = 0$$

or

$$3x + y - 10 = 0.$$

If we set $k = 0$ in (2.17) we obtain the line $x - y - 2 = 0$. However, there is no real k which will reduce (2.17) to the line $2x + y - 7 = 0$, so this line is not included in the family (2.17).

The family of all lines through (a, b) can be represented by setting $k = k_2/k_1$ and writing

$$k_1(x - y - 2) + k_2(2x + y - 7) = 0$$

where the parameters k_1 and k_2 are allowed to assume all possible values. Setting $k_1 = 0$ and $k_2 = 1$ we obtain the line $2x + y - 7 = 0$. The parameters k_1 and k_2 are not independent, since (except for division by zero) we can divide through by either k_1 or k_2.

Similarly, the general equation of a straight line, $Ax + By + C = 0$, contains only two independent constants or parameters.

If we divide by B, we obtain

$$y = -\frac{Ax}{B} - \frac{C}{B},$$

which is of the form $y = mx + b$.

The general form is more "general" than the slope-intercept form, since it includes all possible lines whereas the slope-intercept form does not include vertical lines. Vertical lines are obtained from the general form by setting $B = 0$. We say that the family of lines is a two-parameter family.

PROBLEM LIST 11

1. Write an equation of each family of lines. Draw the graphs of five members of each family:

    (a) having slope 3;

    (b) through $(-2, 3)$;

    (c) parallel to the y-axis;

    (d) having inclination $135°$;

    (e) parallel to the line $2x - 4y - 6 = 0$;

    (f) perpendicular to the line $3x + 4y + 1 = 0$.

2. Write an equation of each family of lines. Draw the graphs of five members of each family:

    (a) parallel to the x-axis;

    (b) through $(4, -1)$;

    (c) having inclination $30°$;

    (d) having y-intercept -2;

    (e) having x-intercept 7;

    (f) through the intersection of $x + 2y - 5 = 0$ and $2x - 4y + 3 = 0$.

3. Describe the property common to each family. Draw the graphs of five members of each family.

    (a) $y = -2x + b$.

    (b) $y = mx + 2$.

    (c) $y + 3 = m(x - 4)$.

    (d) $ky + 3x = 6$.

    (e) $(2x + 3y - 8) + k(5x - y - 3) = 0$.

    (f) $3y - kx = 12$.

4. Write an equation of the family of lines having slope 3. Then find the member of the family which

    (a) passes through $(4, -3)$;

    (b) has y-intercept 6;

    (c) has x-intercept -4;

    (d) passes through $(-1, 3)$.

5. Write an equation of the family of lines through $(3, -2)$. Then find the member of the family

    (a) through $(5, 2)$;

    (b) having slope -3;

    (c) perpendicular to the line $3x - 2y = 1$;

    (d) parallel to the line $4x + 2y = 5$.

6. Write an equation of the family of lines through the intersection of $3x - 2y = 5$ and $2x - y = 4$. Then find the member of the family

    (a) through $(5, -1)$;

    (b) having y-intercept 4;

    (c) having slope -2;

    (d) perpendicular to the line $3x - 4y = 11$.

7. Find the member of the family $y = k|x|$ passing through $(-5, 10)$.

8. Find the member of the family $y = kx^2$ passing through $(2, 7)$.

9. Find the lines of slope 1 which meet the circle $x^2 + y^2 = 1$ in one and only one point.

10. Write an equation of the family of lines through $(3, 2)$. Find the members of the family which form with the coordinate axes first-quadrant triangles of area 16.

11. A triangle has sides $6x - 8y + 48 = 0$, $5x + 4y - 20 = 0$, and $x - 10y + 1 = 0$. Find equations of the altitudes without finding the vertices.

2.18   Equation of a Line in Normal Form

In Fig. 2.27, l is any line that does not pass through the origin. The line ON is normal (meaning perpendicular) to l and the distance p between O and N is assumed to be positive. The angle between the positive x-axis and line segment ON (measured counterclockwise when the coordinate axes are drawn in their usual positions) is denoted by ω (omega). Angle ω is in the interval $0 \leqslant \omega < 2\pi$, and in trigonometry we say that ω is in standard position.

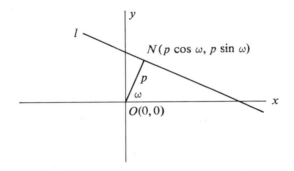

Figure 2.27

Line l has slope $(-\cos \omega)/(\sin \omega)$, since line ON has slope $(p \sin \omega)/(p \cos \omega)$. We employ the point-slope form to obtain an equation of l:

$$y - p \sin \omega = \frac{-\cos \omega}{\sin \omega}(x - p \cos \omega)$$

which after a slight simplification becomes

$$x \cos \omega + y \sin \omega - p = 0. \tag{2.18}$$

Equation (2.18) is called the normal form of l.

Example.   To find the normal form of the line l for which $\omega = 5\pi/6$ and $p = 5$, we replace $\cos \omega$, $\sin \omega$, and p in (2.18) by $-\sqrt{3}/2$, $1/2$, and 5, respectively, to obtain

$$\frac{-\sqrt{3}\,x}{2} + \frac{1y}{2} - 5 = 0.$$

To sketch l we place ω in standard position and locate the point N on the terminal side of ω five units from the origin O. Then l is the line through N normal to line ON. See Fig. 2.28.

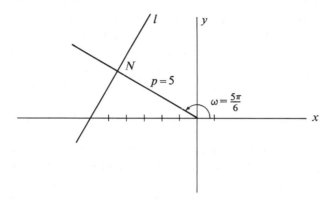

Figure 2.28

Suppose a line l is given in the general form $ax + by + c = 0$. To write l in normal form we seek a number k such that

  (i) $a/k = \cos \omega$.
  (ii) $b/k = \sin \omega$.
  (iii) $c/k = -p < 0$.

Since $a^2/k^2 + b^2/k^2 = \cos^2 \omega + \sin^2 \omega = 1$, **(i)** and **(ii)** will be satisfied if $k = \sqrt{a^2 + b^2}$ or $k = -\sqrt{a^2 + b^2}$.

To satisfy **(iii)**, we choose the k which has the opposite sign from c. Thus there is one and only one value of k which satisfies **(i)**, **(ii)**, and **(iii)**.

Example 1. To write the line $3x - 4y - 10 = 0$ in normal form, we divide both sides by $k = \sqrt{(3)^2 + (4)^2} = 5$ to obtain

$$\frac{3x}{5} - \frac{4y}{5} - 2 = 0$$

from which it is evident that

$$\cos \omega = \frac{3}{5}, \quad \sin \omega = \frac{-4}{5}, \quad \text{and} \quad p = 2.$$

Example 2. To write the line $4x - 5y + 7 = 0$ in normal form, we divide both sides by $k = -\sqrt{(4)^2 + (5)^2} = -\sqrt{41}$ to obtain

$$\frac{-4x}{\sqrt{41}} + \frac{5y}{\sqrt{41}} - \frac{7}{\sqrt{41}} = 0,$$

from which it is evident that

$$\cos \omega = \frac{-4}{\sqrt{41}}, \quad \sin \omega = \frac{5}{\sqrt{41}}, \quad \text{and} \quad p = \frac{7}{\sqrt{41}}.$$

Example 3.   To write $5x - 12y = 0$ in normal form, we divide both sides by $k = -\sqrt{(5)^2 + (12)^2} = -13$ to obtain

$$\frac{-5x}{13} + \frac{12y}{13} = 0.$$

The negative k is chosen so that the coefficient of y will be positive. This makes $\sin \omega > 0$, which amounts to choosing ω in the interval $0 < \omega < \pi$.
We see that $\cos \omega = -5/13$, $\sin \omega = 12/13$, and p must be zero, since the line goes through the origin.

PROBLEM LIST 12

1. Write in normal form the equation of the line for which
   (a) $\omega = 30°, p = 3$;   (e) $\omega = 90°, p = 2$;
   (b) $\omega = 135°, p = 5$;   (f) $\omega = 180°, p = 10$;
   (c) $\omega = 315°, p = 1$;   (g) $\omega = 240°, p = 6$;
   (d) $\omega = 120°, p = 7$;   (h) $\omega = 75°, p = 3$.

2. Sketch each line in Problem 1.

3. Write in normal form the equation of the line for which
   (a) $\omega = \pi, p = 3$;   (e) $\omega = 7\pi/4, p = 5$;
   (b) $\omega = 0, p = 3$;   (f) $\omega = 5\pi/6, p = 3$;
   (c) $\omega = \pi/6, p = 7$;   (g) $\omega = 3\pi/4, p = 0$;
   (d) $\omega = 7\pi/6, p = 4$;   (h) $\omega = \pi/12, p = 7$.

4. Sketch each line in Problem 3.

5. Write each equation in normal form. State the values of $\cos \omega$, $\sin \omega$, and p.
   (a) $3x + 4y - 25 = 0$.   (e) $5x + 2y = 4$.
   (b) $5x - 12y + 26 = 0$.   (f) $x + y = 1$.
   (c) $2x + 3y - 1 = 0$.   (g) $12x + 5y = 0$.
   (d) $7x + 24y = 625$.   (h) $y = 4x/3$.

6. Sketch each line in Problem 5: **(a)** by plotting the intercepts, **(b)** by using ω and p.

7. Write each equation in normal form. State the values of $\cos \omega$, $\sin \omega$, and p.
   (a) $4x + 3y - 5 = 0$.   (e) $8x - 15y = 34$.
   (b) $5x + 12y - 39 = 0$.   (f) $x = 5$.
   (c) $x + 3y = 5$.   (g) $x = -5$.
   (d) $2x - y = 3$.   (h) $y + 2 = 0$.

8. Draw the graphs of five members of each of the following families of lines:
   (a) $x \cos \omega + y \sin \omega - 3 = 0$.
   (b) $(3x/5) - (4y/5) - p = 0$.

9. How far is the line $8x + 15y + 102 = 0$ from the origin?

10. How far is the line $2x - 3y = 1$ from the origin?

11.   A circle has center at the origin and radius 3. Find equations of the lines having slope $-(3/4)$ which are tangent to this circle.

12.   Find an equation of the line through (2, 3) for which $\omega = \pi/4$.

13.   Find an equation of the line which is 11 units from the origin and which passes through (5, 10).

14.   Find an equation of the line which is two units from the origin and which passes through (3, 0).

2.19   Distance from a Line to a Point

In Fig. 2.29, l is a line whose equation in normal form is

$$x \cos \omega + y \sin \omega - p = 0. \tag{2.19}$$

The point $P_1(x_1, y_1)$ is d units from l, where $d > 0$ if P_1 and the origin are on opposite sides of l and $d < 0$ if P_1 and the origin are on the same side of l. The line λ passes through P_1 and is parallel to l.

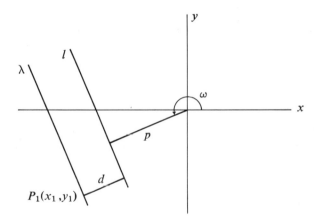

Figure 2.29

The equation of λ in normal form is

$$x \cos \omega + y \sin \omega - (p + d) = 0, \tag{2.20}$$

providing $p + d > 0$.

But (2.20) can be written

$$d = x \cos \omega + y \sin \omega - p. \tag{2.21}$$

Since P_1 lies on λ, its coordinates x_1 and y_1 satisfy (2.21); that is,

$$d = x_1 \cos \omega + y_1 \sin \omega - p. \tag{2.22}$$

But the right member of (2.22) is the left member of (2.19) with x replaced by x_1 and y replaced by y_1. Consequently we have the following rule:

To find the distance from a line l to a point $P_1(x_1, y_1)$, substitute x_1 for x and y_1 for y in the normal form of l.

If $p + d < 0$, the normal form of λ is

$$x \cos(\omega \pm \pi) + y \sin(\omega \pm \pi) + (p + d) = 0.$$

Since this equation reduces to (2.21), the rule also holds in this case.

Example 1.   Find the distance from the line $3x + 4y - 15 = 0$ to the point $(4, 5)$.

Applying the rule, we obtain

$$d = \frac{3(4) + 4(5) - 15}{5} = \frac{17}{5} = 3.4.$$

Since $d > 0$, $(4, 5)$ and $(0, 0)$ are on opposite sides of the given line.

Example 2.   Find the distance from line $2x - 3y + 4 = 0$ to point $(5, -1)$.

Again applying our rule, we have

$$d = \frac{2(5) - 3(-1) + 4}{-\sqrt{13}} = \frac{-17}{\sqrt{13}} \cong -4.7.$$

Since $d < 0$, $(5, -1)$ and $(0, 0)$ are on the same side of the given line.

PROBLEM LIST 13

1. Find the distance from the line to the point. Make a sketch to verify that the answer is reasonable.

   (a) $3x - 4y + 25 = 0$, $(3, -6)$.

   (b) $8x - 15y - 17 = 0$, $(2, 1)$.

   (c) $5x + 12y - 26 = 0$, $(-3, 2)$.

   (d) $2x + y - 4 = 0$, $(3, 0)$.

   (e) $3x + 4y = 12$, $(-5, -2)$.

   (f) $4x - 3y = 7$, $(4, 5)$.

   (g) $3x - y - 1 = 0$, $(-2, 4)$.

   (h) $x + 5 = 0$, $(-13, 8)$.

2. Find the distance from the line to the point. Make a sketch to verify that the answer is reasonable.

   (a) $4x + 3y - 10 = 0$, $(3, -4)$.

   (b) $6x - y = 5$, $(4, 0)$.

   (c) $3x + 3y = 8$, $(-2, -3)$.

   (d) $15x + 8y = 51$, $(4, -5)$.

   (e) $3x - 4y = 11$, $(8, -2)$.

   (f) $3x - 4y = 0$, $(6, 2)$.

   (g) $x + y + 1 = 0$, $(0, 0)$.

   (h) $y - 5 = 0$, $(4, 6)$.

3. Find the distance between the following parallel lines:

   (a) $3x - 4y = 2$, $6x - 8y = 1$.

     (b) $4x + 3y = 11, 4x + 3y = -2$.

     (c) $x + y = 1, 2x + 2y = 3$.

     (d) $2x - 3y = 5, 2x - 3y = 9$.

4.   Find the distance between the following parallel lines:

     (a) $6x - y = 5, 12x - 2y = 7$.

     (b) $4x + 4y = 2, x + y = 0$.

     (c) $3x - 4y - 9, 6x - 8y = 1$.

     (d) $8x + 15y = 51, 16x + 30y = 9$.

5.   Are the points $(-4, 2)$ and $(3, -6)$ on the same or opposite sides of $3x - 4y + 10 = 0$?

6.   Find k if $(3, k)$ is five units from $3x + 4y = 60$. Obtain two answers by allowing d to be either positive or negative.

7.   Find k if $(k, 4)$ is six units from $8x - 15y = 68$. Obtain two answers by allowing d to be either positive or negative.

8.   Does the line $5x + 4y = 20$ intersect the circle $x^2 + y^2 = 9$?

9.   Show that the distance from $ax + by = 0$ to $P_1(x_1, y_1)$ is positive if P_1 is above the line and negative if P_1 is below the line.

10.   A triangle has vertices $(7, 2)$, $(-1, 5)$, and $(9, -3)$. Determine whether $(2, 2)$ is inside or outside the triangle.

11.   A triangle has vertices at $A(-6, 3)$, $B(8, 4)$, and $C(0, -5)$. Find (a) the lengths of the altitudes, (b) the area of the triangle.

12.   A triangle has vertices at $A(-8, 0)$, $B(6, 4)$, and $C(2, -3)$. Find (a) the lengths of the altitudes, (b) the area of the triangle.

13.   Find equations of the bisectors of the angles formed by $3x - 4y = 10$ and $6x + 8y = 5$.

14.   Find equations of the bisectors of the angles formed by $8x + 15y = 17$ and $4x - 3y = 7$.

15.   A triangle has vertices at $A(0, 8)$, $B(1, 0)$, and $C(6, 5)$. Find equations of the bisectors of the three angles.

2.20   *Analytic Proofs of Geometric Theorems*

    The techniques of analytic geometry provide a powerful method of proving geometric propositions. The geometric figures are referred to a system of coordinate axes and the geometric statements of the theorems are translated into algebraic equations involving the coordinates of the points of the geometric figures. The method is best illustrated by examples.

Example 1.   Prove that the midpoint of the hypotenuse of a right triangle is equidistant from the three vertices.

    Locate the origin at the vertex C of the right triangle and let the positive *x*-axis pass through the vertex *B*, which will have abscissa *a* and ordinate 0. Let the positive *y*-axis pass through vertex *A*, which will have abscissa 0 and ordinate *b*. See Fig. 2.30.

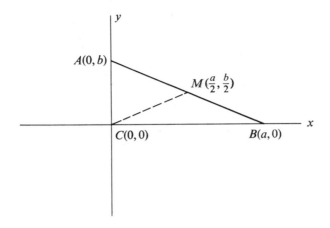

Figure 2.30

By the distance formula

$$AM = \sqrt{\left(\frac{a}{2} - 0\right)^2 + \left(\frac{b}{2} - b\right)^2},$$

$$BM = \sqrt{\left(a - \frac{a}{2}\right)^2 + \left(0 - \frac{b}{2}\right)^2},$$

and

$$CM = \sqrt{\left(\frac{a}{2} - 0\right)^2 + \left(\frac{b}{2} - 0\right)^2}.$$

Since *AM*, *BM*, and *CM* are all equal to $\frac{1}{2}\sqrt{a^2 + b^2}$, the conclusion follows.

It is important to note that the triangle depicted in Fig. 2.30 is an arbitrary right triangle but not an arbitrary triangle. An arbitrary triangle could be assigned vertices *C*(0, 0), *B*(*p*, 0), and *A*(*q*, *r*). It would be permissible to assume that $p > 0$ and $r > 0$, since the *x*- and *y*-axes could always be so chosen. Any assumption regarding the sign of *q* would be improper, since $q < 0$ assumes that *C* is an obtuse angle, $q > 0$ that *C* is an acute angle, and $q = 0$ that *C* is a right angle.

Example 2. Prove that the line segments joining consecutive midpoints of the sides of a quadrilateral form a parallelogram.

A general quadrilateral *ABCD* is referred to *x*- and *y*-axes in Fig. 2.31.

Multiples of 2 are used to designate the vertices of *ABCD*, so that the midpoints *E*, *F*, *G*, and *H* will have simple coordinates. This involves no loss in generality.

The slopes of *EF*, *FG*, *GH*, and *HE* are e/c, $b/(a - f)$, e/c, and $b/(a - f)$, respectively.

The opposite sides of *EFGH* are parallel, since they have equal slopes (or are vertical), and hence *EFGH* is a parallelogram.

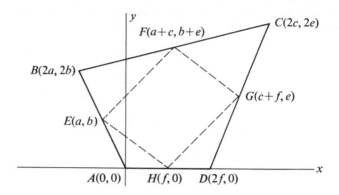

Figure 2.31

PROBLEM LIST 14

Prove the following theorems analytically:

1. The diagonals of a rectangle are equal.

2. The diagonals of a rectangle bisect each other.

3. The line segment joining the midpoints of two sides of a triangle is parallel to the third side and has length one-half that of the third side.

4. The diagonals of a parallelogram bisect each other.

5. The medians from the ends of the base of an isosceles triangle are equal.

6. The sum of the squares of the sides of a parallelogram is equal to the sum of the squares of the diagonals.

7. The sum of the squares of the medians of a triangle is equal to three-fourths the sum of the squares of the three sides.

8. The two lines from a vertex of a parallelogram to the midpoints of the opposite sides trisect the opposite diagonal.

9. The diagonals of a rectangle are perpendicular if and only if the rectangle is a square.

10. The line segments joining the midpoints of opposite sides of a quadrilateral bisect each other. (Use Fig. 2.31.)

11. If two medians of a triangle are equal, the triangle is isosceles.

12. The diagonals of an isosceles trapezoid are equal.

13. The converse of the Pythagorean theorem is true.

14. The sum of the squares of the reciprocals of the legs of a right triangle is equal to the square of the reciprocal of the altitude drawn from the right angle.

15. The altitudes of a triangle intersect in a point.

16. The medians of a triangle intersect in a point which is two-thirds of the distance from any vertex to the midpoint of the opposite side.

REFERENCES

2.1 C. B. BOYER, "History of Analytic Geometry," *Scripta Mathematica*, Yeshiva University, New York, 1956.

2.2 J. G. KEMENY, J. L. SNELL, and G. L. THOMPSON, *Introduction to Finite Mathematics*, Prentice-Hall, Englewood Cliffs, N.J., 1960.

2.3 I. S. SOKOLNIKOFF, *Advanced Calculus*, McGraw-Hill, New York, 1939.

Chapter
3

The differential calculus

3.1 Limit of a Function

Let f be a function defined by $y = f(x)$ and let a be a real number. Assume that f is defined at every point of an open interval containing a except that f may or may not be defined at $x = a$. We are frequently interested in the behavior of $f(x)$ when x is arbitrarily close to a. If, when x is arbitrarily close to a but not equal to a, $f(x)$ is arbitrarily close to a real number L, we say that $f(x)$ approaches L as x approaches a, and we often write $f(x) \rightarrow L$ as $x \rightarrow a$. For example, if $f(x) = x^2$ and $a = 2$, we note that $f(x)$ is close to 4 when x is close to 2.

The preceding discussion is vague, since the meanings of "close" and "arbitrarily close" are not clear. The following definition makes precise the concept of limit of a function.

Definition (*limit of a function*). Let the function f be defined at every point of an open interval containing a except that f may or may not be defined at a. Then the limit of f at a is L, written

$$\lim_{x \to a} f(x) = L \qquad (3.1)$$

if and only if for every positive number ϵ there exists a δ such that

$$|f(x) - L| < \epsilon$$

whenever

$$0 < |x - a| < \delta.$$

Statement (3.1) is also read as "the limit of $f(x)$ as x approaches a is L." Note that $f(x)$ may equal L at a, may be different from L at a, or may be undefined at a. In other words, the character of f at a has nothing to do with the limit of f at a. Note also that δ is positive. If no L exists such that

$$\lim_{x \to a} f(x) = L,$$

we say that $\lim_{x \to a} f(x)$ does not exist.

To prove that the limit of f at a is L, we assume that an *arbitrary* positive number ϵ is given. We then produce a positive number δ such that

$$L - \epsilon < f(x) < L + \epsilon$$

for all x, except possibly $x = a$, satisfying

$$a - \delta < x < a + \delta.$$

In general, the smaller ϵ is, the smaller will be a corresponding acceptable δ. It is often convenient to assume at the outset that ϵ is less than some fixed positive number, say, $\epsilon < 0.01$, since a $\delta = \delta(\epsilon)$ acceptable for every $0 < \epsilon < 0.01$ is clearly acceptable for every $0 < \epsilon$. Finally, if $\delta = \delta(\epsilon)$ is an acceptable δ, it is obvious that any δ_1 satisfying $0 < \delta_1 < \delta$ is also acceptable.

Example 1.   Prove that $\lim_{x \to 3} 2x = 6$.

   Proof.   Given $\epsilon > 0$, we must show that there exists a $\delta > 0$ such that

$$6 - \epsilon < 2x < 6 + \epsilon$$

whenever

$$3 - \delta < x < 3 + \delta \qquad \text{and} \qquad x \neq 3.$$

But

$$6 - \epsilon < 2x < 6 + \epsilon$$

if and only if $3 - (\epsilon/2) < x < 3 + (\epsilon/2)$.

   Thus, if we take $\delta = \epsilon/2$, it will follow that

$$|2x - 6| < \epsilon$$

whenever

$$0 < |x - 3| < \delta = \frac{\epsilon}{2}.$$

Note that the smaller ϵ is, the smaller will be an acceptable δ.

Example 2.   Prove that $\lim_{x \to 2} (3x + 4) = 10$.

   Proof.   Given $\epsilon > 0$, we must show that there exists a $\delta > 0$ such that

$$10 - \epsilon < 3x + 4 < 10 + \epsilon$$

whenever

$$2 - \delta < x < 2 + \delta \qquad \text{and} \qquad x \neq 2.$$

But

$$10 - \epsilon < 3x + 4 < 10 + \epsilon$$

if and only if

$$6 - \epsilon < 3x < 6 + \epsilon,$$

which in turn holds if and only if

$$2 - \frac{\epsilon}{3} < x < 2 + \frac{\epsilon}{3}.$$

Thus, if we take $\delta = \epsilon/3$ it will follow that

$$|(3x + 4) - 10| < \epsilon$$

whenever

$$0 < |x - 2| < \delta = \frac{\epsilon}{3}.$$

Example 3.   Prove that $\lim_{x \to 2} x^2 = 4$.

    Proof.   We note that

$$|x^2 - 4| = |x + 2||x - 2|.$$

We first restrict x so that

$$|x - 2| < 1 = \delta_1;$$

that is, we restrict x to the interval $1 < x < 3$. It then follows that

$$|x^2 - 4| < |3 + 2||x - 2| = 5|x - 2|.$$

    We then restrict x so that $|x - 2| < \epsilon/5 = \delta_2$. Both these restrictions on x will hold if we choose δ the smaller of the numbers δ_1 and δ_2. Then $|x^2 - 4| < \epsilon$ whenever $0 < |x - 2| < \delta$.

Example 4.   Prove that $\lim_{x \to 0} (x/x) = 1$.

    Proof.   We note that

$$\left| \frac{x}{x} - 1 \right| = |1 - 1| = 0 < \epsilon$$

whenever $0 < |x - 0| < \delta$ for every $\delta > 0$. Thus, any $\delta > 0$ is an acceptable δ. This is an exception, since in general an acceptable δ will be dependent upon ϵ. This example also illustrates the fact that $\lim_{x \to a} f(x)$ may exist even though $f(x)$ is undefined at $x = a$. The expression x/x is undefined at $x = 0$ but approaches 1 as x approaches 0.

    The following theorem, the proof of which is left to the Problem List, makes it possible to investigate the limit of a function by employing the concept of the limit of a sequence.

Theorem 3-I.   Let the function f be defined in an open interval I containing $x = a$ except possibly at $x = a$. Then

$$\lim_{x \to a} f(x) = L$$

if and only if

$$\lim_{n \to \infty} f(x_n) = L$$

for *every* sequence $\{x_n\}$ in I such that $\lim_{n \to \infty} x_n = a$ and $x_n \neq a$ for all n.

    Theorem 3-I is particularly useful in proving that the limit of a function f at a does not exist. It is merely necessary to exhibit one sequence $\{x_n\}$ in I such that $\lim_{n \to \infty} x_n = a$, $(x_n \neq a)$, and to verify that $\lim_{n \to \infty} f(x_n)$ does not exist.

Example 5.   Investigate $\lim_{x\to 0}(1/x)$.

Solution.   Consider the sequence $\{1/n\}$. While $\lim_{n\to\infty}(1/n) = 0$, $\lim_{n\to\infty}(n)$ does not exist. Hence, by Theorem 3-I, $\lim_{x\to 0}(1/x)$ does not exist. Note that $1/x$ becomes large without limit when $x \to 0$ along a sequence such as $\{1/n\}$. If $x \to 0$ along $\{-1/n\}$, $|1/x|$ becomes large without limit while $1/x$ remains negative.

Example 6.   The procedure of Example 5 also enables us to show that $\lim_{x\to 0}(1/x^2)$ does not exist. We find it more descriptive to write

$$\lim_{x\to 0}\frac{1}{x^2} = \infty.$$

This means merely that as $x \to 0$ along any $\{x_n\}$ for which $x_n \neq 0$, the corresponding sequence $\{1/x_n^2\} \to \infty$.

Example 7

$$\lim_{x\to 0}\left|\frac{1}{x}\right| = \infty.$$

Example 8

$$\lim_{x\to 0}\frac{-1}{x^2} = -\infty.$$

Example 9.   Consider $\lim_{x\to 0}\sin(1/x)$.

This limit does not exist, since $\sin(1/x)$ oscillates between $+1$ and -1 when $x \to 0$ along the sequence

$$\left\{\frac{2}{(2n-1)\pi}\right\}.$$

Note, however, that when $x \to 0$ along the sequence $\{1/n\pi\}$, $\sin(1/x) \to 0$. This explains why Theorem 3-I states that for *every* sequence $\{x_n\} \to a$, the corresponding sequence $\{f(x_n)\}$ must approach L before we can conclude that $\lim_{x\to a}f(x) = L$.

Example 10.   Consider $\lim_{x\to 0}\sqrt{x}$.

This limit does not exist, since $\sqrt{x}$ is not real when $x < 0$. We can, however, consider the limit of $\sqrt{x}$ as $x \to 0$ through values of x greater than zero. We then write

$$\lim_{x\to 0^+}\sqrt{x} = 0,$$

read as "the limit as x approaches 0 from the right of the square root of x equals 0." This is called a right-hand limit.
Similarly,

$$\lim_{x\to 0^-}\sqrt{-x} = 0$$

illustrates a left-hand limit.

It can be proved (see Problem 18) that $\lim_{x \to a} f(x) = L$ if and only if $\lim_{x \to a^+} f(x) = L$ and $\lim_{x \to a^-} f(x) = L$.

The following theorems on limits play an important role in the subject. In evaluating limits of complicated functions it is simpler to apply these limit theorems than the (ϵ, δ) definition of limit of a function. We will prove Theorem 3-II; additional proofs are given in Ref. 3.3.

Theorem 3-II.   The limit of a sum is equal to the sum of the limits. That is, if

$$\lim_{x \to x_0} f_1(x) = L_1 \quad \text{and} \quad \lim_{x \to x_0} f_2(x) = L_2,$$

then

$$\lim_{x \to x_0} [f_1(x) + f_2(x)] = L_1 + L_2.$$

Proof.   Let $\epsilon > 0$ be assigned arbitrarily. Then, since

$$\lim_{x \to x_0} f_1(x) = L_1,$$

we can find a $\delta_1 > 0$ such that

$$|f_1(x) - L_1| < \frac{\epsilon}{2}$$

whenever $0 < |x - x_0| < \delta_1$.
    Similarly, we can find a $\delta_2 > 0$ such that

$$|f_2(x) - L_2| < \frac{\epsilon}{2}$$

whenever $0 < |x - x_0| < \delta_2$. Then, if δ is the smaller of δ_1 and δ_2,

$$|\{f_1(x) + f_2(x)\} - \{L_1 + L_2\}|$$
$$= |\{f_1(x) - L_1\} + \{f_2(x) - L_2\}|$$
$$\leqslant |f_1(x) - L_1| + |f_2(x) - L_2|$$
$$< \frac{\epsilon}{2} + \frac{\epsilon}{2} = \epsilon$$

whenever $0 < |x - x_0| < \delta$.
    But this is the statement that

$$\lim_{x \to x_0} [f_1(x) + f_2(x)] = L_1 + L_2.$$

Example 11

$$\lim_{x \to 2} (x^3 + x^2) = \lim_{x \to 2} (x^3) + \lim_{x \to 2} (x^2) = 8 + 4 = 12.$$

The following theorems can also be proved by resorting to the definition of a limit.

Theorem 3-III.   The limit of a product is equal to the product of the limits. That is, if

$$\lim_{x \to x_0} f_1(x) = L_1 \quad \text{and} \quad \lim_{x \to x_0} f_2(x) = L_2,$$

then

$$\lim_{x \to x_0} [f_1(x)f_2(x)] = L_1 L_2.$$

Example 12

$$\lim_{x \to 3} [(x^2 + 1)(x^3 - x)] = [\lim_{x \to 3} (x^2 + 1)][\lim_{x \to 3} (x^3 - x)]$$
$$= (10)(24) = 240.$$

Theorem 3-IV.   The limit of a quotient is equal to the quotient of the limits, provided the limit of the denominator is not zero. That is, if

$$\lim_{x \to x_0} f_1(x) = L_1 \quad \text{and} \quad \lim_{x \to x_0} f_2(x) = L_2 \neq 0,$$

then

$$\lim_{x \to x_0} \frac{f_1(x)}{f_2(x)} = \frac{L_1}{L_2}.$$

Example 13

$$\lim_{x \to 5} \frac{x^2}{x^2 - 4} = \frac{\lim_{x \to 5} x^2}{\lim_{x \to 5} (x^2 - 4)} = \frac{25}{21}.$$

Example 14

$$\lim_{x \to 2} \frac{x^2}{x^2 - 4}$$

does not exist, since

$$\lim_{x \to 2} (x^2 - 4) = 0 \quad \text{while} \quad \lim_{x \to 2} (x^2) = 4.$$

Theorem 3-V.   The limit of the nth root is equal to the nth root of the limit. That is, if

$$\lim_{x \to x_0} f(x) = L,$$

then

$$\lim_{x \to x_0} \sqrt[n]{f(x)} = \sqrt[n]{L}.$$

It is assumed that n is a positive integer and that if n is even, $L > 0$.

Example 15

$$\lim_{x \to 2} \sqrt[3]{x^2 + 1} = \sqrt[3]{5}.$$

We are frequently interested in the behavior of the functional values $f(x)$ of a function f as $x \to \infty$ or $x \to -\infty$.

Definition.   Let f be defined for all x greater than some real number x_0. We say that

$$\lim_{x \to \infty} f(x) = L,$$

read as "the limit of f as x becomes infinite is L," if and only if to every $\epsilon > 0$ there corresponds a number A such that

$$|f(x) - L| < \epsilon$$

for all x satisfying $x > A$.

Example 16

$$\lim_{x \to \infty} \frac{1}{x} = 0.$$

This result follows from the definition, since $|(1/x) - 0| < \epsilon$ for all x satisfying $x > 1/\epsilon = A$.

A similar definition holds for the symbolic expression

$$\lim_{x \to -\infty} f(x) = L.$$

Example 17

$$\lim_{x \to -\infty} \frac{2x + 1}{x} = \lim_{x \to -\infty} \left(2 + \frac{1}{x}\right)$$

$$= \lim_{x \to -\infty} 2 + \lim_{x \to -\infty} \frac{1}{x}$$

$$= 2 + 0 = 2.$$

Theorem 3-I has the following analog.

Theorem 3-VI. Let f be defined for all $x \geqslant x_0$. Then

$$\lim_{x \to \infty} f(x) = L$$

if and only if

$$\lim_{n \to \infty} f(x_n) = L$$

for *every* sequence $\{x_n\}$ for which $\lim_{n \to \infty} x_n = \infty$, $(x_n \geqslant x_0$ for all $n)$.

The following examples illustrate applications of the limit theorems we have developed.

Example 18. $\lim_{x \to \infty} x^2$ does not exist, since $\lim_{n \to \infty} n^2 = \infty$. Clearly,

$$\lim_{x \to \infty} x^2 = \infty.$$

Example 19

$$\lim_{x \to \infty} \frac{3x^3 - 2x^2 + 7}{4x^3 + 5x - 3} = \lim_{x \to \infty} \frac{3 - (2/x) + (7/x^3)}{4 + (5/x^2) - (3/x^3)}$$

$$= \frac{\lim_{x \to \infty} [3 - (2/x) + (7/x^3)]}{\lim_{x \to \infty} [4 + (5/x^2) - (3/x^3)]}$$

$$= \frac{3}{4}.$$

Example 20

$$\lim_{x \to -\infty} \frac{x^4 - 7x + 1}{3x^3 + 2} = \lim_{x \to -\infty} \frac{1 - (7/x^3) + (1/x^4)}{(3/x) + (2/x^4)}.$$

This limit does not exist, since the numerator approaches 1 while the denominator approaches 0 as $x \to -\infty$.

Example 21

$$\lim_{x \to \infty} \frac{2x^2 - 5x + 1}{5x^3 + 2x - 7} = \lim_{x \to \infty} \frac{(2/x) - (5/x^2) + (1/x^3)}{5 + (2/x^2) - (7/x^3)} = 0,$$

since the numerator approaches 0 while the denominator approaches 5 as $x \to \infty$.

Example 22

$$\lim_{x \to 2} \frac{x^2 - x - 2}{x - 2} = \lim_{x \to 2} \frac{(x - 2)(x + 1)}{x - 2}$$

$$= \left[\lim_{x \to 2} \frac{x - 2}{x - 2} \right] \left[\lim_{x \to 2} (x + 1) \right]$$

$$= [1][3] = 3.$$

This example shows that it is possible for the limit of a quotient to exist even when the limit of the denominator is zero. The limit of the quotient may exist if the limit of the numerator is also zero.

3.2   *Continuity*

Let us consider a person's height H (in feet) at age t (in years), where $10 \leqslant t \leqslant 30$. A mathematical model appropriate for studying the relationship between t and H is a function f given by $H = f(t)$, having domain $10 \leqslant t \leqslant 30$ and the property that for each t in the domain of f, $f(t)$ is the person's height at time t. We think intuitively of t changing gradually or continuously from $t = 10$ to $t = 30$, while at the same time $f(t)$ changes gradually or continuously from $f(10)$ to $f(30)$. We sometimes say that a person's height varies continuously with time. As time changes, the person's height changes gradually; it does not change abruptly from 5 ft to 6 ft. In our model for describing this situation we cannot think of t and $f(t)$ as moving or changing gradually, since t and $f(t)$ are numbers that do not move or change. The problem is to select from the set of available functions those which can be employed to describe situations involving change without break, or having the property we call continuity.

Many illustrations can be given. We say that the volume of a sphere varies continuously with the radius, the stretch in a spring varies continuously with the applied force, and so forth. The amount of money in a savings account does not vary continuously with time. When interest is applied (either simple or compound) the amount changes abruptly. In a fluid, boundaries called shock waves exist at which the temperature and pressure are discontinuous; that is, their values change abruptly.

Mathematicians long realized that the concept of continuity was of utmost importance in calculus, but it was not until 1821 that a satisfactory precise mathematical definition of this intuitive concept was developed. The following definition was formulated by the French mathematician Augustin-Louis Cauchy (1789–1857), who played a major role in establishing a firm foundation for the calculus. Note that the limit concept is employed to define continuity in terms of real numbers.

Definition (*continuity of a function*).   A function f defined by $y = f(x)$ is continuous at $x = a$ if and only if to every positive number ϵ there corresponds a positive number δ such that

$$|f(x) - f(a)| < \epsilon$$

whenever

$$|x - a| < \delta.$$

If f is defined in an open interval containing a, the following is an equivalent definition. (See Problem 17.)

Definition.   A function f defined by $y = f(x)$ is continuous at $x = a$ if and only if

$$\lim_{x \to a} f(x) = f(a). \tag{3.2}$$

This form of the definition implies that f is defined in some open interval containing a; otherwise f could not approach a limit as $x \to a$. Next, the definition implies that f is defined at $x = a$; otherwise $f(a)$ would be meaningless. Finally, the definition states that f has a limit at a and that this limit is $f(a)$.

Note that in the (ϵ, δ) definition of continuity, the number $x = a$ is not excluded as in the (ϵ, δ) definition of limit of a function. The inequality

$$|f(x) - f(a)| < \epsilon$$

is automatically satisfied when $x = a$.

If f is not continuous at a point a of its domain, we say that f is discontinuous at a.

It is instructive to consider the geometric interpretation of the (ϵ, δ) definition of continuity at $x = a$. The definition states that to every $\epsilon > 0$, there exists an open interval of width 2δ centered at a such that if x is restricted to this interval, the corresponding portion of the graph of f lies between the lines $y = f(a) - \epsilon$ and $y = f(a) + \epsilon$. See Fig. 3.1.

A function f is said to be continuous on the right at $x = a$ if and only if

$$\lim_{x \to a^+} f(x) = f(a),$$

and continuous on the left at $x = a$ if and only if

$$\lim_{x \to a^-} f(x) = f(a).$$

The function f is continuous on the closed interval $a \leqslant x \leqslant b$ if and only if f is continuous on the right at $x = a$, continuous on the left at $x = b$, and continuous

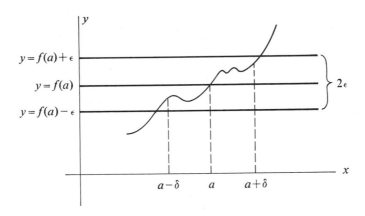

Figure 3.1

at every x_0 satisfying $a < x_0 < b$. If we merely say that f is continuous, we mean that f is continuous at every point in its domain.

Many important theorems in calculus assume in the hypotheses that one or more functions are continuous on a closed interval. Continuous functions provide appropriate mathematical models for studying physical situations involving "continuous" change. The height-age variation previously mentioned is such an example.

Example 1.   The function f defined by $f(x) = 1/x$ is continuous, since it is continuous at every point in its domain of definition D. Note that $x = 0$ is not a point of D.

Example 2.   The function f defined by $f(x) = \sqrt{1 - x^2}$ is continuous on the closed interval $-1 \leqslant x \leqslant 1$.

Example 3.   The function f defined by

$$f(x) = \begin{cases} |x|/x & \text{for} \quad x \neq 0 \\ 1 & \text{for} \quad x = 0 \end{cases}$$

is discontinuous at $x = 0$, since

$$\lim_{x \to 0^+} f(x) = 1 \neq \lim_{x \to 0^-} f(x) = -1.$$

See Fig. 3.2.

By employing the basic theorems on limits, it is possible to show that if the functions f and g are continuous at $x = a$, then their sum and product are also continuous at $x = a$. Also, their quotient f/g is continuous at $x = a$, provided $g(a) \neq 0$.

By showing that the function f defined by $f(x) = cx^n$, where c is constant and n is an integer $\geqslant 0$, is continuous at all x, and then using the fact that the sum of a

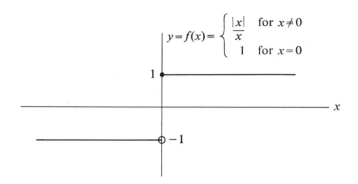

$$y = f(x) = \begin{cases} \dfrac{|x|}{x} & \text{for } x \neq 0 \\ 1 & \text{for } x = 0 \end{cases}$$

Figure 3.2

finite number of continuous functions is continuous, it is possible to show that a polynomial function P, defined by

$$P(x) = a_0 x^n + a_1 x^{n-1} + a_2 x^{n-2} + \cdots + a_{n-1} x + a_n,$$

is continuous at all values of x. Then, using the continuity of the quotient of continuous functions, it follows that a rational function R, defined by $R(x) = P(x)/Q(x)$, where $P(x)$ and $Q(x)$ are polynomials, is continuous at all values of x for which $Q(x) \neq 0$.

The following theorem is useful in evaluating limits and investigating continuity. Let f and g be functions and let the function h be defined by $h(x) = f[g(x)]$. The function h is called the composite of g by f and the domain of h is the set of all real numbers x in the domain of g such that $g(x)$ is in the domain of f. It is assumed that f is defined in an open interval containing b.

Theorem 3-VII. If $\lim_{x \to a} g(x) = g(a) = b$ and if f is continuous at b, then

$$\lim_{x \to a} h(x) = \lim_{x \to a} f[g(x)] = f(b).$$

Example

$$\lim_{x \to 2} \sqrt{x^2 - 1} = \sqrt{3}.$$

A composite function is also termed a function of a function. Theorem 3-VII states that a continuous function of a continuous function is continuous.

In general, the functions we will employ will be continuous, except possibly at isolated points. For example, we will show that the trigonometric function f defined by $f(x) = \sin x$ is continuous at every real x, and that the trigonometric function g defined by $g(x) = \tan x$ is continuous at every x in its domain of definition.

PROBLEM LIST 15

1. Employ the (ϵ, δ) definition of limit to establish the following limits:

(a) $\lim_{x \to a} c = c$, (c = constant).   (c) $\lim_{x \to a} 3x = 3a$.

(b) $\lim_{x \to a} x = a$.   (d) $\lim_{x \to 3} 2x = 6$.

(e) $\lim_{x\to2} (3x + 5) = 11.$

(l) $\lim_{x\to2} (x^3 - 8) = 0.$

(f) $\lim_{x\to4} x^2 = 16.$

(m) $\lim_{x\to0} \sqrt{|x|} = 0.$

(g) $\lim_{x\to0} (3x/x) = 3.$

(n) $\lim_{x\to2} (2/x) = 1.$

(h) $\lim_{x\to2} x^3 = 8.$

(o) $\lim_{x\to a} [kf(x)] = k[\lim_{x\to a} f(x)],$
$(k = \text{constant}).$

(i) $\lim_{x\to5} (3x - 1) = 14.$

(p) $\lim_{x\to2} (x^2 + x + 1) = 7.$

(j) $\lim_{x\to0} (x^2/x) = 0.$

(q) $\lim_{x\to4} \sqrt{x} = 2.$

(k) $\lim_{x\to a} (mx + b) = ma + b.$

(r) $\lim_{x\to a} \sqrt{x} = \sqrt{a},\ (a > 0).$

(s) $\lim_{x\to\infty} c = c,\ (c = \text{constant}).$

2. Show that each of the following limits does not exist:

(a) $\lim_{x\to\infty} x^3.$

(e) $\lim_{x\to2} \sqrt{1 - x^2}.$

(b) $\lim_{x\to0} \dfrac{2}{|x|}.$

(f) $\lim_{x\to0} \sin(1/x^2).$

(c) $\lim_{x\to\infty} \sin x.$

(g) $\lim_{x\to0} (x/x^2).$

(d) $\lim_{x\to1} \sqrt{x - 1}.$

3. State the contrapositive of the statement: If $\lim_{x\to a} f(x) = L$, then $\lim_{x\to\infty} f(x_n) = L$ for *every* sequence $\{x_n\}$ such that $\lim_{n\to\infty} x_n = a$ and $x_n \neq a$ for all n.

4. Employ the limit theorems of this section to evaluate the following limits:

(a) $\lim_{x\to2} (x^3 + 3x - 7).$

(k) $\lim_{x\to\infty} \dfrac{2x^3 - 3x^2}{3x^3 + 2x}.$

(b) $\lim_{x\to3} \dfrac{x^3 + 2x - 1}{x^2 + 4}.$

(l) $\lim_{x\to\infty} \dfrac{x + (1000)^{10}}{x^2}.$

(c) $\lim_{x\to0} \dfrac{x^2 + 2x - 9}{3x^2 + 5}.$

(m) $\lim_{x\to-\infty} \dfrac{-2x^2 + 7x - 1}{4x^2 + 5}.$

(d) $\lim_{x\to1} \dfrac{x^2 - 1}{x - 1}.$

(n) $\lim_{x\to0} \dfrac{x}{|x|}.$

(e) $\lim_{x\to4} \dfrac{x^2 - x - 12}{x - 4}.$

(o) $\lim_{x\to3} \dfrac{1}{x - 3}.$

(f) $\lim_{x\to1} \dfrac{(x - 2)(x - 1)(x + 3)}{(x - 1)(x + 2)}.$

(p) $\lim_{x\to3} \dfrac{1}{(x - 3)^2}.$

(g) $\lim_{x\to0} (5x/x).$

(q) $\lim_{x\to3} \sqrt{x^2 - 9}.$

(h) $\lim_{x\to\infty} (x^3 + 2x).$

(r) $\lim_{x\to\pi/2} (\tan x).$

(i) $\lim_{x\to-\infty} \dfrac{4}{2 - x}.$

(s) $\lim_{x\to\infty} \dfrac{\sin x}{x}.$

(j) $\lim_{x\to-\infty} \left(\dfrac{x}{x^3}\right).$

(t) $\lim_{x\to0} \left(\sin \dfrac{\pi}{x}\right).$

(u) $\lim\limits_{n\to\infty} \dfrac{a(1-r^n)}{1-r}$, $(|r| < 1)$.

(x) $\lim\limits_{h\to 0} \dfrac{1}{h}\left[\dfrac{1}{\sqrt{x+h}} - \dfrac{1}{\sqrt{x}}\right]$.

(v) $\lim\limits_{h\to 0} \dfrac{(x+h)^2 - x^2}{h}$.

(y) $\lim\limits_{x\to 0} \dfrac{\sqrt{x^2+1}-1}{x}$.

(w) $\lim\limits_{h\to 0} \dfrac{1}{h}\left[\dfrac{1}{x+h} - \dfrac{1}{x}\right]$.

(z) $\lim\limits_{x\to 1} \dfrac{1-\sqrt{x}}{1-x}$.

5. Evaluate the following limits:

(a) $\lim\limits_{x\to 0^+} \sqrt[4]{x}$.

(d) $\lim\limits_{x\to 2^+} \sqrt{x-2}$.

(b) $\lim\limits_{x\to 0^+} \dfrac{x}{|x|}$.

(e) $\lim\limits_{x\to 3} \sqrt{1-x^2}$.

(c) $\lim\limits_{x\to 0^-} \dfrac{x}{|x|}$.

(f) $\lim_{x\to 2^+} [x]$, where $[x]$ denotes the greatest integer less than or equal to x.

(g) $\lim\limits_{x\to 2^-} [x]$.

(j) $\lim\limits_{x\to 2^-} \dfrac{1}{x-2}$.

(h) $\lim\limits_{x\to(\pi/2)^-} (\tan x)$.

(k) $\lim\limits_{x\to -3^+} \sqrt{9-x^2}$.

(i) $\lim\limits_{x\to 2^+} \dfrac{1}{x-2}$.

(l) $\lim\limits_{x\to 3^-} \sqrt{9-x^2}$.

6. Given that

$$\lim_{x\to 0} \frac{\sin x}{x} = 1,$$

find

$$\lim_{x\to 0} \frac{1-\cos x}{x^2}.$$

7. A regular polygon of n sides, inscribed in a circle of radius r, has perimeter P_n and area A_n. Assuming that

$$\lim_{x\to 0} \frac{\sin x}{x} = 1,$$

show that

(a) $\lim\limits_{n\to\infty} P_n = 2\pi r$;

(b) $\lim\limits_{n\to\infty} A_n = \pi r^2$.

8. Given that

$$\lim_{x\to a} f_1(x) = L_1,$$

$$\lim_{x\to a} f_2(x) = L_2,$$

$$\lim_{x\to a} f_3(x) = L_3,$$

prove that

$$\lim_{x\to a} [f_1(x) + f_2(x) + f_3(x)] = L_1 + L_2 + L_3.$$

[Assume Theorem 3-II.]

9. Prove that

$$\lim_{x\to 3} x^2 = 9$$

(a) by employing the (ϵ, δ) definition of limit;

(b) by applying Theorem 3-III.

10. The function f is defined by

$$f(x) = \begin{cases} 1/x & \text{for } x \neq 0 \\ 0 & \text{for } x = 0 \end{cases}.$$

Prove that f is discontinuous at $x = 0$.

11. Prove that the function f defined by $f(x) = 2x + 3$ is continuous at $x = 5$.

12. Prove that the function defined by

$$f(x) = \begin{cases} |x|/x & \text{for } x \neq 0 \\ 0 & \text{for } x = 0 \end{cases}$$

is discontinuous at $x = 0$.

13. Prove that the function f defined by $f(x) = |x|$ is continuous at $x = 0$.

14. Prove that the function f defined by

$$f(x) = \begin{cases} \dfrac{x^2 - 9}{x - 3} & \text{for } x \neq 3 \\ 6 & \text{for } x = 3 \end{cases}$$

is continuous at $x = 3$.

15. Prove that the function f defined by

$$f(x) = \begin{cases} x^2 & \text{for } x \neq 0 \\ 1 & \text{for } x = 0 \end{cases}$$

is discontinuous at $x = 0$.

16. Discuss the continuity of the function f defined by $f(x) = [x]$, where $[x]$ denotes the greatest integer less than or equal to x.

17. Prove that the function f defined by $f(x) = \sqrt{-x^2}$ is continuous at $x = 0$ but that $\lim_{x \to 0} f(x) \neq f(0) = 0$.

18. Prove that

$$\lim_{x \to a} f(x) = L$$

if and only if

$$\lim_{x \to a^+} f(x) = L \qquad \text{and} \qquad \lim_{x \to a^-} f(x) = L.$$

19. Prove that if

$$\lim_{x \to a} f(x) = L_1 \qquad \text{and} \qquad \lim_{x \to a} f(x) = L_2,$$

then $L_1 = L_2$. (The limit of a function is unique whenever the limit exists.)

20. Given that $\lim_{x \to a} f(x) = L$, prove that

$$\lim_{x \to a} [f(x) - L] = 0.$$

21. Prove that if $\lim_{x \to a} f(x) = L$ and $f(x) \leqslant k$ for all x, then $L \leqslant k$.

22. Prove Theorem 3-VII.

23. Prove Theorem 3-I.

24. Evaluate

(a) $\displaystyle\lim_{x\to 3^+} \frac{[x]^2 - 9}{x^2 - 9}$,

(b) $\displaystyle\lim_{x\to 3^-} \frac{[x]^2 - 9}{x^2 - 9}$,

where $[x]$ denotes the greatest integer in x.

3.3   Derivative of a Function

If x_1 and x_2 denote real numbers, it is customary to denote the difference $x_2 - x_1$ by Δx, read as "delta x" where Δ may be regarded as a differencing operator; it tells us to take the difference between two values of the quantity to which it applies.

Let the function f given by $y = f(x)$ be defined at every point of an open interval I containing the point $x = a$. Let $a + \Delta x$ denote a point of I distinct from a; that is, assume that f is defined at $a + \Delta x$ and that $\Delta x \neq 0$. The difference Δx between $a + \Delta x$ and a is called an increment (or decrement if Δx is negative). The difference $f(a + \Delta x) - f(a)$ between the corresponding values of $y = f(x)$ is denoted by Δy. We now form the following quotient, called a difference quotient;

$$\frac{\Delta y}{\Delta x} = \frac{f(a + \Delta x) - f(a)}{\Delta x}. \tag{3.3}$$

The quotient (3.3) denotes the average rate of change of $f(x)$, with respect to x, corresponding to or over the interval Δx. For example, if y is measured in dollars and x in fect, then $\Delta y/\Delta x$ is measured in dollars per foot. Thus $\Delta y/\Delta x$ is a measure of the rate at which y is changing with respect to x for the interval Δx. We can compute this average rate of change of y with respect to x for various values of Δx, but regardless of how small we make Δx, we cannot use (3.3) to compute the rate at which y is changing with respect to x at $x = a$. The difficulty in defining the instantaneous rate of change of y with respect to x at $x = a$ is that we have no interval Δx over which to take the average. If, however, the quotient $\Delta y/\Delta x$ approaches a limit as Δx approaches 0, it is natural and reasonable to define the instantaneous rate of change of y with respect to x at $x = a$ as this limit, which Leibniz denoted by the symbol dy/dx, read as "$dy\ dx$." Thus we formulate the following important definition.

Definition (*derivative of a function*).   Let the function f be defined at every point of an open interval containing the point $x = a$. Then

$$\frac{dy}{dx}\bigg]_{x=a} = \lim_{\Delta x \to 0} \frac{\Delta y}{\Delta x}$$

$$= \lim_{\Delta x \to 0} \frac{f(a + \Delta x) - f(a)}{\Delta x}. \tag{3.4}$$

The expression $\dfrac{dy}{dx}\bigg]_{x=a}$ in (3.4) is called the derivative of f with respect to x at $x = a$ and defines the instantaneous rate of change of y with respect to x at $x = a$.

If the limit in (3.4) exists, we say that f is differentiable at a or possesses a derivative at a. It is obvious from the definition that f must be defined at a in order to have a derivative at a. However, we shall see that f may be defined at a and yet not possess a derivative at a.

The function whose domain consists of the set of points at which f is differentiable and whose range consists of the corresponding values of the derivative of f is denoted by f'. The word "derivative" implies that f' is derived from f. Denoting an element of the domain of f' by x and an element of the range of f' by $y' = f'(x)$ (read as "f prime of x"), the function f' is defined by

$$f'(x) = \frac{dy}{dx} = \lim_{\Delta x \to 0} \frac{\Delta y}{\Delta x}$$

$$= \lim_{\Delta x \to 0} \frac{f(x + \Delta x) - f(x)}{\Delta x}. \tag{3.5}$$

The symbol dy/dx suggests that the instantaneous rate of change of y with respect to x is the limit of a difference quotient; however, dy/dx should be regarded as a single symbol and not as a quotient of quantities dy and dx. Later we will give separate interpretations to the quantities dy and dx.

The symbols D_x and d/dx, called differentiation operators, are often employed to indicate the process of differentiation [that of calculating the limit in (3.5)]. For example, $D_x(x^2 + 7x)$ denotes $f'(x)$, where $f(x) = x^2 + 7x$, while $d/dx(x^3 - x)$ denotes $g'(x)$, where $g(x) = x^3 - x$. If

$$\lim_{\Delta x \to 0^+} \frac{f(a + \Delta x) - f(a)}{\Delta x}$$

exists, we say that f possesses a derivative on the right at $x = a$, while if

$$\lim_{\Delta x \to 0^-} \frac{f(b + \Delta x) - f(b)}{\Delta x}$$

exists, we say that f possesses a derivative on the left at $x = b$. The function f is said to be differentiable on the interval $a \leqslant x \leqslant b$ if and only if f has a derivative on the right at a, a derivative on the left at b, and a derivative at every x satisfying $a < x < b$.

The differential calculus is that branch of mathematics which deals with the calculation of the derivatives of functions and with the numerous applications of these derivatives. A few examples of quantities that are derivatives are velocity, acceleration, and curvature in mechanics; power in physics; current in electrical theory; shearing force in the theory of beams; marginal cost in economics; probability density function in statistics, and so forth.

Example 1.   Find dy/dx for the function f defined by $y = f(x) = x^2$.

Solution.   The difference quotient

$$\frac{\Delta y}{\Delta x} = \frac{(x + \Delta x)^2 - x^2}{\Delta x}$$

$$= \frac{2x(\Delta x) + (\Delta x)^2}{\Delta x}$$

$$= 2x + \Delta x.$$

Note that $\Delta y/\Delta x$ depends upon both x and Δx. We now evaluate the limit in (3.5) to obtain:

$$\frac{dy}{dx} = f'(x) = \lim_{\Delta x \to 0} \frac{\Delta y}{\Delta x} = \lim_{\Delta x \to 0} (2x + \Delta x) = 2x.$$

Note that the domain of f' is the same as the domain of f, namely, the set of all real numbers. We say that f is differentiable for all values of x.

The derivative of f at $x = 3$ is given by

$$f'(3) = \frac{dy}{dx}\bigg]_{x=3} = 2x\bigg]_{x=3} = 6.$$

This means that at $x = 3$, y is changing six times as fast as x. If y is measured in feet and x in seconds, $f'(3) = 6$ fps.

Example 2.   If $y = 1/x$, find dy/dx.

Solution.   From (3.5) we have

$$\frac{dy}{dx} = \lim_{\Delta x \to 0} \frac{[1/(x + \Delta x)] - (1/x)}{\Delta x}$$

$$= \lim_{\Delta x \to 0} \frac{x - x - \Delta x}{x(x + \Delta x)(\Delta x)}$$

$$= \lim_{\Delta x \to 0} \frac{-1}{x(x + \Delta x)}$$

$$= \frac{-1}{x^2}, \qquad \text{provided } x \neq 0.$$

Example 3.   If $y = f(x) = 1/x$, find $f'(3)$.
From Example 2 we have

$$f'(3) = \frac{-1}{x^2}\bigg]_{x=3} = \frac{-1}{9}.$$

Example 4.   If $y = f(x) = \sqrt{x}$, find $dy/dx = f'(x)$.
From (3.5) we have

$$f'(x) = \lim_{\Delta x \to 0} \frac{\Delta y}{\Delta x} = \lim_{\Delta x \to 0} \frac{\sqrt{x + \Delta x} - \sqrt{x}}{\Delta x}$$

$$= \lim_{\Delta x \to 0} \left[\frac{\sqrt{x + \Delta x} - \sqrt{x}}{\Delta x} \cdot \frac{\sqrt{x + \Delta x} + \sqrt{x}}{\sqrt{x + \Delta x} + \sqrt{x}} \right]$$

$$= \lim_{\Delta x \to 0} \frac{x + \Delta x - x}{\Delta x(\sqrt{x + \Delta x} + \sqrt{x})}$$

$$= \lim_{\Delta x \to 0} \frac{1}{\sqrt{x + \Delta x} + \sqrt{x}}$$

$$= \frac{1}{2\sqrt{x}}, \qquad \text{provided } x \neq 0.$$

Thus the domain D' of f' consists of the set of positive real numbers, while the domain D of f consists of the set of nonnegative real numbers. Although $\sqrt{x}$ is defined at $x = 0$, f is not differentiable at $x = 0$.

Example 5

$$D_x(x^3 - 2x) = \lim_{\Delta x \to 0} \frac{[(x + \Delta x)^3 - 2(x + \Delta x)] - [x^3 - 2x]}{\Delta x}$$

$$= \lim_{\Delta x \to 0} \frac{3x^2(\Delta x) + 3x(\Delta x)^2 + (\Delta x)^3 - 2(\Delta x)}{\Delta x}$$

$$= \lim_{\Delta x \to 0} [3x^2 + 3x(\Delta x) + (\Delta x)^2 - 2]$$

$$= 3x^2 - 2.$$

PROBLEM LIST 16

1. Find the derivative of f if $f(x)$ is

   (a) $3x - 2$;

   (b) $4x + 1$;

   (c) $x^2 - 3x$;

   (d) $2x^2 + 5x$;

   (e) $\dfrac{2}{x}$;

   (f) $\dfrac{3}{x - 1}$;

   (g) $x^3 + 3x$;

   (h) $x^4 - x$.

2. Find the derivative of f if $f(x)$ is

   (a) $5x + 7$;

   (b) $6x - 3$;

   (c) $3x^2 - 2x$;

   (d) $4x^2 + 5x - 1$;

   (e) $\dfrac{4}{x}$;

   (f) $\dfrac{-2}{x^2}$;

   (g) $2x^3 - x$;

   (h) $2x^4 + x^2$.

3. Evaluate

   (a) $D_x(x - \sqrt{x})$;

   (b) $D_x\left(\dfrac{1}{\sqrt{x}}\right)$;

   (c) $\dfrac{d}{dx}(\sqrt{x + 1})$;

   (d) $\dfrac{d}{dx}\left(\dfrac{3}{x + 1}\right)$.

4. Evaluate

   (a) $D_x(x^2 + \sqrt{x})$;

   (b) $D_x\left(x - \dfrac{1}{\sqrt{x}}\right)$;

   (c) $\dfrac{d}{dx}\sqrt{-x}$;

   (d) $\dfrac{d}{dx}\left(\dfrac{4}{x + 2}\right)$.

5. Show that $dy/dx = 0$ if y is constant.

6. Find dy/dx if $y = f(x) = 3/(x + 1)$.

   Also find $f(2)$, $f'(2)$, $f(-3)$, and $f'(-3)$.

7. Given $f(x) = x^3 + x^2 + 1$, find $f'(2)$, $f'(-2)$, $f'(3)$, and $f'(0)$.

8. A right-circular cylinder has height 3 ft. Find the rate of change of its volume with respect to its radius.

9. Show that the rate of change of the area of a circle with respect to its radius is equal to its circumference.

10. Show that the rate of change of the volume of a sphere with respect to its radius is equal to its surface area.

11. Find $f'(x)$ for the function f defined by $f(x) = \sqrt[3]{x}$. Describe the domain of f and the domain of f'.

3.4   Geometrical Interpretation of the Derivative

In Fig. 3.3, $P(x, y)$ is a point on the graph of $y = f(x)$. The point $Q(x + \Delta x, y + \Delta y)$, located near P, is also on the curve but is distinct from P. The line PQ determined by P and Q, and having inclination α, is called a secant line of the curve. If α approaches a fixed value θ as Q approaches P, P remaining fixed, we define the line L, having inclination θ and passing through P, as the tangent to the curve $y = f(x)$ at P. If α does not approach a limit as $Q \longrightarrow P$, we say that the curve does not possess a tangent at P.

This definition is consistent with the definition employed in plane geometry of a tangent to a circle, but is more useful when applied to more general curves.

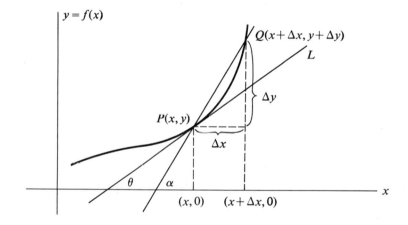

Figure 3.3

From Fig. 3.3 the slope of PQ is

$$m_{PQ} = \tan \alpha = \frac{\Delta y}{\Delta x} = \frac{f(x + \Delta x) - f(x)}{\Delta x}.$$

If the curve possesses a tangent at P, $\alpha \longrightarrow \theta$ as $Q \longrightarrow P$. Therefore, since the tangent function is continuous, $\tan \alpha \longrightarrow \tan \theta$. Hence

$$\lim_{\Delta x \to 0} (\tan \alpha) = \lim_{\Delta x \to 0} \frac{\Delta y}{\Delta x} = \tan \theta = \frac{dy}{dx}$$

$$= f'(x) = m_L.$$

Thus we see that the value of the derivative at a point P on a curve is equal to the slope of the tangent line at P, which may be defined as the slope of the curve at that point. This is the geometrical interpretation of the derivative.

An exception occurs when $\alpha \longrightarrow \pi/2$ as $Q \longrightarrow P$. In this case the derivative will not exist at P and the tangent at P will be vertical. This will be illustrated in Example 6.

Example 1.   Find the slope of the parabola $y = x^2$ at (**a**) $(1, 1)$, (**b**) $(-2, 4)$.

Solution

$$f'(x) = \lim_{\Delta x \to 0} \frac{(x + \Delta x)^2 - x^2}{\Delta x}$$

$$= \lim_{\Delta x \to 0} (2x + \Delta x) = 2x$$

$$f'(1) = 2(1) = 2 \quad \text{and} \quad f'(-2) = 2(-2) = -4.$$

The tangents at the given points are shown in Fig. 3.4.

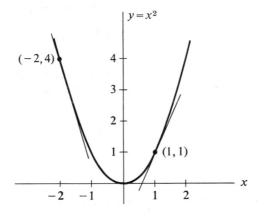

Figure 3.4

Example 2.   Find the points on the parabola $y = x^2$ at which the tangent has slope 6.

Solution.   From Example 1,

$$m = f'(x) = 2x.$$

Setting

$$2x = 6,$$

we obtain

$$x = 3.$$

Thus the tangent to $y = x^2$ has slope 6 only at the point $(3, 9)$.

Example 3.   Find an equation of the tangent to the curve $y = -2/x$ at the point $(1/2, -4)$.

Solution.   The slope of the curve at any point is given by

$$\frac{dy}{dx} = \lim_{\Delta x \to 0} \frac{-2/(x + \Delta x) - (-2/x)}{\Delta x}$$

$$= \lim_{\Delta x \to 0} \frac{2}{x(x + \Delta x)} = \frac{2}{x^2}.$$

Therefore the slope at $(1/2, -4)$ is $2/(1/2)^2 = 8$. An equation of the tangent to the curve at $(1/2, -4)$ is

$$y - (-4) = 8\left(x - \frac{1}{2}\right)$$

or

$$8x - y - 8 = 0. \tag{3.6}$$

It should be noted that when the slope of the curve was being computed, (x, y) denoted an arbitrary point on the curve. In (3.6), however, (x, y) denotes an arbitrary point on the line tangent to the curve at $(1/2, -4)$.

Example 4.   Find an equation of the normal to the curve

$$y = \frac{-2}{x} \quad \text{at} \left(\frac{1}{2}, -4\right).$$

Solution.   In Example 3 we found that the slope of the tangent at $(1/2, -4)$ is 8. The slope of the normal is therefore $-1/8$ and an equation of the normal is

$$y - (-4) = \frac{-1}{8}\left(x - \frac{1}{2}\right)$$

or

$$2x + 16y + 63 = 0.$$

Example 5.   Find the angle ψ between the curves $y = x^2$ and $y = 1/x$. [The angle between two curves is defined as the angle (or its supplement) between their tangents at their point of intersection.]

Solution.   Solving $y = x^2$ and $y = 1/x$ simultaneously, we find that the curves intersect at $(1, 1)$.
    For $y = x^2$,

$$\frac{dy}{dx} = \lim_{\Delta x \to 0} \frac{(x + \Delta x)^2 - x^2}{\Delta x} = 2x$$

and

$$\frac{dy}{dx}\bigg|_{(1,1)} = 2.$$

For $y = 1/x$,

$$\frac{dy}{dx} = \lim_{\Delta x \to 0} \frac{1/(x + \Delta x) - (1/x)}{\Delta x} = \frac{-1}{x^2}$$

and

$$\frac{dy}{dx}\bigg|_{(1,1)} = -1.$$

Therefore

$$\tan \psi = \frac{(-1) - (2)}{1 + (-1)(2)} = 3$$

and

$$\psi \cong 71.6°.$$

(See Fig. 3.5.)

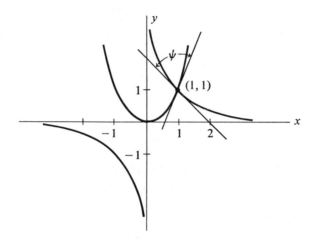

Figure 3.5

Example 6.   Find an equation of the tangent to

$$y = f(x) = x^{1/3} \qquad \text{at} \quad (0, 0).$$

Solution.   At $x = 0$,

$$\frac{\Delta y}{\Delta x} = \frac{f(0 + \Delta x) - f(0)}{\Delta x} = \frac{(\Delta x)^{1/3} - 0}{\Delta x} = \frac{1}{(\Delta x)^{2/3}}.$$

As $\Delta x \to 0$, $\Delta y/\Delta x \to \infty$, but does not approach any real number. Although $f'(0)$ does not exist, the inclination of the secant line through $(0,0)$ and $(\Delta x, [\Delta x]^{1/3})$ approaches $\pi/2$ as $\Delta x \to 0$. Therefore $y = x^{1/3}$ possesses a vertical tangent at $(0, 0)$ and an equation of the tangent at $(0, 0)$ is $x = 0$. The graph of $y = x^{1/3}$ is shown in Fig. 3.6.

We now compute $f'(x)$ for $x \neq 0$.

$$f'(x) = \lim_{\Delta x \to 0} \frac{(x + \Delta x)^{1/3} - x^{1/3}}{\Delta x}$$

$$= \lim_{\Delta x \to 0} \frac{(x + \Delta x)^{1/3} - x^{1/3}}{\Delta x} \cdot \frac{(x + \Delta x)^{2/3} + (x + \Delta x)^{1/3} x^{1/3} + x^{2/3}}{(x + \Delta x)^{2/3} + (x + \Delta x)^{1/3} x^{1/3} + x^{2/3}}$$

$$= \lim_{\Delta x \to 0} \frac{[(x + \Delta x)^{1/3}]^3 - [x^{1/3}]^3}{\Delta x[(x + \Delta x)^{2/3} + (x + \Delta x)^{1/3} x^{1/3} + x^{2/3}]}$$

$$= \lim_{\Delta x \to 0} \frac{1}{(x + \Delta x)^{2/3} + (x + \Delta x)^{1/3} x^{1/3} + x^{2/3}} = \frac{1}{3x^{2/3}}.$$

Thus the function f, which is defined and continuous for all real x, has a derivative at every x except $x = 0$. The graph of $y = x^{1/3}$ has a tangent at every point.

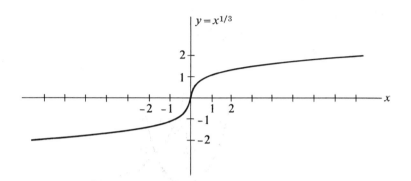

Figure 3.6

Example 7.   Investigate the tangent to the curve

$$y = f(x) = |x| \qquad \text{at} \quad (0, 0).$$

Solution.   At $x = 0$,

$$\frac{\Delta y}{\Delta x} = \frac{|0 + \Delta x|}{\Delta x} = \frac{|\Delta x|}{\Delta x}.$$

As $\Delta x \to 0$, $\Delta y/\Delta x$ does not approach any real number since $|\Delta x|/\Delta x$ is equal to $+1$ for positive Δx and -1 for negative Δx.

The secant line through $(0, 0)$ and $(\Delta x, |\Delta x|)$ does not approach a limiting position as $\Delta x \to 0$, since it has slope $+1$ for every $\Delta x > 0$ and -1 for every $\Delta x < 0$. Thus the curve $y = |x|$ has a "sharp corner" at $(0, 0)$ and does not possess a tangent there. The function given by $y = |x|$, which is defined and continuous for all real x, has a derivative at every x except $x = 0$. (It is easily seen that $f'(x) = +1$ for $x > 0$ and $f'(x) = -1$ for $x < 0$.)

Since

$$\lim_{\Delta x \to 0^+} \frac{f(0 + \Delta x) - f(0)}{\Delta x} = \lim_{\Delta x \to 0^+} \frac{|\Delta x|}{\Delta x} = +1,$$

we say that f has a derivative on the right at $(0, 0)$, and its value is $+1$.

Similarly, f has a derivative on the left at $(0, 0)$, and its value is -1. The graph of $y = |x|$ was shown in Fig. 2.3.

Examples 6 and 7 demonstrate that continuity at a point does not imply differentiability at that point. In 1834 the Bohemian mathematician Bernhard Bolzano (1781–1848) exhibited a remarkable function which is continuous at every point of an interval but which does not possess a derivative at any point of the interval. (See Ref. 3.1.)

If, however, a function f is differentiable at a point, it is continuous at that point. To prove this, let $y = f(x)$ and let f possess a derivative at $x = a$. Then, since

$$f(a + \Delta x) = \frac{f(a + \Delta x) - f(a)}{\Delta x}(\Delta x) + f(a),$$

it follows that

$$\lim_{\Delta x \to 0} f(a + \Delta x) = \left[\lim_{\Delta x \to 0} \frac{f(a + \Delta x) - f(a)}{\Delta x}\right]\left[\lim_{\Delta x \to 0} (\Delta x)\right] + f(a)$$
$$= [f'(a)][0] + f(a) = f(a).$$

This is precisely the statement that f is continuous at $x = a$.

This result provides a method for demonstrating that a function is continuous. For example, we will show later that the function f defined by $f(x) = \sin x$, which is defined for all x, has a derivative at every value of x. It will then follow that f is a continuous function; that is, f is continuous at every x in its domain of definition.

PROBLEM LIST 17

1. Find the slope of the tangent to $y = x^2/4$ at the point where x is (a) -4, (b) -3, (c) -2, (d) -1, (e) 0, (f) 1, (g) 2, (h) 3, (i) 4. Sketch the curve showing the tangent at each of these points.

2. Find the slope of the tangent to $y = 4/x$ at the point where x is (a) -4, (b) -3, (c) -2, (d) -1, (e) 1, (f) 2, (g) 3, (h) 4. Sketch the curve showing the tangent at each of these points.

3. Find equations of the tangent and normal to $y = x^2 - 3x$ at the point where (a) $x = 0$, (b) $x = 3$, (c) $x = -2$. Illustrate graphically.

4. Find equations of the tangent and normal to $y = 1 - x^2$ at the point where (a) $x = 0$, (b) $x = 1$, (c) $x = 2$. Illustrate graphically.

5. Find the point on $y = x^2 - x$ where the tangent has slope 2. Illustrate graphically.

6. Find the point on $y = 1/x^2$ where the tangent has slope -2. Illustrate graphically.

7. Find the slope of the line $y = mx + b$.

8. Find the slope of the line $ax + by + c = 0$.

9. Find the angle between $y = x^2$ and $y = 8/x$. Illustrate graphically.

10. Find the angle between $y = x^2$ and $y = (x^2/4) + (3/4)$ at their first-quadrant intersection.

11. Find the point on $y = x^2 - 1$ at which the tangent has inclination 45°.

12. Find an equation of the tangent to $y = x^{1/5}$ at $(0, 0)$. What is the value of dy/dx at $(0, 0)$?

13. Find the area of the triangle formed by the coordinate axes and the tangent to $y = 5/x$ at $(1, 5)$.

14. Show that the line $6x - y - 9 = 0$ is tangent to $y = x^2$.

15. Find the point on $y = -x^2$ such that the tangent is parallel to $3x - 4y + 10 = 0$. How far apart are these two lines?

16. Determine k such that $y = x^2$ and $y = k/x$ are perpendicular.

17. Determine a and b such that $y = x^2 + ax + b$ has slope -3 at $(0, 2)$.

18. Find equations of the lines which pass through $(1, -3)$ and which are tangent to $y = x^2$.

19. A function f is defined by
$$f(x) = \begin{cases} \sqrt{x} & \text{for } x \geqslant 0 \\ -\sqrt{-x} & \text{for } x < 0 \end{cases}.$$
Find the inclination of the tangent to the curve $y = f(x)$ at the point where (a) $x = 1$, (b) $x = -1$, (c) $x = 0$.

20. A function f is defined by
$$f(x) = \begin{cases} x \sin(1/x) & \text{for } x \neq 0 \\ 0 & \text{for } x = 0 \end{cases}.$$
Show that the curve $y = f(x)$ has no tangent at $(0, 0)$.

21. Two distinct perpendicular lines are tangent to $y = x^2$. Show that they intersect on the line $y = -1/4$.

22. Draw the curve $y = f(x) = \sqrt{(x-1)^2}$. Find the derivative on the right of f at $x = 1$ and the derivative on the left of f at $x = 1$.

3.5   *Differentiation Formulas*

Given a function f defined by $y = f(x)$, the basic method of finding $y' = dy/dx$ is to apply the definition of a derivative given in (3.5) of Sec. 3.3. In this section we employ this definition to develop formulas for finding dy/dx for various types of functions f given by $y = f(x)$. These formulas will enable us to compute derivatives much more rapidly than we can by applying definition (3.5).

———————

Prove that
$$\frac{dc}{dx} = 0. \tag{3.7}$$

(The derivative of a constant is zero.)

Proof. Let $y = c$ where c is an arbitrary constant. Then
$$\frac{\Delta y}{\Delta x} = \frac{c - c}{\Delta x} = 0$$
and
$$\frac{dy}{dx} = \frac{dc}{dx} = \lim_{\Delta x \to 0} \frac{\Delta y}{\Delta x} = 0 \qquad \text{for every } x.$$

It is certainly expected that the rate of change of a constant must be zero. We also know that the line $y = c$ has slope zero at every point.

Example. If $y = 5$, $dy/dx = 0$.

———————

Prove that

$$\frac{d}{dx}(x^n) = nx^{n-1}. \tag{3.8}$$

Proof.   The following proof holds when n is a positive integer. Let $y = x^n$. Then

$$\Delta y = (x + \Delta x)^n - x^n.$$

Applying the binomial theorem, we obtain

$$\Delta y = x^n + nx^{n-1}(\Delta x) + \frac{n(n-1)}{2}x^{n-2}(\Delta x)^2 + \cdots + (\Delta x)^n - x^n,$$

from which

$$\frac{\Delta y}{\Delta x} = nx^{n-1} + \frac{n(n-1)}{2}x^{n-2}(\Delta x) + \cdots + (\Delta x)^{n-1}$$

and

$$\frac{dy}{dx} = \lim_{\Delta x \to 0} \frac{\Delta y}{\Delta x} = nx^{n-1},$$

since all terms except the first approach zero with Δx and since the limit of a sum is the sum of the limits.

Example 1.   If $y = x^5$, $dy/dx = 5x^4$.

Example 2.   If $y = x^1$, $dy/dx = 1x^0 = 1$.

Formula (3.8) holds when n is any real number. Although our proof is valid only for positive integral values of n, we will apply (3.8) for arbitrary n. Later we will present a more general proof. We have already established (3.8) for $n = 1/2$ and $n = 1/3$.

Example 3.   If $y = x^{7/2}$, $dy/dx = (7/2)x^{5/2}$.

Example 4.   If $y = x^{-3/2}$, $dy/dx = (-3/2)x^{-5/2}$.

Example 5.   If $y = x^{\pi}$, $dy/dx = \pi x^{\pi-1}$.

If u and v are differentiable functions of x, then

$$\frac{d}{dx}(u + v) = \frac{du}{dx} + \frac{dv}{dx}. \tag{3.9}$$

This formula states that the derivative of a sum is the sum of the derivatives.

Proof.   Let

$$y = u + v$$

Then

$$\Delta y = (u + \Delta u + v + \Delta v) - (u + v) = \Delta u + \Delta v,$$

where $u + \Delta u$ and $v + \Delta v$ denote the values of u and v at $x + \Delta x$.

Since

$$\frac{\Delta y}{\Delta x} = \frac{\Delta u}{\Delta x} + \frac{\Delta v}{\Delta x},$$

$$\frac{dy}{dx} = \lim_{\Delta x \to 0} \frac{\Delta y}{\Delta x} = \lim_{\Delta x \to 0} \frac{\Delta u}{\Delta x} + \lim_{\Delta x \to 0} \frac{\Delta v}{\Delta x}$$

$$= \frac{du}{dx} + \frac{dv}{dx}.$$

We know that $\Delta u/\Delta x$ and $\Delta v/\Delta x$ approach du/dx and dv/dx as $\Delta x \to 0$ because u and v are assumed to be differentiable at x.

Formula (3.9) is readily extended to apply to the sum of more than two functions. It is also easy to show that

$$\frac{d}{dx}(u - v) = \frac{du}{dx} - \frac{dv}{dx}.$$

Example 1.   If $y = x^3 + x^2$, $dy/dx = 3x^2 + 2x$.

Example 2.   If $y = x + x^{1/2} - x^{-1/2}$, $dy/dx = 1 + (1/2)x^{-1/2} + (1/2)x^{-3/2}$.

If u and v are differentiable functions of x, then

$$\frac{d}{dx}(uv) = u\frac{dv}{dx} + v\frac{du}{dx}. \qquad (3.10)$$

This formula states that the derivative of a product is equal to the first factor times the derivative of the second, plus the second factor times the derivative of the first. (Note that the derivative of a product is not the product of the derivatives.)

Proof.   Let $y = uv$. Then

$$\Delta y = (u + \Delta u)(v + \Delta v) - uv$$
$$= u(\Delta v) + v(\Delta u) + (\Delta u)(\Delta v)$$

and

$$\frac{\Delta y}{\Delta x} = u\frac{\Delta v}{\Delta x} + v\frac{\Delta u}{\Delta x} + \left(\frac{\Delta u}{\Delta x}\right)(\Delta v).$$

Letting $\Delta x \to 0$, we obtain

$$\frac{dy}{dx} = u\frac{dv}{dx} + v\frac{du}{dx} + \left(\frac{du}{dx}\right)(0)$$

$$= u\frac{dv}{dx} + v\frac{du}{dx}.$$

We know that $\Delta v \to 0$ as $\Delta x \to 0$ because v, being a differentiable function of x, is therefore a continuous function of x. The limit of the product $(\Delta u/\Delta x)(\Delta v)$ is equal to the product of the limits.

Example.   If $y = (x^2 + 1)(x^3 - x + 3)$,

$$(x^2 + 1)(x^2 - 1) + (x^3 - x + 3) \cdot 2x$$

$$x^4 + 6x^3 - 2x^2 + 6x + 2$$

$$\frac{dy}{dx} = (x^2 + 1)\frac{d}{dx}(x^3 - x + 3) + (x^3 - x + 3)\frac{d}{dx}(x^2 + 1)$$
$$= (x^2 + 1)(3x^2 - 1) + (x^3 - x + 3)(2x).$$

If the function u is constant, (3.10) reduces to

$$\frac{d}{dx}(cv) = c\frac{dv}{dx} \qquad\qquad \textbf{(3.11)}$$

since $du/dx = 0$ by formula (3.7).

Formula (3.11) states that the derivative of a constant times a function is equal to the constant times the derivative of the function.

Example 1.   If $y = 5x^4$, $dy/dx = 5(4x^3) = 20x^3$.

Example 2.   If $y = 4/x^3$, then $y = 4x^{-3}$ and $dy/dx = -12x^{-4}$.

Example 3.   If $y = 3(2x^5 - 4x^{-1/2} + 1)$, $dy/dx = 3(10x^4 + 2x^{-3/2})$.

If u and v denote differentiable functions of x, then

$$\frac{d}{dx}\left(\frac{u}{v}\right) = \frac{v(du/dx) - u(dv/dx)}{v^2}. \qquad\qquad \textbf{(3.12)}$$

Formula (3.12) states that the derivative of a quotient is equal to the denominator times the derivative of the numerator minus the numerator times the derivative of the denominator, all divided by the square of the denominator. [*Note that* $(d/dx)(u/v) \neq (du/dx)/(dv/dx)$].

Proof.   Let $y = u/v$. Then

$$\Delta y = \frac{u + \Delta u}{v + \Delta v} - \frac{u}{v}$$
$$= \frac{v(\Delta u) - u(\Delta v)}{(v + \Delta v)v},$$
$$\frac{\Delta y}{\Delta x} = \frac{v(\Delta u/\Delta x) - u(\Delta v/\Delta x)}{(v + \Delta v)v},$$

and hence

$$\frac{dy}{dx} = \frac{v(du/dx) - u(dv/dx)}{v^2}.$$

Example.   If $y = (x^2 + 3x)/(x^3 - 5)$,

$$\frac{dy}{dx} = \frac{(x^3 - 5)(2x + 3) - (x^2 + 3x)(3x^2)}{(x^3 - 5)^2}$$
$$= \frac{-x^4 - 6x^3 - 10x - 15}{(x^3 - 5)^2}.$$

PROBLEM LIST 18

1. Differentiate the functions defined by the following equations:

(a) $y = 2$.

(b) $y = 0$.

(c) $y = x^6$.

(d) $y = 3x^5$.

(e) $y = x^3 - x^2 + 1$.

(f) $y = x^{1/2} + x^{3/4} - 2x^{1/3}$.

(g) $y = 3x^{-2} + x^{-1/2} - 1$.

(h) $y = (2x^2 - 3x)^2$.

(i) $y = (x^2 - 1)(x^2 + 1)$.

(j) $y = (3x^2 - x + 1)(2x^3 + x - 2)$.

(k) $y = \sqrt{5x}(x^3 + 1)$.

(l) $y = (x + 1)(x^2 - x + 1)$.

(m) $y = \dfrac{x - 1}{x + 1}$.

(n) $y = \dfrac{x^2 - 2}{x^2 + 1}$.

(o) $y = \dfrac{5}{x^2 - 1}$.

(p) $y = \dfrac{\sqrt{x} + 1}{x - 1}$.

(q) $y = x^3 - \dfrac{2}{x^3}$.

(r) $y = \dfrac{x^2 - 2}{1 + x^3}$.

(s) $y = \dfrac{x^2}{x^2 - 1}$.

(t) $y = \dfrac{x^2 + x + 1}{x^2 - x + 1}$.

2. Find $f'(4)$ if $f(x) = (x^2 + 3x)/(\sqrt{x} + 2)$.

3. Find $g'(3)$ if $g(t) = (t^2 - 1)/(t^2 + 2)$.

4. Find equations of the tangent and normal to $y = x^3 - 3x^2 + x - 2$ at the point where $x = 2$.

5. A body attracts a second body r feet from it with a force of F pounds. If $F = 100/r^2$, find dF/dr when $r = 40$ ft.

6. Prove that $d/dx\,(x^n) = nx^{n-1}$ when n is a negative integer.

7. Generalize (3.10) to obtain a formula for $d/dx\,(uvw)$. Use the result to evaluate $D_x[x^2(x^2 + 1)(x^2 - x + 1)]$.

8. Derive (3.12) from (3.10) by writing $u/v = uv^{-1}$.

3.6 Composite Functions—Chain Rule

The concept of composite function was introduced when Theorem 3-VII was presented. Let f be given by $y = f(u)$ and g by $u = g(x)$. Then the function h given by $y = h(x) = f[g(x)]$ is called the composite of g by f. The domain of h is the set of all real numbers in the domain of g such that $g(x)$ is in the domain of f. The function h is often denoted by $f \circ g$, read as "f circle g."

For example, if $y = f(u) = \sqrt{u}$ and $u = g(x) = 3x$, then $y = h(x) = \sqrt{3x}$. The domain of g is the set of all real numbers, but the domain of h is the set of nonnegative real numbers, since $\sqrt{3x}$ is not real for $x < 0$.

To obtain dy/dx, the derivative of h with respect to x, we can eliminate u and obtain the relationship between y and x. In our example, this yields $y = \sqrt{3x}$

from which dy/dx can be readily obtained. However, it is frequently more convenient to obtain dy/dx without eliminating u. This is accomplished by applying the following important theorem, known as the chain rule for differentiation.

Theorem 3-VIII (*chain rule*).   Let g, defined by $u = g(x)$, be differentiable at x and let f, defined by $y = f(u)$, be differentiable at $u = g(x)$. Then h, defined by $y = h(x) = f[g(x)]$, is differentiable at x and

$$\frac{dy}{dx} = \frac{dy}{du} \cdot \frac{du}{dx}. \tag{3.13}$$

Proof.   Let $\Delta u = g(x + \Delta x) - g(x)$ and $\Delta y = f(u + \Delta u) - f(u)$.

If there exists a number δ such that $\Delta u \neq 0$ whenever $0 < |\Delta x| < \delta$, then for $0 < |\Delta x| < \delta$,

$$\frac{\Delta y}{\Delta x} = \frac{\Delta y}{\Delta u} \cdot \frac{\Delta u}{\Delta x}.$$

As $\Delta x \longrightarrow 0$, $\Delta u \longrightarrow 0$, since g is continuous at x, and

$$\frac{dy}{dx} = \frac{dy}{du} \cdot \frac{du}{dx}.$$

(The remainder of the proof may be omitted, since the portion completed covers all cases which will be of interest to us.)

If no δ exists for which $\Delta u \neq 0$ whenever $0 < |\Delta x| < \delta$, there must exist a sequence $\{(\Delta x)_m\}$ such that the corresponding sequence $\{(\Delta u)_m\}$ has every element zero. As $\Delta x \longrightarrow 0$ along this sequence, $\Delta u/\Delta x$ is identically zero and hence du/dx, which exists by hypothesis, must equal zero.

Now let $\Delta x \longrightarrow 0$ along an *arbitrary* sequence $\{(\Delta x)_n\}$. The corresponding sequence $\{(\Delta y/\Delta x)_n\}$ has limit zero, since its elements are zero if $(\Delta u)_n = 0$ and $(\Delta y/\Delta u)_n \cdot (\Delta u/\Delta x)_n$ if $(\Delta u)_n \neq 0$. If an infinite number of elements of $\{(\Delta u)_n\}$ are $\neq 0$, the corresponding elements of $\{(\Delta y/\Delta x)_n\}$ approach $(dy/du) \cdot (du/dx)$ as $\Delta x \longrightarrow 0$ along $\{(\Delta x)_n\}$. But $du/dx = 0$, and since dy/du exists by hypothesis, the elements in question approach zero as a limit. Thus the sequence $\{(\Delta y/\Delta x)_n\}$ has limit zero, since any number of zero elements, even an infinite number, will not affect its limit. Thus

$$\frac{dy}{dx} = \frac{dy}{du} \cdot \frac{du}{dx} = 0,$$

and (3.13) still holds. (See Problems 13 and 14 for illustrations of this exceptional case.)

The chain rule might have been anticipated, since we know that if A can do something twice as fast as B, and B can do the same task three times as fast as C, then A can do it six times as fast as C. We can also extend the chain rule to longer chains. For example, if

$$y = f(u), \qquad u = g(x), \qquad \text{and} \quad x = h(t)$$

define differentiable functions, then

$$\frac{dy}{dt} = \frac{dy}{du} \cdot \frac{du}{dx} \cdot \frac{dx}{dt}.$$

Example 1. $y = u^2 + 2u$ and $u = x^3 - x$. Then

$$\frac{dy}{dx} = \frac{dy}{du} \cdot \frac{du}{dx} = (2u + 2)(3x^2 - 1).$$

We could replace u in the answer by $x^3 - x$, but this is not essential.

Example 2. $y = u^n$ and $u = g(x)$ (where g is a differentiable function of x). Then

$$\frac{dy}{dx} = \frac{dy}{du} \cdot \frac{du}{dx} = nu^{n-1}\frac{du}{dx}.$$

Example 3. $y = (x^3 + 1)^2$.
We can write $y = x^6 + 2x^3 + 1$ from which

$$\frac{dy}{dx} = 6x^5 + 6x^2 = 6x^2(x^3 + 1).$$

Instead, let us regard y as $y = u^2$, where $u = x^3 + 1$. Then

$$\frac{dy}{dx} = \frac{dy}{du} \cdot \frac{du}{dx} = (2u)(3x^2) = 6x^2(x^3 + 1).$$

Example 4. $y = (x^3 + 1)^{20}$. Then

$$\frac{dy}{dx} = 20(x^3 + 1)^{19}(3x^2) = 60x^2(x^3 + 1)^{19}.$$

In this example it would have been highly inconvenient to raise $x^3 + 1$ to the twentieth power before differentiating.

Example 5. $y = \sqrt[3]{x^2 - 1} = (x^2 - 1)^{1/3}$. Then

$$\frac{dy}{dx} = \frac{1}{3}(x^2 - 1)^{-2/3}(2x) = \frac{2x}{3\sqrt[3]{(x^2 - 1)^2}}.$$

Example 6. $y = \sqrt{u} = u^{1/2}$, where $u = g(x)$ and g is a differentiable function of x. Then

$$\frac{dy}{dx} = \frac{1}{2}u^{-1/2} \cdot \frac{du}{dx} = \frac{du/dx}{2\sqrt{u}}.$$

This result states that the derivative of a square root is the derivative of the radicand divided by twice the square root.
For example

$$\frac{d}{dx}\sqrt{x^3 - 2x + 1} = \frac{3x^2 - 2}{2\sqrt{x^3 - 2x + 1}}.$$

Example 7.   At how many square feet per second is the area of a circle increasing if the radius of the circle is given by

$$r = t^2 + 2t$$

(r in feet and t in seconds)? Also find $dA/dt\,|_{t=3}$.

Solution. $A = \pi r^2$ and $r = t^2 + 2t$, and

$$\frac{dA}{dt} = \frac{dA}{dr} \cdot \frac{dr}{dt} = 2\pi r(2t + 2).$$

When $t = 3$ sec, $r = 15$ ft and

$$\frac{dA}{dt} = 2\pi(15)(8) = 240\pi \frac{ft^2}{sec}.$$

Example 8. $y = \sin(x^2)$

To find dy/dx by the chain rule, we regard y as

$$y = \sin u \qquad \text{where} \quad u = x^2.$$

Then

$$\frac{dy}{dx} = \left[\frac{d}{du}\sin u\right]\left[\frac{du}{dx}\right] = 2x\left[\frac{d}{du}\sin u\right].$$

We cannot complete this example because we do not yet know how to evaluate $d/du \sin u$. The point of this example is to show that when we learn to differentiate a function defined by $y = f(u)$ with respect to its variable u, we will be able to differentiate f with respect to x, where $u = g(x)$, by means of the chain rule [assuming that we know how to differentiate g].

PROBLEM LIST 19

1. Find dy/dx:
    (a) $y = u^2 - u; u = 3x + 1$.
    (b) $y = u^3 + 5u; u = x^2 - 2x$.
    (c) $y = 1/u; u = x^3 - 2x$.
    (d) $y = \sqrt{u}; u = \sqrt{x}$.
    (e) $y = (u^2 - 2u + 1)^3; u = -2x^2 + 3x$.

2. Find dy/dx at $x = 2$:
    (a) $y = u^2 + 3u; u = x^2 - x$.
    (b) $y = (u^2 - 1)^3; u = 3x - 1$.
    (c) $y = \sqrt{2u}; u = x^3 - 2x$.
    (d) $y = 3/u; u = 1 - x^2$.
    (e) $y = \sqrt{u^2 - 1}); u = 4\sqrt{x}$.

3. Find dy/dx:
    (a) $y = (x^3 - x + 1)^2$.
    (b) $y = (x^2 - 1)^9$.
    (c) $y = \dfrac{(x^2 - 1)^2}{x^2 + 1}$.
    (d) $y = (x + 1)(x^2 - 1)^2$.
    (e) $y = \left(\dfrac{1 + x}{1 - x}\right)^2$.
    (f) $y = \sqrt{x^3 - 1}$.
    (g) $y = \sqrt[3]{x^2 - 1}$.
    (h) $y = \dfrac{(x^2 - 1)^2}{(1 - x)^3}$.

(i) $y = \dfrac{\sqrt{x}}{1 + x^2}$.

(k) $y = (3x^2 - x + 1)^{2/3}$.

(j) $y = \sqrt{\dfrac{1 - x}{1 + x}}$.

4. Given $f(x) = (x^2 - 1)^3$, find $f'(3)$ by two different methods.

5. If $y = f(u)$, $dy/du = 1/u$, and $u = 3t^2 - 2t + 1$, find dy/dt when $t = 1$.

6. Find an equation of the tangent to the semicircle $y = \sqrt{169 - x^2}$ at $(12, 5)$. Illustrate graphically.

7. A particle moves upward in quadrant I along $y = x^2$. If its abscissa increases constantly at 3 units per second, how fast is its ordinate increasing with respect to time when it is at $(5, 25)$?

8. If $u = y^2 - 2y + 8$ and $y = 2t - t^2$, find du/dt: (a) when $t = 2$, (b) when $y = -3$.

9. If $d/du \sin u = \cos u$, find $d/dx \sin x^3$ and $d/dx \sin^3 x$ when $x = \pi/4$.

10. If $y = |u| - u$ and $u = 3t - 2$, find dy/dt: (a) when $t = 3$, (b) when $t = -3$.

11. The radius of a sphere is given by $r = t^2 + 3t + 1$ where r is in feet and t in seconds. At how may cubic feet per second is its volume increasing when $t = 3$ sec?

12. If $y = u^2 - 3u$, $u = 1 - x^2$, and $x = \sqrt{t}$, find dy/dt when $t = 4$.

13. If $y = u^3 + 2u^2$ and $u = g(t) \equiv 5$, find dy/dt.

14. If $y = u^2 + 2u$ and

$$u = \begin{cases} x^2 \sin (1/x) & \text{for} \quad x \neq 0 \\ 0 & \text{for} \quad x = 0 \end{cases},$$

show that $(dy/dx)|_{x=0} = 0$. Show also that $\Delta u = u(0 + \Delta x) - u(0)$ is zero for an infinite number of values of Δx in any interval including $x = 0$.

3.7 Higher Derivatives

Given $y = f(x)$, dy/dx defines a function of x denoted by f'. If we differentiate f' with respect to x, we obtain another function of x. This function is called the second derivative of y with respect to x and is denoted by f''. We write

$$\frac{d}{dx}\left(\frac{dy}{dx}\right) = \frac{d^2 y}{dx^2} = \frac{dy'}{dx} = y'' = f''(x).$$

The symbol $d^2 y/dx^2$ is read as "d squared y dx squared" and $d^2/dx^2 = D_x^2$ is an operator which indicates that the function on which it operates is to be differentiated twice. For example,

$$\frac{d^2}{dx^2}(x^3) = D_x^2(x^3) = 6x.$$

Derivatives of order higher than 2 are defined similarly and are denoted by

$$\frac{d^3 y}{dx^3} = D_x^3 = y''' = f'''(x),$$

$$\frac{d^4 y}{dx^4} = D_x^4 = y^{(4)} = f^{(4)}(x),$$

.

.

.

$$\frac{d^n y}{dx^n} = D_x^n = y^{(n)} = f^{(n)}(x).$$

It should be noted that parentheses are employed in $y^{(n)}$ and $f^{(n)}(x)$ but not in $d^n y/dx^n$ and D_x^n. This distinguishes between $y^n = f^n(x) = [f(x)]^n$ and the nth derivative of y with respect to x. For example, if $y = f(x) = x^5$, $y^4 = f^4(x) = x^{20}$, but $y^{(4)} = f^{(4)}(x) = 120x$. On the other hand, $d^4 y/dx^4 = D_x^4(x^5)$ can only refer to $120x$. In general, the nth power F^n of an operator F is an operator which indicates that the operator F is to be applied successively n times.

Example 1

$$y = \frac{x^4}{4} - \frac{4x^3}{3} + 5x - 1$$

$$\frac{dy}{dx} = y' = f'(x) = x^3 - 4x^2 + 5,$$

$$\frac{d^2 y}{dx^2} = y'' = f''(x) = 3x^2 - 8x,$$

$$\frac{d^3 y}{dx^3} = y''' = f'''(x) = 6x - 8,$$

$$\frac{d^4 y}{dx^4} = y^{(4)} = f^{(4)}(x) = 6,$$

$$\frac{d^5 y}{dx^5} = y^{(5)} = f^{(5)}(x) = 0.$$

All higher derivatives of y are also 0.

Example 2.   Given $f(x) = x^{1/3}$, find $f''(8)$.

Solution

$$f'(x) = \left(\frac{1}{3}\right)x^{-2/3},$$

$$f''(x) = \left(\frac{-2}{9}\right)x^{-5/3} = \frac{-2}{9x\sqrt[3]{x^2}},$$

$$f''(8) = \frac{-2}{9(8)(4)} = \frac{-1}{144}.$$

Note that $f'(8)$ did not enter into the computation. We were interested in how fast $f'(x)$ was changing when $x = 8$, not in the value of $f'(x)$ when $x = 8$.

Example 3.   Evaluate $D_x^n(1/x)$.

Solution

$$D_x\left(\frac{1}{x}\right) = D_x(x^{-1}) = -x^{-2},$$

$$D_x^2\left(\frac{1}{x}\right) = +2x^{-3},$$

$$D_x^3\left(\frac{1}{x}\right) = -3\cdot 2x^{-4},$$

.

.

.

$$D_x^n\left(\frac{1}{x}\right) = (-1)^n n!\, x^{-n-1},$$

where $n! = n(n-1)(n-2)\cdots(1)$.

Note that $D_x^n(1/x)$ depnds upon both x and n. For example,

$$D_x^n\left(\frac{1}{x}\right)\Big|_{\substack{n=5\\x=2}} = (-1)^5(5!)2^{-6} = \frac{-15}{8}.$$

PROBLEM LIST 20

1. Find the first and second derivatives of the functions defined by:

(a) $y = x^4 + 3x^2 - 1$.

(b) $y = 2x^6 - 3x^2 - x$.

(c) $y = x - (1/x)$.

(d) $y = 3x + x^{1/2}$.

(e) $y = 2x^{1/3} + 3x^{-2/3} + 1$.

(f) $y = (x^2 - 3x)^2$.

(g) $y = \dfrac{1}{x+1}$.

(h) $y = \dfrac{x}{1-x}$.

2. Find the first and second derivatives of the functions defined by:

(a) $y = 5x^4 - 3x^3 + 2x - 1$.

(b) $y = 4x^3 - x + 7$.

(c) $y = x(x^2 - 1)^2$.

(d) $y = \sqrt{1 - x^2}$.

(e) $y = \dfrac{1-x}{1+x}$.

(f) $y = \dfrac{1}{\sqrt{x}}$.

(g) $y = \dfrac{x^2}{x-1}$.

(h) $y = (1 - x^2)^{2/3}$.

3. Given $f(x) = x/(x^2 + 1)$, find $f(2)$, $f'(2)$, and $f''(2)$.

4. Given $f(t) = t - \sqrt{t}$, find $f(4)$, $f'(4)$, and $f''(4)$.

5. Find $d^n y/dx^n$ for each of the following:

(a) $y = \dfrac{1}{x+1}$.

(b) $y = \dfrac{1}{(x-1)^2}$.

(c) $y = \dfrac{1}{x^3}$.

(d) $y = \sqrt{x}$.

(e) $y = \dfrac{x+1}{x}$.

(f) $y = \dfrac{2x^2 - 3x}{x-1}$.

6. Find the values of x for which $f''(x) = 0$ if $f(x)$ equals

(a) $2x - 1$;   (d) $x^3 - 12x^2 + 1$;

(b) $x^2 - 1$;   (e) $x^4 - 2x^3 - 36x^2 - 1$;

(c) $1 - x^2 - x^3$;   (f) $y = \dfrac{1}{x^2 + 1}$.

7. (a) How fast is the slope of the curve $y = x^3 - 2x^2 + 2$ changing at the point where $x = 2$? (b) What is the slope of the curve at the same point?

8. Given $f(x) = x^{7/3}$, find

(a) $f(0)$.   (c) $f''(0)$.

(b) $f'(0)$.   (d) $f'''(0)$.

9. If $P(x)$ is a polynomial of degree n, show that $D_x^m[P(x)] \equiv 0$ for all positive integers $m > n$.

10. If $y = xu$, where u denotes a differentiable function of x, show that

$$D_x^n y \equiv x\, D_x^n u + n\, D_x^{n-1} u.$$

11. Given that $f(x)$ defines a polynomial of degree 3 for which $f(0) = -1$, $f'(1) = 11$, $f''(1) = 12$, and $f'''(2) = 6$, find $f(1)$.

12. If $y = f(u)$ defines a differentiable function of u and $u = g(x)$ defines a differentiable function of x, show that

$$\frac{dy^2}{dx^2} = \frac{d^2u}{dx^2} \cdot \frac{dy}{du} + \left(\frac{du}{dx}\right)^2 \frac{d^2y}{du^2}.$$

13. If $y = uv$, where u and v denote differentiable functions of x, show that

$$y'' = uv'' + 2u'v' + u''v.$$

Also find y''' and then generalize to obtain a formula for $y^{(n)}$. This formula is known as Leibniz's rule.

3.8   Implicit Differentiation

The chain rule may be employed to calculate the derivative of any differentiable function defined implicitly by an equation of the form $g(x, y) = 0$. Suppose $g(x, y) = 0$ defines a differentiable function given by $y = f(x)$. Then, since $g[x, f(x)]$ is zero for all x in the domain of f, the derivative of $g[x, f(x)]$ with respect to x must be zero. This derivative will involve dy/dx and hence will enable us to compute dy/dx.

Example 1. $g(x, y) = 3x - 4y + 5 = 0$.

Setting

$$\frac{d}{dx}[g(x, y)] = 0,$$

we obtain

$$3 - 4\frac{dy}{dx} = 0,$$

from which

$$\frac{dy}{dx} = \frac{3}{4}.$$

It is important to note that the derivative with respect to x of a function of y is equal to its derivative with respect to y times dy/dx, the derivative of y with respect to x. This follows from the chain rule. In Example 1, the derivative of $-4y$ with respect to x is -4 times dy/dx.

Example 2. $x^2 + y^2 - 1 = 0$. Then

$$2x + 2y\frac{dy}{dx} = 0,$$

and

$$\frac{dy}{dx} = -\frac{x}{y}.$$

Note that the derivative with respect to x of y^2 is $2y$ times dy/dx. Also note that when we find dy/dx in this example, it involves both x and y, where y refers to the function (or functions) determined by $x^2 + y^2 - 1 = 0$. Two functions are actually determined. They are given by

$$y_1 = \sqrt{1 - x^2} \qquad \text{and} \qquad y_2 = -\sqrt{1 - x^2}.$$

Thus

$$\frac{dy_1}{dx} = \frac{-x}{y_1} = \frac{-x}{\sqrt{1 - x^2}} \qquad \text{and} \qquad \frac{dy_2}{dx} = \frac{-x}{y_2} = \frac{x}{\sqrt{1 - x^2}}.$$

We observe that we have obtained the same results we would have obtained if we had solved $x^2 + y^2 - 1 = 0$ for y_1 and y_2 before differentiating.

It is interesting to note that if $P(x, y)$ is a point on the circle $x^2 + y^2 - 1 = 0$ ($x \neq 0$), the slope of a line through the origin O and P is y/x. Thus the tangent at P should have slope $-x/y$ (assuming $y \neq 0$), the negative reciprocal of y/x. This is in agreement with our expression for dy/dx.

Example 3. $y^3 + x^2y - 2x^2 = 0$. Then

$$3y^2\frac{dy}{dx} + \left[x^2\frac{dy}{dx} + y(2x) \right] - 4x = 0,$$

and

$$\frac{dy}{dx} = \frac{4x - 2xy}{3y^2 + x^2}.$$

In this example it would be quite difficult to solve for y in terms of x before differentiating. Note also that the term x^2y is differentiated as a product.

Example 4.   Find $y'' = d^2y/dx^2$ if y is defined implicitly by $x^2 - y^2 - 4 = 0$.

   Solution

$$2x - 2yy' = 0,$$

from which

$$y' = \frac{x}{y}.$$

We now differentiate both sides with respect to x, treating the right member as a quotient:

$$y'' = \frac{y(1) - xy'}{y^2} = \frac{y - x(x/y)}{y^2} = \frac{y^2 - x^2}{y^3}.$$

Finally, we replace $y^2 - x^2$ by -4 (since $x^2 - y^2 - 4 = 0$) to obtain

$$y'' = \frac{-4}{y^3}.$$

After obtaining the relationship

$$x - yy' = 0$$

we could have differentiated implicitly, without solving for y', to obtain

$$1 - yy'' - (y')(y') = 0.$$

Then

$$y'' = \frac{1 - (y')^2}{y} = \frac{1 - (x^2/y^2)}{y} = \frac{y^2 - x^2}{y^3} = \frac{-4}{y^3}.$$

3.9   Derivative of an Inverse Function

It can be proved (see Ref. 3.2) that if f has a nonzero derivative at (x_0, y_0) and if $y = f(x)$ possesses an inverse $x = g(y)$, then $dx/dy = g'(y)$ exists when $y = y_0$. The following argument shows how to compute dx/dy.

Let $y - f(x) = 0$. Then $dy/dx = f'(x)$, and assuming that x is a differentiable function of y, we differentiate both sides of $y - f(x) = 0$ with respect to y to obtain:

$$1 - f'(x)\frac{dx}{dy} = 0$$

or

$$\frac{dx}{dy} = \frac{1}{f'(x)} = \frac{1}{dy/dx}$$

provided $f'(x) \neq 0$.

This result is certainly not unexpected, for if y changes three times as fast as x, it is reasonable to expect that x changes one-third as fast as y. It is also easy to show that if $y = f(x)$ has slope $m \neq 0$ at (x, y), then $y = f^{-1}(x)$ has slope $1/m$ at (y, x), since the two curves are symmetric with respect to the line $y = x$. (See Sec. 2.4.)

Example 1.   Find dx/dy if $y = x^3 + 4x - 1$.

Solution

$$\frac{dy}{dx} = 3x^2 + 4$$

and hence

$$\frac{dx}{dy} = \frac{1}{3x^2 + 4}.$$

Example 2. Find dy/dx if $x = y^3 + 2y - 3$.

Solution A

$$\frac{dx}{dy} = 3y^2 + 2$$

from which

$$\frac{dy}{dx} = \frac{1}{3y^2 + 2}.$$

Solution B. Differentiating both sides with respect to x, we obtain

$$1 = (3y^2 + 2)\frac{dy}{dx}$$

from which

$$\frac{dy}{dx} = \frac{1}{3y^2 + 2}.$$

PROBLEM LIST 21

1. Find dy/dx: (a) by solving for y in terms of x and differentiating, (b) by implicit differentiation. Show that the results of (a) and (b) are equal.

    (a) $3x + 4y - 7 = 0$.   (e) $x^2 - y^2 - 4 = 0$.

    (b) $y - 4x^2 = 0$.   (f) $y^2 + 2y + 1 - x = 0$.

    (c) $x^2 + y^2 - 9 = 0$.   (g) $y^2 - x^3 = 0$.

    (d) $3x - y^2 = 0$.   (h) $x^2 + xy + y^2 = 1$.

2. Assuming that each equation defines one or more differentiable functions of x, find dy/dx by implicit differentiation.

    (a) $4x - 2y + 1 = 0$.   (i) $x^2 - 2xy + 3y^2 = 4$.

    (b) $ax + by + c = 0$.   (j) $x^3 + xy^2 + y^2 - 3x^2 = 0$.

    (c) $xy + y^2 = 5$.   (k) $x^3 + xy^2 - 5y^2 = 0$.

    (d) $xy = 4$.   (l) $x^{2/3} + y^{2/3} = 1$.

    (e) $x^2 y^2 = 6$.   (m) $x^{1/2} + y^{1/2} = 1$.

    (f) $3xy + x^2 = 2$.   (n) $y^4 - 2y^3 + x^2 = 0$.

    (g) $3x^2 + 5y^2 = 4$.   (o) $(x^2 + y^2)^2 = 4(x^2 - y^2)$.

    (h) $6x^2 - 3y^2 = 5$.   (p) $(x^2 + 2y - 1)^2 - y^2(1 - x^2) = 0$.

3. Find y' and y'' by implicit differentiation.

    (a) $xy = 4$.   (e) $x^3 + y^3 = 8$.

    (b) $y^2 - x = 0$.   (f) $y^3 - 5x^2 = 0$.

    (c) $x^2 + y^2 - 4 = 0$.   (g) $y^2 - 4y + 16 = 6x$.

    (d) $y^2 - x^2 = 3$.   (h) $x^{1/2} + y^{1/2} = 3$.

4. Find equations of the tangent and normal to the curve $x^2 - 2xy + y^2 + 5x - 6y + 8 = 0$ at the point $(3, 8)$.

5. Find equations of the tangent and normal to the curve $x^5 + 3x^4 - y^2 = 0$ at the point $(1, 2)$.

6. Find the values of x for which $dy/dx = 0$ if
$$x^3 + y^3 - 3xy = 0.$$

7. Find dy/dx if
    (a) $x = y^3 - 4y^2 + 7$;
    (b) $5x = 3y^2 + 2y - 1$.

8. Find the slope of the curve $2x^3 + 2y^3 - 9xy = 0$ at $(1, 2)$.

9. Find dy/dx:
    (a) $x^3 + xy^2 + x^2 - y^2 = 0$.
    (b) $y^4 - 2y^3 + x^2 = 0$.
    (c) $x^2y + 4y - 9x = 0$.
    (d) $(x^2 + y^2)(x - 1)^2 - 4x^2 = 0$.
    (e) $x^2y^2 - x^2 - 16y^2 = 0$.
    (f) $(x^2 + y^2 - x)^2 - (x^2 + y^2) = 0$.

10. Show that if $y = x^{p/q}$, where p and q are positive integers, defines a differentiable function of x, then
$$\frac{dy}{dx} = \frac{p}{q} x^{(p/q)-1}.$$

11. Find the slope of the curve $y^3 + y^2 = x^3$ at (a) $(2^{1/3}, 1)$, (b) $(0, 0)$.

3.10   *Differential of a Function*

At this stage of our development the symbol dy/dx represents the derivative with respect to x of the function f defined by $y = f(x)$. We now propose to assign separate meanings to the symbols dy and dx. With this objective in mind we set down the following definition.

Definition.   Let $y = f(x)$ define a function of x and let dx be a real variable. The following expression is called the differential dy of the function f:
$$dy = f'(x)\, dx. \tag{3.14}$$

We first note that dy, the differential of f, depends not only upon x but also upon dx. That is, dy is a function of two variables x and dx. We may assign to x any real number for which $f'(x)$ is defined and we may assign to dx any real number whatsoever. The differential of f is sometimes denoted by df.

Example 1.   Find the differential of the function given by $y = x^2 - x$ when $x = 3$ and $dx = 2$.

Solution. $dy = (2x - 1)dx$.
Hence
$$dy \Big|_{\substack{x=3 \\ dx=2}} = 5(2) = 10.$$

Note that to find a particular value of $dy/dx = f'(x)$, it is only necessary to assign x, but to find a particular value of dy it is necessary to assign both x and dx.

———————

Now let us assume that x is given an increment $\Delta x \neq 0$ and let us assign the value Δx to dx. This enables us to interpret the differential dy of f geometrically.

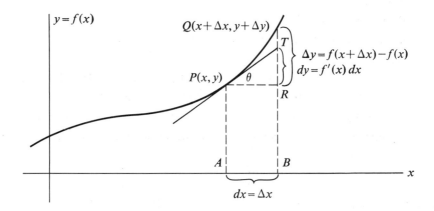

Figure 3.7

In Fig. 3.7 line PT is tangent to $y = f(x)$ at $P(x, y)$. Since

$$f'(x) = \tan \theta = RT \div PR,$$

the distance $RT = (\tan \theta) \, PR = f'(x) \, dx$ provides a geometric interpretation of dy, the differential of f. Observe that to determine RT, we must fix the point P and also fix the distance PR. This is equivalent to saying that dy depends not only upon x but also upon dx.

The height of the curve at a point with abscissa x is denoted by y. At a point where the abscissa is $x + \Delta x = x + dx$, the height is $y + \Delta y$. If dx is sufficiently small, the height of the curve can be approximated by the height of the tangent line drawn to the curve at (x, y), namely, by $y + dy$. We say that the height of the tangent line PT is a linear approximation to the height of the curve $y = f(x)$ in the vicinity or neighborhood of (x, y). This means that dy is an approximation to Δy if $dx = \Delta x$ is sufficiently small. This is verified by the following argument:

$$\lim_{\Delta x \to 0} \frac{\Delta y}{dy} = \lim_{\Delta x \to 0} \frac{\Delta y}{f'(x) \, dx} = \lim_{\Delta x \to 0} \frac{\Delta y}{f'(x) \, \Delta x}$$

$$= \frac{1}{f'(x)} \lim_{\Delta x \to 0} \frac{\Delta y}{\Delta x}$$

$$= \frac{f'(x)}{f'(x)} = 1.$$

The student should realize that $dx = \Delta x$ can be negative as well as positive.

It is also possible for dy to be greater than Δy as well as less than Δy. That is, in Fig. 3.7 point Q could lie between points R and T if the shape of the curve were different.

Example 2.   Find dy when $x = 2$ and $dx = -0.05$ if $y = x^3$.

    Solution. $dy = 3x^2\, dx.$
    Therefore

$$dy\Big|_{\substack{x=2 \\ dx=-0.05}} = 3(2)^2(-0.05) = -0.6.$$

Example 3.   Find dy and Δy when $x = 4$ and $dx = \Delta x = 0.41$ if $y = \sqrt{x}$.

    Solution

$$\Delta y = \sqrt{x + \Delta x} - \sqrt{x} = \sqrt{4.41} - \sqrt{4}$$
$$= 2.1 - 2 = 0.1,$$
$$dy = f'(x)\, dx = \frac{dx}{2\sqrt{x}} = \frac{0.41}{2\sqrt{4}} = 0.1025.$$

In this example, $dy > \Delta y$. The student should draw a graph illustrating dy and Δy.

We have attached separate meanings to the symbols dy and dx and we observe that (provided $dx \neq 0$)

$$dy \div dx = \frac{dy}{dx} = \frac{f'(x)\, dx}{dx} = f'(x).$$

That is, dy/dx has the same meaning it previously had, but now has an extended meaning. It can be interpreted as a fraction having numerator dy and denominator dx. It is no accident that $dy \div dx$ equals the derivative of y with respect to x; if we had defined dy and dx in such a way that $dy \div dx$ did not yield $f'(x)$, we would have been unable to interpret dy/dx as a fraction. To do so would introduce an inconsistency.

The usefulness of differentials is due in large measure to the following important theorem, known as Cauchy's invariant rule.

Theorem 3-IX.   Let f and g be differentiable functions given by $y = f(x)$ and $x = g(t)$, and let h be the composite function given by $y = h(t) = f[g(t)]$. Then dy is given by $f'(x)\, dx$ whether dy denotes the differential df of f or the differential dh of h.

    Proof.   By definition, $dy = f'(x)dx$ for the function f, for which x denotes an element of the domain and y the corresponding element of the range.
    For the function h an element of the domain is denoted by t and the cor-

responding element of the range is denoted by y. By the chain rule,

$$\frac{dy}{dt} = \frac{dy}{dx} \cdot \frac{dx}{dt} = f'(x)g'(t).$$

Hence

$$dy = [f'(x)g'(t)] \, dt = f'(x)[g'(t) \, dt].$$

But $g'(t) \, dt = dx$, the differential dg of g, and therefore dh is given by $dy = f'(x) \, dx$.

The significance of Theorem 3-IX is that the differential df of a function f given by $y = f(u)$ is $f'(u) \, du$ even if u is not an element of the domain of f, but instead is an intermediate variable related to the variable representing an element of the domain of f. When one or more functions are defined by an equation of the form $F(x, y) = 0$, it is often convenient to defer judgment at to whether x or y will denote an element of the domain of the function (or functions) defined implicitly.

Example 4. If $4x^2 + y^2 - 4 = 0$, use differentials to find dy/dx and dx/dy.

Solution. $8x \, dx + 2y \, dy = 0.$

Dividing by dx and solving for dy/dx, we obtain

$$\frac{dy}{dx} = \frac{-4x}{y}.$$

Dividing by dy and solving for dx/dy, we obtain

$$\frac{dx}{dy} - \frac{-y}{4x}.$$

The differential of $4x^2$ is given by $8x \, dx$ and the differential of y^2 is given by $2y \, dy$, whether x or y denotes an element of the domain of any function defined by the given relation.

Example 5. Find dy if $y = x^2 - 2x + 7$ and $x = t^3 + t$.

Solution A

$$y = (t^3 + t)^2 - 2(t^3 + t) + 7$$
$$= t^6 + 2t^4 - 2t^3 + t^2 - 2t + 7.$$

Hence

$$dy = (6t^5 + 8t^3 - 6t^2 + 2t - 2) \, dt.$$

Solution B

$$dy = f'(x) \, dx = (2x - 2)(3t^2 + 1) \, dt$$
$$= [2(t^3 + t) - 2] \, (3t^2 + 1) \, dt$$
$$= (6t^5 + 8t^3 - 6t^2 + 2t - 2) \, dt.$$

Example 6. Find dy/dx if $y = 3t^2 - 5t + 1$ and $x = t^3 + 2t$.

Solution. Since $dy = (6t - 5) \, dt$ and $dx = (3t^2 + 2) \, dt$,

we obtain

$$\frac{dy}{dx} = \frac{6t - 5}{3t^2 + 2}.$$

The symbol d can now be regarded as an operator which indicates that the differential of the function defined by the expression to which d applies should be found. For example, $d(x^2 - 2x) = (2x - 2)\,dx$. The expression $d/dx(x^3 - 1)$ can be interpreted to mean the derivative with respect to x of $x^3 - 1$ or the quotient $d(x^3 - 1) \div dx$. Each differentiation formula gives rise to a differential formula, a few of which follow.

$$dc = 0 \qquad \text{where } c \text{ is a constant.} \tag{3.15}$$

$$d(u + v) = du + dv. \tag{3.16}$$

$$d(uv) = u\,dv + v\,du. \tag{3.17}$$

$$d\left(\frac{u}{v}\right) = \frac{v\,du - u\,dv}{v^2}. \tag{3.18}$$

$$d(u^n) = nu^{n-1}\,du. \tag{3.19}$$

Example 7

$$d(x\sqrt{x-1}) = \frac{x\,dx}{2\sqrt{x-1}} + \sqrt{x-1}\,dx$$
$$= \frac{(3x - 2)\,dx}{2\sqrt{x-1}}.$$

Example 8

$$d(x^{5/3}) = \frac{5}{3}x^{2/3}\,dx.$$

Example 9

$$d\left(\frac{2x}{x^2 + 1}\right) = \frac{(x^2 + 1)(2dx) - (2x)(2x\,dx)}{(x^2 + 1)^2}$$
$$= \frac{(2 - 2x^2)\,dx}{(x^2 + 1)^2}.$$

PROBLEM LIST 22

1. Find the differential of the function defined by each of the following equations:

(a) $y = x^2$.

(b) $y = x$.

(c) $y = x^4 - 3x^2 + 5$.

(d) $y = 2x + \sqrt{x}$.

(e) $y = \sqrt{1 - x^2}$.

(f) $y = x^{2/3} + x^{-1/2} - 1$.

(g) $s = 16t^2$.

(h) $A = s^2$.

(i) $V = (4/3)\pi r^3$.

(j) $A = \pi r^2$.

(k) $V = s^3$.

(l) $T = \pi\sqrt{l/32}$.

2. Given $y = x^2 + 1$, find dy when

(a) $x = 2$ and $dx = 0.1$;

(b) $x = 3$ and $dx = -0.2$;

(c) $x = 4$ and $dx = 0$;

(d) $x = 0$ and $dx = 1$;

(e) $x = -2$ and $dx = 0.3$;

(f) $x = -5$ and $dx = -0.4$.

3. Compute dy for $y = x^3$. Then let $dx = \Delta x$ and compute Δy. Evaluate dy and Δy for $x = 2$ and $dx = 0.01$. How do dy and Δy compare in size for $x = 2$ and $dx = 0.01$?

4. Compute dy for $y = \sqrt{x}$. Let $dx = \Delta x = 0.21$. Illustrate dy and Δy geometrically when $x = 1$.

5. Compute dy for $y = 1/x$. **(a)** Let $dx = \Delta x = -0.5$. Illustrate dy and Δy geometrically when $x = 2$. **(b)** Let $dx = \Delta x = 0.2$. Illustrate dy and Δy geometrically when $x = -1$.

6. Find dy in terms of t and dt by two different methods:

(a) $y = x^2$, $x = 2t$.

(b) $y = x^3 - x$, $x = t^2$.

(c) $y = 1/x$, $x = 3t - 1$.

(d) $y = \sqrt{x}$, $x = 1 - t$.

(e) $y = x + 1$, $x = t^2 - 1$.

(f) $y = ax + b$, $x = ct + d$.

(g) $y = \dfrac{x}{1 + x^2}$, $x = 2t - 1$.

(h) $y = ax^2 + bx + c$, $x = kt + e$.

7. Given $y = x^3 - x + 1$ and $x = t^2 - 1$, find $dy \big|_{\substack{t=1 \\ dt=0.2}}$.

8. Employ differentials to find dy/dx and dx/dy:

(a) $xy = 5$.

(b) $x + 3y^2 = 7$.

(c) $x^2 + y^2 = 9$.

(d) $3x^2 - y^2 = 1$.

(e) $xy^2 + 4 = 0$.

(f) $3y + x^2 - 7x + 2 = 0$.

(g) $x^3 + y^3 - 6xy = 0$.

(h) $x^5 + y^3 = xy^2$.

9. Find dy/dx and dx/dy by means of differentials:

(a) $y = 3t^2 - 2t$, $x = 4t - 5$.

(b) $y = 2t^2 - 4t + 1$, $x = 2t^2 + t$.

(c) $y = \sqrt{t}$, $t = x^2 + 3x$.

10. Evaluate

(a) $d(x^2 - 2x + 3)$;

(b) $d(x + \sqrt{x})$;

(c) $d(x\sqrt{1 - x^2})$;

(d) $d\left(\dfrac{x^2 - 1}{x^3 + 1}\right)$.

REFERENCES

3.1 C. B. BOYER, *The History of the Calculus and Its Conceptual Development*, Dover, New York, 1949.

3.2 R. COURANT, *Differential and Integral Calculus*, Vol. I. Nordemann, New York, 1937.

3.3 I. S. SOKOLNIKOFF, *Advanced Calculus*, McGraw-Hill, New York, 1939.

Chapter

4

The integral calculus

4.1 Introduction

The fundamental problem of the integral calculus can be presented geometrically. We will assume that we are able to find the area of a plane region that is bounded by straight-line segments. This is accomplished by subdividing the region into triangles or rectangles, computing the areas of the triangles or rectangles by elementary geometry, and adding the results. For example, in Fig. 4.1 the area of polygon $ABCD$ can be found by adding the areas of rectangle I and triangles II, III, and IV.

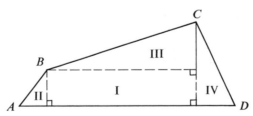

Figure 4.1

We now consider the region in the xy-plane bounded by the x-axis, the line $x = a$, the line $x = b > a$, and the curve $y = f(x)$. We assume that $f(x)$ is nonnegative and continuous on a $a \leqslant x \leqslant b$. The region described is the shaded region R in Fig. 4.2.

Our fundamental problem is to determine the area of a region of the type shown in Fig. 4.2. It is apparent that in general we cannot subdivide the region R into triangles and rectangles as we subdivided the region in Fig. 4.1. Another difficulty is that we are not sure what we mean by the area of a region such as R. Before we can talk precisely about the area of R, it will be necessary to generalize the concept

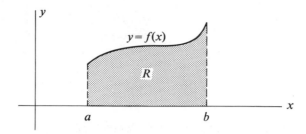

Figure 4.2

of area that is employed when dealing with plane regions bounded by straight-line segments.

The analysis of this area problem, known as the problem of quadrature, leads to the formulation of the concept of a definite integral. The integral concept, in turn, has numerous important applications totally unrelated to the problem of quadrature. Finally, we will discover that a remarkable relationship exists between the integral concept and the differential calculus.

At this point we turn our attention to certain preliminary concepts and theorems which are essential to the logical development of the integral calculus. A few of these theorems will be assumed, since their proofs depend upon properties of the real number system and are more profitably studied in advanced courses. Fortunately, these theorems are easy to state and to illustrate, and their conclusions are intuitively plausible although difficult to prove.

4.2   Increasing and Decreasing Functions

A function f defined by $y = f(x)$ is said to be increasing on a set S of real numbers, provided $f(x_1) < f(x_2)$ for every pair of numbers x_1 and x_2 in S satisfying $x_1 < x_2$. The function is said to be decreasing on S, provided $f(x_1) > f(x_2)$ for every pair of numbers x_1 and x_2 in S satisfying $x_1 < x_2$. If S is an open or closed interval, we say that the function is increasing or decreasing on the interval. See Fig. 4.3.

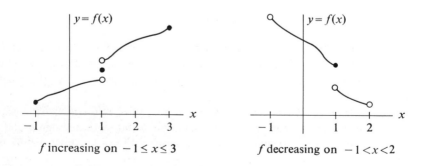

f increasing on $-1 \leq x \leq 3$ f decreasing on $-1 < x < 2$

Figure 4.3

Example 1.   The function defined by $y = x^3$ is an increasing function on the set of real numbers.

Example 2.   The function defined by $y = x^2$ is decreasing on $-\infty < x < 0$ and increasing on $0 \leqslant x < \infty$.

Example 3.   The function defined by $y = f(x) = 1/x$ is decreasing on $-\infty < x < 0$ and decreasing on $0 < x < \infty$. It is neither increasing nor decreasing on its domain of definition, which consists of the positive and negative real numbers. It is not decreasing, since $2 > -2$ but $f(2) = (1/2) > f(-2) = -1/2$.

4.3 *Maximum and Minimum Values of a Function*

A function defined by $y = f(x)$ is said to have an absolute maximum M on a set S if $f(x) = M$ for at least one x in S and $f(x) \leqslant M$ for every x in S. A function defined by $y = f(x)$ is said to have an absolute minimum m on a set S if $f(x) = m$ for at least one x in S and $f(x) \geqslant m$ for every x in S.

Example 1.   The function defined by $y = 3 - x$ has an absolute maximum $M = 2$ and an absolute minimum $m = 0$ on the interval $1 \leqslant x \leqslant 3$.

Example 2.   The function defined by $y = |x| + 1$ has $M = 3$ and $m = 1$ on $-1 \leqslant x \leqslant 2$.

Example 3.   The function defined by $y = 2$ has $M = 2$ and $m = 2$ on every interval.

Examples 1, 2, and 3 are illustrated in Fig. 4.4.

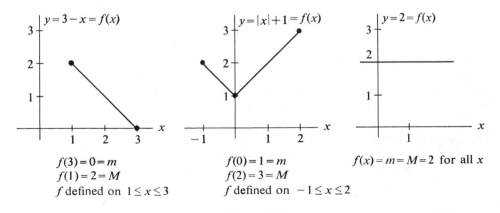

$f(3) = 0 = m$
$f(1) = 2 = M$
f defined on $1 \leq x \leq 3$

$f(0) = 1 = m$
$f(2) = 3 = M$
f defined on $-1 \leq x \leq 2$

$f(x) = m = M = 2$ for all x

Figure 4.4

We now state one of the most important theorems in mathematics. A proof is given in Ref. 4.2.

Theorem 4-I.   A function that is continuous on a closed interval $a \leqslant x \leqslant b$ has an absolute maximum M and an absolute minimum m on $a \leqslant x \leqslant b$.

The first two functions in Fig. 4.4 illustrate Theorem 4-I. The following examples are also instructive.

Example 4.   The function defined by $y = 3 - x$ has an absolute maximum $f(1)$ $= 2 = M$ on $1 \leqslant x < 3$, but does not have an absolute minimum m on $1 \leqslant x < 3$. The interval is not closed.

Example 5.   The function defined by $y = 1/x$ has neither an absolute maximum nor an absolute minimum on $-1 \leqslant x \leqslant 2$. The interval is closed, but the function is not continuous on the interval. The point $x = 0$ is not in the domain of the function.

Example 6.   The function defined by $y = 1/x$ has an absolute minimum $f(-2)$ $= -1/2 = m$ on $-\infty < x \leqslant -2$, but does not have an absolute maximum M on $-\infty < x \leqslant -2$. The interval is not closed. See Fig. 4.5.

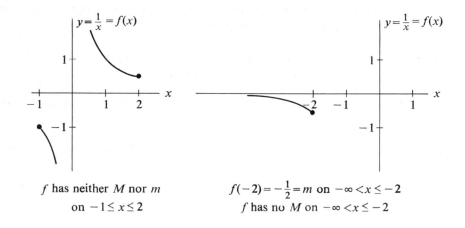

f has neither M nor m
on $-1 \leq x \leq 2$

$f(-2) = -\frac{1}{2} = m$ on $-\infty < x \leq -2$
f has no M on $-\infty < x \leq -2$

Figure 4.5

We next prove a result known as Fermat's theorem. Pierre de Fermat (1601–1665) was a brilliant French mathematician. His investigations on tangents to curves and on maximum and minimum values of functions played a significant role in the development of both analytic geometry and calculus.

Theorem 4-II (*Fermat's theorem*).   Let $y = f(x)$ denote a function that is defined on an interval $a < x < b$ and which assumes an absolute maximum M or an absolute minimum m at $x = c$, where $a < c < b$. If f is differentiable at c, then $f'(c) = 0$.

Proof.   Assume that $f(c) = M$. [If $f(c) = m$, the proof is similar.] Let Δx be any real number different from zero and satisfying $a < c + \Delta x < b$. Then

$$\frac{f(c + \Delta x) - f(c)}{\Delta x} \leqslant 0 \qquad \text{for } \Delta x > 0 \qquad \textbf{(4.1)}$$

and

$$\frac{f(c + \Delta x) - f(c)}{\Delta x} \geqslant 0 \qquad \text{for } \Delta x < 0. \qquad \textbf{(4.2)}$$

The numerators in (4.1) and (4.2) are $\leqslant 0$, since $f(c) = M$ is an absolute maximum. We now allow Δx to approach zero through positive values in (4.1), to obtain

$$\lim_{\Delta x \to 0^+} \frac{f(c + \Delta x) - f(c)}{\Delta x} \leqslant 0.$$

Letting Δx approach zero through negative values in (4.2), we obtain

$$\lim_{\Delta x \to 0^-} \frac{f(c + \Delta x) - f(c)}{\Delta x} \geqslant 0.$$

Since $f'(c)$ exists, $f'(c) = 0$.

The proof depends upon the fact that $\Delta y / \Delta x$, which approaches a limit by hypothesis, must approach zero if it is always $\leqslant 0$ for one manner of approach and always $\geqslant 0$ for another manner of approach.

Example 1.   The function f defined by $y = 3 - x$ has $f(1) = 2 = M$ on $1 \leqslant x \leqslant 3$ and yet $f'(1) \neq 0$. This does not contradict Fermat's theorem, since $x = 1$ does not satisfy $1 < x < 3$. The point $x = c$ in Fermat's theorem must be a point of $a < x < b$. See Fig. 4.4.

Example 2.   The function f defined by $y = |x| + 1$ has $f(0) = 1 = m$ and yet $f'(0) \neq 0$. This does not contradict Fermat's theorem, since $f'(0)$ does not exist. See Fig. 4.4.

Example 3.   The function f defined by $y = f(x) = 1/(1 + x^2)$ satisfies the hypotheses of Fermat's theorem. It is defined on any interval for which $x = 0$ is an interior point. The function is differentiable for all values of x and we see by inspection that $f(0) = 1 = M$. Therefore $f'(0) = 0$. See Fig. 4.6.

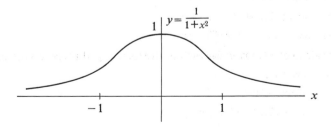

Figure 4.6

Example 4.   The function f given by $y = f(x) = x^3$ is defined on any interval for which $x = 0$ is an interior point. The function is differentiable for all values of x and $f'(0) = 0$. Yet $f(0) = 0$ is neither an absolute maximum nor an absolute minimum. This example does not contradict Fermat's theorem, but merely illustrates that a particular converse of Fermat's theorem is false. See Fig. 4.7.

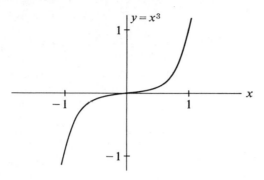

Figure 4.7

PROBLEM LIST 23

1. Determine whether f is increasing or decreasing on the given set of real numbers. Illustrate graphically.

    (a) $f(x) = 3x$, on $-2 < x < 3$.

    (b) $f(x) = x^2$, on $0 < x < 5$.

    (c) $f(x) = x^2$, on $-\infty < x < 0$.

    (d) $f(x) = x^2$, on $-1 < x < 2$.

    (e) $f(x) = |x|$, on $-\infty < x < \infty$.

    (f) $f(x) = \sqrt{x}$, on $1 \leqslant x \leqslant 5$.

    (g) $f(x) = \sqrt{1 - x^2}$, on $-1 \leqslant x \leqslant 1$.

    (h) $f(x) = 2/x$, on $0 < x < \infty$.

    (i) $f(x) = 2/x$, on the domain of definition of f.

    (j) $f(x) = \dfrac{1}{1 + x^2}$, on $1 \leqslant x \leqslant 80$.

    (k) $f(x) = \sin x$, on $0 \leqslant x \leqslant \pi/2$.

    (l) $f(x) = \cos x$, on $0 \leqslant x \leqslant \pi/2$.

    (m) $f(x) = \sin (1/x)$, on $0 < x < \pi/2$.

    (n) $f(x) = x^2 + 2x + 2$, on $0 < x < \infty$.

2. State the values of M and m for each of the following. Illustrate graphically.

    (a) $f(x) = 2x$, on $1 \leqslant x \leqslant 4$.

    (b) $f(x) = x^2$, on $-1 \leqslant x \leqslant 2$.

    (c) $f(x) = |x| - 2$, on $-2 \leqslant x \leqslant 3$.

    (d) $f(x) = \sin x$, on $-\pi/2 \leqslant x \leqslant \pi/4$.

    (e) $f(x) = 3x - 4$, on $-2 \leqslant x \leqslant 1$.

    (f) $f(x) = \pi$, on $-4 < x < 3$.

    (g) $f(x) = -1/x$, on $-5 \leqslant x \leqslant -1$.

(h) $f(x) = x^2 + 2x + 5$, on $-2 \leqslant x \leqslant 3$.

(i) $f(x) = \sin x + \cos x$, on $0 \leqslant x \leqslant 2\pi$.

(j) $f(x) = x/x$, on $-1 < x < 2$.

3. Investigate M and m for each of the following. If either M or m does not exist, explain why Theorem 4-I does not apply. Illustrate graphically.

(a) $f(x) = 3x$, on $1 < x \leqslant 2$.

(b) $f(x) = x^2$, on $0 \leqslant x < 1$.

(c) $f(x) = |x| + 2$, on $-1 < x \leqslant 3$.

(d) $f(x) = \dfrac{2}{1 + x^2}$, on $1 \leqslant x < \infty$.

(e) $f(x) = x^{1/3}$, on $-1 \leqslant x \leqslant 2$.

(f) $f(x) = 3/x$, on $-2 \leqslant x \leqslant 3$.

(g) $f(x) = \sqrt{x}$, on $1 < x \leqslant 2$.

(h) $f(x) = \tan x$, on $-\pi/2 < x < \pi/2$.

(i) $f(x) = \sin x + \sqrt{3} \cos x$, on $0 < x < 2\pi$.

(j) $f(x) = x^2 + 2x - 1$, on $-3 < x \leqslant 0$.

4. In each of the following, investigate to see if Fermat's theorem applies. If the theorem applies, state a conclusion based upon the theorem; if it does not apply, explain the reason. Illustrate graphically.

(a) $f(x) = 4 - x$, on $0 < x < 2$.

(b) $f(x) = x^2$, on $-1 < x < 2$.

(c) $f(x) = \sqrt{4 - x^2}$, on $-1 < x \leqslant 2$.

(d) $f(x) = x^5$, on $-1 < x < 1$.

(e) $f(x) = 3$, on $-3 < x < 2$.

(f) $f(x) = 2 - |x|$, on $-2 < x < 3$.

(g) $f(x) = \dfrac{2}{1 + x^4}$, on $-1 < x < 2$.

(h) $f(x) = \sqrt{3} \sin x - \cos x$, on $0 < x < \pi/2$.

(Assume that $\sin u$ defines a differentiable function of u for all values of u.)

5. Prove Fermat's theorem by showing that if $f'(c)$ exists and is not 0, where $a < c < b$, then f does not assume either an absolute maximum M or an absolute minimum m at c. This is a form of the contrapositive.

4.4   Rolle's Theorem

In this section we prove a result that will be used to establish the powerful mean-value theorem. It is named after Michel Rolle (1652–1719), a French mathematician who applied it to the study of polynomials.

Theorem 4-III (*Rolle's theorem*).   Let the function g defined by $y = g(x)$ be continuous on the closed interval $a \leqslant x \leqslant b$ and differentiable on the open interval $a < x < b$, and let $g(a) = g(b) = 0$. Then $g'(x) = 0$ for *at least* one $x = c$ satisfying $a < c < b$.

Geometrically, Rolle's theorem states that a continuous curve that intersects the x-axis in two distinct points $A(a, 0)$ and $B(b, 0)$, and has a slope at every point (x, y) for which $a < x < b$, must have slope zero at one or more of these latter points. See Fig. 4.8.

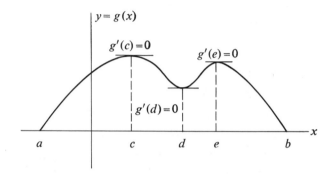

Figure 4.8

Rolle's theorem states that $g'(x) = 0$ for at least one point $x = c$ of an interval $a < x < b$, but does not state how to find c. Theorems of this nature are called existence theorems and play a vital role in mathematics. Note also that $f'(x)$ may be zero for more than one x in $a < x < b$. In Fig. 4.8, $g'(d) = g'(e) = g'(c) = 0$. Rolle's theorem states that *at least* one such x exists.

Proof of Rolle's theorem.   Since g is continuous on $a \leqslant x \leqslant b$, it assumes an absolute maximum M and an absolute minimum m on $a \leqslant x \leqslant b$. This follows from the crucial Theorem 4-I. We now consider two cases.

Case I.   If $m = M$, then $g(x) \equiv 0$ and $g'(x) \equiv 0$ for *all* x in $a < x < b$. The theorem is therefore true in this case, since we can choose c to be any number greater than a and less than b.

Case II.   If $m < M$, then either m or M must be taken on at an interior point c of the interval. Both m and M could not be taken on at the end points, since $g(a) = g(b) = 0$. Let $g(c) = M$. The $g'(c) = 0$ by Fermat's theorem. Similarly, if $g(c) = m$, $g'(c) = 0$ by Fermat's theorem. This completes the proof.

Example 1.   Let $y = g(x) = |x| - 1$ on $-1 \leqslant x \leqslant 1$. Then $g'(x) \neq 0$ for any x in $-1 < x < 1$. This does not contradict Rolle's theorem, since g is not differentiable at $x = 0$.

Example 2.   Let $y = g(x) = 1 - (x^3/x)$ on $-1 \leqslant x \leqslant 1$. Then $g'(x) \neq 0$ for any x in $-1 < x < 1$. The function g is identical with the function f given by $f(x) = 1 - x^2$ for $x \neq 0$, and hence has derivative $-2x$ for $x \neq 0$. Rolle's theorem does not apply since $1 - (x^3/x)$ is undefined at $x = 0$ and hence $x = 0$ is not in the domain of g'.

Example 3. Let $y = g(x) = x^2 - 2x - 8$ on $-2 \leqslant x \leqslant 4$. The function g does satisfy the hypotheses of Rolle's theorem. Differentiating,

$$g'(x) = 2x - 2$$

and setting

$$g'(x) = 2x - 2 = 0$$

we obtain

$$x = 1.$$

Since $g(x) = (x - 4)(x + 2)$, $g(x) = 0$ when $x = -2$ and when $x = 4$. Thus we have verified that Rolle's theorem applies, since $-2 < 1 < 4$.

Examples 1, 2, and 3 are illustrated in Fig. 4.9.

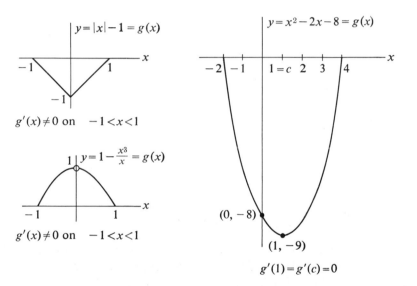

Figure 4.9

4.5   *Mean-Value Theorem*

Our next result is one of the most important theorems in calculus and mathematical analysis. It was first formulated by the Frenchman Joseph Louis Lagrange (1736–1813), regarded by many as the greatest mathematician of the eighteenth century.

Theorem 4-IV (*mean-value theorem*).   Let the function f defined by $y = f(x)$ be continuous on the closed interval $a \leqslant x \leqslant b$ and differentiable on the open interval $a < x < b$. Then

$$\frac{f(b) - f(a)}{b - a} = f'(c) \tag{4.3}$$

or, equivalently,

$$f(b) - f(a) = f'(c)(b - a) \qquad (4.4)$$

for *at least* one $x = c$ satisfying $a < c < b$.

The hypotheses of the mean-value theorem are identical with those of Rolle's theorem except that $f(a)$ and $f(b)$ do not have to equal zero. Equation (4.3) states that the average (or mean) rate of change of f over the interval $b - a$ is equal to the instantaneous rate of change of f somewhere between a and b; that is, somewhere in $a < x < b$. It is this fact that suggests the name "mean-value theorem." The geometric interpretation of the theorem is illustrated in Fig. 4.10.

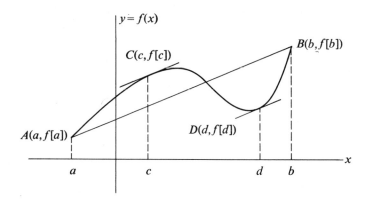

Figure 4.10

The left side of (4.3) is the slope of the line segment AB in Fig. 4.10. The theorem states that the slope of the curve at some point $(c, f[c])$, $a < c < b$, will be the same as the slope of AB. The curve shown in Fig. 4.10 has two such points, C and D.

Proof of the mean-value theorem.   Let $y = h(x)$ be defined by

$$y - f(a) = \frac{f(b) - f(a)}{b - a}(x - a). \qquad (4.5)$$

Note that (4.5) is the point-slope form of line AB in Fig. 4.10 and hence y represents the height of AB.
   Now let $g(x) = f(x) - h(x) = f(x) - y$, or

$$g(x) = f(x) - f(a) - \frac{f(b) - f(a)}{b - a}(x - a). \qquad (4.6)$$

Note that $g(x)$ denotes the difference between the height of the curve $y = f(x)$ and the height of the line AB in Fig. 4.10. Now observe that the function g satisfies the hypotheses of Rolle's theorem. (That $g(a) = g(b) = 0$ is easily verified by direct substitution.) Differentiating (4.6) with respect to x, we obtain

$$g'(x) = f'(x) - \frac{f(b) - f(a)}{b - a}.$$ (4.7)

By Rolle's theorem,

$$g'(c) = f'(c) - \frac{f(b) - f(a)}{b - a} = 0$$

for at least one c in $a < x < b$.
  Hence

$$\frac{f(b) - f(a)}{b - a} = f'(c)$$

for at least one c in $a < x < b$.
  This completes the proof.

It is easy to see that the mean-value theorem holds even if $b < a$. We merely apply (4.3) or (4.4) to the interval $b \leqslant x \leqslant a$ and then multiply both sides of the result by -1.

Example 1.   Let $y = f(x) = |x|$ on $-1 \leqslant x \leqslant 3$. Then

$$\frac{f(3) - f(-1)}{3 - (-1)} = \frac{3 - 1}{4} = \frac{1}{2},$$

but $f'(x) \neq 1/2$ for any x in $-1 < x < 3$. The mean-value theorem does not apply, since f is not differentiable at $x = 0$. See Fig. 4.11.

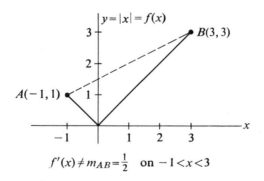

$$f'(x) \neq m_{AB} = \tfrac{1}{2} \quad \text{on } -1 < x < 3$$

Figure 4.11

Example 2.   Let $y = f(x) = x^2/4$ on $-4 \leqslant x \leqslant 2$.
  Then

$$f'(x) = \frac{x}{2} \quad \text{and} \quad \frac{f(2) - f(-4)}{2 - (-4)} = \frac{1 - 4}{6} = \frac{-1}{2}.$$

Setting $x/2 = -1/2$, we obtain $x = -1$. Thus we have verified that the mean-value theorem applies, since $-4 < -1 < 2$. See Fig. 4.12, where the slope at $(-1, 1/4) = $ slope of $AB = -1/2$.

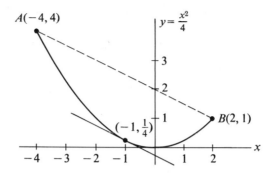

Figure 4.12

We now prove three important theorems which follow immediately from the mean-value theorem.

Theorem 4-V. If a function f defined by $y = f(x)$ has a derivative which is zero for every x in $a < x < b$, then $y = f(x)$ is constant on $a < x < b$.

Proof. Let x_1 and x_2 be any two numbers satisfying $a < x_1 < x_2 < b$. By the mean-value theorem,

$$f(x_2) - f(x_1) = f'(c)(x_2 - x_1)$$

for at least one c in $a < x < b$.

Since $f'(c) = 0$, $f(x_2) - f(x_1) = 0$. Inasmuch as x_1 and x_2 are *any* two distinct points of $a < x < b$, $y = f(x_1) = f(x_2) = $ constant on $a < x < b$.

Theorem 4-VI. If the function f defined by $y = f(x)$ has a positive derivative for every x in $a < x < b$, then the function is increasing on $a < x < b$.

Proof. Let x_1 and x_2 be any two numbers satisfying $a < x_1 < x_2 < b$. By the mean-value theorem,

$$f(x_2) - f(x_1) = f'(c)(x_2 - x_1)$$

for at least one c in $a < x < b$.

Since $f'(c) > 0$ and $x_2 > x_1$, $f(x_2) - f(x_1) > 0$ or $f(x_2) > f(x_1)$. Thus f is increasing on $a < x < b$.

Theorem 4-VII. If the function f defined by $y = f(x)$ has a negative derivative for every x in $a < x < b$, then the function is decreasing on $a < x < b$. The proof is similar to the proof of 4-VI.

PROBLEM LIST 24

1. Determine the value $x = c$ whose existence is guaranteed by Rolle's theorem. Illustrate graphically.

    (a) $f(x) = x^2 - x - 2$, on $-1 \leqslant x \leqslant 2$.

(b) $f(x) = -x^2 + 6x - 8$, on $2 \leqslant x \leqslant 4$.

(c) $f(x) = x^3 - 4x^2 + 3x$, on $1 \leqslant x \leqslant 3$.

(d) $f(x) = \sqrt{4 - x^2}$, on $-2 \leqslant x \leqslant 2$.

2. Explain why Rolle's theorem does not apply. Illustrate graphically.

(a) $f(x) = |x| - 2$, on $-2 \leqslant x \leqslant 2$.

(b) $f(x) = 4 - (x^3/x)$, on $-2 \leqslant x \leqslant 2$.

3. Prove that $x^4 + 4x + 5 = 0$ has at most two distinct real roots.

4. Prove that $ax^5 + bx + c = 0$ has at most three distinct real roots. Assume that a, b, and c are real numbers.

5. Make use of Fig. 4.10 to draw a rough graph of the function g in equation (4.6).

6. Determine the value $x = c$ whose existence is guaranteed by the mean-value theorem. Illustrate graphically.

(a) $y = x^2$, $1 \leqslant x \leqslant 3$.

(b) $y = x^2$, $-3 \leqslant x \leqslant 1$.

(c) $y = \sqrt{x}$, $0 \leqslant x \leqslant 5$.

(d) $y = x^3$, $-3 \leqslant x \leqslant 3$.

7. Explain why the mean-value theorem does not apply. Illustrate graphically.

(a) $y = |x|$, $-3 \leqslant x \leqslant 4$.

(b) $y = 1/x$, $-1 \leqslant x \leqslant 1$.

(c) $y = \dfrac{x^2(x - 2)}{x - 2}$, $0 \leqslant x \leqslant 4$.

(d) $y = 1 - x^{2/3}$, $-1 \leqslant x \leqslant 1$.

(e) $y = \begin{cases} x + 1 & \text{for} & -1 \leqslant x < 0 \\ x + 2 & \text{for} & 0 \leqslant x \leqslant 1. \end{cases}$

8. At what point on $y = ax^2 + bx + c$ is the slope equal to the slope of the line through $P_1(x_1, y_1)$ and $P_2(x_2, y_2)$, P_1 and P_2 being any two distinct points of the same curve?

9. Show that the mean-value theorem can be written in the form

$$f(a + h) = f(a) + hf'(a + \theta h)$$

where

$$0 < \theta < 1.$$

10. Apply the mean-value theorem to the function f defined by $f(x) = \sqrt{x}$ to prove that

$$10 + \frac{17}{22} < \sqrt{117} < 10 + \frac{17}{20}.$$

4.6   The Intermediate-Value Theorem

We will need the following result, which is proved in Ref. 4.2.

Theorem 4-VIII (*intermediate-value theorem*).   Let the function f defined by $y = f(x)$ be continuous on a closed interval $a \leqslant x \leqslant b$ and let k be any real number satisfying $f(a) < k < f(b)$ or $f(a) > k > f(b)$. Then there exists *at least* one $x = c$ between a and b such that $f(c) = k$.

Geometrically the theorem states that the curve $y = f(x)$ intersects the line $y = k$ *at least* once on $a < x < b$. See Fig. 4.13.

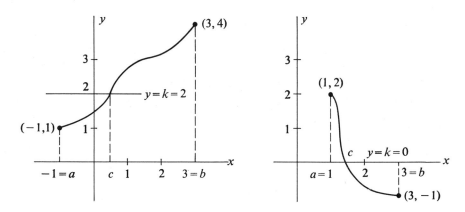

Figure 4.13

The intermediate-value theorem is employed in finding irrational roots of equations.

Example.   To solve $x^3 + x - 4 = 0$, we set $y = f(x) = x^3 + x - 4$ and seek the values of x for which $f(x) = 0$. We next discover the $f(1) = -2$ and $f(2)$

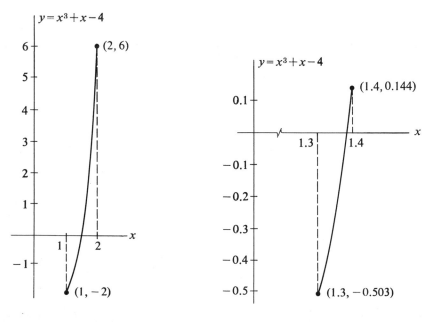

Figure 4.14   **Figure 4.15**

$= +6$. It then follows from the intermediate-value theorem that the equation has at least one root between 1 and 2. From Fig. 4.14 we estimate a root to be approximately 1.4. We next find that $f(1.3) = -0.503$ and $f(1.4) = +0.144$, whereupon we draw the graph shown in Fig. 4.15. Next we find that $f(1.37) < 0$ and $f(1.38) > 0$ and conclude that a root is between 1.37 and 1.38. Continuing in this fashion we are able to obtain a root to any number of decimal places. (It can be shown that the equation has only one root between 1 and 2.)

4.7   An Important Theorem on Sequences

A sequence $\{s_n\}$ is called bounded if there exists a positive number M such that

$$|s_n| \leqslant M \qquad \text{for all } n.$$

Geometrically this means that all points corresponding to the elements of $\{s_n\}$ lie in the interval $-M \leqslant x \leqslant M$.

Example 1.   The sequence

$$\{s_n\} = \left\{ 2 + \frac{(-1)^n}{n} \right\}$$

is bounded. All elements of the sequence lie in the interval $-3 \leqslant x \leqslant 3$. See Fig. 4.16.

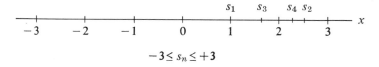

$$-3 \leq s_n \leq +3$$

Figure 4.16

Although we chose $M = 3$, we could just as well have chosen $M = 2.5$.

Example 2.   The sequence $\{n^2\}$ is unbounded. No matter how large an M is selected, $n^2 > M$ for n sufficiently large.

A sequence $\{s_n\}$ is called monotone if either

(i) $s_{n+1} \geqslant s_n$ for all n (monotone nondecreasing), or

(ii) $s_{n+1} \leqslant s_n$ for all n (monotone nonincreasing).

The geometric interpretations of **(i)** and **(ii)** are illustrated in Fig. 4.17.

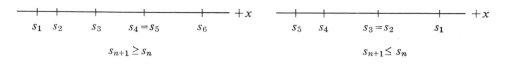

Figure 4.17

Example 3.   The sequence $\{2 + (-1)^n/n\}$ is not monotone.

Example 4.   The sequence $\{n^2\}$ is monotone, since $(n + 1)^2 \geqslant n^2$ for all n.

Example 5.   The sequence $\{1/n\}$ is monotone, since $1/(n + 1) \leqslant 1/n$ for all n. It is also bounded, since $|1/n| \leqslant 1$ for all n.

The following basic theorem on bounded monotone sequences is proved in Ref. 4.2.

Theorem 4-IX.   Every bounded monotone sequence converges.

Example 6.   The sequence $\{1/n\}$ converges to 0; that is

$$\lim_{n \to \infty} \frac{1}{n} = 0.$$

Example 7.   The sequence $\{s_n\} = \{n/(n + 1)\}$ converges to 1. The sequence is bounded since $|n/(n + 1)| \leqslant 1$ for all n. The sequence is monotone, since

$$s_n = \frac{n}{n + 1} = 1 - \frac{1}{n + 1} < 1 - \frac{1}{n + 2} = \frac{n + 1}{n + 2} = s_{n+1}$$

for all n.

Example 8.   Consider the sequence

$$\{s_n\} = \left\{ \frac{1}{2^2} + \frac{1}{3^2} + \cdots + \frac{1}{(n + 1)^2} \right\}.$$

The sequence is obviously monotone, since $s_1 = 1/4, s_2 = 1/4 + 1/9, s_3 = 1/4 + 1/9 + 1/16, \cdots$. We prove that $\{s_n\}$ is bounded by the following argument:

$$s_n = \frac{1}{2 \cdot 2} + \frac{1}{3 \cdot 3} + \frac{1}{4 \cdot 4} + \cdots + \frac{1}{(n + 1)(n + 1)}$$

is clearly less than

$$a_n = \frac{1}{1 \cdot 2} + \frac{1}{2 \cdot 3} + \frac{1}{3 \cdot 4} + \cdots + \frac{1}{n(n + 1)}.$$

But

$$a_n = \left(\frac{1}{1} - \frac{1}{2} \right) + \left(\frac{1}{2} - \frac{1}{3} \right) + \left(\frac{1}{3} - \frac{1}{4} \right) + \cdots + \left(\frac{1}{n} - \frac{1}{n + 1} \right)$$

$$= 1 - \frac{1}{n + 1}$$

which is < 1 for all n.

Hence $|s_n| < 1$ for all n and $\{s_n\}$ converges by Theorem 4-IX.

This example points out the existence character of Theorem 4-IX. Although the theorem states that

$$\lim_{n \to \infty} \left[\frac{1}{2^2} + \frac{1}{3^2} + \cdots + \frac{1}{(n + 1)^2} \right] - L$$

exists, it does not disclose the value of L. Since s_n increases with n but always remains less than 1, it follows that $0.25 < L \leqslant 1$. It can be shown by more advanced methods that $L = \pi^2/6 - 1 \cong 0.64$.

4.8   *Mathematical Induction*

Mathematical induction is an accepted method of proving propositions concerning the natural numbers 1, 2, 3, $\cdots$, n, $\cdots$. Let $P(n)$ be such a proposition. We first show that $P(1)$ is true, meaning that the proposition is true for the natural number 1. Next we demonstrate that the proposition is true for the natural number $k + 1$ whenever it is true for the natural number k, k being arbitrary. In other words, we show that if $P(k)$ is true, then $P(k + 1)$ is also true. Having completed these two steps, we conclude that the proposition $P(n)$ is true for all natural numbers n. The validity of induction is one of the basic assumptions of mathematics; it is the last in a set of postulates for the natural numbers stated by the Italian logician and mathematician Giuseppe Peano (1858–1932).

Example 1.   Prove that

$$1 + 2 + \cdots + n = \frac{n(n + 1)}{2}. \tag{4.8}$$

Proof.   We first verify that the proposition is true for $n = 1$,

$$1 = \frac{1(1 + 1)}{2}.$$

We next assume that

$$1 + 2 + \cdots + k = \frac{k(k + 1)}{2}, \tag{4.9}$$

where k is an arbitrary natural number.

Adding $k + 1$ to both sides of (4.9), we obtain

$$1 + 2 + \cdots + k + (k + 1) = \frac{k(k + 1)}{2} + (k + 1), \tag{4.10}$$

which can be written as

$$1 + 2 + \cdots + (k + 1) = \frac{(k + 1)(k + 2)}{2} = \frac{[k + 1][(k + 1) + 1]}{2}. \tag{4.11}$$

We have shown that if (4.9) is true, then (4.11) is also true. But (4.11) states that proposition (4.8) is true when $n = k + 1$. We therefore conclude that (4.8) is true for all natural numbers n.

Example 2.   Prove that

$$1^2 + 2^2 + \cdots + n^2 = \frac{n(n + 1)(2n + 1)}{6}. \tag{4.12}$$

Proof.   The proposition is true for $n = 1$, since

$$1^2 = \frac{1(1 + 1)(2 + 1)}{6}.$$

Assume that for $n = k$, k arbitrary,

$$1^2 + 2^2 + \cdots + k^2 = \frac{k(k+1)(2k+1)}{6}. \tag{4.13}$$

Adding $(k+1)^2$ to both sides of (4.13), we obtain

$$1^2 + 2^2 + \cdots + k^2 + (k+1)^2 = \frac{k(k+1)(2k+1)}{6} + (k+1)^2$$

or

$$1^2 + 2^2 + \cdots + (k+1)^2 = \frac{(k+1)(k+2)(2k+3)}{6}. \tag{4.14}$$

But (4.14) states that (4.12) is true for $n = k + 1$, since

$$\frac{(k+1)(k+2)(2k+3)}{6} = \frac{(k+1)([k+1]+1)(2[k+1]+1)}{6}.$$

Since (4.12) is true for $n = 1$, and since (4.13) implies (4.14), it follows that (4.12) is true for all natural numbers n.

The method is very powerful even though it does not indicate the origin of any proposition to which it is applied. Frequently one is led to suspect that a proposition is true because he has observed a recurring pattern of some sort in a large number of cases. It is natural to try to prove the proposition by mathematical induction. For a more complete discussion of this topic see Ref. 4.1.

4.9   Summation Notation

The Greek capital letter sigma (Σ) is frequently employed to denote the sum of several terms, each term corresponding to an integer.

Example 1.   The sum of the first n natural numbers $1 + 2 + 3 + \cdots + (n-1) + n$ is denoted by

$$\sum_{i=1}^{n} i,$$

read as "summation from i equals 1 to n of i."

The letter i is called the summation index.

Example 2

$$\sum_{i=1}^{5} i^2 = 1^2 + 2^2 + 3^2 + 4^2 + 5^2 = 55.$$

We also refer to i as a dummy variable or dummy index, since the sum does not involve i.

Example 3

$$\sum_{i=1}^{3} \frac{1}{i^3} = \frac{1}{1^3} + \frac{1}{2^3} + \frac{1}{3^3} = \sum_{k=1}^{3} \frac{1}{k^3}.$$

Sometimes we let the summation index begin at some integer other than 1.

Example 4

$$\sum_{i=0}^{n} 2^i = 2^0 + 2^1 + 2^2 + \cdots + 2^n.$$

Example 5

$$\sum_{k=3}^{5} \sin kx = \sin 3x + \sin 4x + \sin 5x.$$

In general, the symbol $\sum_{i=1}^{n}$ followed by an expression $f(i)$ denotes the sum of the terms obtained by evaluating $f(i)$ at $i = 1, 2, \cdots, n$.

Example 6

$$\sum_{i=0}^{n-1} f(x_i) = f(x_0) + f(x_1) + \cdots + f(x_{n-1}).$$

Example 7

$$\sum_{i=1}^{n} f(x_{i-1}) \Delta x_i = f(x_0) \Delta x_1 + f(x_1) \Delta x_2 + \cdots + f(x_{n-1}) \Delta x_n.$$

Example 8.   The symbol $\sum_{i=1}^{n} c$, where c is a constant, is defined by

$$\sum_{i=1}^{n} c = nc.$$

PROBLEM LIST 25

1. Explain why $x^{30} + 3x^{20} - 2 = 0$ has a real root between 0 and 1.

2. Find $\sqrt{2}$ to two decimal places by applying the intermediate-value theorem.

3. Although $1/x = -1$ at $x = -1$ and $1/x = +1$ at $x = +1$, there is no x between -1 and $+1$ such that $1/x = 0$. Does this contradict the intermediate-value theorem?

4. Use the intermediate-value theorem to show that the curve $y = x^3 - 5x + 1 = 0$ has slope zero for at least one value of x between 1 and 2.

5. Which of the following sequences are bounded? Give reasons for answers and illustrate geometrically.

(a) $\left\{\dfrac{1}{n}\right\}$.

(g) $\left\{\dfrac{n}{2n-1}\right\}$.

(b) $\left\{\dfrac{(-1)^n n)}{n+1}\right\}$.

(h) $\{(-1)^{n+1} n^2\}$.

(c) $\left\{n^3 + \dfrac{1}{n}\right\}$.

(i) $\left\{3 - \dfrac{(-1)^n}{n}\right\}$.

(d) $\left\{\sin\left(\dfrac{n\pi}{2}\right)\right\}$.

(j) $\left\{\tan\left(\dfrac{\pi}{2n-1}\right)\right\}$.

(e) $\left\{2 - \dfrac{1}{n}\right\}$.

(k) $\left\{\tan\left(\dfrac{\pi}{2n+1}\right)\right\}$.

(f) $\left\{\dfrac{1}{2n}\right\}$.

(l) $\left\{\left(1 + \dfrac{1}{n}\right)^2\right\}$.

6. Which of the sequences in Problem 5 are monotone?

7. Which of the sequences in Problem 5 converge?

8. Which of the sequences in Problem 5 converge by Theorem 4-IX?

9. The sequence $\{s_n\}$ is monotone and $|s_n| \leqslant 5$. Does $\{s_n\}$ converge and, if so, what can be said concerning its limit?

10. Prove the following by mathematical induction.

(a) $1 + 3 + \cdots + (2n - 1) = n^2$.

(b) $2 + 4 + \cdots + 2n = n(n + 1)$.

(c) $2^0 + 2^1 + 2^2 + \cdots + 2^{n-1} = 2^n - 1$.

11. Express each sum by using the summation symbol Σ.

(a) $1^4 + 2^4 + 3^4 + \cdots + n^4$.

(b) $1^2 + 2^2 + 3^2 + 4^2 + 5^2$.

(c) $2^0 + 2^2 + 2^4 + \cdots + 2^{2n-2}$.

(d) $f(x_1) + f(x_2) + \cdots + f(x_n)$.

12. Express without using the summation symbol Σ.

(a) $\sum_{k=1}^{n} \dfrac{1}{k^3}$.

(b) $\sum_{k=2}^{5} (k^3 + 1)$.

(c) $\sum_{i=1}^{n} f(c_i) \, \Delta x_i$.

(d) $\sum_{i=1}^{n} f(x_i) g(c_i) \, \Delta x_i$.

(e) $\sum_{i=1}^{4} 2$.

13. Prove that if c is constant,

$$\sum_{i=1}^{n} c f(x_i) = c \sum_{i=1}^{n} f(x_i).$$

14. Prove that

$$\sum_{k=1}^{n} k^3 \neq \left[\sum_{k=1}^{n} k\right]\left[\sum_{k=1}^{n} k^2\right].$$

15. Prove by mathematical induction that

$$\sum_{k=1}^{n} k^3 = \frac{n^2(n + 1)^2}{4}.$$

16. Prove that

$$\sum_{k=1}^{n} ar^{k-1} = \frac{a(1 - r^n)}{1 - r} \qquad (r \neq 1).$$

17. Prove that the sequence

$$\left\{\sum_{k=1}^{n} \frac{1}{n + k}\right\}$$

is convergent by showing that it is monotone and bounded. *Hint:* Consider $s_{n+1} - s_n$ and

$$\sum_{k=1}^{n} \frac{1}{n + n}.$$

18. Prove that

$$\sum_{k=0}^{n} \binom{n}{k} = 2^n$$

where the symbol

$$\binom{n}{k} = \frac{n(n-1)(n-2)\cdots(n-k+1)}{k(k-1)(k-2)\cdots(1)}$$

denotes the number of combinations of n things taken k at a time. *Hint:* Employ the binomial expansion of $(x+y)^n$.

4.10   *Area Under a Curve and the Definite Integral*

We now return to the area problem discussed in Sec. 4.1.

Example 1.   In Fig. 4.18 we consider the area of trapezoid $ABCD$ bounded by the x-axis, the line $x = 1$, the line $x = 9$, and the line $y = f(x) = x$. We will refer to this area as the area under the curve $y = x$ from $x = a = 1$ to $x = b = 9$.

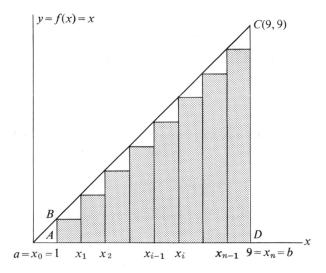

Figure 4.18

We divide line segment AD into n equal parts by inserting $n - 1$ equally spaced points between A and D. These points, together with A and D, are labeled

$$a = x_0 = 1, \qquad x_1 = 1 + (\Delta x), \qquad x_2 = 1 + 2(\Delta x), \cdots,$$
$$x_{n-1} = 1 + (n-1)(\Delta x), \qquad x_n = 9 = b$$

where

$$\Delta x = \frac{b-a}{n} = \frac{9-1}{n} = \frac{8}{n}.$$

We next form the n shaded rectangles by erecting ordinates at $x = x_0$, $x = x_1$, $x = x_2$, $\cdots$, and $x = x_{n-1}$. These are called inscribed rectangles, and it is clear that the sum of their areas will depend upon n. We denote this sum by I_n.

It seems reasonable to expect that I_n will be close to the area of trapezoid $ABCD$ for large values of n. We now investigate the relationship between I_n and n.

$$I_n = f(x_0)(\Delta x) + f(x_1)(\Delta x) + f(x_2)(\Delta x) + \cdots + f(x_{n-1})(\Delta x)$$

$$= (\Delta x) \sum_{i=0}^{n-1} f(x_i) = (\Delta x) \sum_{i=0}^{n-1} x_i$$

$$= (\Delta x)\{[1] + [1 + 1(\Delta x)] + [1 + 2(\Delta x)] + \cdots + [1 + (n-1)(\Delta x)]\}.$$

We now replace Δx by $8/n$ to obtain

$$I_n = \frac{8}{n}\left\{n + \frac{8}{n}[1 + 2 + \cdots + (n-1)]\right\}.$$

$$= 8 + \frac{64}{n^2} \sum_{i=1}^{n-1} i.$$

But

$$\sum_{i=1}^{n-1} i = \frac{(n-1)n}{2}$$

by formula (4.8) of Sec. 4.8 (if we replace n by $n-1$).

Hence

$$I_n = 8 + \frac{64}{n^2} \cdot \frac{(n-1)n}{2} = 8 + 32\left(1 - \frac{1}{n}\right).$$

It is easy to see that the sequence $\{I_n\}$ is bounded, since $|I_n| < 40$. The sequence is also monotone, since $I_{n+1} > I_n$ for all n. We also see by inspection that $\lim_{n\to\infty} I_n = 40$.

The area of trapezoid $ABCD$ is also 40, a result obtained by applying the formula $S = (h/2)(b_1 + b_2)$.

We next approximate the area of trapezoid $ABCD$ by the sum of the areas of the circumscribed rectangles shown in Fig. 4.19. These rectangles have the same bases as those of Fig. 4.18, but each has height equal to the height of $y = x$ at the right end of its base rather than at the left end. The sum of the areas of the circumscribed rectangles is denoted by C_n.

From Fig. 4.19 we obtain

$$C_n = f(x_1)(\Delta x) + f(x_2)(\Delta x) + \cdots + f(x_n)(\Delta x)$$

$$= (\Delta x) \sum_{i=1}^{n} f(x_i) = (\Delta x) \sum_{i=1}^{n} x_i$$

$$= (\Delta x)\{[1 + 1(\Delta x)] + [1 + 2(\Delta x)] + \cdots + [1 + n(\Delta x)]\}$$

$$= \frac{8}{n}\left\{n + \frac{8}{n}[1 + 2 + \cdots + n]\right\} = 8 + \frac{64}{n^2} \sum_{i=1}^{n} i.$$

Replacing

$$\sum_{i=1}^{n} i \quad \text{by} \quad \frac{n(n+1)}{2}$$

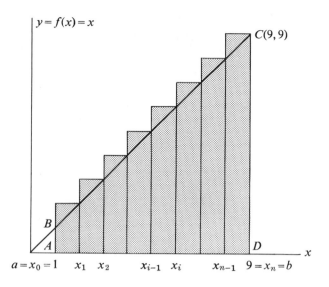

Figure 4.19

from formula (4.8) of Sec. 4.8, we obtain

$$C_n = 8 + \frac{64}{n^2} \cdot \frac{n(n+1)}{2} = 8 + 32\left(1 + \frac{1}{n}\right).$$

The sequence $\{C_n\}$ is bounded, since $|C_n| \leqslant 72$, and is monotone, since $C_{n+1} < C_n$ for all n. The sequence also has limit 40, the area of trapezoid $ABCD$.

Thus, as $n \longrightarrow \infty$, I_n increases and approaches the area under $y = x$, while C_n decreases and approaches the same area. A few values of I_n and C_n are displayed in the following table:

n	1	2	10	100	1000	10,000
I_n	8	24	36.8	39.68	39.968	39.9968
C_n	72	56	43.2	40.32	40.032	40.0032

Since $\lim_{n\to\infty} I_n$, $\lim_{n\to\infty} C_n$, and the area in question under $y = f(x) = x$ all have the same value 40, it is natural to try the same method where $y = f(x)$ is a curve other than a straight line.

Example 2.   In Fig. 4.20 we consider the region bounded by the x-axis, the line $x = 4$, and the curve $y = f(x) = x^2/8$. This curve is called a parabola and will be studied in detail in a later chapter.

Proceeding as in Example 1, we obtain

$$I_n = f(x_0)(\Delta x) + f(x_1)(\Delta x) + \cdots + f(x_{n-1})(\Delta x)$$
$$= (\Delta x) \sum_{i=0}^{n-1} f(x_i) = \frac{(\Delta x)}{8} \sum_{i=0}^{n-1} x_i^2.$$

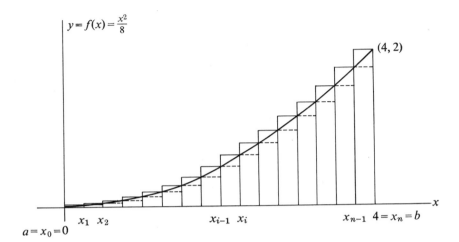

Figure 4.20

Since $\Delta x = 4/n$, we have

$$a = x_0 = 0, \quad x_1 = 1\left(\frac{4}{n}\right),$$

$$x_2 = 2\left(\frac{4}{n}\right), \quad \cdots, \quad x_{n-1} = (n-1)\left(\frac{4}{n}\right),$$

$$x_n = n\left(\frac{4}{n}\right) = 4 = b,$$

and hence

$$I_n = \frac{4}{8n}\left[0^2 + 1^2\left(\frac{4}{n}\right)^2 + 2^2\left(\frac{4}{n}\right)^2 + \cdots + (n-1)^2\left(\frac{4}{n}\right)^2\right]$$

$$= \frac{8}{n^3}[1^2 + 2^2 + \cdots + (n-1)^2].$$

But

$$\sum_{i=0}^{n-1} i^2 = \frac{(n-1)(n)([2n-2]+1)}{6}$$

$$= \frac{(n-1)(n)(2n-1)}{6}$$

by formula (4.12) of Sec. 4.8. Therefore

$$I_n = \frac{8}{n^3}\frac{(n-1)(n)(2n-1)}{6} = \frac{4}{3}\left(1 - \frac{1}{n}\right)\left(2 - \frac{1}{n}\right).$$

It is easy to see that $\{I_n\}$ is bounded and monotone, since $|I_n| < 8/3$ and $I_{n+1} > I_n$ for all n. It is also seen that $\lim_{n\to\infty} I_n = 8/3$.

In this example I_n is the sum of the areas of $n-1$ rather than n rectangles. This is due to the fact that the segment from $x = 0$ to $x = 4/n$ does not have a rectangle associated with it, unless we wish to consider a rectangle with zero height.

We now obtain

$$C_n = f(x_1)(\Delta x) + f(x_2)(\Delta x) + \cdots + f(x_n)(\Delta x)$$

$$= (\Delta x) \sum_{i=1}^{n} f(x_i) = \frac{(\Delta x)}{8} \sum_{i=1}^{n} x_i^2$$

$$= \frac{4}{8n} \left[1^2 \left(\frac{4}{n} \right)^2 + 2^2 \left(\frac{4}{n} \right)^2 + \cdots + n^2 \left(\frac{4}{n} \right)^2 \right]$$

$$= \frac{8}{n^3} [1^2 + 2^2 + \cdots + n^2]$$

$$= \frac{8}{n^3} \frac{n(n + 1)(2n + 1)}{6}$$

by (4.12) of Sec. 4.8.

Therefore,

$$C_n = \frac{4}{3} \left(1 + \frac{1}{n} \right) \left(2 + \frac{1}{n} \right).$$

It is easy to see that $\{C_n\}$ is bounded and monotone, since $|C_n| \leqslant 8$ and $C_{n+1} < C_n$ for all n. It is also clear that

$$\lim_{n \to \infty} C_n = \frac{8}{3} = \lim_{n \to \infty} I_n.$$

As yet we have not defined what we mean by the area under a curve. Now that we have established that I_n increases with n, C_n decreases with n, and that

$$\lim_{n \to \infty} I_n = \lim_{n \to \infty} \sum_{i=0}^{n-1} f(x_i)(\Delta x)$$

$$= \lim_{n \to \infty} C_n = \lim_{n \to \infty} \sum_{i=1}^{n} f(x_i)(\Delta x),$$

we define the area under the curve as this common limit. The limit is called the definite integral of f from a to b and is denoted by the symbol

$$\int_a^b f(x)\, dx,$$

read as "the integral of f of x from a to b." The symbol $\int$ is called an integral sign and is a stylized S which was used in Leibniz's time to indicate a summation. Today it refers to the limit of a sum and the word "integral" implies a process of summation.

The expression $f(x)$ is called the integrand, x the variable of integration, and a and b the limits on the integral. This use of the word "limits" is unfortunate, since we merely mean that a and b denote the endpoints of the interval of integration. The important limit concept we have been using has no relationship to the word "limits" as applied to a and b.

The integral calculus is the branch of mathematics which is devoted to the evaluation and application of definite integrals.

PROBLEM LIST 26

Use the method of Examples 1 and 2 in each of the following problems.

1. Find the area bounded by $x = 1$, $x = 9$, the x-axis, and $y = f(x) = 2x$.

2. Find the area bounded by $x = 12$, the x-axis, and $y = f(x) = x/2$.

3. Show that the area of a right triangle having base b and height h is $bh/2$.

4. Find the area under $y = x^2$ from $x = 0$ to $x = 6$.

5. Find the area under $y = 3x^2$ from $x = 1$ to $x = 2$.

6. Evaluate

$$\int_0^5 x \, dx.$$

7. Evaluate

$$\int_0^r x^2 \, dx.$$

8. Evaluate

$$\int_a^b k \, dx$$

where k is any constant.

9. Evaluate

$$\int_0^2 x^3 \, dx.$$

Hint: Employ the formula of Problem 15 in Problem List 25.

10. The region bounded by $y = h$ and the parabola $y = (4h/b^2)x^2$ is called a parabolic segment. Show that its area is given by $A = 2bh/3$.

11. Assuming that a, b, and c are all positive, evaluate

$$\int_0^1 (ax^2 + bx + c) \, dx.$$

12. In illustrative Example 1, let Q_n denote the sum of the areas of the n rectangles having bases $x_0 < x < x_1$, $\quad x_1 < x < x_2, \cdots, \quad x_{i-1} < x < x_i, \cdots$, and $x_{n-1} < x < x_n$; and heights equal to the height of $y = x$ at the midpoint of the base of each rectangle. Evaluate $\lim_{n \to \infty} Q_n$.

13. Apply the instructions of Problem 12 to illustrative Example 2.

4.11   General Definition of an Integral

In illustrative Examples 1 and 2 of Sec. 4.10, both $\lim_{n \to \infty} I_n$ and $\lim_{n \to \infty} C_n$ existed. It is natural to ask whether this will always be the case. Instead of investigating this question we will give a more general definition of a definite integral and will state a sufficient condition under which the integral will always exist.

We first note that in Examples 1 and 2 it was unnecessary to choose the height of each rectangle at one endpoint or the other. If we had chosen the height of the

ith rectangle as the height of $y = f(x)$ at any point c_i in the base $\Delta x_i = x_i - x_{i-1}$, the limit of the sum of the areas of the corresponding n rectangles would not have been affected. This is due to the fact that f was increasing in $a \leqslant x \leqslant b$ and the corresponding sum for any n would be between I_n and C_n. In this connection see Fig. 4.21 and Problems 12 and 13 of Problem List 26.

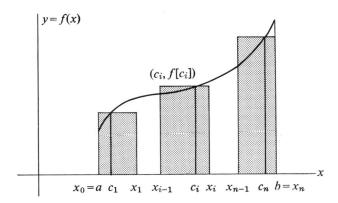

Figure 4.21

We mention this fact concerning the heights of the rectangles because the functional values $f(c_i)$ are so chosen in the general definition of an integral. We will also see that the interval $b-a$ is not necessarily divided into *equal* subintervals.

Definition.   Let the function f be defined on the closed interval $a \leqslant x \leqslant b$ and let this interval be divided into n subintervals (not necessarily of equal length) by $n + 1$ numbers x_i such that

$$a = x_0 < x_1 < x_2 < \cdots < x_{i-1} < x_i < \cdots < x_n = b.$$

Let c_i be *any* number in the ith interval

$$\Delta x_i = x_i - x_{i-1}$$

and let the largest of the Δx_i be denoted by $\max(\Delta x_i)$ (called the norm of the partition). Then

$$\lim_{\max(\Delta x_i) \to 0} \sum_{i=1}^{n} f(c_i)\,\Delta x_i,$$

if it always exists and always has the same value, is called the Riemann definite integral of the function f from a to b and is denoted by

$$\int_a^b f(x)\,dx.$$

Note that $n \longrightarrow \infty$ as $\max(\Delta x_i) \longrightarrow 0$. It would be possible, however, for n to become infinite without having $\max(\Delta x_i) \longrightarrow 0$.

We also note that the limit involved in the definition is more complicated than any limit we have yet encountered. This is due to the fact that the sums

$$\sum_{i=1}^{n} f(c_i)\,\Delta x_i$$

do not form a sequence. A particular sum depends not only upon n, but also upon the points of subdivision

$$x_1, x_2, \cdots, x_i, \cdots, x_{n-1},$$

and also upon the points

$$c_1, c_2, \cdots, c_i, \cdots, c_n.$$

The number c_i is *any* number satisfying

$$x_{i-1} \leqslant c_i \leqslant x_i.$$

The number $\int_a^b f(x)\,dx$ exists if and only if

$$\lim_{\max(\Delta x_i) \to 0} \sum_{i=1}^n f(c_i)\,\Delta x_i$$

exists and has the same value $\int_a^b f(x)\,dx$ for *all* sequences of subdivisions having $\max(\Delta x_i) \to 0$ and *all* proper choices of the points c_i therein.

The statement that

$$\lim_{\max(\Delta x_i) \to 0} \sum_{i=1}^n f(c_i)\,\Delta x_i$$

exists and is equal to the real number $\int_a^b f(x)\,dx$ can also be defined in ϵ, δ terminology. We give this definition and state without proof that it is equivalent to our definition involving sequential limits.

Definition.   The statement

$$\lim_{\max(\Delta x_i) \to 0} \sum_{i=1}^n f(c_i)\,\Delta x_i = \int_a^b f(x)\,dx$$

means that to every $\epsilon > 0$ there corresponds a $\delta > 0$ such that

$$\left| \sum_{i=1}^n f(c_i)\,\Delta x_i - \int_a^b f(x)\,dx \right| < \epsilon$$

for all choices of n and the points $x_1, x_2, \cdots, x_{n-1}$ and the points $c_1, c_2, \cdots, c_n$ such that $\max(\Delta x_i)$ is less than δ.

If the limit in the definition exists, the function f is said to be Riemann integrable over the interval $a \leqslant x \leqslant b$. Bernhard Riemann (1826–1866) was a distinguished German mathematician who made substantial contributions to the theory of integration. The following important theorem, proved in Ref. 4.2, states a sufficient condition for a function to be integrable.

Theorem 4-X.   If a function f is continuous on a closed interval $a \leqslant x \leqslant b$, the function is integrable over the interval.

We emphasize that this theorem states a sufficient condition on f to insure that f be Riemann integrable. It is not necessary. Reference 4.2 also proves that if f has only a finite number of ordinary discontinuities on $a \leqslant x \leqslant b$, then f is integrable on $a \leqslant x \leqslant b$.

Although Theorem 4-X will be sufficient for our purposes, we mention that other more general integrals, applying to more general functions than does the

Riemann integral, have been defined. Certain of these general integrals are required in physics and in the theory of probability.

Although the definition of the Riemann integral developed from the area problem, the definition is purely analytic and depends in no way upon geometric intuition. We will see later than an integral can represent many different types of quantities and that the area under a curve is but one interpretation of an integral.

4.12   *Properties of the Definite Integral*

In the theorems that follow, it is assumed that all integral involved exist. In our first result we assume that $a < c < b$.

Theorem 4-XI

$$\int_a^b f(x)\, dx = \int_a^c f(x)\, dx + \int_c^b f(x)\, dx.$$

This theorem follows immediately from the definition of an integral. In letting $\max(\Delta x_i) \to 0$, we can always choose $x = c$ as one of the x_i. This enables us to separate $\sum_{i=1}^{n} f(c_i)\, \Delta x_i$ into two sums, one of which will approach $\int_a^c f(x)\, dx$ and one of which will approach $\int_c^b f(x)\, dx$. If $f(x) \geqslant 0$, the area interpretation of Theorem 4-XI is that the area under $y = f(x)$ from a to b is the area from a to c plus the area from c to b.

In the definition of an integral we assumed that $a < b$. If $a > b$, we set down the following definition:

$$\int_a^b f(x)\, dx = -\int_b^a f(x)\, dx. \tag{4.15}$$

We could also have arrived at (4.15) by modifying the definition of an integral. For $a > b$ we could have subdivided the interval $b-a$ into n subintervals so that $x_i - x_{i-1} = \Delta x_i$ would always be negative. Then, by factoring out -1 from each term of $\sum_{i=1}^{n} f(c_i)\, \Delta x_i$, we would have been led to (4.15).

If (4.15) is also to hold when $a = b$, it will follow that

$$\int_a^a f(x)\, dx = -\int_a^a f(x)\, dx$$

or

$$2\int_a^a f(x)\, dx = 0.$$

Therefore, in order to be consistent, we define

$$\int_a^a f(x)\, dx = 0. \tag{4.16}$$

We also note that (4.16) is reasonable when the integral is interpreted as an area.

Using (4.15) and (4.16) it is easy to prove that Theorem 4-XI is true for any three numbers a, b, and c. See the Problem List.

Example 1. Show that

$$\int_2^5 x\,dx = \int_2^7 x\,dx + \int_7^5 x\,dx.$$

Solution. $\quad\displaystyle\int_2^7 x\,dx = \int_2^5 x\,dx + \int_5^7 x\,dx,$

$$\int_2^7 x\,dx = \int_2^5 x\,dx - \int_7^5 x\,dx.$$

Transposing, we obtain the desired result.

———————

In the area interpretation of an integral we assumed $f(x) \geqslant 0$. If $f(x) < 0$, and each $\Delta x_i > 0$, the products $f(c_i)\,\Delta x_i$ will be negative and the integral will have a negative value.

Example 2

$$\int_0^2 \left(\frac{x^2}{4} - 1\right) dx < 0.$$

———————

If $f(x) \leqslant 0$ for $a < x < c$ and $\geqslant 0$ for $c < x < b$,

$$\int_a^c f(x)\,dx \leqslant 0, \qquad \int_c^b f(x)\,dx \geqslant 0, \qquad \text{and } \int_a^b f(x)\,dx$$

will yield the algebraic sum of

$$\int_a^c f(x)\,dx \qquad \text{and} \qquad \int_c^b f(x)\,dx.$$

Example 3. We will later develop a simple method to show that

$$\int_0^2 \left(\frac{x^2}{4} - 1\right) dx = \frac{-16}{12} \qquad \text{and} \qquad \int_2^3 \left(\frac{x^2}{4} - 1\right) dx = \frac{+7}{12}.$$

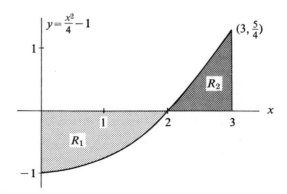

Figure 4.22

In Fig. 4.22 we will say that the area under $y = (x^2/4) - 1$ from 0 to 2 is $-(16/12)$, the area under $y = (x^2/4) - 1$ from 2 to 3 is $7/12$, and that the area under $y = (x^2/4) - 1$ from 0 to 3 is $-(9/12) = -(16/12) + (7/12)$. Since we wish the area of a region to be $\geqslant 0$, we say that the area of region R_1 is $16/12$ and the area of region R_2 is $7/12$.

The next theorems follow readily from the definition of an integral. Their proofs are left to the Problem List.

Theorem 4-XII

$$\int_a^b cf(x)\,dx = c\int_a^b f(x)\,dx$$

for any constant c.

Theorem 4-XIII

$$\int_a^b [f(x) \pm g(x)]\,dx = \int_a^b f(x)\,dx \pm \int_a^b g(x)\,dx.$$

Theorem 4-XIII states that the integral of a sum (difference) is the sum (difference) of the integrals. It is readily extended to more than two functions.

Theorem 4-XIV

$$\left| \int_a^b f(x)\,dx \right| \leqslant \int_a^b |f(x)|\,dx.$$

PROBLEM LIST 27

Assume that all integrals involved exist.

1. Prove the following:

   (a) $\displaystyle\int_2^5 f(x)\,dx = \int_2^8 f(x)\,dx - \int_5^8 f(x)\,dx.$

   (b) $\displaystyle\int_{-2}^6 f(x)\,dx = \int_3^6 f(x)\,dx - \int_3^{-2} f(x)\,dx.$

   (c) $\displaystyle\int_4^{-1} g(x)\,dx - \int_4^2 g(x)\,dx + \int_{-1}^2 g(x)\,dx = 0.$

   (d) $\displaystyle\int_a^b f(x)\,dx = \int_0^b f(x)\,dx - \int_0^a f(x)\,dx.$

2. Simplify:

   (a) $\displaystyle\int_6^{-2} f(x)\,dx + \int_{-2}^5 f(x)\,dx.$

   (b) $\displaystyle\int_3^4 f(x)\,dx - \int_5^5 g(x)\,dx + \int_{-6}^4 f(x)\,dx.$

   (c) $\displaystyle\int_a^{a+5} f(x)\,dx - \int_2^a f(x)\,dx.$

   (d) $\displaystyle\int_a^{t+\Delta t} f(x)\,dx - \int_a^t f(x)\,dx.$

3. Employ definition (4.15) to prove that Theorem 4-XI holds when $c < a < b$.

4. Given that (i) $\int_{-2}^{0} 3x^2\,dx = 8$, (ii) $\int_{0}^{1} 3x^2\,dx = 1$, and (iii) $\int_{1}^{2} 3x^2\,dx = 7$, evaluate:

(a) $\int_{0}^{2} 3x^2\,dx.$ (e) $\int_{3}^{3} 3x^2\,dx.$

(b) $\int_{1}^{-2} 3x^2\,dx.$ (f) $\int_{2}^{5} 3x^2\,dx - \int_{0}^{5} 3x^2\,dx.$

(c) $\int_{2}^{-2} 3x^2\,dx.$ (g) $\int_{4}^{1} 3x^2\,dx + \int_{-2}^{4} 3x^2\,dx.$

(d) $\int_{1}^{0} 3x^2\,dx.$ (h) $\int_{-2}^{1} x^3\,dx + \int_{1}^{-2} x^3\,dx.$

5. Use illustrative Example 3 to evaluate

$$\int_{0}^{3} \left| \frac{x^2}{4} - 1 \right| dx.$$

6. Prove Theorem 4-XII.

7. Prove Theorem 4-XIII.

8. If c and d are arbitrary constants, prove that

$$\int_{a}^{b} [cf(x) \pm dg(x)]\,dx = c \int_{a}^{b} f(x)\,dx \pm d \int_{a}^{b} g(x)\,dx.$$

Hint: Assume Theorems 4-XII and 4-XIII.

9. Prove Theorem 4-XIV.

10. Let f be a certain arbitrary continuous function defined on $a \leqslant x \leqslant b$. Which of the following statements is more likely to be true? Discuss.

(a) The function f is differentiable on $a \leqslant x \leqslant b$.

(b) The function f is integrable over $a \leqslant x \leqslant b$.

4.13   Volume Interpretation of an Integral

An equation of a circle of radius r with center at the origin is $x^2 + y^2 = r^2$, since the distance from $(0, 0)$ to (x, y) is r if and only if $x^2 + y^2 = r^2$. In Fig. 4.23 an equation of the quarter-circle is $y = f(x) = \sqrt{r^2 - x^2}$, where $0 \leqslant x \leqslant r$.

We inscribe rectangles as shown and revolve these rectangles about the x-axis. Each rectangle generates a thin right-circular cylinder, the cylinder generated by the ith rectangle being shown in Fig. 4.24. We assume that we know the formula $\pi a^2 h$ for the volume of a right-circular cylinder. The sum of the volumes of the inscribed cylinders is given by

$$I_n = \sum_{i=1}^{n} \pi (r^2 - x_i^2)\,\Delta x_i$$

$$= \pi r^2 \sum_{i=1}^{n} \Delta x_i - \pi \sum_{i=1}^{n} x_i^2\,\Delta x_i.$$

If we now let every

$$\Delta x_i = \frac{r - 0}{n},$$

$$x_1 = 1\left(\frac{r}{n}\right), \; x_2 = 2\left(\frac{r}{n}\right), \; \cdots, \; x_n = n\left(\frac{r}{n}\right) = r,$$

$y = \sqrt{r^2 - x^2}$
$P_i(x_i, y_i)$
x
$x_0 = 0$
x_1
x_2
x_{i-1}
x_i
x_{n-1}
$x_n = r$

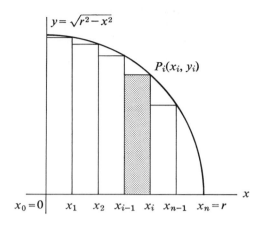

Figure 4.23

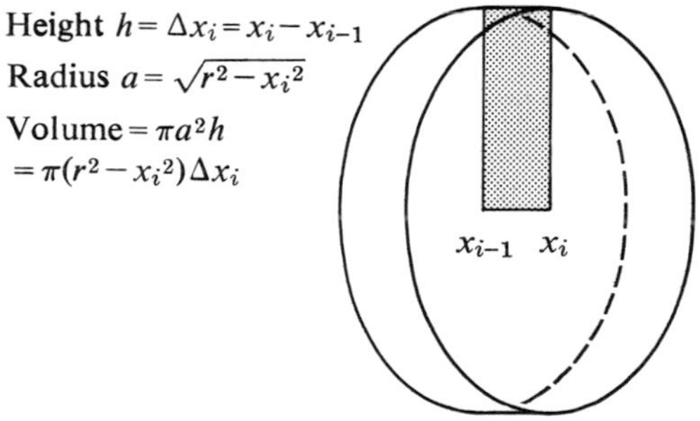

Height $h = \Delta x_i = x_i - x_{i-1}$
Radius $a = \sqrt{r^2 - x_i^2}$
Volume $= \pi a^2 h$
$= \pi(r^2 - x_i^2)\Delta x_i$
x_{i-1}
x_i

Figure 4.24

and hence

$$I_n = \pi r^3 - \frac{\pi r}{n} \cdot \frac{r^2}{n^2}[1^2 + 2^2 + \cdots + n^2],$$

which by formula (4.12) of Sec. 4.8 reduces to

$$\begin{aligned} I_n &= \pi r^3 - \frac{\pi r^3}{n^3} \frac{(n)(n+1)(2n+1)}{6} \\ &= \pi r^3 - \frac{\pi r^3}{6}\left(1 + \frac{1}{n}\right)\left(2 + \frac{1}{n}\right). \end{aligned}$$

Therefore,

$$\begin{aligned} \lim_{\max(\Delta x_i) \to 0} \sum_{i=1}^{n} \pi(r^2 - x_i^2)\,\Delta x_i &= \int_0^r \pi(r^2 - x^2)\,dx \\ &= \lim_{n\to\infty} I_n \\ &= \lim_{n\to\infty}\left[\pi r^3 - \frac{\pi r^3}{6}\left(1 + \frac{1}{n}\right)\left(2 + \frac{1}{n}\right)\right] \\ &= \pi r^3 - \frac{\pi r^3}{3} = \frac{2\pi r^3}{3}. \end{aligned}$$

It is seen by inspection that I_n increases with n. If we set up the corresponding expression C_n for the sum of the volumes of the corresponding circumscribed cylinders, we find that C_n decreases with n and also approaches $2\pi r^3/3$. (See Problem 1.) This prompts us to define the volume of the hemisphere as $\int_0^r \pi(r^2 - x^2)\,dx$. If we multiply by 2 we obtain the well-known formula $V = (4/3)\pi r^3$ for the volume of a sphere.

Thus we have an example in which an integral represents a volume rather than an area. We will encounter other important applications of definite integrals, but we first turn our attention to the matter of evaluating integrals. We have evaluated a few integrals by applying the definition of an integral, but the work was somewhat involved and usually required a special formula such as

$$\sum_{i=1}^n i^2 = \frac{n(n+1)(2n+1)}{6}.$$

In the next section we begin a development that leads to a startling method for evaluating definite integrals.

PROBLEM LIST 28

1. In Fig. 4.23 set up an expression C_n for the sum of the volumes of n cylinders which circumscribe the hemisphere. Show that C_n decreases with n and find $\lim_{n\to\infty} C_n$.

2. Use the method of this section to define the volume of a right-circular cone. Employing the definition selected, derive a formula for the volume.

3. Derive a formula for the volume of a frustrum of a right-circular cone (a) by the method of this section, (b) by applying the result of Problem 2.

4.14   The First Fundamental Theorem of Calculus

Let $y = f(x)$ define a function f continuous on $a \leqslant x \leqslant b$. Then f is integrable on $a \leqslant x \leqslant b$ by Theorem 4-X and consequently, if we regard the lower limit a on the integral as fixed and the upper limit denoted by x as variable, the integral can be regarded as a function F of its upper limit. The domain D of F will, of course, be the interval $a \leqslant x \leqslant b$.

We might be tempted to write

$$F(x) = \int_a^x f(x)\,dx$$

but we would then be using the symbol x to denote both an element of the domain of F and the variable of integration. To avoid this, we write instead

$$F(x) = \int_a^x f(t)\,dt. \qquad (4.17)$$

The variable of integration in a definite integral is often referred to as a dummy variable. This is due to the fact that $\int_a^b f(x)\,dx$ does not depend upon x and has the same value as $\int_a^b f(t)\,dt$ or $\int_a^b f(u)\,du$.

The function F in (4.17) is called an indefinite integral of the function f. We do not say *the* indefinite integral of f, since F depends upon a as well as upon f.

The geometric interpretation of F is given in Fig. 4.25, in which the shaded area represents the value of $F(x)$.

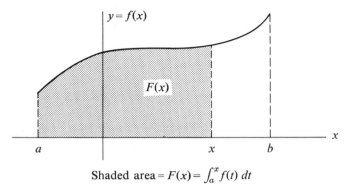

Shaded area $= F(x) = \int_a^x f(t)\,dt$

Figure 4.25

We now state and prove one of the two most important theorems in calculus.

Theorem 4-XV (*first fundamental theorem of calculus*).   Let $F(x) = \int_a^x f(t)\,dt$ be an indefinite integral of the function f, where f is continuous on $a \leqslant x \leqslant b$. Then $F'(x) = D_x[F(x)] = f(x)$ on $a \leqslant x \leqslant b$.

Proof.   Let x be any number satisfying $a \leqslant x < b$ and let Δx be any positive number satisfying $a < x + \Delta x \leqslant b$. Then

$$F(x + \Delta x) - F(x) = \int_a^{x+\Delta x} f(t)\,dt - \int_a^x f(t)\,dt = \int_x^{x+\Delta x} f(t)\,dt.$$

By Theorem 4-I, $f(x)$ assumes a maximum M at some x_M, satisfying $x \leqslant x_M \leqslant x + \Delta x$, and a minimum m at some x_m, satisfying $x \leqslant x_m \leqslant x + \Delta x$. (See Fig. 4.26.)

Since $m = f(x_m) \leqslant f(c) \leqslant f(x_M) = M$ for all numbers c satisfying $x \leqslant c \leqslant x + \Delta x$, it follows from the definition of a definite integral that

$$f(x_m)(\Delta x) \leqslant \int_x^{x+\Delta x} f(t)\,dt \leqslant f(x_M)(\Delta x).$$

(See Problem 8.)

Dividing by Δx, we obtain

$$f(x_m) \leqslant \frac{F(x + \Delta x) - F(x)}{\Delta x} \leqslant f(x_M).$$

If we now let $\Delta x \to 0$, $f(x_m)$ and $f(x_M)$ both approach $f(x)$, since f is continuous at x. Thus

$$\lim_{\Delta x \to 0^+} \frac{F(x + \Delta x) - F(x)}{\Delta x} = f(x).$$

We next let x be any number satisfying $a < x \leqslant b$ and Δx any negative number satisfying $a \leqslant x + \Delta x < b$. It is then easy to show that (see Problem 9)

$$\lim_{\Delta x \to 0^-} \frac{F(x + \Delta x) - F(x)}{\Delta x} = f(x).$$

We finally conclude that $F'(x) = f(x)$ for $a < x < b$, that at $x = a$ the derivative on the right of $F = f(a)$, and that at $x = b$ the derivative on the left of $F = f(b)$. In other words,

$$F'(x) = D_x[F(x)] = f(x) \qquad \text{on } a \leqslant x \leqslant b.$$

The significance of the first fundamental theorem is that it establishes the relationship between integration and differentiation. It states that the derivative of an indefinite integral of a continuous function f is equal to the integrand $f(x)$. In other words, if a continuous function f is integrated and the result differentiated, the integrand $f(x)$ is obtained. *Essentially, the first fundamental theorem establishes the fact that differentiation and integration are inverse processes.*

It is generally believed that the first person to recognize that the problem of tangents and the problem of quadrature were related by the first fundamental theorem was Newton's teacher, Isaac Barrow (1630–1677). In the next section, which concerns the second fundamental theorem of calculus, we will explain why Newton and Leibniz are regarded as the founders of calculus.

The geometric interpretation of the first fundamental theorem is illustrated in Fig. 4.26.

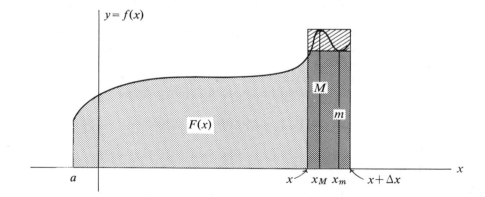

Figure 4.26

The area under the curve from a to x corresponds to $F(x)$, and the area from x to $x + \Delta x$ corresponds to $F(x + \Delta x) - F(x)$. It is clear that the latter area is greater than or equal to the area of the rectangle having base Δx and height m, but less than or equal to the area of the rectangle having base Δx and height M. That is,

$$(\Delta x)f(x_m) \leqslant F(x + \Delta x) - F(x) \leqslant (\Delta x)f(x_M).$$

Dividing by Δx (remembering to reverse the inequality signs if $\Delta x < 0$) and allowing Δx to approach zero, we obtain

$$F'(x) = D_x[F(x)] = f(x).$$

Geometrically, the first fundamental theorem states that the rate of change of the area with respect to the abscissa x is equal to $f(x)$, the height of the curve at $(x, f[x])$.

PROBLEM LIST 29

1. Given that $\int_1^3 3x^2 \, dx = 26$, evaluate $\int_1^3 3y^2 \, dy$.

2. Illustrate geometrically the area represented by

$$\int_{-1}^{x} (t^2 + 1) \, dt.$$

3. Given $F(x) = \int_0^x t \, dt$, evaluate:

   (a) $F(0)$.   (e) $F(y)$.
   (b) $F(1)$.   (f) $F'(x)$.
   (c) $F(3)$.   (g) $F'(5)$.
   (d) $F(3) - F(1)$.   (h) $F''(x)$.

4. Given $F(x) = \int_3^x (t^3 - 2t) \, dt$, evaluate:

   (a) $F(3)$.   (d) $F''(x)$.
   (b) $F'(x)$.   (e) $F''(2)$.
   (c) $F'(4)$.

5. Show that $\int_a^x f(t) \, dt$ and $\int_c^x f(t) \, dt$ differ by a constant.

6. Given that f is continuous, prove that F defined by

$$F(x) = \int_a^x f(t) \, dt$$

   is continuous.

7. In what respect do differentiation and integration resemble multiplication and division?

8. If the continuous function f satisfies $m \leqslant f(x) \leqslant M$ on $a \leqslant x \leqslant b$, prove that

$$m(b - a) \leqslant \int_a^b f(x) \, dx \leqslant M(b - a).$$

9. In the proof of the first fundamental theorem complete the details necessary to show that

$$\lim_{\Delta x \to 0^-} \frac{F(x + \Delta x) - F(x)}{\Delta x} = f(x).$$

4.15 The Second Fundamental Theorem
of Calculus

If the derivative F' of a function F is equal to a second function f, we call F a primitive or antiderivative of f. The word "primitive" suggests that f is derived from F, and the word "antiderivative" implies that F is obtained from f by reversing the process of differentiation. In this terminology the first fundamental theorem states that every indefinite integral $F(x)$ of $f(x)$ is a primitive (or antiderivative) of $f(x)$ whenever f is a continuous function.

We now prove a result that pertains to the set of *all* primitives of a function f.

Theorem 4-XVI.   If $F(x)$ and $G(x)$ are any two primitives of $f(x)$, then $F(x) - G(x)$ is constant.

Proof.

$$D_x[F(x) - G(x)] = D_x[F(x)] - D_x[G(x)]$$
$$= f(x) - f(x) = 0.$$

Hence $F(x) - G(x) = c = $ constant by Theorem 4-V.

The significance of Theorem 4-XVI is that *any* primitive of $f(x)$ must differ from $F(x) = \int_a^x f(t)\, dt$ by a constant.

We now present the second fundamental theorem of calculus. This theorem discloses a powerful method of evaluating many definite integrals and ranks in importance with the first fundamental theorem.

Theorem 4-XVII (*second fundamental theorem of calculus*).   Let G be *any* primitive of a continuous function f. Then

$$\int_a^b f(x)\, dx = G(b) - G(a).$$

Proof.   By Theorem 4-XVI there exists a specific constant c such that

$$\int_a^x f(t)\, dt = G(x) + c. \tag{4.18}$$

Substituting $x = b$ into (4.18), we obtain

$$\int_a^b f(t)\, dt = G(b) + c. \tag{4.19}$$

Substituting $x = a$ into (4.18), we obtain

$$\int_a^a f(t)\, dt = G(a) + c. \tag{4.20}$$

Subtracting (4.20) from (4.19) and recalling that $\int_a^a f(t)\, dt = 0$, we have the final result:

$$\int_a^b f(t)\, dt = G(b) - G(a). \tag{4.21}$$

Equation (4.21) is also written in the form

$$\int_a^b f(x)\, dx = G(x)\Big|_a^b \tag{4.22}$$

where the symbol $G(x)\Big|_a^b$ is used to denote $G(b) - G(a)$.

The second fundamental theorem states that a definite integral, defined in Sec. 4.11 as a rather complicated limit, can be evaluated if we know any primitive of the integrand. Furthermore, it asserts the astonishing fact that only two values of the primitive are required to obtain the exact value of the integral.

If we are to use the second fundamental theorem to evaluate definite integrals, we will want to have a supply of primitives or antiderivatives at our disposal. We will obtain such a supply as we progress, but for the time being we merely note that we obtain an antiderivative formula each time that we develop a new differentiation formula. We merely reverse the differentiation formula. For example, since

$$D_x\left(\frac{x^{n+1}}{n+1}\right) = x^n, \qquad (n \neq -1), \tag{4.23}$$

$x^{n+1}/(n+1)$ is a primitive or antiderivative of x^n.

The symbol D_x^{-1} is a convenient one to denote the general antiderivative of a function. With this notation we write

$$D_x^{-1}(x^n) = \frac{x^{n+1}}{n+1} + C \qquad (n \neq -1), \tag{4.24}$$

where C denotes an arbitrary constant.

We call the right member of (4.24) the general antiderivative of x^n because of the arbitrary constant C. Since C is arbitrary, $(x^{n+1}/(n+1)) + C$ includes all antiderivatives of x^n. The symbol D_x^{-1} is an inverse operator and indicates that the operation which is inverse to differentiation is to be performed on the expression upon which D_x^{-1} operates.

Example 1

$$D_x^{-1}(x^2) = \frac{x^3}{3} + C.$$

Example 2

$$D_x^{-1}(x^{1/2}) = \left(\frac{2}{3}\right)x^{3/2} + C.$$

Example 3

$$D_x[D_x^{-1}(4x^3)] = D_x(x^4 + C) = 4x^3.$$

Example 4

$$D_x^{-1}(x^4 + x^5) = D_x^{-1}(x^4) + D_x^{-1}(x^5)$$
$$= \frac{x^5}{5} + \frac{x^6}{6} + C.$$

The validity of the first step is due to the fact that

$$D_x[D_x^{-1}(x^4) + D_x^{-1}(x^5)] = D_x[D_x^{-1}(x^4)] + D_x[D_x^{-1}(x^5)]$$
$$= x^4 + x^5.$$

This example illustrates the rather simple theorem that the antiderivative of a sum is the sum of the antiderivatives.

We now return to the second fundamental theorem and employ it to evaluate the definite integrals that we previously evaluated by using the definition of a definite integral. We first observe that the second fundamental theorem can be written in the form

$$\int_a^b f(x)\, dx = D_x^{-1} f(x) \Big|_a^b.$$

Example 5.   Find the area under $y = x$ from $x = 1$ to $x = 9$. (This is illustrative Example 1 of Sec. 4.10.)

Solution

$$\int_1^9 x\, dx = D_x^{-1}(x) \Big|_1^9 = \frac{x^2}{2} + C \Big|_1^9$$
$$= \left[\frac{81}{2} + C\right] - \left[\frac{1}{2} + C\right] = 40.$$

Since the constant C disappears when we subtract, we will not bother to include it henceforth.

Example 6.   Find the area under $y = x^2/8$ from $x = 0$ to $x = 4$. (This is illustrative Example 2 of Sec. 4.10.)

Solution

$$\int_0^4 \frac{x^2}{8}\, dx = \frac{x^3}{24} \Big|_0^4 = \frac{8}{3}.$$

The student should reflect upon the remarkable fact that although $y = x^2/8$ gives the height of the parabola over a continuous interval, the second fundamental theorem enables us to compute the exact area under this curve by evaluating $x^3/24$, an antiderivative of $x^2/8$, only at the endpoints of the interval. The values of $x^3/24$ for x between 0 and 4 are not required!

Example 7.   Find the volume of a sphere.

Solution.   In Sec. 4.13 we found that the volume is given by

$$V = 2 \int_0^r \pi(r^2 - x^2)\, dx.$$

Applying the second fundamental theorem, we obtain

$$V = 2\pi \left[r^2 x - \frac{x^3}{3}\right]_0^r$$
$$= 2\pi \left[r^3 - \frac{r^3}{3}\right] = \frac{4\pi r^3}{3}.$$

The power of the second fundamental theorem is perceived when we compare the preceding solutions with those obtained by applying the definition of a definite integral. Newton and Leibniz are regarded as the founders of calculus because they were the first to understand the relationship between differentiation and integration and also to exploit this relationship by applying the second fundamental theorem. Archimedes (287(?)–212 B.C.), the great mathematician of ancient times, solved the problem of quadrature in several instances by applying the essential ideas of the integral calculus. He was also familiar with the problem of tangents. Fermat was familiar with both problems, and Barrow was aware of the first fundamental theorem. But it was Newton and Leibniz who systematized the calculus into an organized body of mathematical knowledge.

The word "calculus" is derived from the Latin word for stone or pebble. Since pebbles were used for counting, "calculus" eventually came to mean "a method of calculation." The method of calculation developed by Newton and Leibniz was considered so remarkable that it was termed THE *calculus*. It furnished science and mathematics with a method so powerful that there resulted an impetus unheard of before the time of Newton and Leibniz.

4.16   Leibniz's Notation for the General Antiderivative

Instead of writing

$$D_x^{-1}[f(x)] = C + \int_a^x f(t)\, dt,$$

Leibniz denoted the general antiderivative of f by the symbol $\int f(x)\, dx$, and wrote

$$\int f(x)\, dx = C + \int_a^x f(t)\, dt.$$

The symbol $\int f(x)\, dx$, read as "the integral of $f(x)$ with respect to x," is not an integral, but is so called because the second fundamental theorem asserts that a definite integral can be evaluated by means of an antiderivative. Although we prefer the notation $D_x^{-1}[f(x)]$, we will yield to convention and adopt the Leibniz notation. After we assemble a collection of antiderivatives, we will list them in a table, which we will term a table of integrals. It should be kept in mind, however, that it will actually be a table of antiderivatives which, by virtue of the second fundamental theorem, are useful for evaluating definite integrals.

Example 1

$$\int (2x^2 - 5)\, dx = \frac{2x^3}{3} - 5x + C.$$

Example 2

$$\int (x^{1/4} + 2x^{-2/3})\, dx = \left(\frac{4}{5}\right)x^{5/4} + 6x^{1/3} + C.$$

PROBLEM LIST 30

1. Find the general antiderivative of each of the following:

(a) $2x^2$.

(b) $x^5 - 3x^2$.

(c) $1 - x^3$.

(d) 6.

(e) 0.

(f) $x^2 - 4x + 5$.

(g) $x^3 + 2x - 7$.

(h) x^{k-1}, $(k \neq 1$ or $0)$.

(i) $x^2 + x^{1/2}$.

(j) $x - \sqrt{x}$.

(k) $x^{1/2} - x^{2/3} + x^{-3/4}$.

(l) $x^4 - 2x^2 + 6x^{1/3}$.

2. Evaluate

(a) $D_x^{-1}(x^2 + 1)$;

(b) $D_x^{-1}(4 - x^3)$;

(c) $D_x^{-1}(\pi)$;

(d) $D_x^{-1}(3x - 4\sqrt{x})$;

(e) $D_x^{-1}\left(\sqrt{x} - \dfrac{1}{\sqrt{x}}\right)$;

(f) $D_x^{-1}[D_x(x^2)]$;

(g) $D_x[D_x^{-1}(x^2)]$;

(h) $D_x\{D_x^{-1}[f(x) - g(x)]\}$.

3. Evaluate

(a) $\int (x^2 + 2)\, dx$;

(b) $\int (x^3 - 3x + 4)\, dx$;

(c) $\int 7\, dx$;

(d) $\int 0\, dx$;

(e) $\int \pi(r^3 - x^3)\, dx$;

(f) $(d/dx) \int 4x^2\, dx$;

(g) $D_x \int f(x)\, dx$;

(h) $\int D_x[f(x)]\, dx$.

4. Evaluate

(a) $\displaystyle\int_0^1 x^5\, dx$;

(b) $\displaystyle\int_1^3 (x^2 + x)\, dx$;

(c) $\displaystyle\int_{-1}^2 (x^2 + 5)\, dx$;

(d) $\displaystyle\int_1^6 (x^2 - 2x + 4)\, dx$;

(e) $\displaystyle\int_{-2}^{-1} (1 - x^2)\, dx$;

(f) $\displaystyle\int_{-1}^{-4} x^2\, dx$;

(g) $\displaystyle\int_0^r \pi(r^4 - x^4)\, dx$;

(h) $\displaystyle\int_2^3 (t^{1/2} - 3t)\, dt$;

(i) $\displaystyle\int_k^x (t^2 + 1)^2\, dt$;

(j) $\displaystyle\int_{-2}^3 |u|\, du$.

5. Find the area under $y = x^2 + 4$ from $x = -1$ to $x = 3$. Illustrate graphically.

6. Find the area under $y = 4 - x^2$ from $x = -1/2$ to $x = 1$. Illustrate graphically.

7. Find the area under $y = x^2 - 2x - 8$ from $x = 0$ to $x = 7$. What portion of the area lies (a) below the x-axis? (b) above the x-axis? Illustrate graphically.

8. Prove that
$$\frac{d}{dx}\int_x^a f(t)\, dt = -f(x).$$

9. Prove the converse of Theorem 4-XVI.

10. Derive the formula for the volume of a right-circular cone.

11. Derive the formula for the volume of a frustrum of a right-circular cone.

12. Derive the formula for the volume of a spherical segment of height h.

13. Find the volume generated by revolving the curve $y = x^3$ from $x = 0$ to $x = 2$ about the x-axis.

14. Explain the significance of the first and second fundamental theorems.

15. Prove the mean-value theorem for integrals:

   Let f be continuous on $a \leqslant x \leqslant b$. Then there exists at least one number c satisfying $a \leqslant c \leqslant b$ such that $\int_a^b f(x)\, dx = f(c)\,(b - a)$. Interpret geometrically.

   (Use the intermediate-value theorem and the result of Problem 8 of Problem List 29.)

REFERENCES

4.1 R. COURANT and H. ROBBINS, *What Is Mathematics?*, Oxford University Press, New York, 1941.

4.2 J. M. H. OLMSTED, *Intermediate Analysis*, Appleton-Century-Crofts, New York, 1956.

4.3 O. TOEPLITZ, *The Calculus: A Genetic Approach*, Univ. of Chicago Press, Chicago, 1963.

Chapter
5 ___

Graph of an equation

In Sec. 2.12 we defined the graph of an equation $f(x,y) = 0$ as the set of all points whose coordinates satisfy the equation. We now investigate various methods and techniques which are effective in drawing the graph of an equation.

5.1 *Intercepts*

The x-intercepts of the curve $f(x,y) = 0$ are the roots of the equation $f(x, 0) = 0$. The y-intercepts of $f(x, y) - 0$ are the roots of $f(0, y) = 0$. That is, to find the x-intercepts, we set $y = 0$ and solve for x; to find the y-intercepts, we set $x = 0$ and solve for y. In Sec. 2.3 the intercepts were employed in drawing the graph of a straight line.

Example 1. Find the intercepts of the curve $y = x^2 - 2x - 8$.

Solution. Setting $y = 0$ and solving for x, we find that the x-intercepts are -2 and 4.
Setting $x = 0$ and solving for y, we find that -8 is the only y-intercept. The graph is shown in Fig. 4.9.

Example 2. Find the intercepts of the curve $y = (x - 2)(x + 3)^2$.

Solution. It is seen by inspection that the x-intercepts are -3 and 2. Setting $x = 0$, we find that -18 is the only y-intercept.

Example 3. Find the intercepts of the curve

$$y = x^3 - 6x^2 + 9x - 3.$$

Solution. Setting $x = 0$, we find that -3 is the only y-intercept. Setting $y = 0$, we find that the x-intercepts are the roots of $x^3 - 6x^2 + 9x - 3 = 0$.

If our objective is merely to draw the graph of $y = x^3 - 6x^2 + 9x - 3$, we do not bother to find the x-intercepts. The graph is shown in Fig. 5.4.

When we find the intercepts of a curve, we locate points on the curve which are also points on the coordinate axes. Essentially, we are plotting certain points which are usually easy to determine.

5.2   Use of the First Derivative

The problem of drawing a curve is greatly simplified if the slope of the curve can be determined at any point where the curve has a slope. Since the first derivative determines the slope at a point, it follows that the first derivative is very useful in drawing curves.

We also know from Theorem 4-VI that a function f is increasing on $a < x < b$ if $f'(x) > 0$ for all x satisfying $a < x < b$. Geometrically, this means that the curve rises as x increases over the interval.

Similarly, Theorem 4-VII states that a function f is decreasing on $a < x < b$ if $f'(x) < 0$ for all x satisfying $a < x < b$. In this case, the curve falls as x increases over the interval.

If $f'(a) = 0$, the curve has slope 0 at $(a, f(a))$. The function f is said to be stationary at $x = a$.

Example 1.   Draw the graph of $y = f(x) = 3 + 2x - x^2$.

Solution.   Setting $x = 0$ and solving for y, we find that the curve has y-intercept 3. Setting $y = 0$ and solving for x, we find that the x-intercepts are -1 and 3.

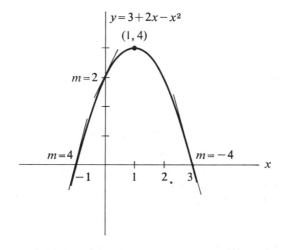

Figure 5.1

From $f'(x) = 2 - 2x = 0$, we find that $f'(1) = 0$.

Since $f'(x) > 0$ whenever $x < 1$, the curve rises for $x < 1$. Since $f'(x) < 0$ whenever $x > 1$, the curve falls for $x > 1$.

The expression $f(x)$ is used to find the height of the curve; the expression $f'(x)$ is used to find the slope of the curve. Thus, $f(1) = 4, f'(0) = 2, f'(-1) = 4$, and $f'(3) = -4$.

The function assumes its absolute maximum $M = 4$ at $x = 1$. See Fig. 5.1.

5.3   *Relative Maxima and Minima*

A function f is said to have a relative maximum at $x = c$ if $f(c)$ is the absolute maximum of f in some interval $a < x < b$ where $a < c < b$.

Similarly, f is said to have a relative minimum at $x = c$ if $f(c)$ is the absolute minimum of f in some interval $a < x < b$ where $a < c < b$.

A maximum or a minimum of a function, whether relative or absolute, is called an extremum. This meaning of the word extremum is therefore different from that usually connected with the word "extreme."

Figure 5.2 displays the graph of a function defined on $x_1 \leqslant x \leqslant x_6$. It is evident that knowing the extrema of a function would be very helpful in drawing its graph.

Figure 5.2

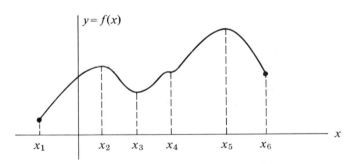

Extrema: $f(x_1), f(x_2), f(x_3), f(x_5), f(x_6)$.   Relative maxima: $f(x_2)$, $f(x_5)$.   Relative minima: $f(x_1), f(x_3), f(x_6)$.   Absolute maximum: $f(x_5)$.   Absolute minimum: $f(x_1)$.

Let us assume that f is differentiable over an interval $p < x < q$ and that $f(c)$ is an extremum of f where $p < c < q$. Then $f(c)$ is the absolute maximum or absolute minimum of f in some interval $a < x < b$ where $a < c < b$. Then, by Theorem 4-II (Fermat's theorem), $f'(c) = 0$.

The contrapositive of this result states that if $f'(c) \neq 0$, then $f(c)$ is not an extremum of f (assuming still that c is an interior point of an interval over which f is differentiable).

Thus, to locate the extrema of f in the interior of an interval, we need examine only those values of x for which $f'(x) = 0$ and those values of x for which $f'(x)$ does not exist. The endpoints of an interval can be tested separately for extrema.

If c is in the domain of definition of f, c is called a critical value of x (for the function f) if $f'(c) = 0$ or if $f'(c)$ does not exist. The point $(c, f(c))$ is called a critical point of the curve $y = f(x)$.

If c is a critical value of x, $f(c)$ is not necessarily an extremum of f. For example, $f(x_4)$ is not an extremum of f in Fig. 5.2.

Example 1.   Draw the graph of $y = -x^3 - x$.

Solution.   When $x = 0$, $y = 0$, and when $y = 0$, $x = 0$. Hence the curve meets the coordinate axes at the origin only. Since every polynomial defines a continuous function, the graph will consist of a single unbroken curve. From

$$y' = -3x^2 - 1$$

we find that $y' < 0$ for all x and hence $y = -x^3 - x$ defines a decreasing function for all x. There are no critical values of x and hence no critical points on the curve. The slope is -1 at the origin and less than -1 at every other point of the curve. See Fig. 5.3.

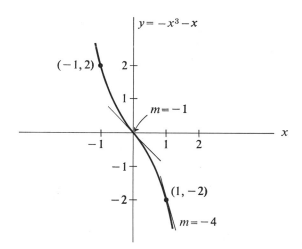

Figure 5.3

Example 2.   Graph $y = \sqrt{x^2}$.

Solution

$$y' = \frac{x}{\sqrt{x^2}} \qquad \text{for } x \neq 0.$$

There are no values of x for which $y' = 0$. However, y' is undefined when $x = 0$ and hence $x = 0$ is a critical value and $(0, 0)$ is a critical point. When $x > 0$, $y' = 1$ and when $x < 0$, $y' = -1$. The function assumes its absolute minimum $m = 0$ at $x = 0$. See Fig. 2.3.

Example 3.   Graph $y = x^3 - 6x^2 + 9x - 3$.

Solution.   The curve has y-intercept -3, but we will not attempt to find the x-intercepts. Setting $y' = 0$, we obtain

$$y' = 3x^2 - 12x + 9 = 3(x - 1)(x - 3) = 0,$$

from which we find that $x = 1$ and $x = 3$ are critical values. The corresponding critical points are $(1, 1)$ and $(3, -3)$. Since $y' > 0$ for $-\infty < x < 1$ and $3 < x < \infty$, y increases on these intervals. Since $y' < 0$ for $1 < x < 3$, y decreases on this interval. Hence it is clear that $y = 1$ is a relative maximum and $y = -3$ is a relative minimum.

After evaluating y and y' for $x = 0$, $x = 2$, and $x = 4$, we draw the graph in Fig. 5.4.

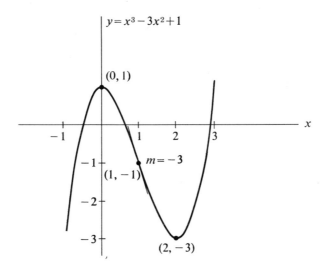

Figure 5.4

Example 4.   Graph $y^3 - x^2 = 0$.

Solution.   The only intercepts are $x = 0$ and $y = 0$.
From

$$y = x^{2/3}$$

we obtain

$$y' = \frac{2}{3} x^{-1/3} = \frac{2}{3\sqrt[3]{x}}.$$

The origin is a critical point, since y' does not exist at $x = 0$. The inclination α of the secant line through $(0, 0)$ and $(x, x^{2/3})$ approaches $\pi/2$ as $x \to 0$, since

$$\tan \alpha = \frac{x^{2/3} - 0}{x - 0} = \frac{1}{\sqrt[3]{x}}.$$

Thus the y-axis is tangent to both the first- and second-quadrant branches of the required curve. Since $y' > 0$ for $x > 0$, y increases for $0 < x < \infty$. Since $y' < 0$ for $x < 0$, y decreases for $-\infty < x < 0$.

After evaluating y and y' for $x = 1$ and $x = 8$, we draw the graph in Fig. 5.5. The curve is called a semicubical parabola. The absolute minimum $m = 0$ of the function is assumed at $x = 0$.

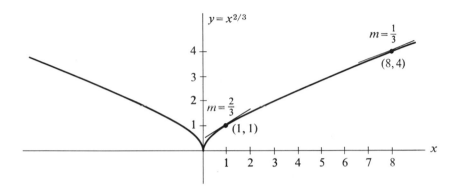

Figure 5.5

PROBLEM LIST 31

1. Find the intercepts of the following curves:

    (a) $3x - 4y + 24 = 0$.

    (b) $y = x^2 - x - 6$.

    (c) $y = 2x^2 + 5x - 12$.

    (d) $y = (x + 2)(x - 3)^2$.

    (e) $y = \sqrt{4 - x^2}$.

    (f) $y^2 + y + x - 6 = 0$.

    (g) $y = x^3 - 2x^2 - 5x + 6$.

    (h) $y = |x - 2| - 3$.

2. Find the intercepts of the following curves:

    (a) $5x + 3y + 30 = 0$.

    (b) $y = x^2 - 3x - 28$.

    (c) $y = 6x^2 - x - 15$.

    (d) $y = (x - 2)^3(x + 3)$.

    (e) $y = \sqrt{x^2 + 4}$.

    (f) $y^2 = x + 3y + 10$.

    (g) $y = 2x^3 - 3x^2 - 3x + 2$.

    (h) $y = |x + 3| - 5$.

3. Graph the functions defined by the following expressions. Exhibit intercepts and extrema, and state the intervals over which each function is increasing or decreasing.

    (a) $y = x^2 - 1$.

    (b) $y = 4 - x^2$.

    (c) $y = x^2 + 3x - 10$.

    (d) $y = 3 + 2x - x^2$.

    (e) $y = 2\sqrt{x}$.

    (f) $y = x^3/8$.

    (g) $y = 1 - x^3$.

    (h) $y = 3x^2 - 5x + 1$.

    (i) $y = x(x^2 - 4)$.

    (j) $y = x^2(x + 2)$.

    (k) $y = x^3 - 3x$.

    (l) $y = x^4$.

    (m) $y = 2x^3 + 9x^2 + 18x + 2$.

    (n) $y = x^3 - 6x^2 + 12x - 2$.

(o) $y = 2x^3 - 15x^2 + 24x - 1$.   (t) $y = \sqrt{4 - x^2}$.

(p) $y = 4 - \sqrt{x}$.   (u) $y = |x(x + 1)|$.

(q) $y = x^{3/2}$.   (v) $y = (\sqrt{x})^2$.

(r) $y^3 = x^2$.   (w) $y = 2 + \sqrt[3]{(x - 1)^2}$.

(s) $y = (x - 1)^{2/3}$.

4. Show that

$$\left(-\frac{b}{2a}, \frac{4ac - b^2}{4a}\right)$$

is a critical point of $y = ax^2 + bx + c$.

5. How does the quantity $b^2 - 3ac$ determine the number of critical points of the cubic curve $y = ax^3 + bx^2 + cx + d (a \neq 0)$?

6. Determine a, b, c, and d so that $(2, -43)$ and $(-3, 82)$ will be critical points of $y = ax^3 + bx^2 + cx + d$.

5.4 Use of the Second Derivative

Given $f'(c) = 0$, our method of determining if $f(c)$ is an extremum of f has been to examine the sign of $f'(x)$ in a small interval $a < x < b$ such that $a < c < b$. We now prove a result that frequently enables us to classify $f(c)$ as a relative maximum or relative minimum merely by examining the sign of $f''(c)$.

Theorem 5-I.   If $f'(c) = 0$ and $f''(c) > 0$, then $f(c)$ is a relative minimum. If $f'(c) = 0$ and $f''(c) < 0$, then $f(c)$ is a relative maximum.

Figure 5.6

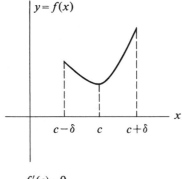

$f'(c) = 0$
$f''(c) > 0$
$f(c)$ is a relative minimum

$f'(c) = 0$
$f''(c) < 0$
$f(c)$ is a relative maximum

Proof.   Assume $f''(c) = p > 0$. Then, given any $\epsilon > 0$, there exists a $\delta > 0$ such that

$$\left|\frac{f'(c+h) - f'(c)}{h} - p\right| = \left|\frac{f'(c+h)}{h} - p\right| < \epsilon$$

whenever $0 < |h| < \delta$. If we let $\epsilon = p/2$,

$$-\frac{p}{2} < \frac{f'(c+h)}{h} - p < \frac{p}{2} \quad \text{or} \quad \frac{p}{2} < \frac{f'(c+h)}{h}$$

whenever $0 < |h| < \delta$.

Since $p/2 > 0$, it follows that $f'(c+h) > 0$ when $0 < h < \delta$ and $f'(c+h) < 0$ when $-\delta < h < 0$. Thus the slope is negative on the interval $c - \delta < x < c$, zero at $x = c$, and positive on the interval $c < x < c + \delta$. The functions f and f' are continuous at $x = c$ and $f(c)$ is a relative minimum.

The proof of the second part of Theorem 5–I is similar. The theorem is illustrated in Fig. 5.6.

Example 1.   Apply Theorem 5–I to the function defined by

$$y = f(x) = x^2.$$

Solution.   From $y' = 2x$ and $y'' = 2$, we obtain

$$f'(0) = 0 \quad \text{and} \quad f''(0) = 2.$$

Since $2 > 0$, $f(0) = 0$ is a relative minimum.

Example 2.   Apply Theorem 5–I to the function defined by $y = f(x) = x^3 - 6x^2 + 9x - 3$.

Solution.   From $f'(x) = 3x^2 - 12x + 9 = 3(x - 1)(x - 3)$ and $f''(x) = 6x - 12$, we obtain

$$f'(1) = 0 \quad \text{and} \quad f''(1) = -6 < 0,$$

while $f'(3) = 0 \quad \text{and} \quad f''(3) = 6 > 0.$

It follows from Theorem 5–I that $f(1) = 1$ is a relative maximum and $f(3) = -3$ is a relative minimum. See Fig. 5.4.

Example 3.   Graph $y = f(x) = 2\sqrt{4 - x^2}$.

Solution.   The function f is defined for $-2 \leqslant x \leqslant +2$. Intercepts are $y = 4$ and $x = \pm 2$. Differentiating, we obtain

$$y' = \frac{-2x}{\sqrt{4 - x^2}}$$

and

$$y'' = -2\left[\frac{\sqrt{4 - x^2}\,(1) - x(-x/\sqrt{4 - x^2})}{4 - x^2}\right] = \frac{-8}{(4 - x^2)^{3/2}}.$$

Since $f'(0) = 0$ and $f'(x)$ does not exist for $x = \pm 2$, $x = 0$, 2, and -2 are critical values. The points $(0,4)$, $(-2, 0)$, and $(2, 0)$ are critical points.

Since $f''(0) = -1 < 0$, $f(0) = 4$ is a relative maximum by Theorem 5–I. Since $y' > 0$ for $-2 < x < 0$, the function increases on this interval. Since $y' < 0$ for $0 < x < 2$, the function decreases on this interval. It is easily seen that the function assumes its absolute minimum $m = 0$ at the end-points $(-2, 0)$ and $(2, 0)$. The relative maximum $f(0)$ is the absolute maximum $M = 4$. See Fig. 5.7.

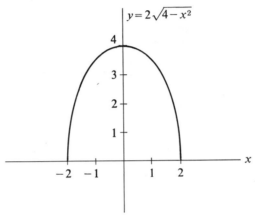

Figure 5.7

We will discover later that the curve in Fig. 5.7 is the upper portion of a curve known as an ellipse. We also note that the curve could have been drawn by first drawing the semicircle $y = \sqrt{4 - x^2}$ and then doubling each ordinate.

If $f'(c) = 0$ and $f''(c) = 0$, no conclusion can be drawn from Theorem 5–I. This is evident from Fig. 5.8. In all four cases $f'(0) = f''(0) = 0$ and yet each curve

Figure 5.8

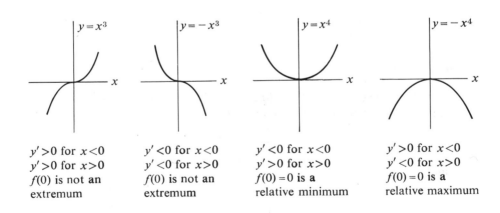

$y = x^3$	$y = -x^3$	$y = x^4$	$y = -x^4$
$y' > 0$ for $x < 0$	$y' < 0$ for $x < 0$	$y' < 0$ for $x < 0$	$y' > 0$ for $x < 0$
$y' > 0$ for $x > 0$	$y' < 0$ for $x > 0$	$y' > 0$ for $x > 0$	$y' < 0$ for $x > 0$
$f(0)$ is not an extremum	$f(0)$ is not an extremum	$f(0) = 0$ is a relative minimum	$f(0) = 0$ is a relative maximum

has a different character at the origin. To determine the shape of each curve in the neighborhood of the origin, we examine the sign of y' on both sides of the origin. In all four cases, $f(0) = f'(0) = f''(0) = 0$. Theorem 5–I does not apply.

PROBLEM LIST 32

1. Determine the extrema of the functions defined by the following expressions. Employ Theorem 5-I whenever possible.

    (a) $y = 3x^2 - 4x + 5$.   (d) $y = 5 + 3x - x^3$.

    (b) $y = 5x^2 - 6x + 2$.   (e) $y = \frac{1}{2}\sqrt{9 - x^2}$.

    (c) $y = 2x^3 - 3x^2 - 36x + 3$.   (f) $y = x^4 - 4x^3$.

2. Show that

$$\left(\frac{-b}{2a}, \frac{4ac - b^2}{4a}\right)$$

is a relative minimum of $y = ax^2 + bx + c$ if $a > 0$ and a relative maximum if $a < 0$.

3. Show that zero is a relative minimum of $y = x^n$ if n is an even integer $\geqslant 2$.

4. Show that if $a < 0$, $y = x^3 + 3ax + b$ has both a relative maximum and a relative minimum.

5.5   Further Use of the Second Derivative
—Concavity and Points of Inflection

Theorem 5–I states that if $f'(c) = 0$ and $f''(c) > 0$, $f(c)$ is a relative minimum of f. This means that there exists an interval $a < x < b$ about c such that, except for the point $(c, f(c))$, all points of the curve $y = f(x)$ are above the tangent to $y = f(x)$ at $x = c$, provided $a < x < b$. It can be proved (see Problem 7) that such an interval always exists when $f''(c) > 0$, even if $f'(c)$ is not zero. We say that the curve is concave upward at $x = c$. Similarly, it can be shown that if $f''(c) < 0$, an interval $a < x < b$ about c exists such that all points of $y = f(x)$, except $(c, f(c))$, are below the tangent to $y = f(x)$ at $x = c$, provided $a < x < b$. In this case we say that the curve is concave downward at $x = c$. See Fig. 5.9.

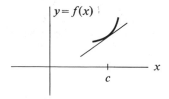

$y = f(x)$ concave upward at $x = c$

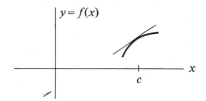

$y = f(x)$ concave downward at $x = c$

Figure 5.9

The curve $y = f(x)$ is said to be concave upward on an interval if it is concave upward at every point of the interval. It is concave downward on an interval if it is concave downward at every point of the interval. In Fig. 5.10, $y = f(x)$ is concave upward on $x_1 < x < x_2$ and on $x_3 < x < x_4$, but concave downward on $x_2 < x < x_3$.

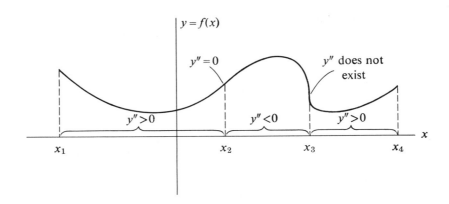

Figure 5.10

Since $y'' = (d/dx)(y')$, the slope in Fig. 5.10 increases for $x_1 < x < x_2$ but decreases for $x_2 < x < x_3$. The fact that the slope increases where the curve is concave upward and decreases where the curve is concave downward indicates that knowledge of the concavity of a curve over various intervals is very useful in curve tracing.

If the curve $y = f(x)$ has a tangent at $x = c$ and if intervals $a < x < c$ and $c < x < b$ exist such that $y = f(x)$ is concave upward in one of these intervals and concave downward in the other, the point $(c, f(c))$ is called a point of inflection. It is a point where the concavity changes and where the tangent crosses the curve.

Since y' assumes an extreme value at a point of inflection, points of inflection can occur only at values of x which are critical values for the function y'. In Fig. 5.10, $(x_2, f(x_2))$ is a point of inflection, since $f''(x_2) = 0$ and $f''(x)$ changes sign at x_2. The point $(x_3, f(x_3))$ is a point of inflection, since the curve has a vertical tangent at x_3 and $f''(x)$ changes sign at x_3. The functions f' and f'' are undefined at $x = x_3$.

In the same way that $f'(c) = 0$ does not imply that $f(c)$ is an extremum of f, $f''(c) = 0$ does not imply that $f'(c)$ is an extremum of f' and that $(c, f(c))$ is a point of inflection of $y = f(x)$. This is illustrated by $y = x^4$ (see Fig. 5.8), where $f''(0) = 0$ but $(0, 0)$ is not a point of inflection. Another illustration will be given in Example 4.

Example 1.   Test $y = x^2 + 4x - 7$ for concavity and points of inflection.

Solution

$$y' = 2x + 4 \qquad \text{and} \qquad y'' = 2$$

Since $y'' > 0$ for all x, the curve is concave upward for all x and has no points of inflection.

Example 2.   Graph $y = x^3 - 3x^2 + 1$.

Solution

$$y' = 3x^2 - 6x = 3x(x - 2),$$
$$y'' = 6x - 6 \;\; = 6\,(x - 1).$$

Setting $y' = 0$, we obtain $x = 0$ and $x = 2$. Since $y'']_{x=0} = -6 < 0$, we have that $y]_{x=0} = 1$ is a relative maximum; and since $y'']_{x=2} = 6 > 0$, we have that $y]_{x=2} = -3$ is a relative minimum. Since $y' > 0$ for $x < 0$ and for $x > 2$, the curve rises over these intervals; $y' < 0$ for $0 < x < 2$, and the curve falls over this interval.

Setting $y'' = 0$, we obtain $x = 1$. The point $(1, -1)$ is a point of inflection since $y']_{x=1} = -3$ exists and y'' changes sign at $x = 1$. The curve is concave downward for $x < 1$ and concave upward for $x > 1$, since $y'' < 0$ for $x < 1$ and $y'' > 0$ for $x > 1$. See Fig. 5.11.

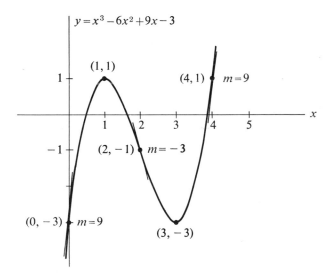

Figure 5.11

Example 3.   Test $y = x^{1/3}$ for concavity and points of inflection.

Solution

$$y' = \frac{1}{3}x^{-2/3} = \frac{1}{3\sqrt[3]{x^2}}$$

and

$$y'' = -\frac{2}{9}x^{-5/3} = \frac{-2}{9x\sqrt[3]{x^2}}.$$

Since y'' is never zero, a point of inflection can occur only at $x = 0$. The point $(0, 0)$ is indeed a point of inflection, since the curve has a vertical tangent at $(0, 0)$ and $y'' > 0$ for $x < 0$, but $y'' < 0$ for $x > 0$. The curve is concave upward for $x < 0$ and concave downward for $x > 0$. See Fig. 3.5.

Example 4.   Graph $y = x + x^4 = x(1 + x^3)$.

Solution

$$y' = 1 + 4x^3$$

and

$$y'' = 12x^2.$$

The curve intersects the x-axis at $x = 0$ and at $x = -1$. Setting $y' = 0$, we find that

$$x = \sqrt[3]{\frac{-1}{4}} = \frac{-\sqrt[3]{16}}{4}.$$

A relative minimum (which is the absolute minimum of y),

$$y = \frac{-3\sqrt[3]{16}}{16},$$

occurs at $x = -\sqrt[3]{16}/4$, since $y'' > 0$ at this point. The curve has no points of inflection. Although $y'' = 0$ at $x = 0$, y'' does not change sign at $x = 0$, and hence the origin is not a point of inflection. The origin is called a flat point of the curve because the slope changes very slowly near $x = 0$ and has zero rate of change at $x = 0$. The curve, shown in Fig. 5.12, is everywhere concave upward.

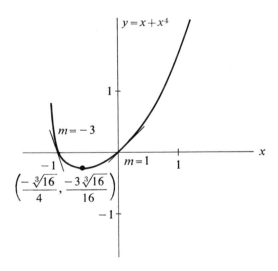

Figure 5.12

PROBLEM LIST 33

1.   Determine the concavity of
    (a) $y = 3x^2 - 2x + 4$;
    (b) $y = 5 + 6x - 2x^2$;
    (c) $y = x^3 - 2$.

2. Discuss the concavity of $y = ax^2 + bx + c$, $(a \neq 0)$.

3. Determine the intervals over which each of the following curves is concave upward. What are the points of inflection?

(a) $y = 4x^3$.

(b) $y = 2x^{1/3}$.

(c) $y = (x - 1)^{2/3}$.

(d) $y = 2x^3 - 6x^2 + 6x - 5$.

(e) $y = 2x^3 + 9x^2 + 12x - 3$.

(f) $y = 5 - 36x + 15x^2 - 2x^3$.

(g) $y = \dfrac{1}{x^2 + 3}$.

(h) $y = \dfrac{1}{x^2 + 12}$.

4. Show that the circle $x^2 + y^2 = 4$ is concave downward at all points where $y > 0$.

5. Draw graphs of each of the following. Show intercepts, critical points, and points of inflection.

(a) $y = 2x^2 - 6x + 5$.

(b) $y = x^2(x - 2)$.

(c) $y = x(x^2 + 6)$.

(d) $y = x^3 + 6x^2 + 9x + 4$.

(e) $y = x^3 + 9x^2 + 15x - 5$.

(f) $y = \dfrac{x}{2} + x^4$.

(g) $y = x^4 - 4x$.

(h) $y = \dfrac{2}{x^2 + 6}$.

(i) $y = \dfrac{x}{x^2 + 1}$.

(j) $y = x^{1/3} + 2x^{4/3}$.

6. The forces acting upon a 10 ft beam cause it to assume the shape of the curve $y = (x^2/10,000)(x - 30)$, known as the elastic curve of the beam. Draw the graph of the elastic curve for $0 \leqslant x \leqslant 10$.

7. Given $y = f(x)$ and $f''(c) > 0$, prove that there exists an interval $a < x < b$ such that $a < c < b$ and such that, for all $x \neq c$ satisfying $a < x < b$, the curve $y = f(x)$ is above the tangent to $y = f(x)$ at $x = c$. *Hint:* Use the mean-value theorem.

8. Show that $(1, 7)$ is not a point of inflection on the curve $y = f(x) = x^4 - 4x^3 + 6x^2 + 4x$ even though $f''(1) = 0$. Show also that $(1, 7)$ is neither a relative maximum nor a relative minimum.

5.6   Symmetry

A curve C is said to be symmetric with respect to a line l if for each point A on C but not on l there is a second point B on C such that l is the perpendicular bisector of line segment AB. The curve $f(x, y) = 0$ is symmetric with respect to the y-axis, provided $f(-x, y) = 0$; that is, provided the equation $f(x, y) = 0$ is unchanged when x is replaced by $-x$. This implies that if (a, b) is on the curve, $(-a, b)$ is also on the curve.

Example 1. The curve $y - x^2 = 0$ is symmetric with respect to the y-axis, since $y - (-x)^2 = 0$ is the same equation as $y - x^2 = 0$.

Example 2. The curve $y^2 - x = 0$ is not symmetric with respect to the y-axis, since $y^2 - (-x) = 0$ is not the same equation as $y^2 - x = 0$.

Example 3. The curves $y = x^4$, $y = x^{2/3}$, $y = |x|$, $x^2 + y^2 = 1$, and $y = 1/(x^2 + 1)$ are all symmetric with respect to the y-axis.

If a curve is symmetric with respect to the y-axis, we need only determine what the curve looks like for $x \geqslant 0$. For $x < 0$, the curve is easily drawn by reflecting the first- and fourth-quadrant portions in the y-axis. Some simple types of symmetry are illustrated in Fig. 5.13.

The curve $f(x, y) = 0$ is symmetric with respect to the x-axis, provided $f(x, -y) = 0$. When this occurs, we draw the curve for $y \geqslant 0$ and then reflect in the x-axis.

Figure 5.13

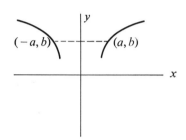

Symmetry with respect
to the y-axis

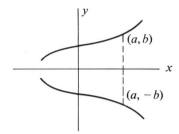

Symmetry with respect
to the x-axis

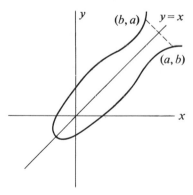

Symmetry with respect
to $y = x$

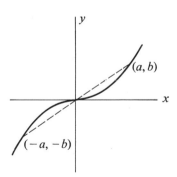

Symmetry with respect
to the origin

Examples. The curves $x = y^2$, $y^2 = x^3$, $4x^2 + y^2 = 4$, $y^4 - y^2 + x = 0$, and $x = 1/(1 + y^2)$ are all symmetric with respect to the x-axis.

The curve $f(x, y) = 0$ is symmetric with respect to the line $y = x$, provided $f(y, x) = 0$. (See Problem 24 of Problem List 6.)

Examples. The curves $y = 1/x$ and $x^2 + xy + y^2 = 4$ are symmetric with respect to $y = x$.

Note: In Sec. 2.4 we found that $y = f(x)$ and its inverse $y = f^{-1}(x)$ are symmetric with respect to $y = x$. This did not mean that either of these curves alone is necessarily symmetric with respect to $y = x$.

A curve C is said to be symmetric with respect to a point P if for every point A different from P on C, there is a second point B on C such that P is the midpoint of line segment AB. The curve $f(x, y) = 0$ is symmetric with respect to the origin, provided $f(-x, -y) = 0$; that is, provided $f(x, y) = 0$ is unchanged when x is replaced by $-x$ and y by $-y$.

Examples.   The curves $y = x^3$, $x^2 + y^2 = 9$, $x^2 + xy + y^2 = 4$, and $xy + 1 = 0$ are all symmetric with respect to the origin. If we know what one of these curves looks like in two adjacent quadrants, we can easily draw it in the other two quadrants.

PROBLEM LIST 34

1. Test for symmetry:
   (a) $2y + x^2 = 0$.
   (b) $2y^2 + 3x = 0$.
   (c) $y - 4x^3 = 0$.
   (d) $y = x^3 - x$.
   (e) $x^2 + y^2 = 5$.
   (f) $xy - 7 = 0$.
   (g) $x^2 - xy + y^2 = 1$.
   (h) $x = |y|$.
   (i) $y = \dfrac{1}{1 + x^2}$.
   (j) $y = \cos x$.
   (k) $y = \sin x$.
   (l) $y = \tan x$.

2. Prove that if $f(x, y) = 0$ is symmetric with respect to both the x- and y-axes, then it is symmetric with respect to the origin. Discuss the converse of this proposition.

3. Under what condition is $f(x, y) = 0$ symmetric with respect to $y = -x$?

4. Show that $y = x^{1/3}$ and $y = x^3$ are symmetric to $y = x$, but that neither curve alone exhibits this type of symmetry.

5.7   *Asymptotes*

Let $P(x, y)$ be an arbitrary point on the curve $f(x, y) = 0$. Let $\rho > 0$ be the distance from the origin to P and let $d \geqslant 0$ be the distance from P to a line l. If

$$\lim_{\rho \to \infty}(d) = 0,$$

the line l is called an asymptote of $f(x, y) = 0$. See Fig. 5.14. Determination of the asymptotes of a curve is often helpful in drawing the curve.

Example 1.   Draw the curve $y = x/(x - 2)$.

Solution.   Since

$$\lim_{x \to 2^+}\frac{x}{x - 2} = \infty \quad \text{and} \quad \lim_{x \to 2^-}\frac{x}{x - 2} = -\infty,$$

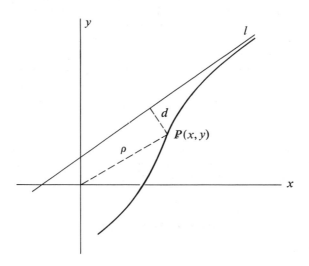

Figure 5.14

the line $x = 2$ is a vertical asymptote. Since

$$\lim_{x\to\infty}\frac{x}{x-2} = \lim_{x\to\infty}\frac{1}{1-(2/x)} = 1 \quad\text{and}\quad \lim_{x\to-\infty}\frac{1}{1-(2/x)} = 1,$$

the line $y = 1$ is a horizontal asymptote. This can also be determined by examining the equation $x = 2y/(y - 1)$, obtained by solving $y = x/(x - 2)$

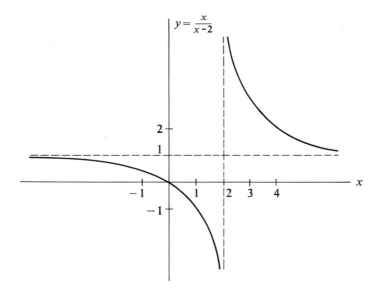

Figure 5.15

for x in terms of y. To draw the curve, we represent the asymptotes by dotted lines and plot a few points. See Fig. 5.15.

Example 2.   Graph $y = x/(x^2 - 9)$.

Solution.   From

$$y = \frac{x}{(x - 3)(x + 3)}$$

we see that the curve has vertical asymptotes $x = \pm 3$, and that, since

$$y = \frac{1/x}{1 - (9/x^2)} \longrightarrow 0 \qquad \text{as } |x| \longrightarrow \infty,$$

$y = 0$ is a horizontal asymptote. We note that the curve passes through and is symmetric with respect to the origin. From

$$y' = \frac{-(x^2 + 9)}{(x^2 - 9)^2} \qquad \text{and} \qquad y'' = 2x\frac{(x^2 + 27)}{(x^2 - 9)^3},$$

we find that the origin is a point of inflection, that the curve falls and is concave downward for $0 < x < 3$, and that the curve falls and is concave upward for $x > 3$. See Fig. 5.16.

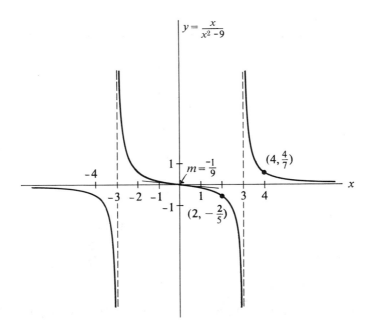

Figure 5.16

The quotient $q = N(x)/D(x)$ of two polynomials defines a function called a rational function of x. If a is a real number such that $D(a) = 0$ and $N(a) \neq 0$, then $x = a$ is a vertical asymptote of the curve $y = N(x)/D(x)$. If the degree of $N(x)$ is less than or equal to the degree of $D(x)$, the curve will always possess one and only one horizontal asymptote. This is found by dividing $N(x)$ and $D(x)$ by the highest power of x appearing in $D(x)$ and then letting $x \to \infty$ (or $-\infty$). If $N(x)$ has degree greater than the degree of $D(x)$, the curve can be studied by writing $N(x)/D(x)$ in the form

$$P(x) + \frac{N_1(x)}{D(x)},$$

where $P(x)$ is a polynomial and $N_1(x)$ is a polynomial of degree less than that of $D(x)$.

PROBLEM LIST 35

1. List the vertical and horizontal asymptotes of the following curves:

(a) $y = 1/x$.

(b) $xy + 2x - 3y = 0$.

(c) $y = \dfrac{x-1}{(x+2)(x-3)}$.

(d) $y = \dfrac{2x^3}{(x-1)^2(x+2)}$.

(e) $y = \dfrac{4}{x^2 + 1}$.

(f) $3x - 5y + xy = 0$.

(g) $xy(x - 3) = 1$.

(h) $y = \dfrac{x^2 - 3}{x^2 + 2x + 2}$.

(i) $y = \dfrac{4(x-1)(x+3)^2}{x^3 - 3x + 2}$.

(j) $y = \dfrac{x^3 - 3x + 2}{x^3 + 2x^2 - 4x - 8}$.

2. Graph each equation. Show all vertical and horizontal asymptotes and utilize symmetry whenever possible. Use first and second derivatives if their use seems appropriate.

(a) $xy + 2x - 3y = 0$.

(b) $xy + 4y = 1$.

(c) $y = \dfrac{x-1}{(x+2)(x-3)}$.

(d) $y = \dfrac{x}{x^2 - 4}$.

(e) $y = \dfrac{3x^2}{x^2 - 16}$.

(f) $y = \dfrac{4}{x^2 + 6}$.

(g) $y = \dfrac{x}{(x-2)^2}$.

(h) $y = \dfrac{x-1}{x^2(x+2)}$.

(i) $y = \dfrac{x^2}{x^2 + 1}$.

(j) $y = \dfrac{-2x^3}{(x-1)(x+2)(x-4)}$.

(k) $y = \dfrac{x^3 + 1}{x}$.

(l) $y = \dfrac{3x}{x^2 + 1}$.

(m) $x = \dfrac{y}{y^2 - 9}$.

(n) $y = \dfrac{x - x^2}{4 - x^2}$.

(o) $y = \dfrac{x^2 - 9}{(x-1)^2}$.

(p) $y = \dfrac{1}{|x|}$.

3. Prove that the graph of a polynomial possesses neither vertical nor horizontal asymptotes.

5.8   Composition of Ordinates

If an equation can be written in the form $y = f_1(x) + f_2(x)$, the graph of the equation can be drawn by adding the heights of the curves $y_1 = f_1(x)$ and $y_2 = f_2(x)$. This is often helpful if $f_1(x)$ and $f_2(x)$ are easy to graph. The addition of the ordinates can be carried out graphically by means of a pair of dividers.

Example 1.   Graph $y = x + 1/x$.

Solution.   In Fig. 5.17 the dotted curves are the graphs of $y_1 = x$ and $y_2 = 1/x$. The height of the required curve at $x = a$ is obtained by adding the heights of y_1 and y_2 at $x = a$. Note that $y = x + (1/x)$ resembles $y = 1/x$ when x is small, and $y = x$ when x is large. The line $y = x$ is an oblique asymptote for $y = x + (1/x)$.

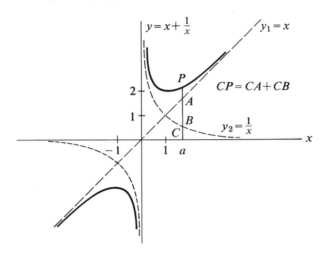

Figure 5.17

Example 2.   The graph of

$$y = \left| \frac{3x}{4} \right| \pm \sqrt{1 - x^2}$$

is shown in Fig. 5.18.

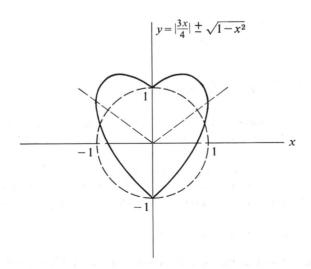

Figure 5.18

Similarly, the graph of $x = f_1(y) + f_2(y)$ can be drawn by adding abscissas. Also, graphs can be drawn by subtracting, multiplying, or dividing ordinates or abscissas.

PROBLEM LIST 36

1. Use the method of this section (in addition to any other methods) to draw the graphs of the following equations:

   (a) $y = x^2 + \dfrac{1}{x}$.

   (b) $y = x + \dfrac{1}{x^2}$.

   (c) $y = 2x - \dfrac{1}{x}$.

   (d) $y = x + \sqrt{x}$.

   (e) $y = 1 + \dfrac{1}{1 + x^2}$.

   (f) $y = 1 - \dfrac{1}{1 - x^2}$.

   (g) $y = x \pm \sqrt{1 - x^2}$.

   (h) $y = x \pm \sqrt{x^2 - 1}$.

   (i) $y = x + x^{3/2}$.

   (j) $y = x + |x|$.

   (k) $x = 4 + y^2$.

   (l) $x = y^3 + \sqrt{y}$.

   (m) $xy + y^2 = 1$.

   (n) $y = \dfrac{x^2 + x + 1}{x + 1}$.

   (o) $y = x + x^4$.

   (p) $|y| + |x| = 1$.

   [See Fig. 5.12 for Problem (o).]

2. On the same set of axes draw the graphs of the lines $y_1 = x$, $y_2 = x - 1$, and $y_3 = x - 3$. From these graphs construct the graph of $y = x(x - 1)(x - 3)$.

3. Draw the graph of $y = x(x - 1)(x - 3)$. From this graph construct the graph of $y^2 = x(x - 1)(x - 3)$.

4. Find the extrema of the curve shown in Fig. 5.18. Separately treat
$$y = \left|\frac{3x}{4}\right| + \sqrt{1 - x^2} \quad \text{and} \quad y = \left|\frac{3x}{4}\right| - \sqrt{1 - x^2}.$$

5. Draw the graph of the equation $y = |3 - |x||$.

5.9 Factorable Equations

Consider an equation of the form $f(x, y) = g(x, y) h(x, y) = 0$. If $g(a, b) = 0$ and $h(a, b)$ is real, then $f(a, b) = 0$ and hence (a, b) is a point of the graph of $f(x, y) = 0$.

Similarly, (a, b) is a point of the graph of $f(x, y) = 0$ if $h(a, b) = 0$ and $g(a, b)$ is real. Thus, to draw the graph of $f(x, y) = 0$, we draw the graphs of $g(x, y) = 0$ and $h(x, y) = 0$ and delete any points at which either $g(x, y)$ or $h(x, y)$ is not real.

Example 1. Graph $(xy - 1)(y - 2x) = 0$.

Solution. The required graph, shown in Fig. 5.19, consists of all points of $xy = 1$ and $y = 2x$. If a point lies on either $xy - 1 = 0$ or $y - 2x = 0$, its coordinates make either $xy - 1$ or $y - 2x$ zero, and hence make the product $(xy - 1)(y - 2x)$ zero. On the other hand, if a point lies on neither $xy - 1 = 0$ nor on $y - 2x = 0$, its coordinates make neither $xy - 1$ nor $y - 2x$ zero, and hence do not make the product $(xy - 1)(y - 2x)$ zero.

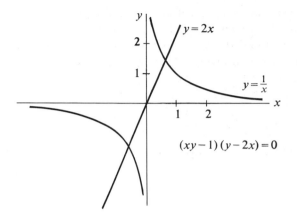

Figure 5.19

Example 2.   The graph of $(x^2 + y^2 + 1)(y - x) = 0$ is the same as the graph of $y - x = 0$, since there are no points at which $x^2 + y^2 + 1 = 0$.

Example 3.   The graph of $(y - x)(y - \sqrt{x}) = 0$ consists of the graph of $y = \sqrt{x}$ plus the first-quadrant portion of the line $y = x$. The third-quadrant portion of $y = x$ is not included, since for $x < 0$, $y - \sqrt{x}$ is not real. For example, even though $(-1) - (-1) = 0$,

$$[(-1) - (-1)][(-1) - \sqrt{-1}] \neq 0,$$

but is undefined, since we are dealing with real numbers only.

PROBLEM LIST 37

Graph the equations in Problems 1–10.

1. $(x + 2y)(y - 3x) = 0$.
2. $(xy - 1)(y - x^2) = 0$.
3. $x(y - x) = 0$.
4. $x^2y + xy^2 + y + x = 0$.
5. $y^2 - x^3y + xy - x^4 = 0$.
6. $(x^2 + y^2)(y + x) = 0$.
7. $x(x + 1) = 0$.
8. $xy = 0$.
9. $(x - 1)y = 0$.
10. $y^3 - x^3 + x^2y - xy^2 - y + x = 0$.
11. Compare the graphs of $y = 3x$ and $xy = 3x^2$.

12. Compare the graphs of $(xy - 1)(y - 2x) = 0$ and $(y - 1/x)(y - 2x) = 0$.

5.10 Summary on Graphing Equations

There is no specific procedure for graphing a given equation. To develop facility in graphing, the student should become familiar with the various techniques of this chapter and should study carefully the various illustrative examples. Skill will be developed only by drawing a large number of curves.

The following illustrative examples and problems involve curves that are more difficult to draw than those heretofore considered.

Example 1.   Graph $y^3 - 3y^2 + x = 0$.

>   **Solution.**   The curve goes through the origin and through $(0, 3)$.
>   From

$$\frac{dy}{dx} = \frac{1}{3y(2 - y)}$$

we find that the curve has vertical tangents at $(0, 0)$ and $(4, 2)$. Also, the slope is positive for $0 < y < 2$ and negative for $y > 2$ and for $y < 0$.
>   From

$$\frac{d^2y}{dx^2} = \frac{2(y - 1)}{9y^3(2 - y)^3}$$

we find that $(2, 1)$ is a point of inflection and that the curve is concave upward for $y < 0$ and $1 < y < 2$, and concave downward for $0 < y < 1$ and $y > 2$.

The graph shown in Fig. 5.20 could also be obtained by drawing the curve $x^3 - 3x^2 + y = 0$ and reflecting it in the line $y - x$.

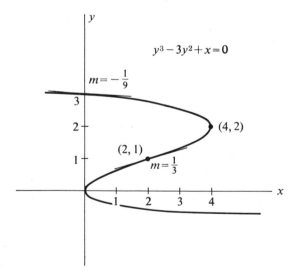

Figure 5.20

Example 2.   Graph $x^2 - xy + y^2 = 3$.

Solution.   The curve is symmetric with respect to the origin and the line $y = x$. Setting $y = x$, we obtain the points $(\sqrt{3}, \sqrt{3})$ and $(-\sqrt{3}, -\sqrt{3})$. The x-intercepts are $\pm\sqrt{3}$ and the y-intercepts are $\pm\sqrt{3}$.
From

$$y = \frac{x \pm \sqrt{3(4 - x^2)}}{2}$$

we find that y is real only for $|x| \leqslant 2$. Similarly, x is real only for $|y| \leqslant 2$, so no points of the curve lie outside a 4×4 square centered at the origin.
From

$$\frac{dy}{dx} = \frac{y - 2x}{2y - x}$$

we find that the curve has horizontal tangents at $(1, 2)$ and $(-1, -2)$, and vertical tangents at $(2, 1)$ and $(-2, -1)$.
For the portion of the curve below the line $y = x/2$, we have

$$y' = \frac{1}{2} + \frac{3x}{2\sqrt{12 - 3x^2}} \qquad \text{and} \qquad y'' = \frac{+18}{(12 - 3x^2)^{3/2}}.$$

From y' we determine the slope at a few points and from y'' we determine that this portion of the curve is concave upward.
The curve, which is an ellipse, is shown in Fig. 5.21.

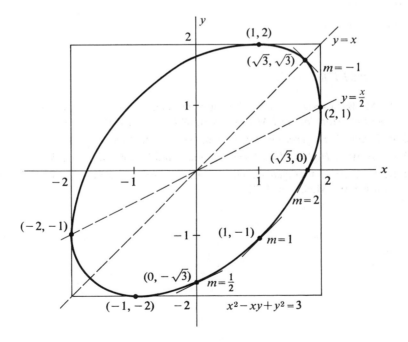

Figure 5.21

PROBLEM LIST 38

Graph the curves in Problems 1–18.

1. $x = y^3 + 3y^2 - 2$.

2. $x^2 - xy + y^2 = 1$.

3. $x^2 - 4xy + y^2 = 3$.

4. $y^2 = x^2(x - 1)$.

5. $2x^2 + 4xy + 3y^2 = 4$.

6. $y = \dfrac{x}{x^2 + 1}$.

7. $y^2 = \dfrac{x^2(x - 1)}{x - 2}$.

8. $4x^2 + 4xy + y^2 - 4x = 0$.

9. $y^2 = x(x - 2)(x - 5)$.

10. $y^2 = x^4(1 - x)$.

11. $y^4 = x^2(1 - y^2)$.

12. $y^2 = x^3(4 - x)$.

13. $y = x^{2/3}(1 - x)^{2/3}$.

14. $y = \dfrac{x^3}{x - 3}$.

15. $y^3 - x^3 + x = 0$.

16. $y^2 = \dfrac{x^3}{2a - x}$.

17. $x^3 + xy^2 - 3ax^2 + ay^2 = 0$.

18. $|x + y| + |x - y| = 1$.

19. Let $(x - a)^k$ be the highest power of $x - a$ which is a factor of the polynomial $P(x)$. Prove that the slope of the curve $y = P(x)$ at $(a, 0)$ is zero when the integer k is greater than 1 and is different from zero when $k = 1$.

20. Draw the graph of

    (a) $y = |x|$;

    (b) $y = |1 - |x||$;

    (c) $y = |1 - |1 - |x|||$.

REFERENCES

5.1 A. M. BRUCKNER, "Some Nonequivalent Definitions of Inflection Points," *American Mathematical Monthly*, Vol. 69 (October, 1962), p. 787.

5.2 P. FROST, *Curve Tracing*, Macmillan, New York, 1892.

5.3 G. SALMON, *Higher Plane Curves*, Hodges and Smith, Dublin, 1852.

5.4 R. C. YATES, *A Handbook on Curves and Their Properties*, J. W. Edwards, Ann Arbor, Michigan, 1947.

Chapter

6

An equation of a graph

In Sec. 2.13 we defined an equation of a graph or set of points in the xy-plane. In Sec. 2.14, after describing the set of points on a line by giving the inclination of the line and specifying a point on the line, we derived an equation of the line. We now proceed to derive equations of some well-known sets of points or curves.

6.1 The Circle

A circle is defined as the set of points that are a constant distance from a fixed point. We denote the constant distance, called the radius, by $r > 0$, and the fixed point, called the center, by $C(h, k)$. In Fig. 6.1, $P(x, y)$ denotes an arbitrary point on the circle. From the distance formula, we have

$$\sqrt{(x - h)^2 + (y - k)^2} = r \qquad (6.1)$$

or

$$(x - h)^2 + (y - k)^2 = r^2. \qquad (6.2)$$

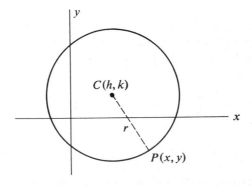

Figure 6.1

Conversely, if x_0 and y_0 are any pair of real numbers satisfying (6.2), x_0 and y_0 also satisfy (6.1), since $r > 0$. Thus (x_0, y_0) is a point of the circle of radius r centered at (h, k). It follows that (6.2) is an equation of the circle.

Example 1. $(x - 2)^2 + (y + 5)^2 = 9$ represents a circle of radius 3 with center at $(2, -5)$.

Example 2.   Find an equation of the circle with center at $(-2, 3)$ and passing through $(6, 5)$.

> **Solution.**   We see immediately that $h = -2$ and $k = 3$. From the distance formula,
>
> $$r = \sqrt{(6 - [-2])^2 + (5 - 3)^2} = \sqrt{68},$$
>
> and by (6.2), an equation of the circle is
>
> $$(x + 2)^2 + (y - 3)^2 = 68,$$
>
> or upon removing parentheses,
>
> $$x^2 + y^2 + 4x - 6y - 55 = 0.$$

Upon removing parentheses in (6.2), we obtain

$$x^2 + y^2 - 2hx - 2ky + h^2 + k^2 - r^2 = 0$$

or

$$x^2 + y^2 + ax + by + c = 0 \tag{6.3}$$

where

$$a = -2h, \qquad b = -2k, \qquad c = h^2 + k^2 - r^2.$$

Thus, every circle has an equation of the form (6.2) and an equation of the form (6.3). Every equation of the form (6.2) represents a circle, so it is natural to ask if every equation of the form (6.3) also represents a circle. The answer is "no," as is shown by the following argument, which employs the process known as "completing the square."

We first write (6.3) in the form

$$\left(x^2 + ax \qquad\right) + \left(y^2 + by \qquad\right) = -c.$$

Each expression in parentheses on the left is now made a perfect square by adding the square of half the coefficient of the second term. This is suggested by the identity $(p + q)^2 = p^2 + (2q)p + q^2$. Adding $(a/2)^2$ and $(b/2)^2$ to both sides, we obtain

$$\left(x^2 + ax + \frac{a^2}{4}\right) + \left(y^2 + by + \frac{b^2}{4}\right) = \frac{a^2}{4} + \frac{b^2}{4} - c$$

or

$$\left(x - \left[\frac{-a}{2}\right]\right)^2 + \left(y - \left[\frac{-b}{2}\right]\right)^2 = \left(\frac{\sqrt{a^2 + b^2 - 4c}}{2}\right)^2. \tag{6.4}$$

Comparing (6.4) with (6.2), we see that—provided $a^2 + b^2 - 4c > 0$—(6.4) represents a circle of radius $(1/2)\sqrt{a^2 + b^2 - 4c}$ with center at $(-a/2, -b/2)$. If $a^2 + b^2 - 4c = 0$, (6.4) represents the single point $(-a/2, -b/2)$. If $a^2 + b^2 - 4c < 0$, (6.4) is not satisfied by the coordinates of any points, since the sum of two squares can never be negative. If the graph of (6.4) consists of a single point, we call the single point a point circle, and if the graph consists of no points, we say that (6.4) represents an imaginary circle. This convention is merely a convenience of language which enables us to say that (6.3) always represents a circle.

Example 3.   Find the center and radius of

$$x^2 + y^2 + 8x - 6y + 21 = 0.$$

Solution.   Completing the square, we obtain

$$(x^2 + 8x \qquad) + (y^2 - 6y \qquad) = -21$$
$$(x^2 + 8x + 16) + (y^2 - 6y + 9) = 16 + 9 - 21 = 4$$
$$(x - [-4])^2 + (y - 3)^2 = (2)^2.$$

The circle has center $(-4, 3)$ and radius 2.

Example 4.   Identify the graph of the equation

$$x^2 + y^2 - 10x + 4y + 29 = 0.$$

Solution

$$(x^2 - 10x \qquad) + (y^2 + 4y \qquad) = -29$$
$$(x^2 - 10x + 25) + (y^2 + 4y + 4) = 25 + 4 - 29 = 0$$
$$(x - 5)^2 + (y - [-2])^2 = 0.$$

The graph is a point circle consisting of the single point $(5, -2)$.

Example 5.   The equation $x^2 + y^2 + 1 = 0$ represents an imaginary circle. Since $x_0^2 + y_0^2 \geqslant 0$ at every point (x_0, y_0), it is impossible for the coordinates of any point to satisfy the given equation.

Example 6.   Find an equation of the circle through

$$A(-2, 0), B(2, 8), \text{ and } C(5, -1).$$

Solution.   Assume that the circle has an equation of the form (6.3):

$$x^2 + y^2 + ax + by + c = 0.$$

Substituting the coordinates of A, B, and C into (6.3), we obtain the three equations

$$4 + 0 - 2a + 0b + c = 0,$$
$$4 + 64 + 2a + 8b + c = 0,$$
$$25 + 1 + 5a - 1b + c = 0.$$

Solving these three equations simultaneously, we obtain $a = -4$, $b = -6$, and $c = -12$.

Substitution of these values of a, b, and c into (6.3) yields the desired result:

$$x^2 + y^2 - 4x - 6y - 12 = 0.$$

Example 7. Find an equation of the circle that passes through $A(3, -4)$ and $B(1, 0)$ and whose center is on the line $2x + y + 8 = 0$.

Solution. Since the coordinates of A and B satisfy (6.2),

$$(3 - h)^2 + (-4 - k)^2 = r^2 \qquad \textbf{(6.5a)}$$

and

$$(1 - h)^2 + (0 - k)^2 = r^2. \qquad \textbf{(6.5b)}$$

Since the center is on $2x + y + 8 = 0$,

$$2h + k + 8 = 0. \qquad \textbf{(6.6)}$$

Subtracting (6.5b) from (6.5a) and simplifying, we obtain

$$h - 2k - 6 = 0. \qquad \textbf{(6.7)}$$

Solving (6.6) and (6.7) simultaneously yields $h = -2$ and $k = -4$. Substituting these values into (6.5b) yields $r = 5$. The following equation of the circle is obtained by substituting these values of h, k, and r into (6.2):

$$(x + 2)^2 + (y + 4)^2 = 25.$$

Example 8. Show that the line $x + y - 3 = 0$ is tangent to the circle $x^2 + y^2 - 4x + 6y + 5 = 0$.

Solution. Replacing x in the equation of the circle by $3 - y$, we obtain

$$(3 - y)^2 + y^2 - 4(3 - y) + 6y + 5 - 0$$

or

$$y^2 + 2y + 1 = (y + 1)^2 = 0$$

from which $y = -1$ and $x = 4$. Hence the line intersects the circle at $(4, -1)$. The slope y' of the circle at any point is obtained by implicit differentiation:

$$2x + 2yy' - 4 + 6y' = 0$$

or

$$y' = \frac{2 - x}{3 + y}.$$

At $(4, -1)$ the slope of the circle is $(2 - 4)/(3 - 1) = -1$. Since -1 is also the slope of $x + y - 3 = 0$, the line and the circle are tangent at $(4, -1)$.

PROBLEM LIST 39

1. Find an equation of the circle (circles)
   (a) with center $(4, -5)$ and radius 6;
   (b) with center $(2, 6)$ and tangent to the y-axis;
   (c) with center $(2, 6)$ and tangent to the x-axis;
   (d) with center $(5, -2)$ and passing through the origin;

    (e) with center $(4, -3)$ and passing through $(7, 2)$;

    (f) having $(6, -4)$ and $(10, 8)$ as ends of a diameter;

    (g) having center $(2, 1)$ and tangent to $3x + 4y = 60$;

    (h) having center $(-3, 2)$ and tangent to $y = 8$;

    (i) having radius 5 and tangent to both axes;

    (j) having center on the x-axis and passing through $(-2, 8)$ and $(6, 2)$;

    (k) having center on $3x - 2y = 22$ and passing through $(10, -8)$ and $(7, 1)$;

    (l) having center on $2x - y = 4$ and tangent to both axes.

2. Find an equation of the circle (circles)

    (a) with center $(5, -3)$ and radius 2;

    (b) with center at $(-4, 2)$ and tangent to the y-axis;

    (c) with center at $(-4, 2)$ and tangent to the x-axis;

    (d) with center at $(-5, 3)$ and passing through the origin;

    (e) with center at $(4, 7)$ and passing through $(-2, 3)$;

    (f) having $(5, -6)$ and $(-1, 4)$ as ends of a diameter;

    (g) having center $(-3, 4)$ and tangent to $x = 5$;

    (h) having center $(-2, 3)$ and tangent to $5x - 12y = 26$;

    (i) having radius 7 and tangent to both axes;

    (j) having center on the y-axis and passing through $(-4, 6)$ and $(5, 2)$;

    (k) having center on $x + y = 1$ and passing through $(3, 3)$ and $(0, 2)$;

    (l) having center on $3x + y = 6$ and tangent to both axes.

3. Find the center and radius of each circle:

    (a) $x^2 + y^2 - 4x + 6y - 3 = 0$.

    (b) $x^2 + y^2 - 8x - 4y - 5 = 0$.

    (c) $x^2 + y^2 - 12x - 2y - 12 = 0$.

    (d) $x^2 + y^2 + 4x + 2y + 10 = 0$.

    (e) $x^2 + y^2 - 10x + 6y + 34 = 0$.

    (f) $3x^2 + 3y^2 - x + 2y = 0$.

4. Find the center and radius of each circle:

    (a) $x^2 + y^2 + 6x - 2y + 9 = 0$.

    (b) $x^2 + y^2 - 8x + 4y - 5 = 0$.

    (c) $x^2 + y^2 + 8x - 6y + 25 = 0$.

    (d) $x^2 + y^2 + x - y - 1 = 0$.

    (e) $2x^2 + 2y^2 + 4x - 3y + 1 = 0$.

    (f) $5x^2 + 5y^2 - 10x - 4 = 0$.

5. Find an equation of the circle determined by

    (a) $(2, 0)$, $(-5, -1)$, and $(-2, 8)$;

    (b) $(-2, 2)$, $(4, -6)$, and $(-4, -2)$;

    (c) $(3, 9)$, $(6, 0)$, and $(-2, 4)$;

   (d) $(-4, 6)$, $(3, 8)$, and $(7, -1)$.
 6. Find an equation of the circle determined by
   (a) $(0, 0)$, $(9, -3)$, and $(10, 0)$;
   (b) $(-1, -1)$, $(1, 0)$, and $(0, 2)$;
   (c) $(6, 9)$, $(2, 5)$, and $(-8, 5)$;
   (d) $(-2, 4)$, $(6, 3)$, and $(5, -2)$.
 7. Find the center of $x^2 + y^2 + ax + by + c = 0$ by differentiating implicitly.
 8. Prove analytically that an angle inscribed in a semicircle is a right angle.
 9. Find an equation of the tangent to $x^2 + y^2 = 25$ at $(3, 4)$.
10. Find an equation of the tangent to
$$x^2 + y^2 + 6x - 4y + 11 = 0 \qquad \text{at } (-2, 3).$$
11. Find the slope of $(x - h)^2 + (y - k)^2 = r^2$ at $P(x, y)$.
12. Find equations of the lines through $(7, 3)$ tangent to $x^2 + y^2 - 4y - 21 = 0$.
13. Find the length of the common chord of
$$x^2 + y^2 + 4x - 8y + 11 = 0 \qquad \text{and} \qquad x^2 + y^2 - 8y + 7 = 0.$$
14. Solve illustrative Example 6 by finding the intersection of the perpendicular bisectors of AB and AC.
15. Determine whether $(1, 3)$ is inside or outside
$$x^2 + y^2 + 4x - 8y + 11 = 0.$$
16. State the common property of each of the following families of circles:
   (a) $x^2 + y^2 + ax + by = 0$.
   (b) $x^2 + y^2 + by + c = 0$.
   (c) $(x - 2)^2 + (y + 3)^2 = r^2$.
   (d) $(x - h)^2 + y^2 = r^2$.
17. Find an equation of the circle passing through $(0, -1)$ and $(6, 3)$ and tangent to $2x - 3y = 16$.
18. Find the center and radius of
$$(x - a)(x - c) + (y - b)(y - d) = 0.$$
19. Show that
$$(x - x_1)(x - x_2) + (y - y_1)(y - y_2)$$
$$+ k[(x_2 - x_1)(y - y_1) - (y_2 - y_1)(x - x_1)] = 0$$
is an equation of a family of circles passing through the points (x_1, y_1) and (x_2, y_2). Employ this result to find an equation of the circle through $(3, -11)$, $(-10, 2)$, and $(6, -10)$.

6.2 *Translation of Axes*

   A curve having equation $f(x, y) = 0$ will sometimes have a simpler equation when referred to a pair of axes other than the x- and y-axes.
   In Fig. 6.2, the u- and v-axes are parallel to the x- and y-axes; the point P has

coordinates x and y in the xy system and u and v in the uv system. The point $(0, 0)$ in the uv system is the point (h, k) in the xy system.

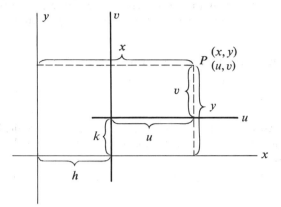

Figure 6.2

The equations

$$x = u + h, \qquad y = v + k, \tag{6.8}$$

are called the equations of translation. If $f(x, y) = 0$ is an equation of a curve C in the xy system, C has equation $f(u + h, v + k) = 0$ in the uv system. We say that the origin has been translated to the point (h, k).

Example 1.   Remove the first-degree terms from

$$xy - 2x - 3y + 4 = 0$$

by a translation.

Solution.   Replacing x by $u + h$ and y by $v + k$ yields

$$(u + h)(v + k) - 2(u + h) - 3(v + k) + 4 = 0$$

which, upon rewriting, becomes

$$uv + (h - 3)v + (k - 2)u + (hk - 2h - 3k + 4) = 0. \tag{6.9}$$

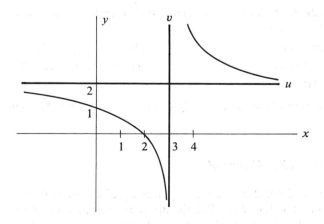

Figure 6.3

Setting the coefficients of u and v, the first-degree terms, equal to zero, we obtain $h = 3$ and $k = 2$. These values reduce (6.9) to $uv - 2 = 0$.

The curve $uv = 2$ in the uv system is the curve $xy - 2x - 3y + 4 = 0$ in the xy system. The uv equation is clearly simpler than the xy equation. See Fig. 6.3.

Example 2. Remove the first-degree terms from

$$x^2 + y^2 - 2x + 6y - 15 = 0$$

by a translation.

Solution. Although the method of Example 1 is applicable, we employ a second method which will be useful in our later work. Completing the square yields

$$(x^2 - 2x + 1) + (y^2 + 6y + 9) = 1 + 9 + 15$$

or

$$(x - 1)^2 + (y + 3)^2 = (5)^2.$$

Replacing $x - 1$ by u and $y + 3$ by v, we obtain the desired result:

$$u^2 + v^2 = 25.$$

Reference to equations (6.8) reveals that the origin has been translated to $(1, -3)$, the center of the circle in the xy system.

PROBLEM LIST 40

1. Remove the first-degree terms of the following equations by a translation.

   (a) $xy - 4x - 3y + 10 = 0$.   (c) $xy - 6x + 1 = 0$.

   (b) $xy + 3y - 5 = 0$.   (d) $xy + 4x + 8y = 0$.

2. Remove the constant term of the following equations by a translation.

   (a) $y = 3x - 12$.   (b) $4x + 3y - 10 = 0$.

3. Simplify the following equations by completing the square and translating axes.

   (a) $x^2 + y^2 - 4x + 12y + 39 = 0$.   (c) $x^2 + y^2 - 3x + 2y + 1 = 0$.

   (b) $x^2 + y^2 + 8x - 6y = 0$.   (d) $5x^2 + 5y^2 + 6x - 7y - 2 = 0$.

4. Simplify each equation by a translation. Draw a graph of each curve showing both the xy- and the uv-axes.

   (a) $y = (x - 1)^2$.   (d) $y + 1 = |x - 3|$.

   (b) $(y + 2)^2 = 4x$.   (e) $(y + 4)(x - 7) = 3$.

   (c) $(y - 3)^2 = (x + 2)^3$.

5. Find an equation of the curve $y^2 + 2y - 4x + 13 = 0$ when the origin is translated to $(3, -1)$.

6.3 The Parabola

A parabola is defined as the set of points equally distant from a line d and a point F not on d. The line d is called the directrix and the point F the focus.

In Fig. 6.4 the line through F perpendicular to d is called the axis of the parabola. It is clear that the point V on this line, halfway from F to d, is a point of the parabola. The point V is called the vertex of the parabola. The parabola is symmetric with respect to its axis, for if P is a point on one side of the axis such that $FP = MP$, there is a point Q on the other side of the axis such that $FQ = FP$ and $NQ = MP$. Thus $FQ = NQ$ and Q is on the parabola.

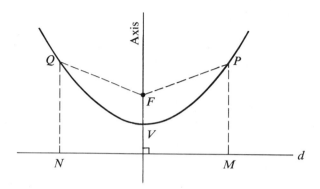

Figure 6.4

The equation we derive for the parabola will depend upon where we locate F and d in the xy-plane. A particularly simple equation is obtained by denoting the distance from F to d by $p > 0$, placing V at the origin, and F at $(0, p/2)$. An equation of d is then $y = -p/2$.

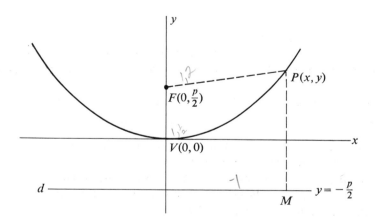

Figure 6.5

If $P(x, y)$ in Fig. 6.5 is an arbitrary point on the parabola,

$$FP = MP$$

so x and y satisfy

$$\sqrt{(x - 0)^2 + \left(y - \frac{p}{2}\right)^2} = y - \left(\frac{-p}{2}\right). \qquad \textbf{(6.10)}$$

Squaring, x and y satisfy

$$x^2 + y^2 - py + \frac{p^2}{4} = y^2 + py + \frac{p^2}{4} \qquad \textbf{(6.11)}$$

and also

$$x^2 = 2py. \qquad \textbf{(6.12)}$$

Conversely, if the coordinates x_0 and y_0 of $P_0(x_0, y_0)$ satisfy (6.12), they also satisfy (6.11) and also (6.10). Therefore $FP_0 = MP_0$ and P_0 is a point on the parabola. This proves that (6.12) is an equation of the parabola.

If we place F at $(0, -p/2)$ and V at the origin, the parabola has equation

$$x^2 = -2py \qquad \textbf{(6.13)}$$

and opens downward rather than upward.

If V is placed at (h, k) and F at $(h, k + p/2)$, the parabola has equation

$$(x - h)^2 = 2p(y - k), \qquad \textbf{(6.14)}$$

which is graphed in Fig. 6.6(a).

This follows from the fact that a translation of the origin to (h, k) transforms (6.14) into $u^2 = 2pv$.

Similarly,

$$(x - h)^2 = -2p(y - k), \qquad \textbf{(6.15)}$$

graphed in Fig. 6.6(b), represents a parabola with V at (h, k), F at $(h, k - p/2)$, and which opens downward.

If, in (6.14), x and y are interchanged, and also h and k, we obtain the equation

$$(y - k)^2 = 2p(x - h), \qquad \textbf{(6.16)}$$

which is graphed in Fig. 6.6(c).

Since the interchange reflects the parabola (6.14) in the line $y = x$, (6.16) represents a parabola with V at (h, k), F at $(h + p/2, k)$ and which opens to the right.

The same interchange (x with y and h with k) in (6.15) yields

$$(y - k)^2 = -2p(x - h), \qquad \textbf{(6.17)}$$

graphed in Fig. 6.6(d), which represents a parabola with V at (h, k), F at $(h - p/2, k)$, and which opens to the left.

The student should be familiar with the standard equations (6.14), (6.15), (6.16), and (6.17), and should know the type parabola represented by each equation. A graphic summary is presented in Fig. 6.6.

Example 1.   Identify the curve $y^2 = 8x$.

Solution.   The equation is of the form (6.16) with $h = 0$, $k = 0$, and $p = 4$. Hence the curve is a parabola with V at $(0, 0)$, F at $(2, 0)$, directrix $x = -2$, and axis $y = 0$. After plotting a point such as $(2, 4)$, the parabola is readily drawn.

Example 2.   Find an equation of the parabola with V at $(2, 3)$ and F at $(2, -2)$.

Figure 6.6

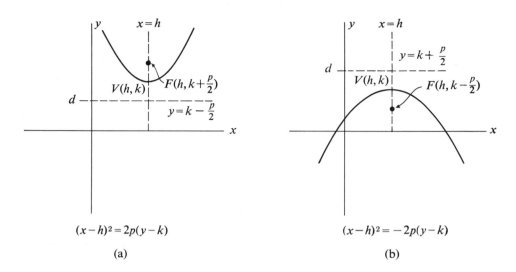

$$(x-h)^2 = 2p(y-k)$$

(a)

$$(x-h)^2 = -2p(y-k)$$

(b)

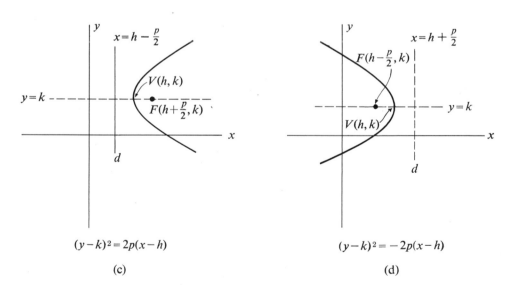

$$(y-k)^2 = 2p(x-h)$$

(c)

$$(y-k)^2 = -2p(x-h)$$

(d)

Solution.   Reference to Fig. 6.6 indicates that equation (6.15) can be used to represent the parabola. From the location of V we obtain $h = 2$ and $k = 3$, and since F is five units below V, $p/2 = 5$ and hence $p = 10$. Substituting these values of h, k, and p into (6.15) yields the answer

$$(x - 2)^2 = -20(y - 3).$$

Example 3.   A chord of a parabola is a line segment joining two distinct points of the parabola. Find the length of the chord through the focus and perpendicular to the axis. This chord is called the latus rectum of the parabola.

Solution. Substituting $y = p/2$ into $x^2 = 2py$, we obtain $x = \pm p$. Hence the latus rectum joins $(-p, p/2)$ and $(p, p/2)$ and has length $2p$.

Removal of parentheses from (6.14) or (6.15) yields an equation of the form

$$x^2 + ax + by + c = 0. \qquad (6.18)$$

Hence, a parabola with a vertical axis always has an equation of the form (6.18). We now show that if $b \neq 0$, every equation of the form (6.18) represents a parabola with vertical axis:

$$x^2 + ax + \frac{a^2}{4} = -by - c + \frac{a^2}{4},$$

$$\left(x - \left[\frac{-a}{2}\right]\right)^2 = -b\left(y - \frac{a^2 - 4c}{4b}\right). \qquad (6.19)$$

By comparison with (6.14) and (6.15), we see that (6.19) represents a parabola with vertical axis, $h = -a/2$, $k = (a^2 - 4c)/4b$, and $p = |b/2|$. The parabola opens upward if $b < 0$ and downward if $b > 0$.

Similarly,

$$y^2 + ay + bx + c = 0 \qquad (6.20)$$

represents a parabola with horizontal axis if $b \neq 0$.

Given an equation of the form (6.18) or (6.20), we complete the square and compare the result with the standard forms of Fig. 6.6.

Example 4. Graph the parabola

$$y^2 + 2y + 12x - 47 - 0.$$

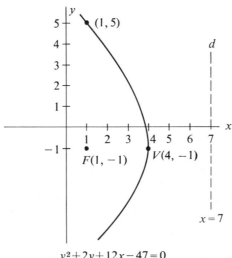

$$y^2 + 2y + 12x - 47 = 0$$

Figure 6.7

Solution.   Completing the square, we obtain

$$y^2 + 2y + 1 = -12x + 47 + 1$$

from which

$$(y - [-1])^2 = -12(x - 4).$$

Since this equation is of the form (6.17), the parabola has vertex $(4, -1)$, $p = 6$, focus at $(1, -1)$, directrix $x = 7$, and opens to the left. After plotting the end $(1,5)$ of the latus rectum, we draw the graph in Fig. 6.7.

Example 5.   Prove that the tangent to a parabola at an end of the latus rectum intersects the axis on the directrix.

Solution.   When placed in the position shown in Fig. 6.5, the parabola has equation $y = x^2/2p$ and one end of the latus rectum is at $Q(p, p/2)$. Since $dy/dx = x/p$, the slope of the parabola at Q is 1. Hence the tangent has equation

$$y - \frac{p}{2} = 1(x - p).$$

Setting $x = 0$, we find that $y = -p/2$. Since $(0, -p/2)$ is on the directrix, the proof is complete.

PROBLEM LIST 41

1. For each parabola, find V, F, and d and draw the graph.
    (a) $y^2 = 10x$.
    (b) $x^2 = -8y$.
    (c) $y^2 = -14x$.
    (d) $x^2 = -4y$.
    (e) $y^2 + 3x = 0$.
    (f) $x^2 - 15y = 0$.
    (g) $2y^2 + 5x = 0$.
    (h) $3x^2 + 7y = 0$.

2. Write an equation of the parabola with
    (a) vertex at $(0, 0)$, directrix $y = -16$;
    (b) vertex at $(0, 0)$, directrix $x = 7$;
    (c) focus at $(0, 0)$, directrix $y = 8$;
    (d) focus at $(4, 2)$, vertex at $(4, -10)$;
    (e) vertex at $(-3, 6)$, directrix $x = -9$;
    (f) focus at $(2, -4)$, vertex at $(2, 1)$.

3. Find V, F, and d and draw the graph.
    (a) $x^2 - 4x - 10y - 36 = 0$.
    (b) $y^2 + 8y + 6x + 10 = 0$.
    (c) $x^2 + 10x + 8y + 41 = 0$.
    (d) $y^2 + 6y - 14x + 23 = 0$.
    (e) $y^2 = kx(k > 0)$.
    (f) $2x^2 + 5x - 4y + 10 = 0$.
    (g) $3y^2 + 4y + 2x - 5 = 0$.

4. Find an equation of the parabola that has vertex at the origin, focus on the y-axis, and which passes through $(7, 4)$.

5. State the common properties of each of the following families of parabolas:
   (a) $y^2 = kx(k < 0)$.
   (b) $(x - 2)^2 = 2p(y + 4)$.
   (c) $(y + 1)^2 = -2p(x - h)$.
   (d) $x^2 = 2p(y - k)$.

6. Find an equation of the parabola that has its axis parallel to the y-axis and which passes through $(1, 9)$, $(-2, -6)$, and $(-1, -3)$.

7. On the same set of axes draw the graphs of $x^2 = 2py$ for $p = 1/4, 1/2, 1$, and 2. How does the shape of the parabola depend upon the parameter p?

8. Find the length of the focal chord (chord passing through the focus) of $y^2 = 16x$ if one end of the chord is at $(1, 4)$.

9. Find, by differentiation, the vertex of each of the following parabolas:
   (a) $x^2 + 6x - 4y + 17 = 0$.
   (b) $y^2 + 4y + 8x - 28 = 0$.
   (c) $x^2 + ax + by + c = 0$.
   (d) $y^2 + ay + bx + c = 0$.

10. Find the length of the common chord of the parabolas $y = x^2$ and $y^2 = 8x$. Illustrate graphically.

11. Determine b so that $y = x + b$ will be tangent to $y^2 = 4x$. Also determine the point of tangency.

12. The period t of a pendulum is given approximately by $t = 2\pi\sqrt{l/g}$, where t is in seconds, l is the length of the pendulum in feet, and g is the acceleration of gravity in feet per second per second. Solve for l in terms of t and graph the resulting equation for $0 \leqslant t \leqslant 2$. Use $g = 32$ and $\pi^2 \cong 10$.

13. A suspension bridge cable hangs in the form of a parabola. Find an equation of the cable of the form $y = kx^2$, given that the span of the bridge is 400 ft and the sag of the cable is 40 ft. Find the height of the cable above the x-axis at $x = 100$ ft.

14. A parabolic arch has a 20-ft base and height 10 ft. Find the height of the arch at a point on the base 4 ft from the center of the base.

15. A cross section of a headlight is a parabola with vertex at the origin, axis $y = 0$, and passing through $(3, 4)$. Find the focus of the parabola.

16. A projectile fired from the origin with initial speed v_0 feet per second at an angle θ with the x-axis follows (under certain simplifying assumptions) the parabolic path having equation
$$y = x \tan \theta - \frac{16x^2 \sec^2 \theta}{v_0^2}$$
where x and y are in feet. Find the vertex of the parabolic path if $v_0 = 512$ fps and $\theta = 45°$.

17. Let P be any point on a parabola other than the vertex. If the tangent to the parabola at P intersects the directrix at D, prove that $DF \perp PF$, where F denotes the focus.

18. In Fig. 6.8, line t is tangent to the parabola and line n is normal to the parabola at P, and F denotes the focus. Prove that if angle α equals angle β, then PR is parallel to the axis of the parabola.

   According to the reflection principle of optics, a light ray traveling from F to P will be reflected in the direction PR such that α, called the angle of incidence, will equal β, the angle of reflection. Hence, as a consequence of the geometric fact that

$\alpha = \beta$ implies that PR is parallel to the axis of the parabola, all light rays emanating from the focus F will be reflected along paths parallel to the axis of the parabola. This geometric property also accounts for the use of parabolic surfaces in telescopes, radar screens, lamps, and similar devices.

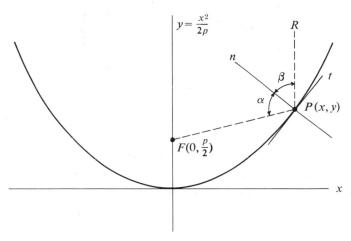

Figure 6.8

19. On the same set of axes draw the graphs of the functions f and g given by

$$f(x) = \begin{cases} -3(x-1)^2 + 3 & \text{for } 0 \leqslant x \leqslant 1 \\ \left[-\dfrac{1}{2}(x-3)\right]^{1/2} + 2 & \text{for } 1 < x \leqslant 3 \\ 2 & \text{for } 3 < x \leqslant 5 \\ -2(x-5)^2 + 2 & \text{for } 5 < x \leqslant 6 \end{cases},$$

$$g(x) = \begin{cases} 0 & \text{for } 0 \leqslant x \leqslant 1,\, 2 < x \leqslant 4, \\ & \qquad \text{and } 5 < x \leqslant 6 \\ -\sqrt{-\left(x-\dfrac{3}{2}\right)^2 + \dfrac{1}{4}} & \text{for } 1 < x \leqslant 2 \\ -\sqrt{-x^2 + 9x - 20} & \text{for } 4 < x \leqslant 5 \end{cases}$$

6.4 The Ellipse

An ellipse is defined as the set of points the sum of whose distances from two fixed points is constant. The two fixed points, denoted by F and F' in Fig. 6.9, are called the foci. The distance $F'F$ is denoted by $2c$ and the constant sum by $2a$. Since $2a > 2c > 0$, $a > c > 0$. To visualize the appearance of an ellipse, imagine that a piece of string·having length $2a$ has one end attached at F' and the other at F. If a pencil or marker draws the string taut, the possible positions of the pencil constitute the set of points of the ellipse. This is sometimes referred to as the gardener's method for constructing an ellipse, since it is used by gardeners to mark out elliptical flower beds. In Fig. 6.9,

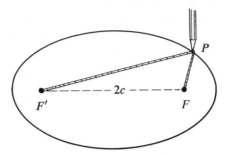

Figure 6.9

$$F'P + FP = 2a > 2c.$$

A simple equation of an ellipse is obtained by placing the foci at $(-c, 0)$ and $(c, 0)$. In Fig. 6.10 an arbitrary point on the ellipse in denoted by $P(x, y)$.

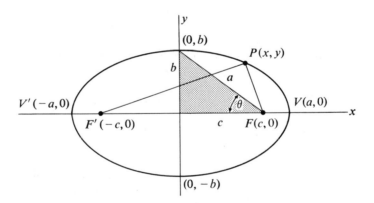

Figure 6.10

Since $F'P + FP = 2a$, x and y satisfy

$$\sqrt{(x + c)^2 + (y - 0)^2} + \sqrt{(x - c)^2 + (y - 0)^2} = 2a. \qquad (6.21)$$

Transposing the second radical, squaring both sides, and simplifying, we find that x and y also satisfy

$$a^2 - cx = a\sqrt{(x - c)^2 + y^2}. \qquad (6.22)$$

Squaring again and simplifying, we find that x and y satisfy

$$x^2(a^2 - c^2) + a^2y^2 = a^2(a^2 - c^2). \qquad (6.23)$$

Noting that $a^2 - c^2 > 0$, since $a > c$, we find it convenient to let $b^2 = a^2 - c^2(b > 0)$. Dividing both sides of (6.23) by a^2b^2, we find that x and y satisfy

$$\frac{x^2}{a^2} + \frac{y^2}{b^2} = 1. \qquad (6.24)$$

Conversely, if the coordinates x_0 and y_0 of $P_0(x_0, y_0)$ satisfy (6.24), they also satisfy (6.23), (6.22), and (6.21). Hence, $F'P_0 + FP_0 = 2a$ and P_0 is a point on the ellipse. This completes the proof that (6.24) is an equation of the ellipse.

An ellipse having equation (6.24) is symmetric with respect to the x-axis, the y-axis, and the origin. The curve has x-intercepts $\pm a$, and y-intercepts $\pm b$, the latter fact furnishing a geometric interpretation of the quantity b, assumed to be positive. The points $V'(-a, 0)$ and $V(a, 0)$ are called the vertices; the line segment $V'V$, the major axis; and the line segment from $(0, -b)$ to $(0, b)$, the minor axis. The origin is called the center C of the ellipse.

The ellipse is easily drawn from $y = (\pm b/a)\sqrt{a^2 - x^2}$, obtained by solving (6.24) for y in terms of x.

The slope and the concavity at any point are determined from

$$y' = \frac{-b^2 x}{a^2 y} \quad \text{and} \quad y'' = \frac{-b^4}{a^2 y^3},$$

obtained from (6.24) by implicit differentiation. (See Problem 5.)

Since $b^2 + c^2 = a^2$, the points $(0, 0)$, $(0, b)$ and $(c, 0)$ are vertices of a right triangle with hypotenuse having length a. The foci can be located by drawing an arc of radius a with center at $(0, b)$. This arc will cut the x-axis in F' and F.

The ratio $e = c/a = 2c/2a$, also equal to $\cos \theta$ in Fig. 6.10, is called the eccentricity of the ellipse. The eccentricity is a measure of the flatness of the ellipse and it is easily seen from Fig. 6.10 that $0 < e < 1$. For e close to zero, the ellipse is nearly circular and for e close to 1, the ellipse is long and narrow. The earth travels around the sun in a nearly circular elliptical orbit having $e = 0.0167$, while Halley's comet travels in a long, narrow elliptical orbit having $e = 0.98$.

If we permitted F' and F to coincide, c would be zero and the ellipse would be a circle radius $2a/2 = a$. Thus, a circle is sometimes regarded as an ellipse of eccentricity zero. If we allowed a to equal c, the ellipse would degenerate into the line segment $F'F$.

If center C of the ellipse is placed at (h, k), F at $(h + c, k)$ and F' at $(h - c, k)$, the ellipse has equation

$$\frac{(x - h)^2}{a^2} + \frac{(y - k)^2}{b^2} = 1, \tag{6.25}$$

which is graphed in Fig. 6.11(a).

This follows from the fact that a translation of the origin to (h, k) transforms (6.25) into (6.24).

If, in (6.25), x and y are interchanged, and also h and k, we obtain the equation

$$\frac{(y - k)^2}{a^2} + \frac{(x - h)^2}{b^2} = 1, \tag{6.26}$$

which is graphed in Fig. 6.11(b).

Since the interchange of x and y reflects the ellipse (6.25) in the line $y = x$, (6.26) represents an ellipse with center (h, k), vertices $(h, k \pm a)$, and foci $(h, k \pm c)$.

The important equations to remember are (6.25) and (6.26). The ellipses they represent are shown in Fig. 6.11.

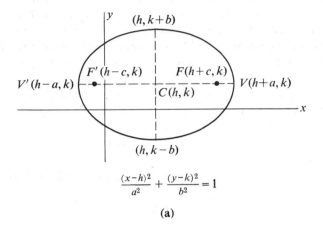

$$\frac{(x-h)^2}{a^2} + \frac{(y-k)^2}{b^2} = 1$$

(a)

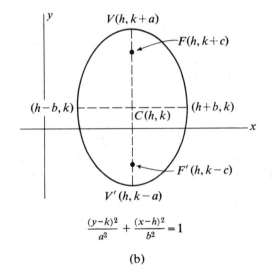

$$\frac{(y-k)^2}{a^2} + \frac{(x-h)^2}{b^2} = 1$$

(b)

Figure 6.11

Example 1. Identify the curve $x^2/16 + y^2/9 = 1$.

Solution. Since $16 > 9$, the equation is of the form (6.25) rather than (6.26) and hence represents an ellipse with horizontal major axis. From $h = 0$, $k = 0$, $a = 4$, and $b = 3$, we find that the center is at $(0, 0)$, the vertices at $(\pm 4, 0)$, and the ends of the minor axis at $(0, \pm 3)$. From $c^2 = a^2 - b^2$, we obtain $c = \sqrt{7}$, and hence the foci are at $(\pm\sqrt{7}, 0)$. The eccentricity $e = c/a = \sqrt{7}/4 \cong 0.66$.

Example 2. Find an equation of the ellipse having foci at $(2, 9)$ and $(2, -3)$ and minor axis of length 10.

Solution.   Since the major axis is vertical, we use the form (6.26). The center is at $(2, 3)$; $h = 2$, $k = 3$, $c = 6$, and $b = 5$. From $a^2 = b^2 + c^2$, we obtain $a^2 = 25 + 36 = 61$. An equation of the ellipse is

$$\frac{(y - 3)^2}{61} + \frac{(x - 2)^2}{25} = 1.$$

Removal of parentheses from (6.25) or (6.26) yields an equation of the form

$$ax^2 + by^2 + cx + dy + e = 0, \qquad\qquad (6.27)$$

where a and b have the same sign and are both different from zero. Thus every ellipse whose major axis is parallel to either the x- or y-axis has an equation of the form (6.27).

The process of completing the square can be used to show that an equation of the form (6.27) always represents an ellipse, provided we allow for a point ellipse or an imaginary ellipse.

Example 3.   Graph the equation

$$25x^2 + 144y^2 + 50x - 576y - 2999 = 0.$$

Solution.   We complete the square as follows:

$$25(x^2 + 2x \qquad) + 144(y^2 - 4y \qquad) = 2999.$$

We next add 1 and 4 inside the parentheses on the left. Since the 1 and 4 are multiplied by 25 and 144, we also add $25 \times 1 = 25$ and $144 \times 4 = 576$ on the right side, yielding

$$25(x^2 + 2x + 1) + 144(y^2 - 4y + 4) - 2999 + 25 + 576 = 3600.$$

Dividing by 3600, we obtain

$$\frac{(x + 1)^2}{144} + \frac{(y - 2)^2}{25} = 1.$$

Since this equation is of the form (6.25), the curve is an ellipse having $a = 12$ and $b = 5$. The center is at $(-1, 2)$, vertices at $(-13, 2)$ and $(11, 2)$, and ends of the minor axis at $(-1, 7)$ and $(-1, -3)$. The student should draw the graph.

Note: If the right member had been 0 instead of 3600, the equation would represent a point ellipse, while if the right member had been negative, the ellipse would be termed imaginary.

PROBLEM LIST 42

1. Find the vertices, ends of the minor axis, foci, and eccentricity, and graph each ellipse.

   (a) $\dfrac{x^2}{9} + \dfrac{y^2}{16} = 1.$

   (b) $\dfrac{x^2}{25} + \dfrac{y^2}{4} = 1.$

   (c) $36x^2 + y^2 = 36.$

   (d) $49x^2 + 4y^2 = 196.$

(e) $64x^2 + 100y^2 = 6400$.   (g) $x^2 + 2y^2 = 1$.

(f) $3x^2 + y^2 = 3$.

2. Find an equation of the ellipse with

     (a) foci at $(\pm 6, 0)$, and major axis of length 16;

     (b) vertices at $(0, \pm 8)$, and minor axis of length 6;

     (c) foci at $(\pm 5, 0)$, and vertices at $(\pm 8, 0)$;

     (d) vertices at $(4, -2)$ and $(4, 10)$, and minor axis of length 10;

     (e) foci at $(-2, 3)$ and $(8, 3)$, and eccentricity 2/3;

     (f) vertices at $(\pm 2, 0)$, and passing through $(1, 1)$;

     (g) foci at $(0, \pm 2\sqrt{3})$, and passing through $(1, 2\sqrt{3})$.

3. Graph each equation:

     (a) $4x^2 + y^2 - 16x + 6y + 21 = 0$.

     (b) $x^2 + 9y^2 + 8x - 18y + 16 = 0$.

     (c) $16x^2 + 9y^2 + 36y - 108 = 0$.

     (d) $9x^2 + 4y^2 - 36x + 8y + 4 = 0$.

     (e) $4x^2 + 5y^2 + 8x - 50y + 129 = 0$.

     (f) $2x^2 + y^2 + 12x - 2y + 20 = 0$.

4. Find an equation of the tangent to the ellipse
$$x^2 + 4y^2 + 2x - 3y - 13 = 0 \text{ at } (1, 2).$$

5. Given $x^2/a^2 + y^2/b^2 = 1$, show that
$$\frac{dy}{dx} = \frac{-b^2x}{a^2y} \quad \text{and} \quad \frac{d^2y}{dx^2} = \frac{-b^4}{a^2y^3}.$$

6. State the common properties of each of the following families of ellipses:

     (a) $x^2/k^2 + y^2/9 = 1$, $(k > 3)$.

     (b) $x^2/k^2 + y^2/9 = 1$, $(k < 3)$.

     (c) $\dfrac{(x + 2)^2}{a^2} + \dfrac{(y - 3)^2}{b^2} = 1$, $(a > b)$.

     (d) $\dfrac{(x - 1)^2}{9} + \dfrac{(y - k)^2}{16} = 1$.

7. A latus rectum of an ellipse is a chord through a focus perpendicular to the major axis. Show that a latus rectum of $x^2/a^2 + y^2/b^2 = 1$ has length $2b^2/a$.

8. Find the slope of $x^2/a^2 + y^2/b^2 = 1$ at the first-quadrant end of a latus rectum. Write the answer in terms of the eccentricity.

9. Find the intersections of the ellipse
$$25x^2 + 9y^2 + 50x - 18y - 191 = 0$$
and the line $5x + 3y = 19$.

10. By using the definition of an ellipse, show that $(4, 1)$ is a point on $5x^2 + 20y^2 = 100$.

11. Prove that the product of the distances from the foci of an ellipse to any tangent to the ellipse is constant.

12. An arch in the form of a semiellipse is 20 ft high and has a 50 ft base. Find the height of the arch at a point on the base 15 ft from an end of the base.

13. Find an equation of an ellipse having axes parallel to the coordinate axes and passing through $(-9, 3)$, $(-7, 6)$, $(1, -2)$, and $(7, -1)$.

14. In Fig. 6.12, line n is normal to the ellipse at P. Prove that if angle α equals angle β, F' is on PR. This establishes the reflection principle for the ellipse. A sound or light wave emanating from F will be reflected toward F'. In an elliptical whispering gallery a sound made at one focus F may be heard at the other focus F', even though it may be inaudible at points between F and F'. (See Problem 18 of Problem List 41.)

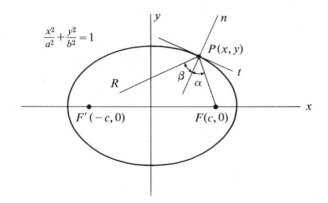

Figure 6.12

15. The Colosseum at Rome is elliptical in shape, having length 615 ft and width 510 ft. Find the position of the foci.

6.5   The Hyperbola

A hyperbola is defined as the set of points, the difference of whose distances from two fixed points is constant. The two fixed points, denoted by F and F' in Fig. 6.13, are called the foci. The distance $F'F$ is denoted by $2c$ and the constant difference by $2a$, a and c both being positive. If P denotes a point on the hyperbola, and $F'P = F'P_1 = FP_2 = FP_3$, and $FP = FP_1 = F'P_2 = F'P_3$, it is clear that P_1, P_2, and P_3 are also on the hyperbola. This symmetry will be evident when we obtain an equation of the hyperbola. We also note that since

$$F'F + FP > F'P,$$

then

$$2a = F'P - FP < F'F = 2c$$

and hence

$$a < c.$$

A simple equation of the hyperbola is obtained by placing the foci at $(-c, 0)$ and $(c, 0)$. In Fig. 6.14, an arbitrary point of the hyperbola is denoted by $P(x, y)$.

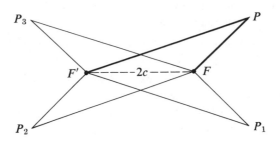

Figure 6.13

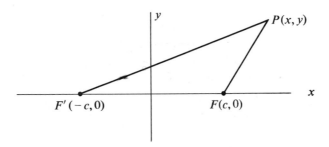

Figure 6.14

Since $F'P - FP = \pm 2a$, x and y satisfy

$$\sqrt{(x + c)^2 + (y - 0)^2} - \sqrt{(x - c)^2 + (y - 0)^2} = \pm 2a. \qquad \textbf{(6.28)}$$

Simplifying, as in the discussion of the ellipse, we find that x and y satisfy

$$(c^2 - a^2)x^2 - a^2 y^2 = a^2(c^2 - a^2). \qquad \textbf{(6.29)}$$

Since $c > a$, $c^2 - a^2 > 0$, and we find it convenient to let $b^2 = c^2 - a^2 (b > 0)$. Dividing both sides of (6.29) by $a^2 b^2$, we find that x and y satisfy

$$\frac{x^2}{a^2} - \frac{y^2}{b^2} = 1, \qquad \textbf{(6.30)}$$

which is represented in Fig. 6.15.

By reversing the steps in the preceding argument, it is readily shown that if x_0 and y_0 satisfy (6.30), $P_0(x_0, y_0)$ is a point of the hyperbola. Thus (6.30) is an equation of the hyperbola.

To draw the graph of (6.30), we need only sketch the first-quadrant portion, since the curve is symmetric to both axes and the origin. From $y = (b/a)\sqrt{x^2 - a^2}$, we see that the curve has x-intercept a and that y, defined for $x \geqslant a$, increases with x. When x is large, $x^2 - a^2$ is only slightly less than x^2, and hence y is only slightly less than $(b/a)\sqrt{x^2} = (b/a)x$. More precisely,

$$\lim_{x \to \infty} \left[\frac{(b/a)x}{(b/a)\sqrt{x^2 - a^2}} \right] = \lim_{x \to \infty} \left[\frac{1}{\sqrt{1 - (a/x)^2}} \right] = 1.$$

Consequently the line $y = (b/a)x$ is an asymptote of the first-quadrant portion of the hyperbola. From

$$y' = \frac{bx}{a\sqrt{x^2 - a^2}} = \frac{b}{a}\sqrt{\frac{1}{1 - (a/x)^2}},$$

we see that as $x \longrightarrow \infty$, the slope of the hyperbola approaches b/a, the slope of its asymptote $y = (b/a)x$. From

$$y'' = \frac{-ab}{(x^2 - a^2)^{3/2}},$$

we see that the first-quadrant portion of the hyperbola is concave downward for $x > a$. To draw the graph of (6.30) we draw a rectangle of base $2a$ and height $2b$ and having center at the origin, as shown in Fig. 6.15. After drawing the diagonals of the rectangle, which are the asymptotes $y = \pm(b/a)x$, the hyperbola is readily drawn. Since $c^2 = a^2 + b^2$, a circle which passes through the four corners of the rectangle will cut the x-axis in the foci.

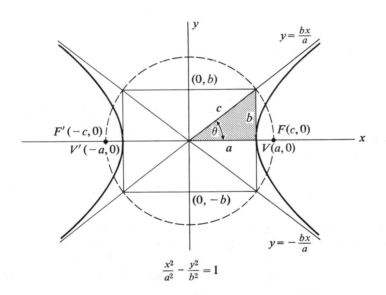

Figure 6.15

The origin is called the center of the hyperbola, the points V and V' the vertices, the line segment $V'V$ the transverse axis, and the line segment from $(0, -b)$ to $(0, b)$ the conjugate axis.

The ratio $e = (c/a) > 1$ is called the eccentricity of the hyperbola. Since $e = c/a = \sec \theta$ in Fig. 6.15, the eccentricity is a measure of the size of the angle 2θ between the asymptotes, If e is close to 1, 2θ is close to 0, while if e is very large, 2θ is close to π.

If the center C of the hyperbola is placed at (h, k), F at $(h + c, k)$, and F' at $(h - c, k)$, the hyperbola will have equation

$$\frac{(x - h)^2}{a^2} - \frac{(y - k)^2}{b^2} = 1. \tag{6.31}$$

This follows from the fact that a translation of the origin to (h, k) transforms (6.31) into (6.30).

If, in (6.31), x and y are interchanged, and also h and k, we obtain the equation

$$\frac{(y - k)^2}{a^2} - \frac{(x - h)^2}{b^2} = 1. \tag{6.32}$$

Since the interchange of x and y reflects the hyperbola (6.31) in the line $y = x$, (6.32) represents a hyperbola with center (h, k), vertices $(h, k \pm a)$, and foci $(h, k \pm c)$.

The asymptotes of (6.31) have equations

$$y - k = \pm\frac{b}{a}(x - h), \tag{6.33}$$

while the asymptotes of (6.32) have equations

$$y - k = \pm\frac{a}{b}(x - h). \tag{6.34}$$

Example 1.   Identify the curve $x^2/16 - y^2/9 = 1$.

> **Solution.**   The equation is of the form (6.31) and hence represents a hyperbola whose branches open to the right and to the left. Since $h = 0$, $k = 0$, $a = 4$, and $b = 3$, the center is at the origin, the vertices are at $(\pm 4, 0)$, and the asymptotes are the lines $y = \pm(3/4)x$. Since $c = \sqrt{a^2 + b^2} = 5$, the foci are at $(\pm 5, 0)$. The graph is shown in Fig. 6.15, provided a, b, and c are replaced by 4, 3, and 5.

Example 2.   Find an equation of the hyperbola having foci at $(8, 17)$ and $(8, -9)$ and vertices at $(8, 9)$ and $(8, -1)$.

> **Solution.**   Since the center is at $(8, 4)$, the hyperbola has an equation of the form (6.32) with $h = 8$, $k = 4$, $a = 5$, and $c = 13$. These values, together with $b = \sqrt{c^2 - a^2} = 12$, yield $[(y - 4)^2/25] - [(x - 8)^2/144] = 1$.
>
> The branches of the hyperbola open upward and downward, and from (6.34), the asymptotes have equations
>
> $$y - 4 = \pm\frac{5}{12}(x - 8).$$
>
> Note that a may be less than, equal to, or greater than b, while in the equations of the ellipse, a is always greater than b.

Removal of parentheses from (6.31) or (6.32) yields an equation of the form

$$ax^2 + by^2 + cx + dy + e = 0 \tag{6.35}$$

where a and b have opposite signs and are both different from zero. Thus every hyperbola whose transverse axis is parallel to one of the coordinate axes has an equation of the form (6.35).

The process of completing the square can be used to show that an equation of the form (6.35) represents a hyperbola or two straight lines.

Example 3.   Graph the equation

$$9x^2 - 25y^2 + 36x - 50y + 236 = 0.$$

Solution.   We complete the square as follows:

$$9(x^2 + 4x \quad) - 25(y^2 + 2y \quad) = -236.$$

We next add 4 and 1 inside the parentheses on the left side. Since the 4 is multiplied by 9 and the 1 by -25, we add $9 \times 4 = 36$ and $-25 \times 1 = -25$ on the right side, yielding

$$9(x^2 + 4x + 4) - 25(y^2 + 2y + 1) = -236 + 36 - 25 = -225.$$

Dividing by -225, we obtain

$$\frac{(y + 1)^2}{9} - \frac{(x + 2)^2}{25} = 1.$$

Since this equation is of the form (6.32), the curve is a hyperbola with center at $(-2, -1)$, vertices at $(-2, 2)$ and $(-2, -4)$, and asymptotes [from (6.34)] $y + 1 = \pm(3/5)(x + 2)$. The foci are at $(-2, -1 \pm \sqrt{34})$. See Fig. 6.16.

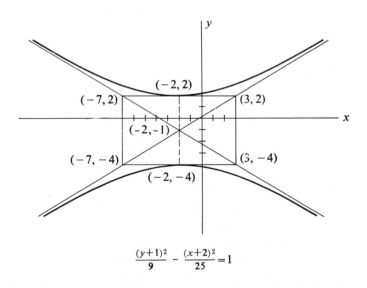

$$\frac{(y+1)^2}{9} - \frac{(x+2)^2}{25} = 1$$

Figure 6.16

Example 4.   Identify the graph of

$$x^2 - 4y^2 + 10x + 24y - 11 = 0.$$

Solution.   Completing the square, we obtain

$$\frac{(x + 5)^2}{4} - \frac{(y - 3)^2}{1} = 0.$$

Factoring the left member, we see that the graph consists of the two straight lines

$$\frac{x+5}{2} \pm \frac{y-3}{1} = 0.$$

PROBLEM LIST 43

1. Find the vertices and foci, and draw the graph of each hyperbola and its asymptotes.

(a) $\dfrac{x^2}{9} - \dfrac{y^2}{16} = 1.$ (e) $16x^2 - y^2 = 16.$

(b) $\dfrac{y^2}{25} - \dfrac{x^2}{1} = 1.$ (f) $y^2 - 2x^2 = 1.$

(c) $4x^2 - 9y^2 = 36.$ (g) $y^2 - x^2 = 10.$

(d) $16y^2 - 9x^2 = 144.$ (h) $7x^2 - 4y^2 = 28.$

2. Find an equation of the hyperbola with
   (a) vertices at $(\pm 3, 0)$, and foci at $(\pm 5, 0)$;
   (b) vertices at $(0, \pm 4)$, and foci at $(0, \pm 5)$;
   (c) foci at $(-3, 2)$ and $(7, 2)$, and transverse axis 8;
   (d) foci at $(3, 15)$ and $(3, -11)$, and conjugate axis 10;
   (e) vertices at $(-5, -1)$ and $(7, -1)$, and eccentricity 2;
   (f) vertices at $(\pm 4, 0)$, and passing through $(16, 15)$.

3. Graph each equation:
   (a) $x^2 - 4y^2 - 8y = 8.$
   (b) $4y^2 - x^2 + 6x + 16y + 3 = 0.$
   (c) $16y^2 - 9x^2 - 36x - 32y - 164 = 0.$
   (d) $x^2 - 25y^2 + 10x + 50y - 25 = 0.$
   (e) $x^2 - y^2 - 6x - 4y + 1 = 0.$
   (f) $9x^2 - 4y^2 + 108x - 16y + 308 = 0.$

4. Find an equation of the tangent to
   $$x^2 - 4y^2 + 2x - 4y = 0 \qquad \text{at } (2, 1).$$

5. Given $(x^2/a^2) - (y^2/b^2) = 1$, show that
   $$\frac{dy}{dx} = \frac{b^2 x}{a^2 y} \qquad \text{and} \qquad \frac{d^2 y}{dx^2} = \frac{-b^4}{a^2 y^3}.$$

6. A latus rectum of a hyperbola is a chord through a focus perpendicular to the transverse axis. Show that a latus rectum of $(x^2/a^2) - (y^2/b^2) = 1$ has length $2b^2/a$.

7. Find an equation of the hyperbola with foci at $(\pm 10, 0)$ and asymptotes $4y \pm 3x = 0.$

8. On the same set of axes draw the hyperbolas having vertices at $(\pm a, 0)$ and eccentricity (a) $2/\sqrt{3}$, (b) $\sqrt{2}$, (c) 2.

9. On the same set of axes draw the hyperbolas having foci at $(\pm c, 0)$ and eccentricity (a) 1.1, (b) 1.5, (c) 3.

10. The transverse axis of $(x^2/a^2) - (y^2/b^2) = 1$ is the conjugate axis of $(y^2/b^2) - (x^2/a^2)$ $= 1$. The hyperbolas have the same asymptotes and are called conjugate hyperbolas. Draw the hyperbolas $(x^2/49) - (y^2/576) = 1$ and $(y^2/576) - (x^2/49) = 1$ on the same set of axes.

11. Find the slope of $(x^2/a^2) - (y^2/b^2) = 1$ at the point in the first quadrant where x equals (a) $2a$, (b) $3a$, (c) $4a$, (d) $10a$.

12. By using the definition of a hyperbola, show that $(4\sqrt{3}, 6)$ is a point on $(y^2/9) - (x^2/16) = 1$.

13. Show that the product of the distances from the foci to any tangent to the hyperbola $b^2x^2 - a^2y^2 = a^2b^2$ is constant.

14. Show that the distance from a focus to an asymptote of a hyperbola is equal to half the length of the conjugate axis.

15. A hyperbola whose asymptotes are perpendicular is known as a rectangular (or equilateral) hyperbola. Show that the rectangular hyperbola having foci at $(c/\sqrt{2}, c/\sqrt{2})$ and $(-c/\sqrt{2}, -c/\sqrt{2})$ has an equation $xy = c^2/4$.

16. If, in $f(x, y) = 0$, x and y are replaced by

$$x = u \cos \theta - v \sin \theta \Big\}$$
$$y = u \sin \theta + v \cos \theta \Big\} \qquad \textbf{(6.36)}$$

the equation $f(u \cos \theta - v \sin \theta, u \sin \theta + v \cos \theta) = 0$ represents the curve $f(x, y) = 0$, referred to a set of axes each of which makes an angle θ with the x- and y-axes as shown in Fig. 6.17. Equations (6.36) are known as the equations of rotation. Transform the equation $x^2 - y^2 = a^2$ by rotating the axes through (a) $\pi/4$, (b) $-\pi/4$.

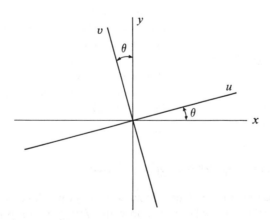

Figure 6.17

17. Boyle's law states that, under certain conditions, the product of the pressure and volume of a gas remains essentially constant. Depict graphically the manner in which the pressure varies with the volume.

18. In Fig. 6.18, line n is normal to the hyperbola at P. Prove that if angle α equals

angle β, then F is on PR extended. Points F' and F represent the foci. This establishes the reflection property of the hyperbola, utilized in hyperbolic mirrors and other devices.

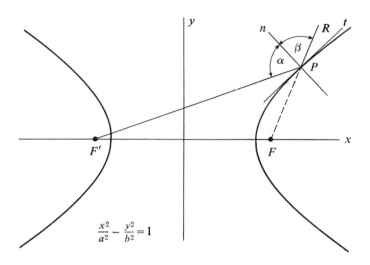

Figure 6.18

19. In Fig. 6.18, two signals are transmitted simultaneously from points F' and F. An observer at P receives the signal from F at a time t seconds before he receives the signal from F'. Knowing the rate r at which the signal travels, the observer at P can find $F'P - FP = rt$. He then knows he is somewhere on the hyperbola with foci at F' and F and having constant difference $2a = rt$. If he also receives signals transmitted simultaneously from F and F'', he knows he is on a second hyperbola with foci at F and F''. His position is at the obvious intersection of the two hyperbolas. This is the basis of the important system of navigation known as LORAN (for LOng RAnge Navigation).

A first-quadrant point P is on the hyperbola with foci at $(\pm 5, 0)$ and having constant difference $2a = 8$. Find graphically the approximate coordinates of P if it is also on the hyperbola with foci at $(5, 0)$ and $(5, -26)$ and having constant difference $2a = 24$.

6.6 *An Equation of a Conic*

Let d be a fixed line and let F be a fixed point not on d. The set of points P such that the ratio r of FP to DP (where D is on d and $DP \perp d$) is a positive constant is known as a conic or conic section. The point F is called the focus and the line d the directrix of the conic. Let $p > 0$ denote the distance from F to d.

To derive an equation of the conic we let the directrix coincide with the y-axis and place F at $(p, 0)$. In Fig. 6.19, $P(x, y)$ denotes an arbitrary point on the conic, and hence, since

$$FP = r \cdot DP,$$

x and y satisfy

$$\sqrt{(x - p)^2 + (y - 0)^2} = rx.$$

Simplifying, we find that x and y satisfy

$$x^2(1 - r^2) - 2px + y^2 + p^2 = 0. \tag{6.37}$$

Conversely, if x_0 and y_0 satisfy (6.37), we can show by reversing our steps that $P_0(x_0, y_0)$ is on the conic. Thus (6.37) is an equation of the conic.

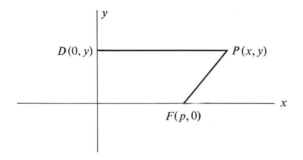

Figure 6.19

If $r = 1$, (6.37) reduces to $y^2 = 2p(x - p/2)$ and hence represents a parabola.

If $r < 1$, (6.37) represents an ellipse of eccentricity r, while if $r > 1$, (6.37) represents a hyperbola of eccentricity r. Thus an ellipse has two foci and two directrices, and the same is true for a hyperbola.

It can be shown that a curve represented by (6.37) can be obtained as the intersection of a plane and a right-circular cone of two nappes. This accounts for the term "conic section." Figure 6.20 exhibits the parabola, ellipse, and hyperbola as conic sections.

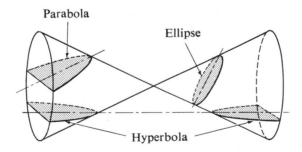

Figure 6.20

The ancient Greeks, particularly Appollonius (260?–200? B.C.) and Pappus (second half of the third century), discovered many interesting properties of the conic sections. Much of this pure mathematics later became applied mathematics when numerous applications of the conics were discovered in science and technology. For example, the fact that the orbits of many celestial bodies and satellites are conic sections gives the theory of conics an importance in modern space mechanics.

Example 1. Discuss (6.37) when $r = 1$ and $p = 4$.

Solution. The equation reduces to $y^2 = 8(x - 2)$ and hence represents a parabola with focus at $(4, 0)$, vertex at $(2, 0)$, axis the x-axis, and directrix the y-axis.

Example 2. Show that when $r < 1$, (6.37) represents an ellipse with eccentricity $e = r$.

Solution. Dividing by $1 - r^2$ and completing the square yields

$$x^2 - \frac{2px}{1 - r^2} + \frac{p^2}{(1 - r^2)^2} + \frac{y^2}{1 - r^2} = \frac{-p^2}{1 - r^2} + \frac{p^2}{(1 - r^2)^2}$$

or

$$\left(x - \frac{p}{1 - r^2}\right)^2 + \frac{y^2}{1 - r^2} = \frac{p^2 r^2}{(1 - r^2)^2}.$$

Dividing by $p^2 r^2/(1 - r^2)^2$, we obtain

$$\frac{\left(x - \dfrac{p}{1 - r^2}\right)^2}{\left(\dfrac{pr}{1 - r^2}\right)^2} + \frac{y^2}{\left(\dfrac{pr}{\sqrt{1 - r^2}}\right)^2} = 1.$$

We recognize this as an equation of an ellipse for which

$$a = \frac{pr}{1 - r^2}, \qquad b = \frac{pr}{\sqrt{1 - r^2}}, \qquad c = \sqrt{a^2 - b^2} = \frac{pr^2}{1 - r^2}.$$

The eccentricity $e = c/a = r$. The center of the ellipse is at

$$\left(\frac{p}{1 - r^2}, 0\right)$$

and hence the distance from the center to the y-axis, which is a directrix of the ellipse, is

$$\frac{p}{1 - r^2} = \frac{a}{r} = \frac{a}{e}.$$

By symmetry, the line $x = 2a/e$ is a second directrix of the ellipse.

PROBLEM LIST 44

1. Draw the graph of (6.37) for

   (a) $r = 1$ and $p = 6$;

   (b) $r = 1$ and $p = 10$;

   (c) $r = \frac{4}{5}$ and $p = \frac{9}{4}$;

   (d) $r = \frac{12}{13}$ and $p = \frac{25}{12}$;

   (e) $r = \frac{5}{4}$ and $p = \frac{9}{5}$;

   (f) $r = \sqrt{2}$ and $p = 4$.

2. Discuss the graph of (6.37) when $r \to 0$.

3. Show that when $r > 1$, (6.37) represents a hyperbola with eccentricity $e = r$.

4. Derive an equation of a conic with focus at $(0, p)$ whose directrix is the x-axis.

5. Prove that the tangents to a conic at the extremities of a focal chord meet on the directrix.

6.7   *Equations of Miscellaneous Graphs*

In this section the method of deriving an equation of a set of points will be the same as that used in the preceding sections.

Example 1.   Find an equation of the set of points the sum of whose distances from $(0, 0)$ and $(4, 4)$ is 8.

Solution.   Denoting an arbitrary point on the graph by $P(x, y)$, x and y satisfy

$$\sqrt{x^2 + y^2} + \sqrt{(x - 4)^2 + (y - 4)^2} = 8.$$

Transposing the first radical, squaring, and simplifying, we find that x and y satisfy

$$2\sqrt{x^2 + y^2} = 4 + x + y.$$

Squaring again and simplifying, x and y satisfy

$$3x^2 + 3y^2 - 2xy - 8x - 8y - 16 = 0. \tag{6.38}$$

Conversely, if x_0 and y_0 satisfy (6.38), it can be shown, by reversing the steps employed in obtaining (6.38), that $P_0(x_0, y_0)$ is a point on the graph. Hence, (6.38) is an equation of the set of points having the given property.

The graph of (6.38) could easily be drawn, since the set of points constitute an ellipse with foci at $(0, 0)$ and $(4, 4)$ and for which $c = 2\sqrt{2}$, $a = 4$, and $b = 2\sqrt{2}$. The presence of an xy term is due to the fact that the axes of the ellipse are not parallel to the x -and y-axes.

Example 2.   Find an equation of the set of points which are vertices of a right triangle whose hypotenuse is the line segment from $A(-a, 0)$ to $B(a, 0)$.

Solution.   Letting $P(x, y)$ denote an arbitrary point of the set, $AP \perp BP$ implies that x and y satisfy

$$\frac{y - 0}{x + a} = -\frac{x - a}{y - 0}. \tag{6.39}$$

Conversely, if x_0 and y_0 satisfy (6.39), $P_0(x_0, y_0)$ is a point of the set, since $AP_0 \perp BP_0$. Thus (6.39) is an equation of the given set of points. If $x \neq -a$ and $y \neq 0$, (6.39) is equivalent to the equation $y^2 = -(x^2 - a^2)$ or $x^2 + y^2 = a^2$. Hence the set of points consists of the points of the circle $x^2 + y^2 = a^2$ minus the points A and B.

PROBLEM LIST 45

1. Find an equation of the set of points
   - (a) equidistant from $(8, 4)$ and $(-6, -3)$;
   - (b) each of which is three times as far from $(8, 0)$ as from $(-8, 0)$;
   - (c) the sum of whose distances from $(0, 0)$ and $(6, 8)$ is 26;
   - (d) the difference of whose distances from $(4, 4)$ and $(-4, -4)$ is 8;
   - (e) which are midpoints of the ordinates of the circle $x^2 + y^2 = 16$ (consider an ordinate the line segment from $(x, 0)$ to the point (x, y) on the circle);
   - (f) which are midpoints of a line segment 12 units long having one end on the x-axis and the other end on the y-axis;
   - (g) equidistant from the origin and the line
   $$3x + 4y - 60 = 0;$$
   - (h) which are centers of circles tangent to both axes;
   - (i) which are centers of circles tangent to the x-axis and tangent to the circle $x^2 + (y - r)^2 = r^2$;
   - (j) which are centers of circles tangent to the x-axis and passing through $(0, a)$. Assume $a \neq 0$.

2. Find an equation of the set of points having the property that the slope of the line segment joining each point and the origin is equal to the square of the abscissa of that point. Draw the graph of the equation.

3. Find an equation of the set of points having the property that the slope of the line segment joining each point and the origin has absolute value twice the distance from the origin to that point. Draw the graph of the equation.

4. Find an equation of the set of points the product of whose distances from two fixed points is constant. Place the fixed points at $(-c, 0)$ and $(c, 0)$ and denote the constant product by a^2. Draw the graph of the equation when (a) $a = 5$ and $c = 3$, (b) $a = 3$ and $c = 5$. These curves are known as ovals of Cassini.

5. Let $a = c$ in the equation of Problem 4. Draw the graph of the resulting equation when $a = c = 1$. This curve is known as a lemniscate of Bernoulli.

6. Find an equation of the set of points which are intersections of the altitudes of triangles having two vertices at $(-1, 0)$ and $(1, 0)$ and the third vertex on the line $y = 1$. Draw the graph of the equation.

7. Circle A has center $(6, 0)$ and radius 6; circle B has center $(8, 0)$ and radius 8; circle C has center $(14, 0)$ and radius 2; and circle D is tangent internally to circle B and externally to circles A and C. Find the center and radius of circle D. *Hint:* Note that the center of circle D lies on a certain ellipse and also on a certain hyperbola.

REFERENCES

6.1 G. SALMON, *A Treatise on Conic Sections*, Longmans, Green, London, 1917.

6.2 B. SPAIN, *Analytical Conics*, Pergamon Press, New York, 1957.

Chapter

7

Applications of differential calculus

7.1 Rectilinear Motion

A body moving in a straight line is said to undergo a rectilinear motion. If the dimensions of the body are small in comparison to the distance the body moves during a discussion, the body is often referred to as a particle, and it is assumed that at a given instant the entire body is located at a point. We will call the straight line on which the particle moves the s-axis and we select an origin O where $s = 0$ on this axis. A positive s-axis is selected and the points of the s-axis are assumed to be in one-to-one correspondence with the real numbers.

An appropriate mathematical model describing this idealized physical situation consists of a function f, given by $s = f(t)$, with the property that, for each t in the domain D of f, $f(t)$ is the point where the particle is located at time t. The domain D of f is usually an interval $0 \leqslant t \leqslant t_0$, although D may contain negative values of t. The function f is called the position function of the particle and s denotes the displacement or signed distance of the particle from the origin.

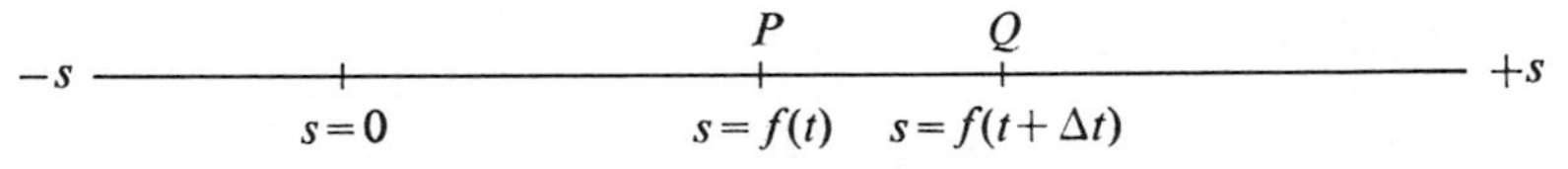

$$-s \ \text{———————} \overset{P}{+} \quad \overset{Q}{+} \text{————} \ +s$$
$$s=0 \qquad\qquad s=f(t) \quad s=f(t+\Delta t)$$

Figure 7.1

In Fig. 7.1 let us assume that P is the position of the particle at time t and Q its position at time $t + \Delta t$. In the time interval Δt, the change Δs in displacement is

$$\Delta s = f(t + \Delta t) - f(t).$$

207

The average velocity during the interval $\Delta t \neq 0$ is

$$v_{av} = \frac{\Delta s}{\Delta t} = \frac{f(t + \Delta t) - f(t)}{\Delta t}. \tag{7.1}$$

Formula (7.1) yields the average velocity over an interval Δt regardless of how small $|\Delta t|$ may be, except that Δt must be different from zero. If this average velocity approaches a limit as $\Delta t \to 0$, we define the velocity v at P, which is the instantaneous velocity at t, as the limit approached by the average velocity $\Delta s/\Delta t$ as $\Delta t \to 0$. In symbols,

$$v = \lim_{\Delta t \to 0} \frac{\Delta s}{\Delta t} = \lim_{\Delta t \to 0} \frac{f(t + \Delta t) - f(t)}{\Delta t} = \frac{ds}{dt} = f'(t). \tag{7.2}$$

Thus the first derivative of the position function f, defined by $s = f(t)$, yields the instantaneous velocity of the moving particle. Since the differentiability of f implies the continuity of f, $\lim_{\Delta t \to 0} f(t + \Delta t) = f(t)$.

After obtaining $v = ds/dt = f'(t)$, we regard t as a variable, and hence the velocity of the particle defines a function of t, namely, the function f'.

It follows from Theorems 4-VI and 4-VII that s increases with t (the particle moves in the positive s direction) during any time interval over which $f'(t) > 0$, and that s decreases with t (the particle moves in the negative s direction) during any time interval over which $f'(t) < 0$. If $f'(t_0) = 0$, the particle is said to be at rest at $t = t_0$. The absolute value of v, $|v| = |ds/dt| = |f'(t)|$, is called the speed of the particle.

Purely for convenience, we will assume that s is measured in feet, t in seconds, and that $t \geqslant 0$.

Example 1. For the rectilinear motion governed by $s = t^2$, find the average velocity for the period beginning at the end of 3 sec and lasting (a) 1 sec, (b) 0.5 sec, (c) 0.1 sec, (d) 0.01 sec, (e) 0.0001 sec, (f) 0.000001 sec. Also find the velocity at $t = 3$, the end of 3 sec.

Solution. From (7.1), the average velocity for the interval from $t = 3$ to $t = 3 + \Delta t$ is

$$v_{av} = \frac{\Delta s}{\Delta t} = \frac{(3 + \Delta t)^2 - (3)^2}{\Delta t} = 6 + \Delta t.$$

The required average velocities, in feet per second, are given by

Δt	1	0.5	0.1	0.01	0.0001	0.000001
v_{av}	7	6.5	6.1	6.01	6.0001	6.000001

From (7.2), the velocity at $t = 3$ is

$$v_3 = \frac{ds}{dt}\bigg|_{t=3} = 2t \bigg|_{t=3} = 6 \text{ fps.}$$

Note that since $v = 2t > 0$ for $t > 0$, the particle moves in the positive s direction for $t > 0$. At $t = 0$, the particle is at rest.

Example 2. Study the rectilinear motion described by

$$s = 2t^3 - 15t^2 + 24t + 3.$$

Solution.   Differentiating with respect to t yields

$$v = 6t^2 - 30t + 24 = 6(t-1)(t-4).$$

We note that $v = 0$ at $t = 1$ and $t = 4$, and that $v > 0$ except when $1 \leqslant t \leqslant 4$. Thus the particle moves in the positive direction except when $1 \leqslant t \leqslant 4$. The motion is illustrated graphically in Fig. 7.2.

Figure 7.2

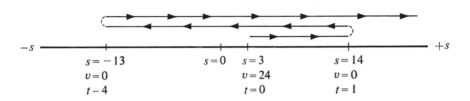

$$
\begin{array}{cccc}
s = -13 & s = 0 \quad s = 3 & s = 14 \\
v = 0 & v = 24 & v = 0 \\
t - 4 & t = 0 & t = 1
\end{array}
$$

Example 3.   Find the total distance traveled by the particle of Example 2 in the first 3 sec.

Solution.   At $t = 0$, $s = 3$, and at $t = 3$, $s = -6$. Thus the change in displacement during the first 3 sec is -9 ft. However, to find the total distance traveled, we must take into consideration the fact that the particle changed its direction at $t = 1$. In the first second the particle traveled from $s = 3$ to $s = 14$ or 11 ft, while from $t = 1$ to $t = 3$ the particle traveled from $s = 14$ to $s = -6$ or 20 ft. Hence the total distance traveled in the first 3 sec is $11 + 20 = 31$ ft.

The quotient

$$a_{\text{av}} = \frac{\Delta v}{\Delta t} = \frac{f'(t + \Delta t) - f'(t)}{\Delta t},$$

called the average acceleration, is the average rate of change of the velocity during the time interval Δt. The acceleration is defined as the limit, if it exists, of this quotient. In symbols,

$$a = \lim_{\Delta t \to 0} \frac{\Delta v}{\Delta t} = \lim_{\Delta t \to 0} \frac{f'(t + \Delta t) - f'(t)}{\Delta t}$$

$$= \frac{dv}{dt} = \frac{d^2 s}{dt^2} = f''(t). \tag{7.3}$$

Example 4.   A projectile, shot vertically upward along the y-axis, moves according to the law $y = -16t^2 + 160t$. Describe its motion.

Solution.   It is appropriate to use the symbol y in place of the symbol s.

From

$$v = \frac{dy}{dt} = -32t + 160 = -32(t - 5)$$

and

$$a = \frac{dv}{dt} = \frac{d^2y}{dt^2} = -32,$$

we find that $v = 0$ when $t = 5$, that $v > 0$ for $0 \leqslant t < 5$, that $v < 0$ for $t > 5$, and that v decreases constantly at the rate of 32 feet per second per second (written 32 ft/sec²). Since $y = 0$ when $t = 0$ and $y = 400$ when $t = 5$, the projectile rises 400 ft during the first 5 sec and then falls indefinitely, unless, of course, the law governing its motion no longer applies. Note that for $t > 5$, $v < 0$, and v is decreasing, since $a < 0$. Although v is decreasing, the speed $|v|$ is actually increasing when $t > 5$.

PROBLEM LIST 46

1. A particle moves in a straight line according to the law $s = t^2 + t$. Find the average velocity for the period beginning at the end of 2 sec and lasting (a) 1 sec, (b) 0.5 sec, (c) 0.01 sec, (d) 0.001 sec, (e) 0.00001 sec. Also find its velocity at $t = 2$.

2. A particle moves along the y-axis according to the law $y = t^3 - 6t^2 + 9t + 3$. Determine (a) when the particle is at rest, (b) when the particle moves in the negative y-direction, (c) the total distance traveled during the first 2 sec, (d) when the velocity is increasing, (e) the displacement, velocity, and acceleration when $t = 4$.

3. A projectile, shot vertically upward along the y-axis, moves according to the law $y = -16t^2 + 192t$. Determine its initial velocity, how long it rises, how high it goes, and its displacement, velocity, and acceleration at the end of 10 sec.

4. Given that $b \neq 0$, find the velocity and acceleration at time t of a particle moving in a straight line according to (a) $s - bt + c$, (b) $s = bt^2 + ct + d$.

5. A particle moves along the x-axis according to $x = t^2 - 4t + 7$. Find, for the first 3 sec, the change in displacement, the total distance traveled, the average velocity, and the average speed.

6. Describe the rectilinear motion governed by

   (a) $s = 5$;   (f) $s = 2t^3 - 15t^2 + 36t$;
   (b) $s = t + 2$;   (g) $s = 3t^2 - t^3 - 3$;
   (c) $s = t^2 - 1$;   (h) $s = t^4 - t^2 + 1$;
   (d) $s = t^3 + 9t^2$;   (i) $s = t + \sqrt{t}$.
   (e) $s = t^3 - 3t^2 + 3$;

7. Two particles start at the same time and move along the x-axis according to $x_1 = t^2 + 4t$ and $x_2 = t^2 - 8t + 36$. Find the velocities and accelerations of the two particles at the instant when their displacements are equal.

8. A baseball is dropped from the top of the Washington monument, 555 ft high. If it falls straight downward according to the law $s = 16t^2$, find its velocity when it hits the ground.

9. The height of a ball, thrown vertically upward from a point 100 ft above the ground, is given by $y = -16t^2 + 64t + 100$. Find the distance the ball rises, its velocity when it passes its initial position on its return flight, and its velocity when it strikes the ground.

10. An object moves in a straight line according to the law $s = f(t)$, where f is a differentiable function of t. What does Theorem 4-IV, the mean-value theorem, state concerning the average velocity during the interval from $t = t_1$ to $t = t_2$? Apply the mean-value theorem to the motion $s = t^2 + 1$ for the interval from $t = 2$ to $t = 5$.

11. The time rate of change of acceleration, $da/dt = d^3s/dt^3$, is termed "jerk." In designing certain vehicles, an effort is made to limit the magnitude of the jerk in order to obtain maximum riding comfort. Find the jerk of an elevator that moves according to the law $s = t^3 + 4t^2$.

7.2   Applied Maxima and Minima

In Chapter 5 we developed methods for determining the absolute maximum and the absolute minimum of a function. We now apply these methods to a number of interesting and practical situations. Our first step is to obtain an equation $y = f(x)$ or $g(x, y) = 0$ relating y, the quantity to be maximized or minimized, and a convenient variable x in the problem. The method is best illustrated by examples.

Example 1.   Find two *positive* numbers whose sum is 9, if the product of one number and the square of the other is a maximum.

>   **Solution.**   Let x denote one number and P the product to be maximized. Then $9 - x$ denotes the other number and
>
> $$P = x^2(9 - x) = 9x^2 - x^3,$$
>
>   where $x > 0$ and $9 - x > 0$.

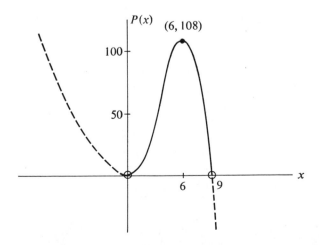

Figure 7.3

Thus we seek the absolute maximum of the function P defined by $P(x) = 9x^2 - x^3$ having domain $0 < x < 9$.

From $P'(x) = 18x - 3x^2 = 3x(6 - x)$, we find that $x = 6$ is the only critical value of $P(x)$. Since $P''(x) = 18 - 6x$, $P''(6) = -18 < 0$, and we conclude that $P(6)$ is the absolute maximum of P.

The required numbers are $x = 6$ and $9 - x = 3$, and the maximum product is $P(6) = (6)^2(9 - 6) = 108$.

Note that 108 is not the maximum ordinate of the cubic curve $P(x) = 9x^2 - x^3$. Actually, the curve has no maximum ordinate, but we are interested only in the ordinates of points (x, y) for which $0 < x < 9$. See Fig. 7.3.

Example 2.   A rectangular field of area 200 sq ft is to be fenced off along the bank of a river. If no fence is required along the river, what dimensions of the field will require the least number of feet of fence?

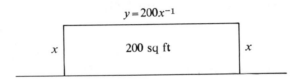

$$y = 200x^{-1}$$

| x | 200 sq ft | x |

Figure 7.4

Solution.   In Fig. 7.4 let x and y denote the required dimensions. Then L, the required length of fencing, is given by $L = 2x + y$. But $xy = 200$ and hence $L(x) = 2x + 200x^{-1}$, where $x > 0$ and $y = 200x^{-1} > 0$.

From $L'(x) = 2 - 200x^{-2} = 0$, we obtain $x^2 = 100$, and hence $x = 10$ ft is the only critical value of x. From $y = 200x^{-1}$, we find that the dimension $y = 20$ ft.

It is obvious that $L(10) = 40$ ft is the minimum number of feet of fencing required, since L varies continuously with x, is very large when x is close to zero, and is also very large when x is large. It is easy to verify that $L(10)$ is a minimum by showing that $L''(10) > 0$.

Example 3.   The strength of a beam is a measure of its resistance to being bent

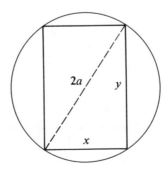

Figure 7.5

by applied forces. If the strength of a rectangular beam is proportional to the breadth and the square of the depth, find the shape of the strongest rectangular beam that can be cut from a circular cylindrical log of radius a.

Solution.   In Fig. 7.5, x denotes the breadth and y the depth of the beam. Denoting the strength of the beam by S and the constant of proportionality by k, we have

$$S = kxy^2$$

or, since $y^2 = 4a^2 - x^2$,

$$S(x) = kx(4a^2 - x^2) = 4ka^2x - kx^3,$$

where

$$0 < x < 2a \qquad \text{and} \qquad 0 < y < 2a.$$

From $S'(x) = 4ka^2 - 3kx^2 = 0$, we obtain

$$x = \frac{2a}{\sqrt{3}}.$$

The required depth y is given by

$$y = \sqrt{4a^2 - \frac{4a^2}{3}} = \frac{2a\sqrt{2}}{\sqrt{3}} = \sqrt{2}\,x.$$

It is clear from the nature of the problem that these dimensions will make the strength of the beam a maximum.

Example 4.   A right-circular cylindrical can is to have a volume of $90\,\pi$ cubic inches. Find the height h and the base radius r such that the cost of the can will be a minimum, given that the top and bottom cost 5 cents per square inch and the lateral surface 3 cents per square inch.

Solution.   Since the top and bottom have combined area $2\pi r^2$ and the lateral surface has area $2\pi rh$, the cost C of the can is given by

$$C = 5(2\pi r^2) + 3(2\pi rh). \tag{7.4}$$

From $\pi r^2 h = 90\pi$ we obtain $h = 90r^{-2}$. Substituting this expression for h into (7.4) yields

$$C = C(r) = 10\pi r^2 + 540\pi r^{-1}.$$

Differentiating,

$$C'(r) = 20\pi r - 540\pi r^{-2} = 0 \qquad \text{for } r = 3 \text{ in.}$$

The corresponding value of h is $90(3)^{-2} = 10$ in. These dimensions clearly yield the minimum possible cost, since there does not exist a maximum cost.

Example 5.   Find the point on the circle $x^2 + y^2 = 4$ which is nearest to $(3, -4)$.

Solution.   To minimize s we need only minimize s^2, and hence we obtain, from Fig. 7.6,

$$s^2 = (x - 3)^2 + (y + 4)^2. \tag{7.5}$$

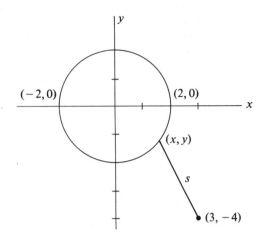

Figure 7.6

Instead of expressing s^2, the quantity to be minimized, in terms of x or y alone, let us differentiate (7.5) with respect to x, where y denotes either of the two functions of x defined implicitly by $x^2 + y^2 = 4$. This method is often effective. Thus,

$$\frac{d}{dx}(s^2) = 2(x - 3) + 2(y + 4)\frac{dy}{dx} = 0$$

only when

$$\frac{dy}{dx} = \frac{3 - x}{y + 4}.$$

But, from $x^2 + y^2 = 4$ we have $2x + 2y\, dy/dx = 0$, or $dy/dx = -x/y$. Solving

$$x^2 + y^2 = 4 \qquad \text{and} \qquad \frac{3 - x}{y + 4} = \frac{-x}{y}$$

simultaneously, we obtain $x = \pm(6/5)$ and $y = \mp(8/5)$. It is easy to see from Fig. 7.6 that $(6/5, -8/5)$ must be the point closest to $(3, -4)$. The point $(-6/5, 8/5)$ is the point farthest from $(3, -4)$.

Note: Since $d/dx\,(s^2)$ is not defined when $y = 0$, the distances from $(3, -4)$ to $(2, 0)$ and $(-2, 0)$ must be investigated separately. Neither yields a maximum or a minimum.

PROBLEM LIST 47

1. Find two numbers whose sum is 8, if the product of one number and the cube of the other is a maximum.

2. Find the number that exceeds its square by the maximum amount.

3. A rectangular field is to be enclosed and divided into two smaller rectangles, as shown in Fig. 7.7. If the total area of the field is to be 600 sq ft, find the dimensions that will require the least number of feet of fence.

Figure 7.7

4. A box can be made from a piece of cardboard by cutting equal squares from the four corners and turning up the four sides. Find the maximum possible volume of the box if the cardboard is **(a)** 12 in. × 12 in., **(b)** 16 in. × 6 in.

5. Find the highest and lowest points on the curve $y = (x/9) + (1/x)$ for the interval **(a)** $1 \leqslant x \leqslant 4$, **(b)** $4 \leqslant x \leqslant 6$.

6. Find the relationship between the height and base radius of a right-circular cylinder of prescribed volume if the total surface is a minimum.

7. A Norman window consists of a rectangle surmounted by a semicircle. Find the dimensions of the rectangle if the window admits maximum light for a fixed perimeter.

8. The stiffness of a beam is a measure of its resistance to being deflected by applied forces. If the stiffness of a rectangular beam is proportional to the breadth and the cube of the depth, find the shape of the stiffest rectangular beam that can be cut from a circular cylindrical log of radius a.

9. Find the point on the line $3x - 4y = 12$ which is closest to $(1, 3)$.

10. Find the first-quadrant point on the curve $y = x + (1/x)$ which is closest to the origin.

11. A poster is to contain 216 sq in. of printed material. Find the most economical dimensions for the poster if it is to have a 2-in. margin at the bottom and 1-in. margins on the other three sides.

12. A rectangular lot adjacent to a highway is to be enclosed by a fence. If the fencing costs $3.00 per foot along the highway and $2.00 per foot on the other three sides, find the dimensions of the lot of maximum area that can be fenced off for $1000.

13. Find the rectangle of maximum area with upper vertices on the x-axis and lower vertices on the parabola $y = x^2 - 27$.

14. A 12-in. line segment is divided into two segments, each having length greater than zero. One segment is employed as the circumference of a circle and the other as the perimeter of a square. What division yields the minimum total area for the circle and the square? Show that no division will yield a maximum total area.

15. Assume that the x-axis lies along a lake shore, that town A is located at $(0, 6)$ and town B at $(21, 8)$. Water is to be pumped to both towns from a point P on the x-axis. Where should P be located to make the total distance $AP + PB$ a minimum?

16. Towns B, C, and A are located 6 miles west, 6 miles east, and 10 miles south, respectively, of a point D. A road is to run north from A to a point P, and from P a branch is to run to B and another branch to C. Find the length of PC if the total length of road $l = AP + PC + PB$ is a minimum.

17. A motor launch is to run from a ship anchored at $A(0, 6)$ to a bus station located at a point P on the x-axis. A bus is to run from P to $C(5, 0)$. If the launch averages 10 mph and the bus 40 mph, where should P be located to minimize the time for a trip from A to C?

18. Ship A is 40 miles west of ship B. If ship A sails east at 20 mph and ship B, starting at the same time, sails north at 10 mph, find the time when the ships will be closest together.

19. A club maintains a membership of from 200 to 350 members. When the membership is 200, each member pays \$300 yearly dues, but when the membership exceeds 200, each member's dues is decreased by \$1.00 for each member over 200. What membership yields a maximum yearly income to the club from members' dues?

20. Find the altitude of the right-circular cone of maximum volume which can be inscribed in a sphere of radius a.

21. Find the altitude of the right-circular cone of maximum volume which can be circumscribed about a sphere of radius a.

22. Find correct to the nearest tenth the abscissa of the point on the parabola $y = x^2$ which is nearest to $(4, -1)$.

23. The optical principle of least time states that a light ray traveling between two points describes the path requiring the least time. Let a light ray travel from $A(0, a)$ to $B(k, b)$, and assume that its velocity is v_1 in the medium of quadrant I but v_2 in the medium of quadrant IV. Show that the ray will travel from A to P to B in Fig. 7.8, where P is the point on the x-axis such that

$$\frac{\sin \alpha}{\sin \beta} = \frac{v_1}{v_2}. \tag{7.6}$$

Equation (7.6) is Snell's law of refraction.

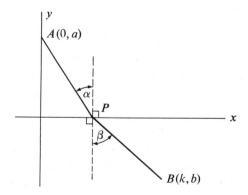

Figure 7.8

24. Find the length of the longest beam that can be moved horizontally from a hall of width a into a hall of width b if the two halls are perpendicular.

25. A curve having equation $y = k/x$ is to be drawn so that the sum of the squares of the vertical deviations of the points $(1, 3)$, $(2, 2)$, and $(3, 1)$ from the curve shall be

a minimum. Find k. [The vertical deviation of the point (x_1, y_1) from the curve $y = f(x)$ is $f(x_1) - y_1$.]

26. A straight fence is 100 ft long. A rectangular enclosure of perimeter 300 ft is to be formed in such a way that the 100 ft of straight fence is included in one of the dimensions of the rectangle. Find the dimensions of the rectangle for which its area will be maximum.

27. Find the point on the curve $y = 4\sqrt{x}$ which is closest to (a) $(12, 0)$, (b) $(8, 0)$, (c) $(5, 0)$.

28. Two chords of the ellipse $(x^2/a^2) + (y^2/b^2) = 1$ are perpendicular and pass through the center of the ellipse. Show that the maximum product of their lengths is $8a^2b^2/(a^2 + b^2)$ and that this maximum is attained when the chords lie along the lines $y = \pm x$.

7.3   Related Rates

Let us assume that a set of variables are related by an equation

$$f(x, y, z, \ldots) = 0, \tag{7.7}$$

and that each of the variables in the equation is a function of the time t. If equation (7.7) is differentiated with respect to t by the chain rule, the result will be an equation of the form

$$g\left(x, \frac{dx}{dt}, y, \frac{dy}{dt}, z, \frac{dz}{dt}, \ldots\right) = 0. \tag{7.8}$$

Equation (7.8) relates not only the variables in the problem but also their time derivatives. Consequently, problems of this type are called related rate problems.

Suppose, for example, that the variables x, y, and z satisfy the equation

$$4x^2 + y^2 - z + 5 = 0,$$

and that x, y, and z are functions of the time t. As t changes, each term on the left side changes, but the entire left member remains zero and hence the time derivative of the left member is zero for all values of t. Differentiating the left member as a sum and applying the chain rule to each term, we have

$$\frac{d}{dt}[4x^2 + y^2 - z + 5] = \frac{d}{dt}(4x^2) + \frac{d}{dt}(y^2) - \frac{d}{dt}(z) + \frac{d}{dt}(5)$$

$$= 8x\frac{dx}{dt} + 2y\frac{dy}{dt} - \frac{dz}{dt} + 0 = 0.$$

The last equation is of the form (7.8) and can be used to determine one of the time derivatives at an instant when the other time derivatives and the values of x, y, and z are known.

It should be emphasized that equation (7.7) must hold at *arbitrary* time t. No specific values of the variables may be substituted before differentiating with respect to time. The rate at which a quantity is changing cannot be determined from the value of the quantity at a specific instant.

Example 1.   Each edge of a cube is increasing at the constant rate of 2 in. per sec. How fast is the volume increasing when x, the length of an edge, is 5 in. long?

   Solution.   At arbitrary time t, the volume V is given by

$$V = x^3.$$

Differentiating with respect to time, we obtain

$$\frac{dV}{dt} = 3x^2 \frac{dx}{dt}.$$

Hence $dV/dt \big|_{x=5} = 3(5)^2(2) = 150$ cu in./sec.

Example 2.   A right triangle has hypotenuse 5 ft and variable legs x and y. If x increases at the constant rate of 6 fpm, how fast is y changing when x is 4 ft long?

   Solution.   At arbitrary time t,

$$x^2 + y^2 = 25 \tag{7.9}$$

and hence

$$2x \frac{dx}{dt} + 2y \frac{dy}{dt} = 0,$$

or

$$\frac{dy}{dt} = \frac{-x(dx/dt)}{y} \qquad (y \neq 0).$$

   Since dy/dt depends not only upon x and dx/dt but also upon y, we must determine the value of y when $x = 4$. This is easily found from (7.9) to be 3. Therefore,

$$\frac{dy}{dt} \bigg|_{x=4} = \frac{-4(6)}{3} = -8 \text{ fpm.}$$

   Since $dy/dt < 0$, y is decreasing as t increases at the instant when $x = 4$. This follows from Theorem 4-VII of Chapter 4.

Example 3.   Water is poured into the right-circular conical container shown in Fig. 7.9 at the rate of 12 cfm. How fast is the water level rising when the water is 7 ft deep?

   Solution.   At arbitrary time t, the volume of water in the container is given by

$$V = \frac{\pi}{3} r^2 h.$$

From the similar triangles in Fig. 7.9,

$$\frac{h}{r} = \frac{12}{3} \qquad \text{or} \qquad r = \frac{h}{4}.$$

Hence $$V = \frac{\pi}{3} \left(\frac{h}{4} \right)^2 h = \frac{\pi h^3}{48}.$$

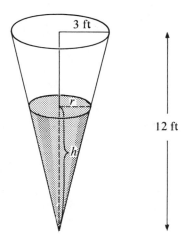

Figure 7.9

Differentiating with respect to time, we obtain

$$\frac{dV}{dt} = \frac{\pi h^2}{16}\frac{dh}{dt}$$

or

$$\frac{dh}{dt} = \frac{16(dV/dt)}{\pi h^2} = \frac{192}{\pi h^2}. \qquad (7.10)$$

When $h = 7$, the rate at which the water level is rising is given by

$$\left.\frac{dh}{dt}\right|_{h=7} = \frac{192}{49\pi} \cong 1.2 \text{ fpm.}$$

Note that equation (7.10) gives the rate at which the water level is rising at arbitrary time t. The rate is very large when h is small, but decreases as h increases. This phenomenon is readily observed when water is poured at a constant rate into a conical paper cup.

Example 4.   At a certain instant one side x of a triangle is 5 ft long and is increasing at the rate of 2 fps. At the same instant, side y is 3 ft long and is decreasing at the rate of 15 fps. If the angle between x and y is always $\pi/3$ radians, determine whether the third side s is increasing or decreasing at the instant in question. See Fig. 7.10.

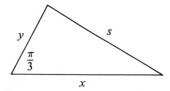

Figure 7.10

Solution.   Applying the law of cosines, we obtain

$$s^2 = x^2 + y^2 - 2xy\left(\frac{1}{2}\right)$$

or

$$s^2 = x^2 + y^2 - xy. \tag{7.11}$$

Differentiating with respect to time yields

$$2s\frac{ds}{dt} = 2x\frac{dx}{dt} + 2y\frac{dy}{dt} - x\frac{dy}{dt} - y\frac{dx}{dt}.$$

At the instant in question,

$$\frac{ds}{dt}\Big|_{x=5} = \frac{2(5)(2) + 2(3)(-15) - (5)(-15) - 3(2)}{2s}$$

$$= \frac{-1}{2s}. \tag{7.12}$$

Since $ds/dt\,|_{x=5}$ is negative,, side s is decreasing with time at the instant in question. The exact value of $ds/dt\,|_{x=5}$ can be found from (7.12) by first finding $s\,|_{x=5}$ from (7.11).

PROBLEM LIST 48

1. Each side x of a square is increasing at the constant rate of 3 ips. How fast is the area increasing when $x = 5$?

2. The area of a circle decreases at the constant rate of 9 sq in./sec. How fast is the radius r decreasing when r is 4 in.?

3. How fast does the diagonal of a cube increase if each side of the cube increases at the constant rate of 5 ipm?

4. A particle moves along the parabola $y = x^2$ in such a manner that its abscissa increases at the constant rate of 7 units/sec. How fast is its ordinate increasing when the particle is at $(3, 9)$?

5. Gas is pumped into a spherical balloon at the constant rate of 50 cu ft/sec. How fast is the surface of the balloon increasing when the radius is 12 ft?

6. At a certain instant $t = t_0$, the base radius r of a right-circular cylinder is 3 in. and the height h is 5 in. If, at $t = t_0$, r is increasing at 2 ips, and h is decreasing at 2 ips, find $dV/dt|_{t=t_0}$, where V denotes the volume of the cylinder.

7. A 20-ft ladder leans against a vertical wall. If the base of the ladder is pulled away from the wall at the constant rate of 4 fps, how fast is the top of the ladder sliding down the wall when the base of the ladder is 12 ft from the wall?

8. The area of a rectangle is constant. If the base b increases at the constant rate of 5 meters/sec, how fast is the height h decreasing when b is 60 meters and h is 90 meters?

9. A right-circular cone for which $h = r$ is used as a reservoir. If water is drawn off at

the constant rate of 8 cfm, how fast is the water level decreasing when the water is 15 ft deep?

10. A balloon is released 100 ft east of an observer. If the balloon rises vertically at the constant rate of 15 fps, how fast is the distance from the observer to the balloon changing 10 sec after the balloon is released?

11. A ship leaves point A and sails north at the constant rate of 20 knots. Two hours later a second ship leaves A and sails east at the constant rate of 30 knots. How fast are the ships separating when the first ship is 60 nautical miles from A?

12. At a certain instant an angle θ is equal to $\pi/6$ and its sine is increasing at the rate of $1/10$ per second. How fast is its cosine changing at the same instant?

13. Particle A starts from $(-10, 0)$ and moves along the x-axis while particle B starts from $(0, 15)$ at the same time and moves along the y-axis. If the abscissa of A increases at the constant rate of 5 units/sec and the ordinate of B decreases at the constant rate of 2 units/sec, where will the two particles be located when they are closest together?

14. Boyle's law states that under certain conditions the product of the pressure p of a gas and the volume v of the gas is constant. At a certain instant the pressure is 8 psi, the volume is 200 cu in., and the volume is decreasing at the rate of 3 cu in./min. How fast is the pressure changing at the same instant? Solve the same problem if $pv = 1600$ is replaced by $pv^{1.4} = 8(200)^{1.4}$.

15. A man 6 ft tall walks away from a light that is 15 ft above the ground. If he walks at the constant rate of 4 mph, find the rate at which his shadow is lengthening.

16. A pulley is located at $(0, 25)$ and a crate at $(0, 0)$. A 50-ft rope is passed over the pulley and one end of the rope is fastened to the crate while the other end is moved along the x-axis at the constant rate of 4 units/sec. How fast is the crate rising when it is at $(0, 10)$? Neglect the dimensions of the pulley.

17. The radius of a sphere changes with time. Compare the time rates of change of the volume and the surface.

18. At a certain instant one side x of a triangle is 9 ft long and is decreasing at the rate of 3 fps. At the same instant side y is 56 ft long and is decreasing at the rate of 5 fps. If the angle between x and y is always $2\pi/3$ radians, find the rate at which the third side is changing at the instant in question.

19. Water flows out of a hemispherical tank at the constant rate of 15 cfm. If the radius of the tank is 8 ft, how fast is the water level falling when the water is 4 ft deep? [Use the formula $V = (\pi h^2/3)(3r - h)$ for the volume of a spherical segment.]

20. Water is poured into the container shown in Fig. 7.9. Determine the variable rate at which the water must flow in so that the water level will rise at the constant rate of 2 fpm.

21. The intensity I of illumination at a point P is inversely proportional to the square of the distance r from P to the source of light. If $I = 500$ units when r is 1 ft, find dI/dt when $r = 8$ ft, given that P is approaching the source of light at the constant rate of 64 fps.

7.4   Approximations

In Sec. 3.10 the differential of a function f given by $y = f(x)$ was defined as
$$dy = f'(x)\, dx.$$
It was shown that if $dx = \Delta x$ is small, then dy furnishes an approximation to
$$\Delta y = f(x + \Delta x) - f(x).$$
Consequently, if we wish to find $f(x + \Delta x) = f(x) + \Delta y$, we can approximate its value by $f(x) + dy = f(x) + f'(x)\, dx$. In Fig. 3.7 this involves using the height BT of the tangent to the curve at P as an approximation to the actual height BQ of the curve. It is often simpler to compute dy than Δy.

To summarize, if the height of $y = f(x)$ at $x + dx$ is to be approximated by $f(x) + f'(x)\, dx$, x and dx must be chosen so that dx is small and x is a value for which $f(x)$ and $f'(x)$ are easily found. It is difficult to specify how small dx must be, since this would in general depend upon the function f and the desired accuracy of the approximation.

Example 1.   The side of a square is 3.02 in. long. Approximate the area of the square.

Solution.   The area of a square of side x is exactly x^2. We want the approximate value of x^2 when $x = 3.02$. We choose $x = 3$ and $dx = 0.02$, since 3 is close to 3.02 and x^2 and its derivative $2x$ are easily evaluated at $x = 3$.
From $A = x^2$ we obtain $dA = 2x\, dx$ and hence $A + dA = x^2 + 2x\, dx$. Thus
$$A + dA \big|_{\substack{x=3 \\ dx=0.02}} = (3)^2 + 2(3)(0.02) = 9.12 \text{ sq in.}$$

The exact area is $(3.02)^2 = 9.124$ sq in. The difference between the exact area,
$$(x + dx)^2 = x^2 + 2x\, dx + (dx)^2,$$
and the approximation $x^2 + 2x\, dx$ is $(dx)^2$. This difference is small if dx is small. For a geometric interpretation, see Fig. 7.11.

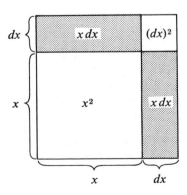

Figure 7.11

Example 2.   Find the approximate value of $\sqrt{622}$.

Solution.   We want the height of $y = \sqrt{x}$ at $x = 622$, so we choose $x = 625$, the perfect square nearest to 622, and $dx = -3$. From $y = \sqrt{x}$ we obtain $dy = dx/2\sqrt{x}$ and hence

$$y + dy = \sqrt{x} + \frac{dx}{2\sqrt{x}}.$$

Thus

$$y + dy\big|_{\substack{x=625 \\ dx=-3}} = 25 + \frac{-3}{2(25)} = 24.94.$$

Example 3.   Find the approximate volume of metal in a spherical shell of inner radius 4 in. and thickness 0.1 in.

Solution.   From $V = (4/3)\pi r^3$ we obtain

$$dV = 4\pi r^2 \, dr$$

and $\Delta V \cong dV\big|_{\substack{r=4 \\ dr=0.1}} = 4\pi(16)(0.1) = 6.4\pi$ cu in.

Example 4.   A company wishes to manufacture a cube of side x. If x can be measured to within 2% of its specified value, what is the maximum possible percentage error in the volume of the cube?

Solution.   From $V = x^3$ we obtain

$$dV = 3x^2 \, dx.$$

Dividing both sides by $V = x^3$ yields

$$\frac{dV}{V} = \frac{3x^2 \, dx}{x^3} = 3\left(\frac{dx}{x}\right). \tag{7.13}$$

If we let x be the specified value of the side and $|dx|$ the maximum numerical error in measuring x, then $|dx/x|$ is called the maximum relative error in x. This is 0.02, since x can be in error by at most 2%. The maximum relative error in V is $|\Delta V/V|$, which we approximate by $|dV/V|$. It is clear from (7.13) that $|dV/V|$ will be a maximum when $|dx|$ is a maximum and that the maximum relative error in V is $3(0.02) = 0.06$. Thus the volume of the cube can differ from its specified value by (approximately) at most 6%.

If the specifications had demanded that the volume be accurate to within 3%, the side x would have to be accurate to within (approximately) 1/3 of 3%, or 1%.

It is interesting to note that the result is independent of the value of x stated in the specifications.

PROBLEM LIST 49

1.   Find the approximate value of $x^2 - 2x$ when $x = 3.001$.

2.   Find the approximate height of the curve $y = x^3 - 2x^2 + 7$ at $x = 2.98$.

3.   Find the approximate area of a square of side $5\frac{1}{8}$ in.

4. Let r denote the radius of a circle. If r is increased by dr, show that the area of the circle is increased approximately by dr times the original circumference.

5. Two concentric spheres have radii 6 in. and 6.12 in. Find the approximate difference in their volumes.

6. A right-circular cylinder has height 6 in. and base radius 4 in. If the base radius is decreased by 1/16 in., find the approximate volume of the new cylinder.

7. A wooden cube has volume 8 cu ft. Approximately what size slab must be cut from each of three adjacent faces in order that the volume of the resulting cube will be 7 cu ft?

8. Show that the volume of a thin cylindrical shell is approximately equal to the inner lateral surface times the thickness.

9. Show that the approximate height of $y = ax + b$, obtained by using differentials, is equal to the exact height.

10. Given $x \neq 0$, find the approximate change in the reciprocal of x due to a small change dx in x.

11. Find the approximate value of each of the following:

    (a) $\sqrt{82}$.   (d) $\dfrac{1}{\sqrt{226}}$.   (g) $\sqrt[3]{730}$.

    (b) $\sqrt{123}$.   (e) $\sqrt[5]{31}$.   (h) $\sqrt[4]{255}$.

    (c) $\dfrac{1}{100.02}$.   (f) $(65)^{2/3}$.   (i) $\sqrt{3.6}$.

12. A simple pendulum of length l feet takes $t = \pi\sqrt{l/32}$ seconds to complete one oscillation. If $l = 1$ ft, find the approximate change in l necessary to cause a change of 0.05 sec in t.

13. If the percentage error in measuring the radius of a sphere does not exceed 3%, find the approximate maximum percentage error in (a) the volume, (b) the surface.

14. Find the approximate y-intercepts of the curve $y^2 = x^3 + 3x^2 + 122$.

15. If the volume of a cube must be accurate to within 3%, what is the approximate maximum allowable percentage error in measuring an edge of the cube?

16. Approximately how much wood is required to make a cubical box of volume 27 cu ft, using 1/2-in. boards?

17. A rope extends around the earth at the equator, assumed to be a circle. By how many feet must the rope be lengthened in order that it remain circular, with each of its points in the plane of the equator and 1 ft above the equator?

18. The volume v of a gas is 30 cu in. and the pressure p is 20 psi. If Boyle's law (pv = constant) is satisfied, find the approximate change in v when p decreases from 20 psi to 19 psi.

19. Find the approximate slope of the curve $y = x^3 + 3x^2 - 4x - 6$ at the point where $x = -1.98$.

20. Let E denote the maximum relative error in x. Find the approximate maximum relative error in the nth power of x.

7.5   *The Newton-Raphson Method*

The method to be described is useful for finding close approximations to the real roots of an equation of the form $f(x) = 0$. Let us assume that we have found two numbers a and b such that a is close to b and $f(a)$ and $f(b)$ have opposite signs. In most simple cases, $f(x) = 0$ will have just one root r between a and b. From a rough graph (see Fig. 7.12) we make a first estimate x_1 of r.

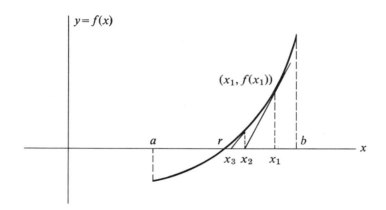

Figure 7.12

The curve $y = f(x)$ passes through $(x_1, f(x_1))$ and intersects the x-axis in $(r, 0)$. The method consists of replacing the curve by its tangent at $(x_1, f(x_1))$ and finding the point $(x_2, 0)$ where the tangent intersects the x-axis. In general, x_2 will be a better approximation than x_1 to the root r. The process is then repeated, letting x_2 play the role x_1 played originally. This iterative process yields a sequence $\{x_n\}$, which in most cases converges to r with remarkable rapidity. Such iterative processes are easily handled by computing machines, since a computer can carry out a large number of repetitions in a short period of time.

To find the iterative formula that enables us to find x_{n+1} from x_n, we write an equation of the tangent at $(x_1, f(x_1))$:

$$y - f(x_1) = f'(x_1)(x - x_1).$$

Setting $y = 0$ and solving for x, we obtain

$$x = x_2 = x_1 - \frac{f(x_1)}{f'(x_1)}.$$

By repeating the process, with x_2 as the approximation to r, we obtain

$$x_3 = x_2 - \frac{f(x_2)}{f'(x_2)}.$$

Thus we see that

$$x_{n+1} = x_n - \frac{f(x_n)}{f'(x_n)}. \qquad (7.14)$$

By examining the expression $-[f(x_n)/f'(x_n)]$, called the correction, which must be added to x_n to find x_{n+1}, it is easy to see that the method is most effective when $f(x_n)$ is small and $f'(x_n)$ is large. Figure 7.13 illustrates a situation in which $\{x_n\}$ may not even converge. The difficulty is that $f'(x_1)$ is too small, and hence the curve and the tangent are not close together when they cross the x-axis. For a more complete discussion of the method, sometimes referred to simply as Newton's method, see Ref. 7.1.

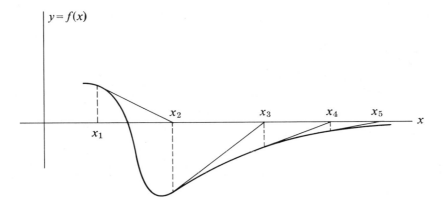

Figure 7.13

As a general rule of procedure the iteration is continued until x_n and x_{n+1} agree to the required number of decimal places.

Example 1. Find $\sqrt{2}$ to three decimal places.

Solution. Since $\sqrt{2}$ satisfies $x^2 - 2 = 0$, we want the positive root of this equation. Taking $x_1 = 1.5$ and using $f'(x) = 2x$, we obtain

$$x_2 = 1.5 - \frac{0.25}{3} \cong 1.42.$$

Using $x_2 = 1.42$, we obtain

$$x_3 = 1.42 - \frac{0.0164}{2.84} \cong 1.414.$$

Using $x_3 = 1.414$, we obtain

$$x_4 = 1.414 - \frac{-0.000604}{2.828} = 1.414$$

to three decimal places. Since x_3 and x_4 agree to the required number of decimal places, we accept the answer $\sqrt{2} \cong 1.414$. Reference to a table of square roots verifies that this answer is correct to three decimal places.

Example 2. Find the real roots of $x^3 - 3x^2 + 4x - 5 = 0$ correct to two decimal places.

Solution. A rough graph of $y = f(x) = x^3 - 3x^2 + 4x - 5$ reveals that the equation has one real root between 2 and 3. Using $x_1 = 2.2$ and $f'(x) = 3x^2 - 6x + 4$, we obtain

$$x_2 = 2.2 - \frac{-0.072}{5.32} \cong 2.21.$$

Using $x_2 = 2.21$, we obtain

$$x_3 = 2.21 - \frac{-0.018439}{5.3923} \cong 2.21.$$

The equation has a real root 2.21 correct to two decimal places.

PROBLEM LIST 50

1. Find the roots of each equation correct to two decimal places, using the Newton-Raphson method. Check the roots by using the quadratic formula.

   (a) $x^2 - 4x + 1 = 0.$ (c) $2x^2 - 4x + 1 = 0.$

   (b) $x^2 - 6x + 7 = 0.$ (d) $3x^2 + 5x - 1 = 0.$

2. Find correct to two decimal places:

   (a) $\sqrt{3}$.   (e) $\sqrt[3]{3}$.

   (b) $\sqrt{10}$.   (f) $\sqrt[3]{315}$.

   (c) $\sqrt{53}$.   (g) $\sqrt[3]{-459}$.

   (d) $\sqrt{7.83}$.   (h) $\sqrt[4]{9}$.

3. Given that $x^3 - 2x - 5 = 0$ has a root between 2 and 3, find the root to two decimal places.

4. Given that $x^3 + 3x^2 - 2x - 5 = 0$ has a root between 1 and 2, find the root to two decimal places.

5. Find all the real roots of $x^3 + 2x^2 - 5x - 4 = 0$ correct to one decimal place.

6. The equation $x^3 - 3x^2 - 2x + 5 = 0$ has a root between 3 and 4. Find the root to three decimal places.

7. Find all the real roots of $x^3 - 3x - 1 = 0$ correct to two decimal places.

8. Find to two decimal places the abscissa of the point of intersection of the line $y = 3 - x$ and the cubic $y = x^3$.

9. A cube has edge 2 in. Find to three decimal places the edge of a cube having twice the volume of the given cube.

10. Find to two decimal places the abscissa of the point on $y = x^2/4$ closest to $(4, 0)$.

11. An open box is constructed from a 10 in. × 10 in. square of tin by cutting equal squares from each corner and turning up the sides. Find to two decimal places the side x of each square cut out, given that the volume of the box is 68 cu in. and that the height of the box exceeds 2 in.

12. The volume of a spherical segment is given by $V = (\pi h^2/3)(3r - h)$, where r is the radius of the sphere and h the height of the segment. Find h correct to two decimal places if $r = 3$ ft and $V = 9\pi$ cubic feet (1/4 the volume of the sphere).

13. Given points $A(0, 3)$, $B(2, -1)$, $C(6, 3)$, and $P(x, 3)$, where $0 \leqslant x \leqslant 6$, let ϕ = angle CBP and ψ = angle PBA. Find x to the nearest tenth if $\phi = 2\psi$.

7.6   *Antiderivatives*

In Chapter 4 we called $F(x)$ an antiderivative of $f(x)$ over an interval on the x-axis if $F'(x) = f(x)$ for every x in the interval. In Theorem 4-XVI we proved that if $F(x)$ and $G(x)$ are any two antiderivatives of $f(x)$, then $F(x)$ and $G(x)$ differ by a constant. We termed $F(x) + C$ the general antiderivative of $f(x)$, C being an arbitrary constant. At this point our only formula for a general antiderivative is (4.24):

$$D^{-1}(x^n) = \frac{x^{n+1}}{n+1} + C \qquad (n \neq -1).$$

Later we will develop more formulas for general antiderivatives, called integrals.

Let us assume that a problem involves the variables x and y. In many important applications we do not know the relationship between x and y, but we do know the relationship involving x, y, and certain derivatives of y with respect to x. Such a relationship is of the form

$$F(x, y, y', y'', \cdots, y^{(n)}) = 0 \tag{7.15}$$

and is called a differential equation. A solution of (7.15) is a relationship involving x and y but no derivatives. Most physical laws, such as Newton's law of motion relating force and acceleration, are expressed as differential equations. The subject of differential equations is an important branch of mathematics and an active area of current research. In this section we consider some simple differential equations and their applications. This subject will be pursued further in Chapter 20.

Example 1.   Solve the differential equation

$$\frac{dy}{dx} = 3x^2 + 2x - 1. \tag{7.16}$$

Solution.   Using the fact that the antiderivative of a sum is the sum of the antiderivatives, we obtain

$$y = x^3 + x^2 - x + C. \tag{7.17}$$

This is the general solution of (7.16), since every solution can be obtained by assigning the proper value to C. To show that (7.17) is a solution of (7.16) we verify that

$$\frac{d}{dx}(x^3 + x^2 - x + C) = 3x^2 + 2x - 1.$$

Example 2.   Solve the differential equation

$$\frac{dy}{dx} = x^2,$$

given that $y = 2$ when $x = 1$.

Solution.   The general solution is $y = (x^3/3) + C$. Substituting $x = 1$ and $y = 2$, we obtain

$$2 = \frac{1}{3} + C,$$

and hence C must equal 5/3 in order to satisfy the given condition. Hence the required solution is $y = (x^3/3) + (5/3)$.

Note that x and y can be made to satisfy one condition, since the general solution contains one arbitrary constant. A problem of this type is called an initial-value problem because in many applications one variable is the time and the specified condition gives the value of the other variable at the initial time $t = 0$.

Example 3.   Solve the initial-value problem

$$y'' = 6x; \qquad y = 3, \; y' = 2 \quad \text{when } x = 0.$$

Solution.   In $y' = 3x^2 + C$ we set $x = 0$ and $y' = 2$ to obtain $y' = 3x^2 + 2$. In $y = x^3 + 2x + k$ we set $x = 0$ and $y = 3$ to obtain $y = x^3 + 2x + 3$.

Example 4.   Solve the differential equation $y'' = 12x$, given that $y = 0$ when $x = 0$, and $y = 6$ when $x = 2$.

Solution.   Forming antiderivatives, we obtain

$$y' = 6x^2 + c$$

and

$$y = 2x^3 + cx + k. \tag{7.18}$$

Application of the given conditions to (7.18) yields

$$0 = k \qquad \text{and} \qquad 6 = 16 + 2c + k.$$

The required solution $y = 2x^3 - 5x$ is obtained by substituting $k = 0$ and $c = -5$ in (7.18).

Note that x and y were made to satisfy two conditions and that (7.18) contained two arbitrary constants. This type of problem is called a two-point boundary-value problem, since the given conditions usually involve the endpoints of the interval which is of interest and importance in the problem.

Example 5.   Find an equation of a curve passing through (2, 3) for which

$$\frac{dy}{dx} = \frac{x}{2} \tag{7.19}$$

at every point of the curve.

Solution.   In order that (7.19) be satisfied, it is necessary that

$$y = \frac{x^2}{4} + c. \tag{7.20}$$

Equation (7.20) represents a one-parameter family of curves, called integral curves of the differential equation (7.19). A few members of the family are displayed in Fig. 7.14. Equation (7.19) is called a differential equation of the family (7.20). To find the particular integral curve passing through (2, 3), we substitute $x = 2$ and $y = 3$ in (7.20), obtaining

$$3 = 1 + c$$

which yields $c = 2$. The required curve, and there is only one, has equation $y = (x^2/4) + 2$.

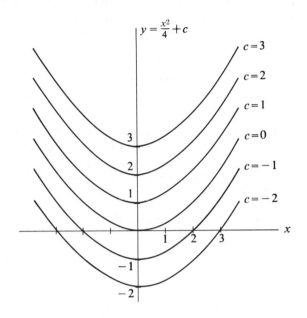

Figure 7.14

Example 6.   A particle moves on the x-axis with acceleration $a = 6t - 4$ ft/sec². If the particle is at the origin and has velocity 10 fps when $t = 0$, find its position and velocity at $t = 3$.

Solution.   We first solve the initial-value problem:

$$a = \frac{dv}{dt} = \frac{d^2x}{dt^2} = 6t - 4, \qquad v = 10, \ x = 0, \ t = 0:$$

$$v = 3t^2 - 4t + c$$

$$10 = 0 - 0 + c;$$

and

$$\frac{dx}{dt} = v = 3t^2 - 4t + 10 \tag{7.21}$$

$$x = t^3 - 2t^2 + 10t + k$$

$$0 = 0 - 0 + 0 + k$$

$$x = t^3 - 2t^2 + 10t. \tag{7.22}$$

Substituting $t = 3$ in (7.21) and (7.22), we obtain $v_3 = 25$ fps and $x_3 = 39$ ft.

Example 7.   A ball is released from a balloon that is 192 ft above the ground and which is rising at 64 fps. Find the distance the ball continues to rise and the time elapsed before the ball strikes the ground.

Solution.   Let the displacement s of the ball be measured from the point where the ball is released and let s be positive upward. Also let the time t be measured from the instant the ball is released. Assume that the ball has constant acceleration $a = dv/dt = -32$ ft/sec². The acceleration, known as the acceleration of gravity, is negative, since the velocity decreases with time. Because the initial velocity of the ball is the same as the velocity of the balloon, we must solve the initial-value problem:

$$a = \frac{dv}{dt} = \frac{d^2s}{dt^2} = -32; \quad \begin{Bmatrix} t = 0 \\ v = 64 \end{Bmatrix}, \quad \begin{Bmatrix} t = 0 \\ s = 0 \end{Bmatrix}.$$

From $v = -32t + c$ we obtain $64 = 0 + c$ and hence

$$v = \frac{ds}{dt} = -32t + 64.$$

From $s = -16t^2 + 64t + k$ we obtain $0 = 0 + 0 + k$ and hence

$$s = -16t^2 + 64t.$$

The ball continues to rise until $v = -32t + 64 = -32(t - 2) = 0$ or $t = 2$ sec. The distance traveled in the first 2 sec is

$$S_2 = -16t^2 + 64t \, |_{t=2} = 64 \text{ ft}.$$

To find the time before the ball strikes the ground, we set $s = -192$ and solve for t:

$$-192 = -16t^2 + 64t,$$

$$t^2 - 4t - 12 = 0,$$

$$(t - 6)(t + 2) = 0.$$

The answer is 6 sec, since $t \geqslant 0$.
The flight of the ball is depicted in Fig. 7.15.

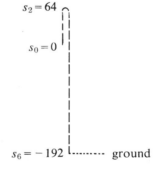

Figure 7.15

Remark.   If we had decided to measure s positive downward, v_0 would have been -64 and a would have been $+32$. We could also have chosen $s = 0$ at the ground level. The important point is that we must first choose our coordinate system and then use it consistently throughout the problem.

PROBLEM LIST 51

1.   Solve the following differential equations:

(a) $y' = x^2 - 2x$.

(b) $y' = x^3 + x - 2$.

(c) $y' = 3x^4 - 4x^2$.

(d) $y' = 2x^3 - x^2 + x - 4$.

2.   Solve the following initial-value problems:

(a) $y' = 6x; \; x = 0, \; y = 4$.

(b) $y' = -2x$; $x = 0$, $y = 7$.

(c) $y' = 4$; $x = 0$, $y = -3$.

(d) $y' = x - 3$; $x = 0$, $y = 8$.

(e) $y' = x^2 - 2x - 3$; $x = 3$, $y = 1$.

(f) $y' = 3x^2 + 4$; $x = -2$, $y = 3$.

3. Solve the following initial-value problems:

(a) $y'' = 3x$; $y = 5$, $y' = 2$ when $x = 0$.

(b) $y'' = 6x + 8$; $y = 2$, $y' = -1$ when $x = 0$.

(c) $y'' = 6x + 10$; $y = 8$, $y' = 13$ when $x = 1$.

(d) $y'' = 12x^2$; $y = -1$, $y' = -7$ when $x = -1$.

(e) $y''' = 24x + 6$; $y = 1$, $y' = 0$, $y'' = 2$ when $x = 0$.

(f) $y''' = 60x^2$; $y = 2$, $y' = 3$, $y'' = 18$ when $x = 0$.

4. Solve the following two-point boundary-value problems:

(a) $y'' = 2$; $x = 0$, $y = -1$; $x = 1$, $y = 5$.

(b) $y'' = 12x$; $x = 0$, $y = -3$; $x = 1$, $y = 0$.

(c) $y'' = -6x + 2$; $x = 1$, $y = -3$; $x = 3$, $y = -21$.

(d) $y'' = 12x^2$; $x = -1$, $y = -3$; $x = 2$, $y = 21$.

5. Find a one-parameter family of integral curves for each of the following differential equations. Illustrate each family graphically.

(a) $y' = 2x$.

(b) $y' = 4$.

(c) $y' = 0$.

(d) $y' = -6x$.

(e) $y' = -2x + 3$.

(f) $y' = x^2$.

(g) $y' = -3x^2$.

(h) $y' = x^{-1/2}$.

6. Find an equation of a curve passing through $(0, -3)$ if the slope of the curve at every point is four times the abscissa of the point.

7. A curve has a differential equation $y'' = 6x - 2$. Find an equation of the curve if it has slope 6 at $(1, 5)$.

8. The variables x and y satisfy the differential equation $y' = -14x + 14$. If $y = -1$ when $x = 0$, find the maximum value of y.

9. A particle moves on the x-axis with velocity $v = dx/dt = 2t + 3$ fps. If it starts from the point $(-4, 0)$ at time $t = 0$, find its position and velocity at time $t = 2$.

10. A particle moves on the y-axis with velocity $v = dy/dt = 3t^2 - 4$. If it is at $(0, 3)$ at time $t = 2$, find its position and velocity at time $t = 3$.

11. A particle moves on the x-axis with acceleration $a = 2t$ ft/sec². If the particle is at $(8, 0)$ and has velocity 4 fps when $t = 1$, find its position and velocity at $t = 3$.

12. A particle moves in a straight line with acceleration $a = 2t - 3$ ft/sec². If $s = 0$ and $v = -4$ when $t = 0$, find (a) when the particle reverses its direction and (b) the total distance the particle moves in the first 5 sec.

13. A particle moves on the x-axis with acceleration $a = 5 - 2t$. If the particle starts from the origin with $v = 0$, how far does it move in the positive direction? Assume $t \geqslant 0$.

14. A particle moves in a straight line with constant acceleration a. This type of motion is called uniformly accelerated rectilinear motion. If $s = 0$ and $v = v_0$ when $t = 0$, show that

(a) $v = v_0 + at$;

(b) $s = v_0 t + (1/2) at^2$;

(c) $v^2 = v_0^2 + 2as$;

(d) $s = (1/2)(v + v_0)t$.

It is important to remember that these formulas, although useful, are valid only when the acceleration is *constant*.

15. A body is uniformly accelerated from 20 fps to 100 fps in 16 sec. Find the distance traveled in that time.

16. Particle A has acceleration $6t$ ft/sec^2 and starts from the origin with $v = 0$ at $t = 0$. Particle B has constant acceleration 2 ft/sec^2 and starts from $(15, 0)$ with $v = 1$ fps at $t = 0$. If A and B move along the x-axis, where does A overtake B?

17. A bullet is shot upward at 640 fps. Find the distance the bullet rises and the velocity with which it strikes the ground. (Use $g = -32$.)

18. A ball is released from a balloon that is 320 ft above the ground and which is rising at 32 fps. Find the length of time the ball continues to rise and the velocity with which it strikes the ground. (Use $g = -32$.)

19. If the brakes on a certain car can produce a constant deceleration of 20 ft/sec^2, what is the maximum allowable velocity if the car is to be stopped in 60 ft or less after the brakes are applied?

20. A box slides down an inclined plane with constant acceleration 12 ft/sec^2. If $v_0 = 6$ fps, how long does it take for the box to slide 120 ft?

REFERENCE

7.1 J. B. SCARBOROUGH, *Numerical Mathematical Analysis*, The Johns Hopkins Press, Baltimore, 1962.

Chapter

8____

Applications of
integral calculus

8.1   *Areas Bounded by Curves*

Let us assume that in Fig. 8.1 we wish to find the area bounded by the curves $y = f_1(x)$, $y = f_2(x)$, and the lines $x = a$ and $x = b$. We assume that $f_2(x) \geqslant f_1(x)$ for $a \leqslant x \leqslant b$. If $f_1(x)$ and $f_2(x)$ are positive for $a \leqslant x \leqslant b$, it is clear that the required area is equal to the area under $y = f_2(x)$ minus the area under $y = f_1(x)$. If f_2 and f_1 are continuous functions of x, this difference is equal to

$$\int_a^b f_2(x)\,dx - \int_a^b f_1(x)\,dx,$$

or

$$A = \int_a^b [f_2(x) - f_1(x)]\,dx. \tag{8.1}$$

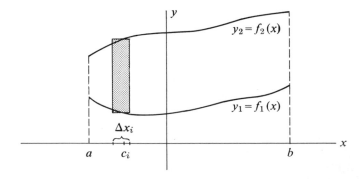

Figure 8.1

234

It is easy to verify that (8.1) gives the required area even if $f_2(x)$ or $f_1(x)$ is negative over part or all of the interval $a \leqslant x \leqslant b$. For example, if $f_1(x) < 0$ and $f_2(x) > 0$ for $a \leqslant x \leqslant b$, the expression $\int_a^b f_1(x) \, dx$ is negative and when this negative quantity is subtracted from the positive quantity $\int_a^b f_2(x) \, dx$, it gives the required area. Similarly, it is easy to see that (8.1) holds when both $f_2(x)$ and $f_1(x)$ are negative. It is important to remember that in using (8.1), the equation of the *lower* curve must be subtracted from the equation of the *upper* curve; this ensures that the area will be nonnegative.

We also note that if we had subdivided the interval $a \leqslant x \leqslant b$ as we did in Sec. 4.11, the expression $[f_2(c_i) - f_1(c_i)] \, \Delta x_i$ would represent the area of the shaded rectangle in Fig. 8.1. Since the difference between two continuous functions is a continuous function, it would follow from Theorem 4-X that

$$\int_a^b [f_2(x) - f_1(x)] \, dx = \lim_{\max(\Delta x_i) \to 0} \sum_{i=1}^n [f_2(c_i) - f_1(c_i)] \, \Delta x_i$$

would exist. Since this integral does give the area between the curves by (8.1), it is convenient to think of the area as the limit of the sum of elementary rectangles of the type shown in Fig. 8.1. The expression $f_2(x) - f_1(x)$ can be regarded as the length of the elementary rectangle, and dx as the width of the elementary rectangle.

If the roles of x and y are interchanged, (8.1) is replaced by

$$A = \int_c^d [g_2(y) - g_1(y)] \, dy. \tag{8.2}$$

Equation (8.2) gives the area bounded by the curves $x = g_2(y)$, $x = g_1(y)$, and lines $y = c$ and $y = d$. It is assumed that $g_2(y) \geqslant g_1(y)$ for all y in $c \leqslant y \leqslant d$. Under these conditions, (8.2) yields a nonnegative area.

Example 1.   Find the area bounded by $y = (x^2/4) + 3$, $y = 1 - x^2$, $x = -1$, and $x = 2$.

   Solution.   The required area and a typical elementary rectangle are shown in Fig. 8.2. Applying (8.1) we have

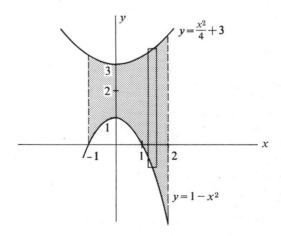

Figure 8.2

$$A = \int_{-1}^{2} \left[\left(\frac{x^2}{4} + 3 \right) - (1 - x^2) \right] dx$$

$$= \int_{-1}^{2} \left(\frac{5x^2}{4} + 2 \right) dx$$

$$= \frac{5x^3}{12} + 2x \Big]_{-1}^{2} = \left(\frac{88}{12} \right) - \left(\frac{-29}{12} \right)$$

$$= \frac{117}{12} \quad \text{square units.}$$

Example 2.   Find the area bounded by $y = x^2$ and $x + y - 2 = 0$.

Solution.   Solving the equations simultaneously, we find that the parabola and the line intersect at $(-2, 4)$ and at $(1, 1)$. Applying (8.1) we obtain

$$A = \int_{-2}^{1} [(-x + 2) - x^2] \, dx$$

$$= -\frac{x^2}{2} + 2x - \frac{x^3}{3} \Big]_{-2}^{1}$$

$$= \frac{9}{2} \quad \text{square units.}$$

See Fig. 8.3.

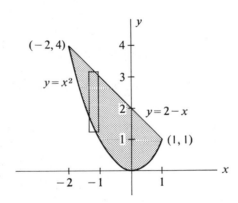

Figure 8.3

Example 3.   Find the area bounded by $y^2 - x = 0$ and $y - x + 6 = 0$.

Solution.   We first solve the equations simultaneously to find that the parabola and the line intersect at $(4, -2)$ and at $(9, 3)$. We see from Fig. 8.4 that formula (8.1) is not applicable because the required area is bounded below by both the parabola and the line. It is possible to apply (8.1) to the portion of the area to the left of $x = 4$, using $f_2(x) = \sqrt{x}$ and $f_1(x) = -\sqrt{x}$, and then to the portion to the right of $x = 4$, using $f_2(x) = \sqrt{x}$ and $f_1(x) = x - 6$. It is simpler, however, to apply (8.2) to the entire area. Using the elementary rectangle shown in Fig. 8.4, we have

$$A = \int_{-2}^{3} [(y + 6) - y^2] \, dy$$

$$= \frac{y^2}{2} + 6y - \frac{y^3}{3} \bigg]_{-2}^{3}$$

$$= \frac{125}{6} \quad \text{square units.}$$

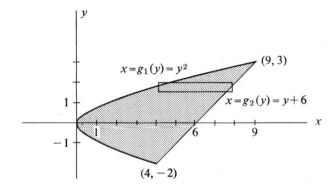

Figure 8.4

PROBLEM LIST 52

1. Find the areas bounded by the following curves. In each case draw a graph showing the required area and the elementary rectangle or element of area employed.

(a) $y = x^2 + 1$, $y = x/2$, $x = 0$, $x = 4$.

(b) $y = -x^2$, $y = x + 1$, $x = -1$, $x = 3$.

(c) $y = x^2$, $y = x^3$, $x = 1/2$.

(d) $y = x^2 - 5$, $y = 4$.

(e) $y = 1 - x^2$, $y = (1/2)(x^2 - 1)$.

(f) $y = x^3$, $y = \sqrt{x}$.

(g) $y = x^4$, $y = 8x$.

(h) $y = -x^2$, $y + x + 2 = 0$.

(i) $y = x^2/2$, $y + x - 4 = 0$.

(j) $y = x^{3/2}$, $y = x$.

(k) $y = x^{2/3}$, $y = x$.

(l) $y = x^2 + x - 2$, $5x + 4y - 5 = 0$.

(m) $y^2 = x$, $x + y - 2 = 0$.

(n) $y^2 + x - 1 = 0$, $x = 0$.

(o) $y = x^3$, $y = 8x$.

(p) $y = x^4$, $y = 32 - x^4$.

(q) $y = x^3$, $y = |x|$, $x = -2$.

(r) $y^2 - 4y + 1 - x = 0$, $y^2 - 5x + 5 = 0$.

2. Follow the instructions of Problem 1 and find the enclosed areas using both (8.1) and (8.2).

   (a) $y = x^2$, $y = x$.

   (b) $y = x^2$, $y^2 = x$.

   (c) $y = x^{3/2}$, $y = x^{2/3}$.

   (d) $y = x^3$, $y = |x|$.

3. For the parabola $y^2 = 2px$, find the

   (a) area bounded by the parabola and $y = 2x$;

   (b) area bounded by the parabola and $x = k$;

   (c) value of c such that the area bounded by the parabola and $x = c$ is equal to the area bounded by the parabola from $x = c$ to $x = p/2$.

4. Find the area bounded by $x^2y - 1 = 0$, $x - 8y = 0$, and $x - 64y = 0$.

5. Solve illustrative Example 3 by using vertical elements of area.

6. Find the area bounded by the cubic $y = x^3/3$ and its tangent at $(1, 1/3)$.

7. Find the area cut off from the parabola $y^2 - 6y - 4x + 1 = 0$ by the chord joining $(-1, 5)$ and $(2, -1)$.

8. The equation $y = kx(x - a)$ determines a two-parameter family of parabolas. Find the member of this family which passes through $(4, 1)$ and which determines with the x-axis the least area. Assume $k < 0$.

9. Show that if $f(x) = ax^2 + bx + c$, the area bounded by $y = f(x)$, the x-axis, $x = -h$, and $x = h$ is given by $(h/3)[f(-h) + 4f(0) + f(h)]$. Show that the result also holds for $f(x) = ax^3 + bx^2 + cx + d$.

8.2   Volumes

Consider the problem of finding the volume of a solid extending from the plane perpendicular to the x-axis at $x = a$ to the plane perpendicular to the x-axis at $x = b$. See Fig. 8.5. We assume that for all x in $a \leqslant x \leqslant b$, the plane perpendicular to the x-axis at $x = x$ intersects the solid in a plane section of area $A = A(x)$, where A is a continuous function on $a \leqslant x \leqslant b$. As x increases from a to b, $A(x)$ changes gradually from $A(a)$ to $A(b)$, and $A(x)$ is often referred to as the area of a moving cross section.

By subdividing the interval from a to b into n parts, as we did in Chapter 4, and passing planes through the points of subdivision perpendicular to the x-axis, the solid is divided into n thin slabs. The sum of the volumes of these slabs is approximately

$$\sum_{i=1}^{n} A(c_i) \, \Delta x_i,$$

where $x_{i-1} \leqslant c_i \leqslant x_i$, and the volume of the solid is defined by

$$V = \lim_{\max(\Delta x_i) \to 0} \sum_{i=1}^{n} A(c_i) \, \Delta x_i. \qquad (8.3)$$

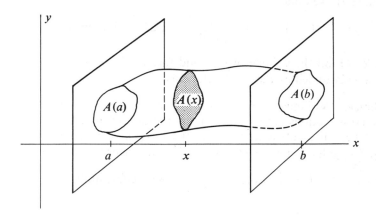

Figure 8.5

Since A is a continuous function on $a \leqslant x \leqslant b$, it follows from Theorem 4-X that the limit in (8.3) exists, and hence

$$V = \int_a^b A(x)\,dx. \qquad (8.4)$$

By using inscribed and circumscribed slabs, each of constant cross section, it can be shown that definition (8.3) is reasonable. The development would be analogous to that used for areas in Chapter 4.

Example 1.   The base of a solid lies in the xy-plane and is bounded by $y = x^2/10$, $x = 5$, and the x-axis. Find the volume of the solid if every cross section perpendicular to the x-axis is a square.

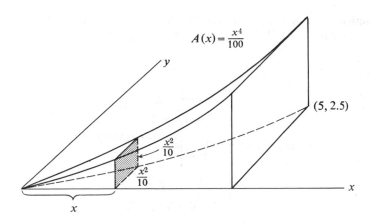

Figure 8.6

Solution.   We see from Fig. 8.6 that $A(x) = (x^2/10)^2 = x^4/100$. Hence, from (8.4), we obtain

$$A = \int_0^5 \frac{x^4}{100}\,dx = \frac{x^5}{500}\Big]_0^5 = 6.25 \quad \text{cubic units.}$$

Example 2.   Find the volume of the solid formed by revolving about the x-axis the area bounded by the x-axis, the curve $y = \sqrt{x}$, and the line $x = 4$.

Solution.   Volumes of revolution are special cases to which (8.4) applies. The cross sections are circles and the radius r of an arbitrary cross section must be expressed in terms of x. If $r = r(x)$, then $A(x) = \pi[r(x)]^2$. From Fig. 8.7 we have $A(x) = \pi(\sqrt{x})^2 = \pi x$, and hence

$$V = \int_0^4 \pi x\,dx = \frac{\pi x^2}{2}\Big]_0^4 = 8\pi \quad \text{cubic units.}$$

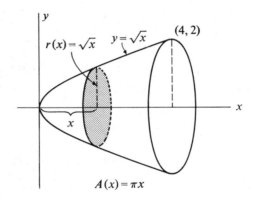

Figure 8.7

Example 3.   Find the volume of the solid formed by revolving about the y-axis the area bounded by the y-axis, the curve $y = x^3$, the line $y = 2$, and the line $y = 8$.

Solution.   Since the cross sections are circles perpendicular to the y-axis, the coordinate x in (8.4) must be replaced by y and an arbitrary cross section

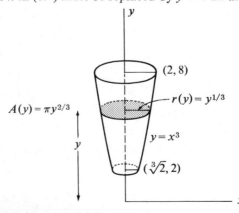

Figure 8.8

must be expressed in terms of y. From Fig. 8.8 we have

$$V = \int_2^8 A(y)\, dy = \int_2^8 \pi y^{2/3}\, dy$$

$$= \frac{3\pi}{5} y^{5/3} \Big]_2^8$$

$$= \frac{3\pi}{5} [32 - 2^{5/3}] \quad \text{cubic units.}$$

Example 4.   Find the volume generated by revolving about the x-axis the area bounded by $y^2 = 4x$ and $x^2 = 4y$.

Solution.   The parabolas intersect at $(0, 0)$ and at $(4, 4)$ as shown in Fig. 8.9. An arbitrary cross section perpendicular to the x-axis is an annular ring for which

$$A(x) = \pi(2\sqrt{x})^2 - \pi\left(\frac{x^2}{4}\right)^2 = \pi\left[4x - \frac{x^4}{16}\right].$$

From (8.4) we find that

$$V = \int_0^4 \pi\left[4x - \frac{x^4}{16}\right] dx$$

$$= \pi\left[2x^2 - \frac{x^5}{80}\right]_0^4$$

$$= \frac{96\pi}{5} \quad \text{cubic units.}$$

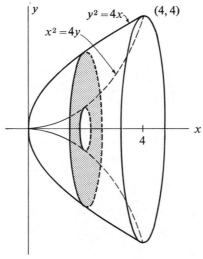

$$A(x) = \pi (2\sqrt{x})^2 - \pi(\tfrac{x^2}{4})^2$$

$$= \pi [4x - \tfrac{x^4}{16}]$$

Figure 8.9

Example 5.   Find the volume generated by revolving about the line $x = 4$ the first-quadrant area bounded by $y^2 = x$, the line $x = 4$, and the x-axis.

Solution.   We see from Fig. 8.10 that an arbitrary cross section perpendicular to the line $x = 4$ is a circle for which
$$A(y) = \pi(4 - y^2)^2.$$
Hence

$$V = \int_0^2 \pi(4 - y^2)^2 \, dy$$

$$= \pi \int_0^2 \pi(16 - 8y^2 + y^4) \, dy$$

$$= \pi \left[16y - \frac{8y^3}{3} + \frac{y^5}{5} \right]_0^2$$

$$= \frac{256\pi}{15} \quad \text{cubic units.}$$

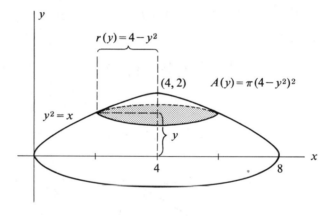

Figure 8.10

Example 6.   Find the volume of a wedge cut from a right-circular cylinder of radius a by a plane that passes through a diameter of the base and makes a $45°$ angle with the plane of the base.

Solution.   One-half of the wedge is shown in Fig. 8.11. The base of the cylinder has equation $x^2 + y^2 = a^2$ and an arbitrary section of the wedge perpendicular to the x-axis is a right isosceles triangle for which
$$A(x) = \frac{y^2}{2} = \frac{a^2 - x^2}{2}.$$
The volume of the entire wedge is given by

$$V = 2 \int_0^a \frac{a^2 - x^2}{2} \, dx$$

$$= a^2 x - \frac{x^3}{3} \Big]_0^a$$

$$= \frac{2a^3}{3} \quad \text{cubic units.}$$

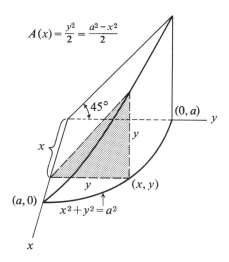

Figure 8.11

PROBLEM LIST 53

1. The base of a solid lies in the xy-plane and is bounded by $y = x^2/4$, $x = 4$, and the x-axis. Find the volume of the solid if every cross section perpendicular to the x-axis is

   (a) a square;

   (b) an isosceles right triangle with one end of the hypotenuse on the parabola $y = x^2/4$;

   (c) an isosceles right triangle with one end of the hypotenuse on the x-axis;

   (d) an isosceles right triangle with hypotenuse in the xy-plane.

2. The base of a solid is a circle of radius 4 in. Find the volume of the solid if every section perpendicular to a diameter of the base is

   (a) a square;

   (b) a semicircle whose diameter lies in the base of the solid.

3. Find the volume of a right pyramid having altitude h and a square base of side a.

4. The base of a solid lies in the xy-plane and is bounded by $xy = 1$, the y-axis, the line $y = 2$, and the line $y = 5$. Find the volume of the solid if every cross section perpendicular to the y-axis is a square.

5. Find the volume generated by revolving about the x-axis the area in the xy-plane bounded by

   (a) $y = 2\sqrt{x}$, $x = 5$, $y = 0$;

   (b) $y = x^2$, $y = 0$, $x = 2$, $x = 5$ $(2 \leqslant x \leqslant 5)$;

   (c) $y = x^3$, $y = 0$, $x = -4$, $x = -1$;

   (d) $y = x^2 + 3$, $y = 1$, $x = 0$, $x = 4$;

(e) $y = x^{3/2}$, $x = 4$;

(f) $y = \sqrt{x}$, $3y = x$.

6. Find the volume generated by revolving about the y-axis the first-quadrant area in the xy-plane bounded by

(a) $y = x^2$, $y = 4$, $x = 0$;

(b) $y = x^2$, $x = 2$, $y = 0$;

(c) $y = 4 - x^2$, $y = 0$, $x = 0$;

(d) $y^2 = 3x$, $x^2 = 3y$;

(e) $xy = 4$, $x = 0$, $y = 2$, $y = 7$;

(f) $xy = 8$, $x + y - 9 = 0$.

7. Find the volume generated by revolving about the line $x = 3$ the area bounded by $y = x^2$, $x = 3$, and $y = 0$.

8. Find the volume generated by revolving about the line $y = -4$ the area bounded by $y = -x^2$ and $y = -4$.

9. Find the volume generated by revolving about the line $x = 6$ the area bounded by $y = 2x$, $x = 4$, and $y = 0$.

10. Find the volume of the cone generated by revolving about the x-axis the area of the triangle having vertices $(0, 0)$, $(6, 0)$, and $(6, 2)$.

11. Derive the formula for the volume of a sphere of radius a.

12. Derive the formula $V = (\pi h^2/3)(3a - h)$ for the volume of a spherical segment, where a is the radius of the sphere and h the height of the segment.

13. Derive the formula for the volume of a right-circular cone of height h and base radius r.

14. Find the volume of the prolate spheroid generated by revolving the ellipse $b^2x^2 + a^2y^2 = a^2b^2$ $(a > b)$ about the x-axis.

15. Find the volume of the oblate spheroid generated by revolving the ellipse $b^2x^2 + a^2y^2 = a^2b^2$ $(a > b)$ about the y-axis.

16. Determine n so that the first-quadrant area bounded by $y = x^n$, $x = 0$, and $y = 1$ and the area bounded by $y = x^n$, $x = 1$, and $y = 0$ will generate the same volume when revolved about the y-axis.

17. The base of a solid lies in the xy-plane and is bounded by $9x^2 - 4y^2 = 36$ and $x = 4$. Find the volume if every cross section perpendicular to the x-axis is a square.

18. Find the volume of a wedge cut from a right-circular cylinder of radius 8 in. by a plane that passes through a diameter of the base and makes a $30°$ angle with the plane of the base.

19. Find the volume common to two right-circular cylinders, each having base radius a, if the axes of the cylinders intersect at right angles.

Volumes by the Cylindrical Shell Method

The preceding method for calculating volumes is known as the slab method, or the moving cross-section method. We now present an alternate method which is more convenient for certain volumes. Given that $y = f(x)$ defines a continuous function on $a \leqslant x \leqslant b$, we consider the problem of finding the volume generated by revolving about the y-axis the area in Fig. 8.12 bounded by $y = f(x)$, the x-axis, the line $x = a$, and the line $x = b$.

We divide the interval from a to b into n parts in the usual manner and then form n rectangles by erecting ordinates at the midpoints of the n subintervals. In Fig. 8.12 the shaded rectangle is the ith rectangle,

$$c_i = \frac{x_i + x_{i-1}}{2}$$

is the midpoint of the subinterval $\Delta x_i = x_i - x_{i-1}$, and $f(c_i)$ is the height of the ith rectangle. It is clear that if all n of these rectangles are revolved about the y-axis, they will generate a total volume which will be an approximation to the required volume. The ith rectangle will generate a cylindrical shell whose volume will equal the volume of a right-circular cylinder of height $f(c_i)$ and base radius x_i minus the volume of a right-circular cylinder of height $f(c_i)$ and base radius x_{i-1}. Denoting this volume by ΔV_i, we apply the formula $V_c = \pi r^2 h$ for the volume of a right-circular cylinder to obtain

$$\begin{aligned}
\Delta V_i &= \pi x_i^2 f(c_i) - \pi x_{i-1}^2 f(c_i) \\
&= \pi f(c_i)(x_i + x_{i-1})(x_i - x_{i-1}) \\
&= 2\pi \frac{x_i + x_{i-1}}{2} f(c_i)(x_i - x_{i-1}) \\
&= 2\pi c_i f(c_i)\, \Delta x_i.
\end{aligned}$$

The function having value $2\pi x f(x)$ at x, being the product of the continuous functions having values $2\pi x$ and $f(x)$ at x, is continuous on $a \leqslant x \leqslant b$. It follows from Theorem 4-X that

$$\lim_{\max(\Delta x_i) \to 0} \sum_{i=1}^{n} 2\pi c_i f(c_i)\, \Delta x_i = 2\pi \int_a^b x f(x)\, dx \qquad (8.5)$$

exists. We state without proof that the limit in (8.5) is equal to the required volume. It will be possible to establish this fact after we have studied double integrals in Chapter 17. See Problem 15 of Problem List 101. However, we will see in the exercises that the shell method produces the same answer as the slab method when a volume is computed by both methods.

An alternate approach is to define the required volume as the limit in (8.5). It would then be possible to show that this definition is consistent with the slab definition. That is, both the slab definition and the shell definition would yield the same volume when applied to the same region. It is interesting to note that the slab method would be inconvenient if applied in Fig. 8.12. The difficulty is that we would not obtain a single expression $A(y)$ for an arbitrary cross section perpendicular to the y-axis. We could subdivide the required volume into three subregions and apply the slab method to each one, but this would be much more complicated than using the shell method.

It is easy to extend the shell method to volumes obtained by revolving about the y-axis an area bounded by $y = f_2(x)$, $y = f_1(x)$, $x = a$, and $x = b$. Assuming that

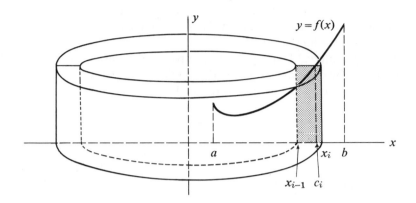

Figure 8.12

$f_2(x) \geqslant f_1(x)$ on $a \leqslant x \leqslant b$, $f(x)$ in (8.5) is replaced by $h(x) = f_2(x) - f_1(x)$ and h is regarded as the height of an elementary shell.

The basic formula for volumes obtained by revolving areas about the y-axis is

$$V = 2\pi \int_a^b xh(x)\, dx. \tag{8.6}$$

Note that if a shell of inner radius x, height h, and thickness dx could be rolled out into a slab, the slab would have dimensions $2\pi x$, h, and dx, and hence volume $2\pi xh\, dx$. Note also that if $V = \pi x^2 h$, then $dV = 2\pi xh\, dx$. In other words, if a right-circular cylinder of height h and radius x has its radius changed by dx, its volume is changed by approximately $2\pi xh\, dx$. These observations render it easier to remember (8.6).

If an area is revolved about the x-axis, the roles of x and y are interchanged and the shell formula becomes

$$V = 2\pi \int_c^d yh(y)\, dy. \tag{8.7}$$

Example 1.   Find the volume generated by revolving about the y-axis the area bounded by $y = x + (4/x)$, the x-axis, the line $x = 1$, and the line $x = 3$.

Solution.   Applying (8.6) to Fig. 8.13, we obtain

$$V = 2\pi \int_1^3 x \left(x + \frac{4}{x} \right) dx$$

$$= 2\pi \int_1^3 (x^2 + 4)\, dx$$

$$= 2\pi \left[\frac{x^3}{3} + 4x \right]_1^3 = \frac{100\pi}{3} \quad \text{cubic units.}$$

It is important to note that the interval of integration extends only from $x = 1$ to $x = 3$ even though the cylindrical shells extend back to $x = -3$. We also point out that the slab method would be quite difficult to apply in this problem.

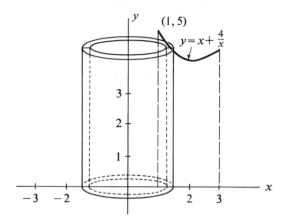

Figure 8.13

Example 2. Find the volume generated by revolving about the y-axis the first-quadrant area bounded by $y = x^2$, the line $y = 4$, and the y-axis.

    Solution. Applying (8.6) to Fig. 8.14, we obtain

$$V = 2\pi \int_0^2 x(4 - x^2)\, dx$$

$$= 2\pi \int_0^2 (4x - x^3)\, dx$$

$$= 2\pi \left[2x^2 - \frac{x^4}{4} \right]_0^2 = 8\pi \quad \text{cubic units.}$$

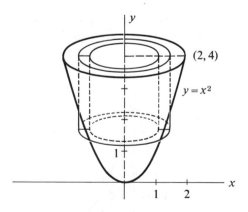

Figure 8.14

We observe that the slab method applied to Fig. 8.14 also yields

$$V = \pi \int_0^4 y\, dy = \pi \frac{y^2}{2} \Big]_0^4 = 8\pi \quad \text{cubic units.}$$

Example 3. Find the volume generated by revolving about the x-axis the area bounded by $x = y^2 - 4y$ and $x = -y$.

Solution. The curves intersect at $(0, 0)$ and at $(-3, 3)$. Applying (8.7) with $h(y) = -y - (y^2 - 4y)$ to Fig. 8.15, we obtain

$$V = 2\pi \int_0^3 y[-y - (y^2 - 4y)]dy$$

$$= 2\pi \int_0^3 (3y^2 - y^3)\, dy$$

$$= 2\pi \left[y^3 - \frac{y^4}{4} \right]_0^3 = \frac{27\pi}{2} \quad \text{cubic units.}$$

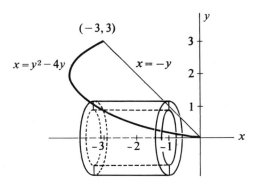

Figure 8.15

Example 4. Find the volume generated by revolving about the line $x = 2$ the area bounded by $y = x^2 + 1$, the x-axis, the y-axis, and the line $x = 2$.

Solution. Since the elementary shell in Fig. 8.16 has radius $r = 2 - x$, we must replace x in (8.6) by $2 - x$. This yields

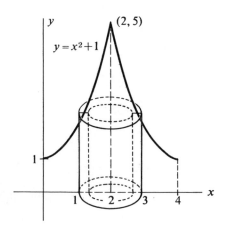

Figure 8.16

$$V = 2\pi \int_0^2 (2 - x)(x^2 + 1)\, dx$$

$$= 2\pi \int_0^2 (-x^3 + 2x^2 - x + 2)\, dx$$

$$= 2\pi \left[\frac{-x^4}{4} + \frac{2x^3}{3} - \frac{x^2}{2} + 2x \right]_0^2 = \frac{20\pi}{3} \quad \text{cubic units.}$$

PROBLEM LIST 54

1. Find by the shell method the volume generated by revolving about the y-axis the area in the xy-plane bounded by

   (a) $y = x^2 + 1$, $y = 0$, $x = 0$, $x = 3$;

   (b) $y = \sqrt{x}$, $y = 0$, $x = 1$, $x = 4$ $(1 \leqslant x \leqslant 4)$;

   (c) $y = 6x - x^2$, $y = 0$;

   (d) $y = x + 1$, $y = 1 - x^2$;

   (e) $y = x^2 - 4x + 3$, $y = x - 1$;

   (f) $y = x^3$, $y = x$;

   (g) $y = x + (9/x)$, $y = x$, $x = 1$, $x = 4$;

   (h) $xy = 1$, $2y + 1 = 0$, $x + 1 = 0$.

2. Find by the shell method the volume generated by revolving about the x-axis the area in the xy-plane bounded by

   (a) $x = y^2$, $x = 0$, $y = 4$;

   (b) $x = y^2 - 4y$, $x = 0$;

   (c) $y = 2x$, $xy = 8$, $y = 1$;

   (d) $y^2 = x^3$, $y = x$;

   (e) $2y + x + 2 = 0$, $x + y + 1 = 0$, $y = 0$;

   (f) $x = y^3 - 2y^2 + y$, $x = 0$;

   (g) $y = |x|$, $x - 2y + 3 = 0$;

   (h) $y^2 = 2px$, $x = p/2$.

3. Find by the shell method and the slab method the volume generated by revolving about the y-axis the area in the xy-plane bounded by

   (a) $y = x^2$, $x = y^2$;

   (b) $y = 4 - x^2$, $y = 1$.

4. Find the volume generated by revolving the area bounded by $y = x^2 + 3$, $y = 0$, $x = 0$, and $x = 3$ about

   (a) $x = 0$,   (b) $x = 3$,   (c) $x = 5$.

5. Derive the formula for the volume of a right-circular cone by the shell method.

6. Find the volume generated by revolving about the y-axis the area of the triangle having vertices $(1, 1)$, $(3, 4)$, and $(6, 0)$. Use the shell method.

7. Find the volume generated by revolving the area of a circle of radius a about a line tangent to the circle.

8.3   Arc Length

The curve shown in Fig. 8.17 is the graph of a function f defined by $y = f(x)$ which is continuous on $a \leqslant x \leqslant b$. We consider the problem of finding the distance *along the curve* from $(a, f(a))$ to $(b, f(b))$. Although we have an intuitive feeling that the curve has a length between these two points, we have not as yet given a precise mathematical definition of arc length. We do know how to find the non-negative length of a line segment by using the distance formula, so it is natural that we attempt to generalize this concept of length.

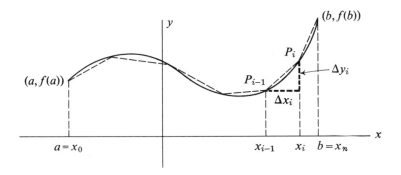

Figure 8.17

We subdivide the interval from a to b into n subintervals in the usual fashion. The $n + 1$ points $P_i(x_i, f(x_i))$ on the curve determine n line segments. If n were very large and each of the corresponding n line segments were very small in length, our intuition tells us that the sum of the lengths of the n line segments would be close to what we think the required arc length should be. This observation prompts us to define the required arc length L by

$$L = \lim_{\max(\Delta x_i) \to 0} \sum_{i=1}^{n} P_{i-1} P_i. \tag{8.8}$$

At this point we might feel that definition (8.8) will yield a length L, provided f is continuous on $a \leqslant x \leqslant b$. The matter is not so simple, however, and it is shown in Ref. 8.2 that the curve given by

$$f(x) = \begin{cases} x \sin (1/x) & \text{for } x \neq 0 \\ 0 & \text{for } x = 0 \end{cases}$$

is continuous on $0 \leqslant x \leqslant 1$ but has no length over this interval because the limit in (8.8) does not exist. Curves for which the limit (8.8) exists are said to be rectifiable over $a \leqslant x \leqslant b$.

We shall prove that $y = f(x)$ is rectifiable, provided f has a continuous derivative on $a \leqslant x \leqslant b$. By the distance formula we have

$$P_{i-1} P_i = \sqrt{(\Delta x_i)^2 + (\Delta y_i)^2}$$

$$= \sqrt{1 + \left(\frac{\Delta y_i}{\Delta x_i}\right)^2} \, \Delta x_i.$$

By Theorem 4-IV (mean-value theorem) there exists at least one c_i satisfying $x_{i-1} < c_i < x_i$ such that

$$\frac{\Delta y_i}{\Delta x_i} = f'(c_i).$$

Therefore

$$P_{i-1}P_i = \sqrt{1 + [f'(c_i)]^2}\, \Delta x_i.$$

It follows from Theorem 4-X that

$$\lim_{\max(\Delta x_i) \to 0} \sum_{i=1}^{n} \sqrt{1 + [f'(c_i)]^2}\, \Delta x_i$$

exists, since the function whose value at x is $\sqrt{1 + [f'(x)^2]}$, being the square root of the sum of two continuous functions, is continuous on $a \leqslant x \leqslant b$. The curve $y = f(x)$ is rectifiable on $a \leqslant x \leqslant b$ and

$$L = \int_a^b \sqrt{1 + \left(\frac{dy}{dx}\right)^2}\, dx. \tag{8.9}$$

It is customary to denote arc length by the letter s. If we now regard $P_0(a, f(a))$ as a fixed point, called the origin of arcs, the distance s from P_0 to $(x, f(x))$ is given by

$$s = \int_a^x \sqrt{1 + [f'(u)]^2}\, du. \tag{8.10}$$

The dummy variable u is employed in (8.10) so that x will not have two different meanings. If $x > a$, s is positive, while if $x < a$, s is negative, assuming, of course, that the curve in question is rectifiable over the interval where (8.10) is employed.

Applying Theorem 4-XV (first fundamental theorem of calculus) to (8.10), we obtain

$$\frac{ds}{dx} = \sqrt{1 + \left(\frac{dy}{dx}\right)^2}. \tag{8.11}$$

Equation (8.11) is the formula for the rate of change of arc length with respect to the abscissa. We would have introduced this formula in Chapter 7, but we had not defined arc length at that stage. Note that s increases at the same rate as x (that is, $ds/dx = 1$) at points where the slope dy/dx of the curve is zero, that $ds/dx \geqslant 1$ at all points of the curve, and that s increases much more rapidly than x at points of the curve where $|dy/dx|$ is large.

If the roles of x and y are interchanged, (8.9) becomes

$$L = \int_c^d \sqrt{1 + \left(\frac{dx}{dy}\right)^2}\, dy, \tag{8.12}$$

where $c = f(a)$ and $d = f(b)$.

If both sides of (8.11) are multiplied by dx, we obtain

$$ds = \sqrt{1 + \left(\frac{dy}{dx}\right)^2}\, dx, \tag{8.13}$$

which can also be written in the form

$$ds^2 = dx^2 + dy^2. \tag{8.14}$$

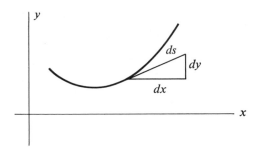

Figure 8.18

Formula (8.14) furnishes us with the geometric interpretation of the quantity ds, called the differential of arc. This is illustrated in Fig. 8.18.

From (8.14) it is easy to obtain the alternate formula

$$ds = \sqrt{1 + \left(\frac{dx}{dy}\right)^2}\, dy. \tag{8.15}$$

In order to apply Theorem 4-XVII (second fundamental theorem of calculus) to the evaluation of the integral in (8.9), we require an antiderivative of the function defined by $\sqrt{1 + (dy/dx)^2}$. Since our supply of antiderivative (or integral) formulas is limited, there are not many curves we can rectify at the present time. After we have increased our supply of these formulas, we will be able to rectify certain other curves. In cases where an antiderivative of $\sqrt{1 + (dy/dx)^2}$ is not available, the integral in (8.9) can be evaluated approximately by numerical methods, two of which will be presented in Chapter 11.

The following important integral formula will enable us to rectify the semicubical parabola $y^2 = x^3$.

$$\int u^n\, du = \frac{u^{n+1}}{n+1} + C \qquad (n \neq -1). \tag{8.16}$$

The proof of (8.16), in which u denotes a differentiable function of some variable x, and du denotes the differential of u, is simple. We merely verify that

$$\frac{d}{dx}\left(\frac{u^{n+1}}{n+1} + C\right) = \frac{(n+1)u^n}{n+1} \cdot \frac{du}{dx} = u^n \frac{du}{dx},$$

which is the integrand when the left member of (8.16) is written in the form $\int [u^n(du/dx)]\, dx$.

Example 1

$$\int (x+1)^3\, dx = \frac{(x+1)^4}{4} + C$$

The function defined by $x + 1$ plays the role of u, and dx the role of du.

Example 2

$$\int (2x + 1)^3 \, dx = \frac{1}{2} \int (2x + 1)^3 2 \, dx$$

$$= \frac{1}{2} \frac{(2x + 1)^4}{4} + C = \frac{(2x + 1)^4}{8} + C$$

The function defined by $2x + 1$ plays the role of u and hence dx had to be multiplied by 2 so that the integral would be in the form $\int u^n \, du$. The differential of $2x + 1$ is $2dx$.

Example 3

$$\int \sqrt{1 + 5x} \, dx = \frac{1}{5} \int (1 + 5x)^{1/2} 5 \, dx$$

$$- \frac{1}{5} \frac{(1 + 5x)^{3/2}}{3/2} + C$$

$$= \frac{2(1 + 5x)^{3/2}}{15} + C$$

Example 4

$$\int x\sqrt{4 - x^2} \, dx = -\frac{1}{2} \int (4 - x^2)^{1/2}(-2x) \, dx$$

$$= -\frac{1}{2} \frac{(4 - x^2)^{3/2}}{3/2} + C$$

$$= \frac{-(4 - x^2)^{3/2}}{3} + C$$

Example 5

$$\int \sqrt{4 - x^2} \, dx$$

We are unable to evaluate this integral by (8.16). If we let $4 - x^2$ play the role of u, there is no way to introduce $du = -2x \, dx$, since it contains the variable x. Later we will develop methods for handling this integral.

We note that formula (4.24),

$$\int x^n \, dx = \frac{x^{n+1}}{n + 1} + C \qquad (n \neq -1),$$

is a special case of (8.16), x playing the role of u and dx the role of du.

Example 6.   Find the length of the semicubical parabola $y^2 = x^3$ between $(0, 0)$ and $(2, 2\sqrt{2})$. See Fig. 8.19.

Solution.   From $y = x^{3/2}$ we obtain $y' = (3/2)x^{1/2}$. We then apply (8.9) to obtain

$$L = \int_0^2 \sqrt{1 + \frac{9x}{4}} \, dx = \frac{4}{9} \int_0^2 \left(1 + \frac{9x}{4}\right)^{1/2} \frac{9}{4} \, dx.$$

By (8.16) we find

$$L = \frac{4}{9} \cdot \frac{2}{3}\left(1 + \frac{9}{4}x\right)^{3/2}\Big]_0^2 = \frac{8}{27}\left[\frac{11\sqrt{22}}{4} - 1\right] \cong 3.53 \quad \text{units.}$$

By comparison, the distance between the two points, easily obtained by the distance formula, is $\sqrt{12} \cong 3.46$ units.

With the exception of the straight line and the circle, the semicubical parabola was the first curve to be rectified. This was accomplished by the English mathematician William Neil (1637–1670).

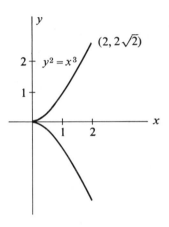

Figure 8.19

Example 7. Find the length of $y = (x^3/3) + 1/(4x)$ between $(1, 7/12)$ and $(2, 67/24)$.

Solution. From $y' = x^2 - 1/(4x^2)$ and (8.9) we obtain

$$L = \int_1^2 \sqrt{1 + \left(x^2 - \frac{1}{4x^2}\right)^2}\, dx$$

$$= \int_1^2 \sqrt{1 + x^4 - \frac{1}{2} + \frac{1}{16x^4}}\, dx$$

$$= \int_1^2 \sqrt{x^4 + \frac{1}{2} + \frac{1}{16x^4}}\, dx$$

$$= \int_1^2 \sqrt{\left(x^2 + \frac{1}{4x^2}\right)^2}\, dx$$

$$= \int_1^2 \left(x^2 + \frac{x^{-2}}{4}\right) dx$$

$$= \frac{x^3}{3} - \frac{x^{-1}}{4}\Big]_1^2 = \frac{59}{24} \quad \text{units.}$$

PROBLEM LIST 55

1. Find ds/dx for each of the following:

   (a) $y = x^2$.   (b) $y^2 = x^3$.

(c) $y = 2x^2 - x + 1$.   (d) $y = \frac{1}{3}(x^2 + 2)^{3/2}$.

2. Find ds/dy for each of the following:

   (a) $x = y^2$.   (c) $x^2 + y^2 = 1$.

   (b) $(x - 1)^2 = (y + 2)^3$.   (d) $x = \frac{y^4}{4} + \frac{1}{8y^2}$.

3. Draw a graph illustrating dx, dy, and ds at $(1, 1)$ for the function defined by $y = \sqrt{x}$. Assume $dx > 0$.

4. Find the point on $y = x^2 - 4x + 1$ where $ds/dx = 1$. Find the points where $ds/dx = 2$.

5. Evaluate the following integrals:

   (a) $\int (x - 3)^2 \, dx$.   (d) $\int \sqrt{1 + (8x/9)} \, dx$.

   (b) $\int (2x + 1)^4 \, dx$.   (e) $\int x\sqrt{x^2 - 9} \, dx$.

   (c) $\int \sqrt{1 - 6x} \, dx$.   (f) $\int x(4 - x^2)^{2/3} \, dx$.

6. Find the distance from $(0, 1)$ to $(3, 7)$ along $2x - y + 1 = 0$
   (a) by the distance formula;
   (b) by formula (8.9).

7. Find the distance from $(1, 1)$ to $(3, 3\sqrt{3})$ along $y^2 = x^3$.

8. For the function defined by $y = (x^3/3) + 1/(4x)$
   (a) draw the graph of the function;
   (b) determine the points on the curve where $ds/dx = 1$;
   (c) determine the distance along the curve from $(1/2, 13/24)$ to $(1, 7/12)$;
   (d) determine the distance along the curve from the point where $x = -4$ to the point where $x = -2$.

9. Find the length of $x^2 = 4y^3$ from $(2, 1)$ to $(54, 9)$.

10. Find the length of $y = (x^3/4) + 1/(3x)$ from the point where $x = 1$ to the point where $x = 2$.

11. Find the length of the first-quadrant portion of $x = y^4 + 1/(32y^2)$ from the point where $y = 1$ to the point where $y = 2$.

12. Find the perimeter of the area bounded by $y^3 = x^2$ and $x + 3y - 4 = 0$.

13. Find the perimeter of the area bounded by $x^4 - 6xy + 3 = 0$ and $11x - 12y - 3 = 0$.

14. Find the perimeter of the area enclosed by $x^{2/3} + y^{2/3} = a^{2/3}$.

15. Find the length of the curve $9y^2 = x(3 - x)^2$ from $(1, 2/3)$ to $(3, 0)$.

16. Show that $1 + y'^2$ is a perfect square for the function defined by $y = ax^n + bx^{2-n}$ whenever $4abn \, (n - 2) = 1$.

17. Set up, but do not evaluate, integrals for the length of
    (a) $y = x^2$ from $(0, 0)$ to $(3, 9)$;

(b) $y = x^3$ from $(-1, -1)$ to $(2, 8)$;

(c) $xy = 1$ from $(1, 1)$ to $(4, 1/4)$.

8.4 Areas of Surfaces of Revolution

In Fig. 8.20 it is assumed that, for $a \leqslant x \leqslant b$, $y = f(x)$ defines a continuous and nonnegative function f and that f' is continuous. We propose to investigate the lateral surface of the solid of revolution obtained by revolving $y = f(x)$ about the x-axis, from $x = a$ to $x = b$. The surface obtained is known as a surface of revolution. Our investigation will include the formulation of a satisfactory definition of such an area.

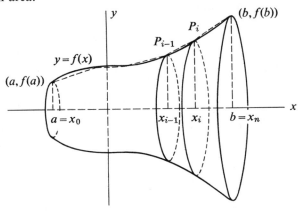

Figure 8.20

We subdivide the interval from a to b in the usual manner and form the corresponding polygonal path from $(a, f(a))$ to $(b, f(b))$ as we did in the arc-length problem. When the curve and the polygonal path are revolved about the x-axis, each segment of the path, such as $P_{i-1}P_i$, generates the lateral area of a frustrum of a right-circular cone. If n is large and all segments $P_{i-1}P_i$ are small in length, our intuition tells us that the sum of the lateral areas of the n frustra will be close to what we think the surface of revolution should be. Hence we define the surface of revolution S as the limit as $\max (\Delta x_i) \to 0$ of the sum of the lateral areas of the n approximating frustra.

To obtain a formula for S, we first obtain a formula for the lateral area S_f of a frustrum of a right-circular cone. We assume that the lateral surface of a right-circular cone is given by $S_c = \pi r s$, where r is the base radius and s the slant height.

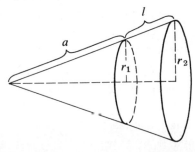

Figure 8.21

From Fig. 8.21 we obtain

$$S_f = \pi r_2(a + l) - \pi r_1 a$$

or

$$S_f = \pi(r_2 a - r_1 a) + \pi r_2 l.$$

Similar triangles yield

$$\frac{r_1}{a} = \frac{r_2}{a + l}$$

from which it easily follows that

$$r_2 a - r_1 a = r_1 l.$$

Substituting into the last expression for S_f, we obtain the required formula:

$$S_f = \pi r_1 l + \pi r_2 l = \pi(r_1 + r_2)l. \qquad (8.17)$$

Applying (8.17) to Fig. 8.20 with $r_1 = f(x_{i-1})$, $r_2 = f(x_i)$, and $l = P_{i-1}P_i$, we obtain

$$S = \lim_{\max(\Delta x_i) \to 0} \sum_{i=1}^{n} [\pi f(x_{i-1})P_{i-1}P_i + \pi f(x_i)P_{i-1}P_i].$$

We now replace $P_{i-1}P_i$ by the expression which was used for it in Sec. 8.3, namely,

$$P_{i-1}P_i = \sqrt{1 + [f'(c_i)]^2}\, \Delta x_i$$

where $x_{i-1} < c_i < x_i$. Thus

$$S = \lim_{\max(\Delta x_i) \to 0} \sum_{i=1}^{n} \pi f(x_{i-1})\sqrt{1 + [f'(c_i)]^2}\, \Delta x_i$$

$$+ \lim_{\max(\Delta x_i) \to 0} \sum_{i=1}^{n} \pi f(x_i)\sqrt{1 + [f'(c_i)]^2}\, \Delta x_i. \qquad (8.18)$$

Since the function defined by the expression $\pi f(x)\sqrt{1 + [f'(x)]^2}$ is continuous on $a \leqslant x \leqslant b$, one might conclude that Theorem 4-X is applicable to (8.18). However, there is a difficulty involved, since $x_{i-1} \neq c_i$ in the first sum and $x_i \neq c_i$ in the second sum. This difficulty is resolved by the following extension of Theorem 4-X, proved in Ref. 8.1 and due to the American mathematician G. A. Bliss (1876–1951).

Theorem 8-I (*Bliss's theorem*).   If f and g are continuous on $a \leqslant x \leqslant b$, and if the interval from a to b is subdivided into n parts in the usual manner, and if c_i and c_i' are any two points in the ith subinterval Δx_i, then

$$\lim_{\max(\Delta x_i) \to 0} \sum_{i=1}^{n} g(c_i)h(c_i')\, \Delta x_i = \int_a^b g(x)h(x)\, dx.$$

Applying Bliss's theorem to each term of (8.18), with $g(x) = \pi f(x)$ and $h(x) = \sqrt{1 + [f'(x)]^2}$, and adding the two equal results, we obtain

$$S = 2\pi \int_a^b f(x)\sqrt{1 + [f'(x)]^2}\, dx. \qquad (8.19)$$

Using (8.13) and (8.15), formula (8.19) can also be written as

$$S = 2\pi \int y\, ds \qquad (8.20)$$

or

$$S = 2\pi \int_c^d y\sqrt{1 + \left(\frac{dx}{dy}\right)^2}\, dy. \tag{8.21}$$

In (8.21), $c = f(a)$ and $d = f(b)$. The limits are omitted in (8.20), since the integration can be performed with respect to either x or y. In fact, the integration can be performed with respect to s or some other variable if (under certain conditions) the integrand can be expressed in terms of that other variable. This changing of the variable of integration will be studied in Chapter 11.

If the function f is negative on $a \leqslant x \leqslant b$, the integrand in (8.19) will be negative, and hence S will be negative. Thus, (8.19) should be applied over intervals where $f(x)$ does not change sign.

If a curve $y = f(x)$ is revolved about the y-axis, formula (8.20) becomes

$$S = 2\pi \int x\, ds, \tag{8.22}$$

and ds can be replaced by either

$$\sqrt{1 + \left(\frac{dy}{dx}\right)^2}\, dx \qquad \text{or} \qquad \sqrt{1 + \left(\frac{dx}{dy}\right)^2}\, dy.$$

If a curve is revolved about a line parallel to the x- or y-axis, the preceding formulas are readily modified to obtain the areas of the resulting surfaces of revolution.

Example 1.   Find the surface generated by revolving the curve $y = 2\sqrt{x}$ from $x = 1$ to $x = 9$ about the x-axis.

Solution I.   Using $y' = x^{-1/2}$ and (8.19) we find

$$S = 2\pi \int_1^9 2x^{1/2}\sqrt{1 + \frac{1}{x}}\, dx$$

$$= 4\pi \int_1^9 (x + 1)^{1/2}\, dx$$

$$= 4\pi \cdot \frac{2}{3}(x + 1)^{3/2}\Big]_1^9$$

$$= \frac{8\pi}{3}[(10)^{3/2} - 2^{3/2}] \quad \text{square units.}$$

Solution II.   Using $x = y^2/4$, $dx/dy = y/2$, and (8.21), we find

$$S = 2\pi \int_2^6 y\sqrt{1 + \frac{y^2}{4}}\, dy$$

$$= \frac{\pi}{2}\int_2^6 (4 + y^2)^{1/2}(2y)\, dy$$

$$= \frac{\pi}{2} \cdot \frac{2}{3}(4 + y^2)^{3/2}\Big]_2^6$$

$$= \frac{8\pi}{3}[(10)^{3/2} - 2^{3/2}] \quad \text{square units.}$$

Example 2.   Find the area generated by revolving the curve $y = x^2$ from $(0, 0)$ to $(2, 4)$ about the y-axis.

Solution.   Using $y' = 2x$, $ds = \sqrt{1 + 4x^2}\, dx$, and (8.22), we obtain

$$S = 2\pi \int_0^2 x\sqrt{1 + 4x^2}\, dx$$

$$= \frac{\pi}{4} \int_0^2 (1 + 4x^2)^{1/2}(8x)\, dx$$

$$= \frac{\pi}{4} \cdot \frac{2}{3}(1 + 4x^2)^{3/2}\Big]_0^2$$

$$= \frac{\pi}{6}(17\sqrt{17} - 1) \quad \text{square units.}$$

PROBLEM LIST 56

1.   Find the surface area generated when the given arc is revolved about the x-axis:

   (a) $y = 4\sqrt{x}$ from $x = 1$ to $x = 4$.

   (b) $y = 2x$ from $x = 0$ to $x = 5$.

   (c) $3x - 4y + 1 = 0$ from $x = 1$ to $x = 5$.

   (d) $x + y = -1$ from $x = -1$ to $x = 1$.

   (e) $y = x^3$ from $x = 0$ to $x = 2$.

   (f) $y^2 = 4 - x$ from $(0, 2)$ to $(4, 0)$.

   (g) $y = (x^4/4) + 1/(8x^2)$ from $x = 1$ to $x = 2$.

   (h) $y = (x^5/5) + 1/(12x^3)$ from $x = 1$ to $x = 2$.

   (i) $3x = 2(y^2 + 1)^{3/2}$ from $y = 1$ to $y = 3$.

2.   Find the surface area generated when the given arc is revolved about the y-axis:

   (a) $y = x^2/2$ from $x = 0$ to $x = 1$.

   (b) $3x - 2y = 1$ from $x = 1$ to $x = 5$.

   (c) $y = 2x$ from $x = 0$ to $x = 4$.

   (d) $y = 4 - x^2$ from $(0, 4)$ to $(2, 0)$.

   (e) $y = (x^4/4) + 1/(8x^2)$ from $x = 1$ to $x = 2$.

   (f) $y = (x^5/5) + 1/(12x^3)$ from $x = 1$ to $x = 2$.

3.   Find the surface area generated by revolving the line segment from $(0, 0)$ to (h, r) about the x-axis.

4.   The portion of a sphere between two parallel planes h units apart is called a zone of altitude h. If a denotes the radius of the sphere, show that the lateral area of a zone is given by $S_z = 2\pi a h$.

5.   Find the surface area generated by revolving the parabola $x^2 = 2py$ from $(0, 0)$ to $(p, p/2)$ about the y-axis.

8.5   Average Value

The average or arithmetic mean m of a set of n numbers $y_1, y_2, \ldots, y_n$ is defined by

$$m = \frac{y_1 + y_2 + \cdots + y_n}{n}. \tag{8.23}$$

The number m is representative of the set in the sense that the set would have the same sum if every member y_i was replaced by m. For example, if a student had grades of 90, 70, 80, and 60, his average grade would be 300/4, or 75. Here all four grades were considered equally important, but let us now assume that the grade of 90 has twice the importance of each of the other three grades. We then assign a weight of 2 to the grade of 90 and a weight of 1 to each of the other grades. If we now multiply each grade by its weight, add the results, and divide by the sum of the weights, we obtain the weighted mean, or weighted average. For the four grades this would be

$$\frac{90(2) + 70(1) + 80(1) + 60(1)}{2 + 1 + 1 + 1} = \frac{390}{5} = 78.$$

The formula for the weighted mean $\bar{y}$ is

$$\bar{y} = \frac{y_1 w_1 + y_2 w_2 + \cdots + y_n w_n}{w_1 + w_2 + \cdots + w_n}, \tag{8.24}$$

where w_i is the weight assigned to y_i.

We now consider the problem of finding the average height of the curve $y = f(x)$ from $x = a$ to $x = b$ in Fig. 8.22. It is assumed that f is continuous on $a \leqslant x \leqslant b$. We must formulate a satisfactory definition for the average ordinate $\bar{y}_x$, since (8.23) and (8.24) apply only when a finite number of quantities are to be averaged.

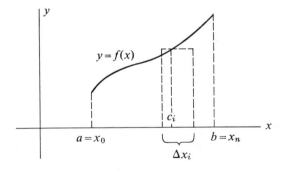

Figure 8.22

We subdivide the interval from a to b into n parts in the usual manner and choose an arbitrary ordinate $f(c_i)$ in each subinterval Δx_i. If n is large and max (Δx_i) small in length, it seems plausible that the mean of the n ordinates chosen would be a good approximation to what we think $\bar{y}_x$ should be, provided each ordinate $f(c_i)$ is weighted with the length of the corresponding subinterval Δx_i. With this motivation, we define $\bar{y}_x$ by

$$\bar{y}_x = \lim_{\max(\Delta x_i) \to 0} \left[\frac{\sum\limits_{i=1}^{n} f(c_i) \Delta x_i}{\sum\limits_{i=1}^{n} \Delta x_i} \right].$$

Applying Theorem 4-X, we obtain

$$\bar{y}_x = \frac{\int_a^b f(x)\, dx}{b - a}. \tag{8.25}$$

An alternate approach is to subdivide $b - a$ into n equal parts and apply (8.23) to the n midordinates. This yields

$$m = \frac{\sum\limits_{i=1}^{n} f(m_i)}{n} = \frac{\sum\limits_{i=1}^{n} f(m_i)(\Delta x)}{n(\Delta x)},$$

where

$$m_i = \frac{x_{i-1} + x_i}{2} \quad \text{and} \quad \Delta x = \frac{b - a}{n}.$$

It is easy to see that $m \to \bar{y}_x$ in (8.25) as $n \to \infty$.

Geometrically, $\bar{y}_x$ represents the altitude of a rectangle having base $b - a$ and area equal to the area under $y = f(x)$ from a to b. See Fig. 8.23. In this interpretation, area must be regarded as negative over intervals where $f(x) < 0$.

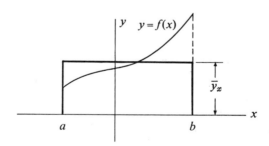

Figure 8.23

In (8.25) the subscript on $\bar{y}_x$ indicates that the ordinates are averaged with respect to x. The average value of a quantity $v = F(u)$ with respect to a variable u upon which v depends over an interval $u_1 \leqslant u \leqslant u_2$ is given by

$$\bar{v}_u = \frac{\int_{u_1}^{u_2} F(u)\, du}{u_2 - u_1}. \tag{8.26}$$

As will be seen in the examples, the average value of a quantity with respect to one variable need not be the same as the average value of that quantity with respect to a different variable.

Example 1.   Find the average height with respect to x of $y = 4 - x^2$ from $(0, 4)$ to $(2, 0)$.

Solution

$$\bar{y}_x = \frac{\int_0^2 (4 - x^2)\, dx}{2 - 0}$$

$$= \frac{4x - (x^3/3)]_0^2}{2} = \frac{8}{3} \text{ units.}$$

Example 2.   Find the average height of $x^{2/3} + y^{2/3} = 1$ from $(2^{-3/2}, 2^{-3/2})$ to $(0, 1)$ with respect to the arc length s.

Solution.   By implicit differentiation, it is easily shown that $dx/dy = -x^{1/3}/y^{1/3}$. Hence

$$\bar{y}_s = \frac{\int y\, ds}{\int ds} = \frac{\int_{2^{-3/2}}^1 y\sqrt{1 + (x^{2/3}/y^{2/3})}\, dy}{\int_{2^{-3/2}}^1 \sqrt{1 + (x^{2/3}/y^{2/3})}\, dy}$$

$$= \frac{\int_{2^{-3/2}}^1 y^{2/3}\, dy}{\int_{2^{-3/2}}^1 y^{-1/3}\, dy} = \frac{4}{5}(1 - 2^{-5/2}).$$

Note that s is positive upward along the curve with $s = 0$ at $(2^{-3/2}, 2^{-3/2})$. See Fig. 8.24.

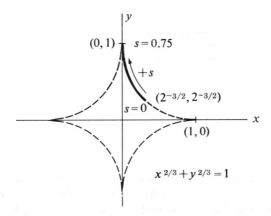

Figure 8.24

The average height of the same arc with respect to x is given by

$$\bar{y}_x = \frac{\int_0^{2^{-3/2}} (1 - x^{2/3})^{3/2}\, dx}{2^{-3/2} - 0} \, .$$

This integral, which we will be able to evaluate in Chapter 11, has a value different from $\bar{y}_s$.

Example 3. Find the average abscissa of $y = x^2/2$ from $(0, 0)$ to $(2, 2)$ with respect to (a) the ordinate y, (b) the shaded area A shown in Fig. 8.25.

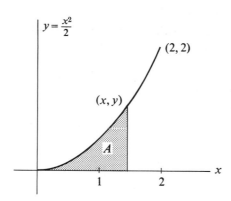

Figure 8.25

Solution

(a)
$$\bar{x}_y = \frac{\int_0^2 x\, dy}{\int_0^2 dy} = \frac{\int_0^2 \sqrt{2}\, y^{1/2}\, dy}{2} = \frac{4}{3} \text{ units.}$$

(b) To find $\bar{x}_A$ we first find
$$A = \int_0^x \frac{u^2}{2}\, du = \frac{x^3}{6},$$

from which we obtain
$$A]_{x=2} = \frac{4}{3} \quad \text{and} \quad x = 6^{1/3} A^{1/3}.$$

Then
$$\bar{x}_A = \frac{\int x\, dA}{\int dA} = \frac{\int_0^{4/3} 6^{1/3} A^{1/3}\, dA}{4/3}$$

$$= \frac{3}{4}(6^{1/3}) \frac{3}{4} A^{4/3}\Big]_0^{4/3}$$

$$= \frac{3}{2} \neq \bar{x}_y.$$

PROBLEM LIST 57

1. Find the average height of each arc with respect to x. Illustrate $\bar{y}_x$ graphically, as in Fig. 8.23.

   (a) $y = x^2$ from $(0, 0)$ to $(2, 4)$.

  (b) $y = x^2 + 2x + 2$ from $(-2, 2)$ to $(1, 5)$.

  (c) $y = |x|$ from $x = -1$ to $x = 2$.

  (d) $y = 2x + 3$ from $x = 1$ to $x = 4$.

  (e) $y = x^2(3 - x)$ from $(0, 0)$ to $(4, -16)$.

  (f) $y = \sqrt{x}$ from $(1, 1)$ to $(9, 3)$.

  (g) $y = x\sqrt{1 + x^2}$ from $x = 1$ to $x = 3$.

2. Find the average abscissa of each arc with respect to y. Illustrate $\bar{x}_y$ graphically.

  (a) $y = 2x$ from $(0, 0)$ to $(3, 6)$.

  (b) $y^2 = x^3$ from $(0, 0)$ to $(4, 8)$.

  (c) $y^2 = x$ from $(1, 1)$ to $(9, 3)$.

  (d) $x = y^3$ from $(-1, -1)$ to $(8, 2)$.

3. For the segment of $2x - y - 3 = 0$ from $(2, 1)$ to $(4, 5)$ find

  (a) $\bar{y}_x$,   **(b)** $\bar{y}_y$,   **(c)** $\bar{y}_s$,   **(d)** $\bar{x}_y$.

4. Find the average height with respect to x of the first-quadrant portion of the circle $x^2 + y^2 = a^2$.

5. Find the average value of y^2 with respect to x for the first-quadrant portion of the ellipse $b^2x^2 + a^2y^2 = a^2b^2$.

6. Find the average height of $x^{2/3} + y^{2/3} = a^{2/3}$ with respect to s from $(a, 0)$ to $(\sqrt{2}\,a/4, \sqrt{2}\,a/4)$.

7. Find the average squared abscissa of $b^2x^2 + a^2y^2 = a^2b^2$ with respect to x from $x = 0$ to $x = a$.

8. The distance s that a body falls from rest under the influence of gravity is given by $s = (1/2)gt^2$. The velocity v satisfies $v^2 = 2gs$. Find, for the first t seconds, the average velocity

  (a) with respect to the time t;

  (b) with respect to the distance s.

9. Find the average abscissa of $y = x^2$ from $(0, 0)$ to $(2, 4)$ with respect to

  (a) the ordinate y;

  (b) the area A bounded by $y = x^2$, $y = 0$, and $x = x$.

10. Find the average height of $y = x^3/3 + 1/(4x)$ with respect to the arc length s from $x = 1$ to $x = 2$.

REFERENCES

8.1 G. A. Bliss, "A Substitute for Duhamel's Theorem," *Annals of Mathematics*, Vol. 16 (1914–15).

8.2 J. M. H. Olmsted, *Advanced Calculus*, Appleton-Century-Crofts, New York, 1961.

Trigonometric and inverse

trigonometric functions

9.1 Trigonometric Functions of a Real Variable

In elementary trigonometry $\sin x$ is regarded as a real number which is associated with an angle x, where x may be measured in degrees, radians, revolutions, or some other unit of angular measure. In the calculus it is more convenient to regard both x and $\sin x$ as real numbers. Then $y = f(x) = \sin x$ defines a function of the real variable x. We propose to study this function.

In Fig. 9.1 the unit circle shown has equation $t^2 + y^2 = 1$ when referred to the ty-axes. The arc from $P(t_1, y)$ to $A(1, 0)$ has equation $y = \sqrt{1 - t^2}$. Since $y = \sqrt{1 - t^2}$ is continuous on $t_1 \leqslant t \leqslant 1$ and

$$\frac{dy}{dt} = \frac{-t}{\sqrt{1 - t^2}}$$

is continuous on $t_1 < t < 1$, the arc $\overset{\frown}{PA}$ has a length s. The angle x subtended by $\overset{\frown}{PA}$ is an angle of s radians and $x = s$. (If a circle has radius r, the radian measure θ of the central angle subtended by an arc s of the circle is given by $\theta = s/r$.)

A one-to-one correspondence is established between the set of all angles and the set of real numbers. The point A is chosen as origin of arcs on the circle and the distance $\overset{\frown}{AP}$ corresponds to the angle x. Distance is taken as positive counterclockwise around the circle and as negative clockwise around the circle. Thus, positive angles correspond to positive distances and negative angles to negative distances. The ratio of the circumference C to the diameter 2 of the circle is denoted by π and hence the distance in the positive direction from A around the circle and back to

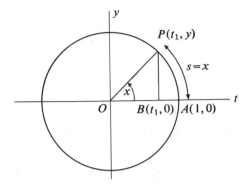

Figure 9.1

A is 2π. The distance from A to $(0, 1)$ in the positive direction is $\pi/2$; the distance from A to $(-1, 0)$ in the negative direction is $-\pi$, and so forth.

The sine of x is equal to $BP \div OP = BP = y$. Since x corresponds to the directed arc length $s = \overset{\frown}{AP}$, $\sin x$ can be regarded as the sine of the real number which measures the directed distance from A to P along the circle.

For points in the lower semicircle, $y = -\sqrt{1 - t^2}$ and $\sin x$ is negative.

We now construct the graph of the function defined by $y = \sin x$. Since $\sin (x + 2n\pi) \equiv \sin x (n = 0, \pm 1, \pm 2, \cdots)$, we will draw the graph for $0 \leqslant x \leqslant 2\pi$ only. Since $y = f(x) = \sin x$ defines a periodic function of period 2π, its graph outside $0 \leqslant x \leqslant 2\pi$ is readily obtained.

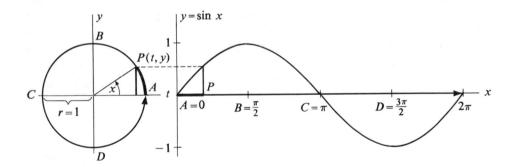

Figure 9.2

In Fig. 9.2 the curve on the right is the graph of $y = \sin x$ for $0 \leqslant x \leqslant 2\pi$. The abscissa of a point on the curve corresponds to the positive arc of the same length measured in the positive direction from A on the circumference of the unit circle shown on the left. The ordinate is the same as the ordinate of the corresponding point on the unit circle.

Henceforth, the six basic trigonometric functions will each be regarded as a function of a real variable. The graphs of the other five functions are drawn in Fig. 9.3 for ready reference. One period of each function is shown.

Figure 9.3

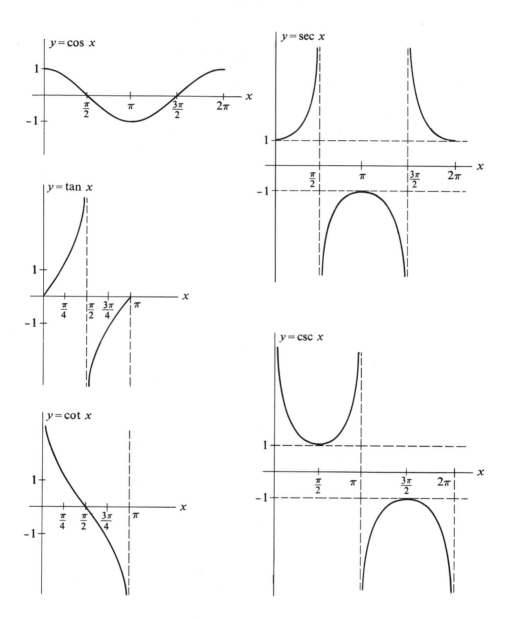

9.2   *An Important Limit*

In order to differentiate the function defined by $y = \sin x$, it is necessary to know

$$\lim_{x \to 0} \frac{\sin x}{x}.$$

We first observe that since

$$\frac{\sin(-x)}{(-x)} \equiv \frac{-\sin x}{-x} \equiv \frac{\sin x}{x},$$

$$\lim_{x \to 0^-} \frac{\sin x}{x} = \lim_{x \to 0^+} \frac{\sin x}{x}.$$

Hence we need only investigate the limit as $x \to 0$ through positive values. Let us assume that in Fig. 9.1, $0 < x < \pi/2$.

We subdivide BA into n parts such that $\Delta x_1 = \Delta x_2 = \cdots = \Delta x_n$. The ordinates at the points of subdivision on the t-axis produce a polygonal path $P_0 P_1 P_2 \cdots P_n$ from P to A (P_0 denotes P and P_n denotes A). We know that as $n \to \infty$, the limit of the length of the nth polygonal path exists and is equal to $s = x$. Since $s = x$ is greater than or equal to the length of PA, the polygonal path when $n = 1$, and $BP < PA$, it follows that

$$\sin x < x. \tag{9.1}$$

For the nth polygonal path,

$$P_0 P_1 < \Delta x_1 + |\Delta y_1|,$$
$$P_1 P_2 < \Delta x_2 + |\Delta y_2|,$$

$$\cdot$$
$$\cdot$$
$$\cdot$$

$$P_{n-1} P_n < \Delta x_n + |\Delta y_n|.$$

Now adding, we find the length of the nth polygonal path must be less than

$$\sum_{i=1}^{n} \Delta x_i + \sum_{i=1}^{n} |\Delta y_i| = BA + BP$$

$$= (1 - \cos x) + \sin x,$$

since $OB = \cos x$. Since every polygonal path has length less than $(1 - \cos x) + \sin x$, it follows that x, the limit approached by the length of the nth polygonal path as $n \to \infty$, must satisfy

$$x \leqslant (1 - \cos x) + \sin x. \tag{9.2}$$

We also note by (9.1) that

$$1 - \cos x < (1 - \cos x)(1 + \cos x) = \sin^2 x < x \sin x. \tag{9.3}$$

Combining (9.1), (9.2), and (9.3) yields

$$\sin x < x < x \sin x + \sin x = (x + 1) \sin x.$$

Dividing through by $\sin x$ and taking reciprocals, we obtain

$$1 > \frac{\sin x}{x} > \frac{1}{x + 1}.$$

Since

$$\lim_{x \to 0} \frac{1}{x + 1} = 1,$$

it follows that

$$\lim_{x \to 0} \frac{\sin x}{x} = 1. \tag{9.4}$$

9.3 Continuity of the Trigonometric Functions

We first note that

$$\lim_{x \to 0} \sin x = \lim_{x \to 0} \left(\frac{\sin x}{x} \cdot x \right) = \left(\lim_{x \to 0} \frac{\sin x}{x} \right) \left(\lim_{x \to 0} x \right)$$
$$= (1)(0) = 0 = \sin 0. \tag{9.5}$$

This proves that the function defined by $y = \sin x$ is continuous at $x = 0$. The function defined by $y = \cos x$ is also continuous at $x = 0$, since

$$\lim_{x \to 0} \cos x = \lim_{x \to 0} \sqrt{1 - \sin^2 x} = 1 = \cos 0. \tag{9.6}$$

We next employ the formula $\sin(x + h) = \sin x \cos h + \cos x \sin h$ to show that $\sin x$ is continuous at $x = x_0$. We have

$$\lim_{x \to x_0} \sin x = \lim_{h \to 0} \sin (x_0 + h)$$
$$= \lim_{h \to 0} [\sin x_0 \cos h + \cos x_0 \sin h]$$
$$= (\sin x_0) \Big[\lim_{h \to 0} \cos h \Big] + (\cos x_0) \Big[\lim_{h \to 0} \sin h \Big]$$
$$= (\sin x_0)(1) + (\cos x_0)(0) = \sin x_0.$$

Similar proofs for the other functions are left to the exercises.

Formula (9.4) will enable us to show that each of the six trigonometric functions is differentiable at all values of x for which it is defined. Since differentiability at a point implies continuity at that point, it will then follow that each trigonometric function is continuous at all values of x for which it is defined.

PROBLEM LIST 58

1. Extend Fig. 9.1 so that each of the six trigonometric functions will be represented by a line segment.

2. In Fig. 9.1 what points on the circle correspond to (a) $3\pi/2$, (b) 4π, (c) $-3\pi/2$, (d) -3π?

3. State the period of each of the six trigonometric functions.

4. Draw the graph of the function defined by $y = \cos x$ by using the technique of Fig. 9.2.

5. Draw the graph of the function defined by $y = 3 \sin (2x + \pi/6)$ by using the technique of Fig. 9.2. State the period and the amplitude of the function.

6. Evaluate the following limits:

   (a) $\displaystyle\lim_{x \to 0} \frac{\sin 2x}{x}$.

   (b) $\displaystyle\lim_{x \to 0} \frac{\sin x}{3x}$.

   (c) $\displaystyle\lim_{x \to 0} \frac{\tan x}{x}$.

   (d) $\displaystyle\lim_{x \to 0} \frac{\sin kx}{x}$.

   (e) $\displaystyle\lim_{x \to 0} \frac{x - \sin x}{x}$.

   (f) $\displaystyle\lim_{x \to 0} \frac{1 - \cos x}{x}$.

(g) $\lim\limits_{x \to 0} \dfrac{\tan 5x}{3x}$.

(i) $\lim\limits_{x \to 0^+} \dfrac{\sqrt{\sin 2x}}{\sqrt{x}}$.

(h) $\lim\limits_{x \to 0} \dfrac{\sin x - \tan x}{x^3}$.

7. Prove (9.4) by comparing the areas of triangle OBP, sector OAP, and triangle OAT in Fig. 9.4. This proof is simpler than the one in the text, but requires the formula $A = r^2\theta/2$ for the area of a sector of a circle.

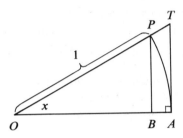

Figure 9.4

8. Prove that the function defined by $y = \cos x$ is continuous at $x = x_0$.

9. Prove that the function defined by $y = \tan x$ is continuous at $x = x_0$
   (a) by using the formula

$$\tan (x + h) = \frac{\tan x + \tan h}{1 - \tan x \tan h};$$

   (b) by using the formula $\tan x = \sin x/\cos x$.

9.4   The Derivative of the Sine Function

To find $(d/dx) \sin x$ we resort to the definition of a derivative. From

$$y = \sin x$$

we obtain $\Delta y = \sin (x + \Delta x) - \sin x$. Replacing $\sin (x + \Delta x)$ by $\sin x \cos (\Delta x) + \cos x \sin (\Delta x)$ and dividing by Δx yields

$$\frac{\Delta y}{\Delta x} = \frac{\sin x \cos (\Delta x) + \cos x \sin (\Delta x) - \sin x}{\Delta x}$$

$$= \frac{\cos x \sin (\Delta x) - \sin x[1 - \cos (\Delta x)]}{\Delta x}.$$

Letting $\theta = \Delta x/2$ in the double-angle formula $\cos 2\theta = 1 - 2 \sin^2 \theta$, we find that

$$1 - \cos (\Delta x) = 2 \sin^2 \frac{\Delta x}{2}.$$

Thus,

$$\frac{\Delta y}{\Delta x} = \cos x \left[\frac{\sin (\Delta x)}{\Delta x} \right] - \sin x \left(\sin \frac{\Delta x}{2} \right) \left(\frac{\sin (\Delta x/2)}{\Delta x/2} \right).$$

Taking the limit of each side as $\Delta x \longrightarrow 0$, we apply (9.4) and (9.5) to obtain

$$\frac{dy}{dx} = \lim_{\Delta x \to 0} \frac{\Delta y}{\Delta x} = [\cos x][1] - [\sin x][0][1] = \cos x.$$

We emphasize that this formula is true only if x is a real number or the radian measure of an angle. Otherwise it would not be true that

$$\lim_{\Delta x \to 0} \frac{\sin (\Delta x)}{\Delta x} = 1.$$

If u denotes a differentiable function of x, it follows from the chain rule that

$$\frac{d}{dx} \sin u = \frac{d}{du} \sin u \cdot \frac{du}{dx} = \cos u \frac{du}{dx}. \tag{9.7}$$

Example 1. $d/dx \sin 2x = 2 \cos 2x.$

Example 2. $d/dx \sin x^2 = 2x \cos x^2.$

Example 3. $d/dx \sin^2 x = (d/dx)(\sin x)^2 = 2 \sin x \cos x.$

Example 4. $d/dx \sin^3 4x = 3 \sin^2 4x \cdot (d/dx) \sin 4x = 12 \sin^2 4x \cos 4x.$

9.5   *Derivatives of the Other Trigonometric Functions*

We could differentiate the other trigonometric functions by using the definition of a derivative, but it is simpler to apply (9.7).

To differentiate $\cos u$ with respect to x, we write

$$\frac{d}{dx} \cos u = \frac{d}{dx} \sin \left(\frac{\pi}{2} - u \right) = \left[\cos \left(\frac{\pi}{2} - u \right) \right] [-1] \frac{du}{dx}$$

or

$$\frac{d}{dx} \cos u = -\sin u \frac{du}{dx}. \tag{9.8}$$

The other trigonometric functions may be differentiated by writing them in terms of the sine and cosine. The results are:

$$\frac{d}{dx} \tan u = \sec^2 u \frac{du}{dx}, \tag{9.9}$$

$$\frac{d}{dx} \cot u = -\csc^2 u \frac{du}{dx}, \tag{9.10}$$

$$\frac{d}{dx} \sec u = \sec u \tan u \frac{du}{dx}, \tag{9.11}$$

$$\frac{d}{dx} \csc u = -\csc u \cot u \frac{du}{dx}. \tag{9.12}$$

For example, we obtain (9.9) by writing $\tan u = \sin u/\cos u$ and differentiating the right member as a quotient. Thus,

$$\frac{d}{dx}\tan u = \frac{d}{dx}\frac{\sin u}{\cos u}$$

$$= \frac{\cos u[\cos u(du/dx)] - \sin u[-\sin u(du/dx)]}{\cos^2 u}$$

$$= \frac{\cos^2 u + \sin^2 u}{\cos^2 u}\frac{du}{dx} = \sec^2 u\,\frac{du}{dx}.$$

The derivations of (9.10), (9.11), and (9.12) are left to the exericses.

Example 1

$$\frac{d}{dx}\tan\frac{x}{2} = \frac{1}{2}\sec^2\frac{x}{2}.$$

Example 2

$$\frac{d}{dx}\cot^3 2x = 3\cot^2 2x\frac{d}{dx}\cot 2x$$

$$= 3\cot^2 2x(-\csc^2 2x)(2)$$

$$= -6\cot^2 2x\,\csc^2 2x.$$

Example 3

$$\frac{d}{dx}(x^2\sec x) = x^2\sec x\tan x + 2x\sec x.$$

Example 4.   A gutter is constructed from a sheet of metal of width a by rotating one-third of the sheet on each side through an angle θ as shown in Fig. 9.5. Determine θ so that the cross-sectional area A will be a maximum, thereby enabling the gutter to carry the maximum amount of water.

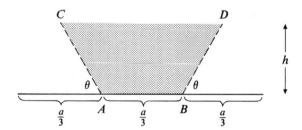

Figure 9.5

Solution.   The area of trapezoid $ABCD$ is equal to half its height $h = [a/3]\sin\theta$, multiplied by the sum of its bases $AB = a/3$ and $CD = a/3 + 2([a/3]\cos\theta)$. From

$$A = \frac{1}{2}\cdot\left[\frac{a}{3}\right]\sin\theta\left[\frac{2a}{3} + \left(\frac{2a}{3}\right)\cos\theta\right]$$

$$= \frac{a^2}{9}(\sin\theta + \sin\theta\cos\theta)$$

we obtain

$$\frac{dA}{d\theta} = \frac{a^2}{9}[\cos\theta + (\sin\theta)(-\sin\theta) + (\cos\theta)(\cos\theta)].$$

Setting $dA/d\theta = 0$ and replacing $-\sin^2 \theta$ by $\cos^2 \theta - 1$ yield

$$2 \cos^2 \theta + \cos \theta - 1 = 0$$

or

$$(2 \cos \theta - 1)(\cos \theta + 1) = 0.$$

Since $\cos \theta = -1$ when $\theta = n\pi$, it is clear that maximum area is obtained when $\cos \theta = 1/2$, or $\theta = \pi/3$ or $60°$. One could also verify that $d^2 A/d\theta^2 |_{\theta = \pi/3} < 0$.

Example 5.   In Fig. 9.6, BC is the connecting rod of a direct-acting engine. The crank AB is one-fourth as long as BC and is rotating counterclockwise at 400 rpm. As end B of rod BC moves around the circle of radius a, end C moves back and forth along AC. Find $d\phi/dt$, the angular velocity of rod BC, when $\theta = \pi/6$.

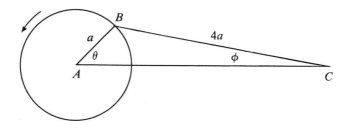

Figure 9.6

Solution.   Applying the law of sines to $\triangle ABC$ yields

$$\frac{\sin \phi}{a} = \frac{\sin \theta}{4a} \qquad \text{or} \qquad \sin \phi = \frac{\sin \theta}{4}.$$

Differentiating implicitly with respect to time, we obtain

$$\cos \phi \frac{d\phi}{dt} = \frac{\cos \theta}{4} \frac{d\theta}{dt} \qquad \text{or} \qquad \frac{d\phi}{dt} = \frac{\cos \theta}{4 \cos \phi} \frac{d\theta}{dt}.$$

When $\theta = \pi/6$, $\sin \theta = 1/2$, $\cos \theta = \sqrt{3}/2$, $\sin \phi = 1/8$, and

$$\cos \phi = \sqrt{1 - \sin^2 \phi} = \sqrt{1 - \frac{1}{64}} = \frac{\sqrt{63}}{8}.$$

Therefore,

$$\frac{d\phi}{dt}\Big|_{\theta = \pi/6} = \frac{(\sqrt{3}/2)(400)}{4\sqrt{63}/8} = \frac{400}{\sqrt{21}} \cong 87 \text{ rpm}.$$

PROBLEM LIST 59

1.   Find $\dfrac{dy}{dx}$:

(a) $y = \sin 3x.$

(c) $y = \tan \dfrac{x}{5}.$

(b) $y = x + \cos 4x.$

(d) $y = \sec 3x - x^2.$

(e) $y = \csc^2 x$.

(l) $y = \dfrac{\sin 2x}{1 + \tan x}$.

(f) $y = \cot (1 + x^2)$.

(m) $y = \sin^4 2x \cos^2 3x$.

(g) $y = \sin^2 (2 - x)$.

(n) $y = \sqrt{1 - \csc^3 x}$.

(h) $y = \sin (2 - x)^2$.

(o) $y = \dfrac{\sec 2x}{3 + \sin x}$.

(i) $y = \cos^3 2x$.

(p) $y = (1 - 2 \sin^2 x)^3$.

(j) $y = 3 \cos^2 \dfrac{x}{2}$.

(q) $y = x + \sqrt{1 - \sin^3 x}$.

(k) $y = 2 \sin^3 x \cos x$.

2. Find y' and y'':
    (a) $y = \sin x - \cos x$.

    (d) $y = \sqrt{1 - 2 \cos x}$.

    (b) $y = 3 \sin^2 2x$.

    (e) $y = x \csc 2x$.

    (c) $y = x - \tan x$.

    (f) $y = \cot^3 x$.

3. Verify:
    (a) $\dfrac{d}{dx} \sin 2x = \dfrac{d}{dx}(2 \sin x \cos x)$.

    (b) $\dfrac{d}{dx} \cos 2x = \dfrac{d}{dx}(\cos^2 x - \sin^2 x)$.

    (c) $\dfrac{d}{dx} \tan 2x = \dfrac{d}{dx} \dfrac{2 \tan x}{1 - \tan^2 x}$.

4. Verify that $y = a \cos kx + b \sin kx$ defines a solution of the differential equation $(d^2y/dx^2) + k^2y = 0$. Verify that $y = a \sin(kx + \phi)$ also defines a solution.

5. Derive (9. 10).

6. Derive (9.11).

7. Derive (9.12).

8. Find $(d/dx) \sin x$ if x is measured in degrees.

9. Find dy/dx by implicit differentiation:
    (a) $\sin 2x + \cos y - x = 0$.
    (b) $x - 2 \sin(x + y) = 0$.

10. Derive the formula $(d/dx) \cos x = -\sin x$ by evaluating
$$\lim_{\Delta x \to 0} \frac{\cos (x + \Delta x) - \cos x}{\Delta x}.$$

11. Derive the formula $(d/dx) \sin x = \cos x$ by using the formula
$$\sin A - \sin B = 2 \cos \frac{A + B}{2} \sin \frac{A - B}{2}.$$

12. Given $y = \sin^3 2x$, find y' and y'' when $x = \pi/6$.

13. Each of the two equal sides of an isosceles triangle has constant length 5 ft. If the angle θ between these sides increases at the constant rate of 20 rad/sec, find the rate at which the area of the triangle is increasing when $\theta = \pi/3$.

14. Find the dimensions of the rectangle of maximum area which can be inscribed in a circle of radius a.

15. Find the dimensions of the right-circular cylinder of maximum lateral surface which can be inscribed in a sphere of radius a.

16. A horizontal searchlight, located at $(0, 5)$, is revolving counterclockwise at constant angular velocity of 20 rpm. How fast is the light beam moving along the x-axis when the searchlight is pointed toward $(5, 0)$?

17. Find the approximate value of $\tan [(\pi/4) + (1/100)]$, using differentials.

18. Find the length of the shortest ladder which will reach from the ground level to a high vertical wall if it must clear an 8-ft vertical fence which is 27 ft from the wall.

19. Find the maximum and minimum values of $y = 3 \cos x + 4 \sin x$.

20. Find the altitude of an isosceles triangle of minimum area which can be circumscribed about a circle of radius a.

21. Find the dimensions of the right-circular cylinder of maximum volume which can be inscribed in a sphere of radius a.

22. Find the dimensions of the right-circular cone of maximum volume which can be inscribed in a sphere of radius a.

23. Find the dimensions of the right-circular cone of minimum volume which can be circumscribed about a sphere of radius a.

24. Find the radius of the right-circular cone of maximum volume that can be constructed with a given slant height s.

25. In Fig. 9.6, determine the velocity of point C when $\theta = \pi/2$.

26. Given that f is defined by $f(x) = \sin x$, find $f'(0)$ by applying the definition of a derivative.

27. Employ the formula

$$\tan (x + y) = \frac{\tan x + \tan y}{1 - \tan x \tan y}$$

and the fact that

$$\lim_{h \to 0} \frac{\tan h}{h} = 1$$

to show that

$$\lim_{h \to 0} \frac{\tan (x + h) - \tan x}{h} = \sec^2 x.$$

28. Let $f(t) = \cos (x + y) - \cos (x + t) \cos (y - t) + \sin (x + t) \sin (y - t)$. Show that

(a) $\frac{d}{dt} f(t) = f'(t) \equiv 0$;

(b) $f(y) = 0$, and hence that $f(t) \equiv 0$;

(c) $\cos(x + y) \equiv \cos x \cos y - \sin x \sin y$.

9.6 *Graphs Involving Trigonometric Functions*

In drawing graphs involving trigonometric functions it is often convenient to indictate multiples of π on the x-axis. This can be accomplished approximately by choosing a unit distance along the y-axis and then locating the point $(\pi, 0)$ slightly more than three units from the origin ($\pi \cong 3.14$). Another useful fact is that $y = a \sin(kx + \phi)$ [or $y = a \cos(kx + \phi)$] has amplitude a, amplitude denoting the maximum displacement of the graph from the x-axis. If $f(x)$ has period p, then $f(kx + \phi)$ has period p/k. This follows from the fact that

$$(kx_2 + \phi) - (kx_1 + \phi) = p$$

when

$$x_2 - x_1 = \frac{p}{k}.$$

The calculus is not required to construct simple trigonometric graphs. However, as a matter of interest, let us consider the graph of $y = \sin x$. From $y' = \cos x$ and $y'' = -\sin x = -y$, we note that the curve has intercepts and points of inflection at $x = n\pi$, maxima at $x = (\pi/2) + 2n\pi$, and minima at $x = (3\pi/2) + 2n\pi$, ($n = 0, \pm1, \pm2, \cdots$). We note also that $|y'| \leqslant 1$ and that the curve is concave downward for $y > 0$ and concave upward for $y < 0$. These observations are verified by reference to Fig. 9.2.

For more complicated trigonometric graphs, the calculus is very useful. We combine our previous methods for constructing graphs with our newly acquired formulas for differentiating the trigonometric functions.

Example 1.   Draw the graph of $y = \sin^2 x$ for $0 \leqslant x \leqslant 2\pi$.

Solution.   From $y' = 2 \sin x \cos x = \sin 2x$ and

$$y'' = 2 \cos 2x = 2 - 4 \sin^2 x = 2 - 4y,$$

we find that $y = 0$ at $x = n\pi$, $y' = 0$ when $2x = n\pi$ or at $x = n\pi/2$, and $y'' = 0$ when $2x = (\pi/2) + n\pi$ or at $x = (\pi/4) + (n\pi/2)$.

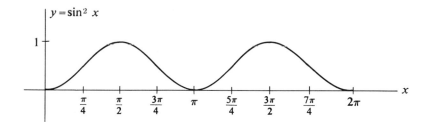

Figure 9.7

It is easily determined that maxima occur at $x = n\pi/2$ when n is odd, and minima at $x = n\pi/2$ when n is even. Points of inflection occur at $x = (\pi/4) + (n\pi/2)$, and $y = 1/2$ and $y' = \pm1$ at each of these points. Since $0 \leqslant y \leqslant 1$, $2 - 4y < 0$ when $1 \geqslant y > 1/2$, and $2 - 4y > 0$ when $0 \leqslant y < 1/2$. The curve is concave downward when $y > 1/2$ and concave upward when $y < 1/2$. The graph is shown in Fig. 9.7.

Example 2.   Draw the graph of $y = 2 \cos x + \cos 2x$ for $0 \leqslant x \leqslant 2\pi$.

Solution.   The graph has period 2π, the larger of the periods of the two terms. The method of composition of ordinates is very helpful, since the curves $y_2 = 2 \cos x$ and $y_3 = \cos 2x$ are easily drawn. From

$$y' = -2 \sin x - 2 \sin 2x = -2 \sin x \, (1 + 2 \cos x),$$

we find that the slope is zero at $x = 0$, π, 2π, $2\pi/3$, and $4\pi/3$.

From $y'' = -2 \cos x - 4 \cos 2x$, we find that $(0, 3)$, $(\pi, -1)$, and $(2\pi, 3)$ are maximum points, while $(2\pi/3, -3/2)$ and $(4\pi/3, -3/2)$ are minimum points. The equations $y = 0$ and $y'' = 0$ could be solved for $\cos x$ by the quadratic formula, but we will merely note that in $0 \leqslant x \leqslant 2\pi$, there are two intercepts and four points of inflection. The two intercepts and the intersections of the curve with the component curves $y_2 = 2 \cos x$ and $y_3 = \cos 2x$ are easily determined graphically. In drawing the graph it is also helpful to compute the slope at $x = \pi/4$, $\pi/2$, $3\pi/4$, and so forth. The graph is shown in Fig. 9.8.

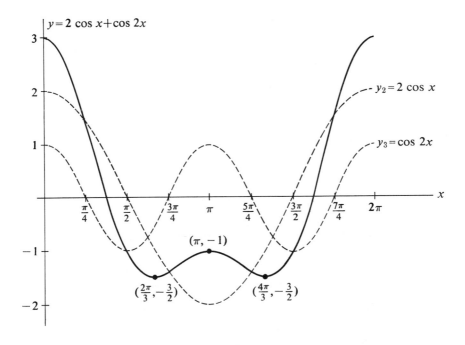

Figure 9.8

In physics many waves can be represented by periodic functions defined by expressions of the form $y = a \sin (kx + \phi)$ or $y = a \cos (kx + \phi)$. These are called fundamental waves; and other waves, called harmonic waves, are sums of fundamental waves. The harmonic waves are said to be obtained from the fundamental waves by superposition, which corresponds to the composition of ordinates in Fig. 9.8.

PROBLEM LIST 60

1. Draw the graphs of the following equations for the indicated intervals:

    (a) $y = 2 \sin (x + \pi/3),\ 0 \leqslant x \leqslant 2\pi$.

    (b) $y = 3 \cos (2x - \pi/4),\ 0 \leqslant x \leqslant 2\pi$.

    (c) $y = \cos^2 x,\ -2\pi \leqslant x \leqslant 2\pi$.

    (d) $y = \sqrt{3} \sin x - \cos x,\ 0 \leqslant x \leqslant 2\pi$.

    (e) $y = \sin x + \cos x,\ -2\pi \leqslant x \leqslant 2\pi$.

    (f) $y = 1 + \sin x,\ -2\pi \leqslant x \leqslant 2\pi$.

    (g) $y = x - \tan x,\ -\pi \leqslant x \leqslant \pi$.

    (h) $y = 3 \sin \pi x,\ -4 \leqslant x \leqslant 4$.

    (i) $y = \cos x - x,\ 0 \leqslant x \leqslant 2\pi$.

    (j) $y = \sec x + \cos x,\ 0 \leqslant x \leqslant 2\pi$.

    (k) $y = \tan x - \sin x,\ 0 \leqslant x \leqslant 2\pi$.

    (l) $y = 64 \sec x + 27 \csc x,\ 0 < x < \pi/2$.

    (m) $y = \sec x - \csc x,\ 0 < x < 2\pi$.

    (n) $y = (\cot x + 1)^{-1},\ 0 < x < \pi/2$.

    (o) $y = 1 - x + \tan x,\ -2\pi \leqslant x \leqslant 2\pi$.

    (p) $y = 4 \sec x + 3 \cos x,\ -2\pi \leqslant x \leqslant 2\pi$.

    (q) $y = \sin 2x + 2 \sin x,\ 0 \leqslant x \leqslant 2\pi$.

    (r) $y = \cos 2x + 2 \sin x,\ 0 \leqslant x \leqslant 2\pi$.

    (s) $y = \cos 3x - \sin x,\ 0 \leqslant x \leqslant 2\pi$.

    (t) $y = 3 \sin x - 4 \sin^3 x,\ 0 \leqslant x \leqslant 2\pi$.

    (u) $y = |x| + \sin x,\ -\pi < x < \pi$.

2. The function defined by $y = 1 - \sin x$ is called the coversine of x, and the function defined by $y = (1 - \cos x)/2$ is called the haversine of x. Draw the graphs of these functions for $0 \leqslant x \leqslant 2\pi$.

3. Prove that the slope of the curve $y = \tan x$ is never less than 1.

4. Draw the graph of $y = \sin x + \sqrt{3} \cos x$. Then write $y = 2[(1/2) \sin x + (\sqrt{3}/2) \cos x]$ and use the formula $\sin (A + B) = \sin A \cos B + \cos A \sin B$ to write y as a fundamental sine wave. Verify that the graph is correct.

5. Find the angle between

    (a) $y = \sin x$ and $y = \cos x$;

    (b) $y = \tan x$ and $y = \cot x$;

    (c) $y = \cos x$ and $3x - 2\pi y = 0$.

9.7   The Inverse Trigonometric Functions

We wish to construct an inverse of the function defined by $y = f(x) = \sin x$, using the methods of Secs. 2.4 and 3.9. We must select a subset D' of the domain D of f such that to each y in $-1 \leqslant y \leqslant 1$, the range R of f, there corresponds one and only one x in D'. As shown in Fig. 9.9, the interval $-\pi/2 \leqslant x \leqslant \pi/2$ is a natural choice for D'. Since f is continuous and differentiable on D', the inverse of this function, denoted by f^{-1} and defined by $y = f^{-1}(x) = \text{Sin}^{-1} x$, is continuous on $-1 \leqslant x \leqslant 1$ and differentiable on $-1 < x < 1$. Since $f'(-\pi/2) = f'(\pi/2) = 0$, $\text{Sin}^{-1} x$ does not possess a derivative at $x = -1$ or at $x = +1$.

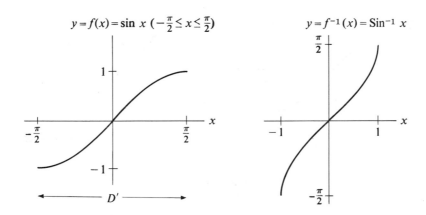

$$y = f(x) = \sin x \ \left(-\tfrac{\pi}{2} \leq x \leq \tfrac{\pi}{2}\right) \qquad\qquad y = f^{-1}(x) = \text{Sin}^{-1} x$$

Figure 9.9

Note that the two curves in Fig. 9.9 are symmetric with respect to the line $y = x$.

In elementary trigonometry the expression $\sin^{-1} x$ is often employed to denote any number whose sine is x. The particular number which we are now denoting by $\text{Sin}^{-1} x$ is referred to as the principal value of $\sin^{-1} x$. When we write $y = \text{Sin}^{-1} x$, we will always mean the value at x of the function whose graph is shown in Fig. 9.9.

We again point out that the "-1" in $\text{Sin}^{-1} x$ is not an exponent but rather, as explained in Sec. 2.4, a symbol employed to denote an inverse function. To avoid confusion we will write the reciprocal of $\sin x$ as $\csc x$ or $(\sin x)^{-1}$, rather than as $\sin^{-1} x$. The expression $y = \sin x$ is sometimes written $x = \text{Arcsin } y$. Although we will not use this notation, it is very suggestive, since, in Fig. 9.1, x is indeed an arc whose sine is y.

Examples

$$\text{Sin}^{-1}(-1) = -\frac{\pi}{2}; \qquad \text{Sin}^{-1}\left(-\frac{1}{2}\right) = -\frac{\pi}{6}; \qquad \text{Sin}^{-1}(0) = 0;$$

$$\text{Sin}^{-1}\left(\frac{1}{\sqrt{2}}\right) = \frac{\pi}{4}; \qquad \text{Sin}^{-1}(1) = \frac{\pi}{2}.$$

In constructing an inverse of the function defined by $y = f(x) = \cos x$ we are guided by the same considerations as in the case of $y = \sin x$. We cannot choose the interval $-\pi/2 \leqslant x \leqslant \pi/2$ for D', since for every y in $0 \leqslant y < 1$ there are two values of x in $-\pi/2 \leqslant x \leqslant \pi/2$ satisfying $y = \cos x$.

The natural choice for D' is the interval $0 \leqslant x \leqslant \pi$. The graph of the inverse cosine function defined by $y = f^{-1}(x) = \text{Cos}^{-1} x$ is shown in Fig. 9.10.

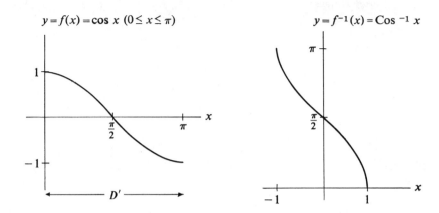

$y = f(x) = \cos x \ (0 \leq x \leq \pi)$

$y = f^{-1}(x) = \text{Cos}^{-1} x$

Figure 9.10

Examples

$$\text{Cos}^{-1}(-1) = \pi; \qquad \text{Cos}^{-1}\left(-\frac{1}{2}\right) = \frac{2\pi}{3}; \qquad \text{Cos}^{-1}(0) = \frac{\pi}{2};$$

$$\text{Cos}^{-1}\left(\frac{\sqrt{3}}{2}\right) = \frac{\pi}{6}; \qquad \text{Cos}^{-1}(1) = 0.$$

In constructing the inverse of the function defined by $y = \tan x$, we choose D' as the interval $-\pi/2 < x < \pi/2$. The graph of $y = \text{Tan}^{-1} x$ is shown in Fig. 9.11.

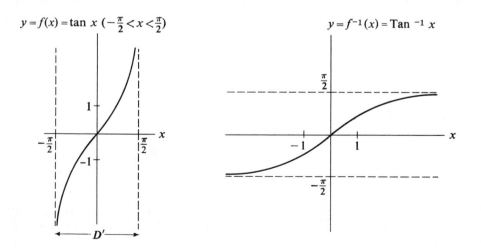

$y = f(x) = \tan x \ (-\frac{\pi}{2} < x < \frac{\pi}{2})$

$y = f^{-1}(x) = \text{Tan}^{-1} x$

Figure 9.11

In constructing the inverse of the function defined by $y = \cot x$, we choose D' as the interval $0 < x < \pi$. The graph of $y = \mathrm{Cot}^{-1} x$ is shown in Fig. 9.12.

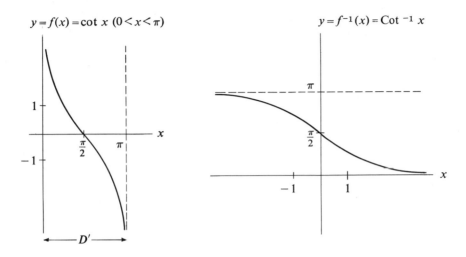

$$y = f(x) = \cot x \ (0 < x < \pi)$$

$$y = f^{-1}(x) = \mathrm{Cot}^{-1} x$$

Figure 9.12

Examples

$$\mathrm{Tan}^{-1}(-1) = -\frac{\pi}{4}; \qquad \mathrm{Tan}^{-1}(0) = 0; \qquad \mathrm{Tan}^{-1}(\sqrt{3}) = \frac{\pi}{3};$$

$$\mathrm{Cot}^{-1}(-1) = \frac{3\pi}{4}; \qquad \mathrm{Cot}^{-1}(0) = \frac{\pi}{2}; \qquad \mathrm{Cot}^{-1}(1) = \frac{\pi}{4}.$$

The function defined by $y = \mathrm{Sec}^{-1} x$ is not always constructed with the same choice of D'; and the same is true for the function defined by $y = \mathrm{Csc}^{-1} x$. These

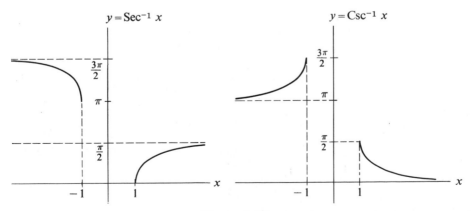

$$y = \mathrm{Sec}^{-1} x$$

$$y = \mathrm{Csc}^{-1} x$$

Figure 9.13

functions can usually be avoided in applications. The graphs of these functions for one method of construction are shown in Fig. 9.13.

9.8 Derivatives of the Inverse Trigonometric Functions

To differentiate $y = \text{Sin}^{-1} x$, we write $\sin y = x$ and differentiate implicitly with respect to x. Thus

$$\cos y \frac{dy}{dx} = 1$$

and

$$\frac{dy}{dx} = \frac{1}{\cos y} = \frac{1}{\sqrt{1 - \sin^2 y}} = \frac{1}{\sqrt{1 - x^2}}. \tag{9.13}$$

In (9.13) $\cos y > 0$, since $-\pi/2 < y < \pi/2$. Since dy/dx gives the slope of the curve $y = \text{Sin}^{-1} x$ shown in Fig. 9.9, it is easy to see that dy/dx does not exist at $x = \pm 1$, that $dy/dx > 0$ for $-1 < x < 1$, and that $dy/dx = 1$ at $x = 0$. From

$$\frac{d^2 y}{dx^2} = \frac{x}{(1 - x^2)^{3/2}}$$

it is easy to see that $(0, 0)$ is a point of inflection, that the curve is concave downward for $-1 < x < 0$, and concave upward for $0 < x < 1$.

———————

The other inverse trigonometric functions are differentiated similarly. For example, writing $y = \text{Tan}^{-1} x$ in the form $\tan y = x$, we obtain, upon differentiating implicitly with respect to x,

$$\sec^2 y \frac{dy}{dx} = 1$$

or

$$\frac{dy}{dx} = \frac{1}{\sec^2 y} = \frac{1}{1 + \tan^2 y} = \frac{1}{1 + x^2}.$$

Upon application of the chain rule, the following formulas are easily obtained; in each case u denotes a differentiable function of x:

$$\frac{d}{dx} \text{Sin}^{-1} u = \frac{1}{\sqrt{1 - u^2}} \frac{du}{dx}, \tag{9.14}$$

$$\frac{d}{dx} \text{Cos}^{-1} u = \frac{-1}{\sqrt{1 - u^2}} \frac{du}{dx}, \tag{9.15}$$

$$\frac{d}{dx} \text{Tan}^{-1} u = \frac{1}{1 + u^2} \frac{du}{dx}, \tag{9.16}$$

$$\frac{d}{dx} \text{Cot}^{-1} u = \frac{-1}{1 + u^2} \frac{du}{dx}. \tag{9.17}$$

One of the main reasons for the importance of the inverse trigonometric functions is that the preceding differentiation formulas give rise to useful integral or antiderivative formulas. These will be studied in Chapter 11.

Example 1

$$\frac{d}{dx} \text{Sin}^{-1} 2x = \frac{2}{\sqrt{1 - 4x^2}}.$$

Example 2

$$\frac{d}{dx} \text{Cos}^{-1} (3x - 1) = \frac{-3}{\sqrt{1 - (3x - 1)^2}} = \frac{-\sqrt{3}}{\sqrt{2x - 3x^2}}.$$

Example 3

$$\frac{d}{dx} \text{Tan}^{-1} \left(\frac{1}{x}\right) = \frac{1}{1 + (1/x^2)}\left(\frac{-1}{x^2}\right) = \frac{-1}{x^2 + 1}.$$

Example 4

$$\frac{d}{dx}(x \, \text{Cot}^{-1} x) = \frac{-x}{1 + x^2} + \text{Cot}^{-1} x.$$

Example 5. A balloon is released at point C which is 400 ft horizontally from point A. Find the rate at which angle θ is changing 10 sec after the balloon is released, if the balloon rises at the constant rate of 20 fps. See Fig. 9.14.

Solution. From $\theta = \text{Tan}^{-1} (20t/400) = \text{Tan}^{-1} (t/20)$ we obtain

$$\frac{d\theta}{dt} = \frac{1/20}{1 + (t/20)^2} = \frac{20}{400 + t^2},$$

and hence

$$\frac{d\theta}{dt}\Big|_{t=10} = \frac{20}{400 + 100} = \frac{2}{50} \, \text{rad/sec}.$$

Figure 9.14

Example 6. Draw the graph of $y = 2 \, \text{Sin}^{-1} (x/3)$.

Solution. Since $-1 \leqslant x/3 \leqslant 1$, y is defined for $-3 \leqslant x \leqslant 3$. When $x = -3$, $y = -\pi$, and when $x = 3$, $y = \pi$. The curve goes through the origin and, from

$$y' = \frac{2(1/3)}{\sqrt{1 - (x/3)^2}},$$

has slope 2/3 at the origin. Additional information may be gleaned from the equation $x = 3 \sin(y/2)$. The graph is shown in Fig. 9.15.

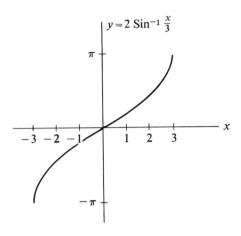

Figure 9.15

PROBLEM LIST 61

1. Evaluate

   (a) $\mathrm{Sin}^{-1}(\sqrt{3}/2)$;

   (b) $\mathrm{Cos}^{-1}(-\sqrt{3}/2)$;

   (c) $\mathrm{Tan}^{-1}(-\sqrt{3})$;

   (d) $\mathrm{Cot}^{-1}(-1/\sqrt{3})$;

   (e) $\mathrm{Sin}^{-1}(1/\sqrt{2}) + \mathrm{Sin}^{-1}(-1/\sqrt{2})$;

   (f) $\mathrm{Cos}^{-1}(1/\sqrt{2}) + \mathrm{Cos}^{-1}(-1/\sqrt{2})$;

   (g) $\mathrm{Tan}^{-1}(1/2) + \mathrm{Tan}^{-1}(1/3)$;

   (h) $\mathrm{Sin}^{-1}(24/25) + \mathrm{Sin}^{-1}(7/25)$.

2. Given $x = \mathrm{Sin}^{-1}(-1/2)$, find $\cos x$, $\tan x$, $\cot x$, $\sec x$, and $\csc x$.

3. Find dy/dx. Simplify when possible.

   (a) $y = \mathrm{Sin}^{-1}(5x)$.

   (b) $y = \mathrm{Cos}^{-1}(x - 1)$.

   (c) $y = \mathrm{Tan}^{-1}(3x^2)$.

   (d) $y = \mathrm{Cot}^{-1}\sqrt{x}$.

   (e) $y = 3\,\mathrm{Sin}^{-1}(2x - 1)$.

   (f) $y = x^2\,\mathrm{Sin}^{-1}(2x)$.

   (g) $y = \mathrm{Cos}^{-1}(2/x^3)$.

   (h) $y = \mathrm{Tan}^{-1}\left(\dfrac{2}{1 - x^2}\right)$.

   (i) $y = \dfrac{\sqrt{9 - x^2}}{x} + \mathrm{Sin}^{-1}\left(\dfrac{x}{3}\right)$.

   (j) $y = x - (x^2 + 1)\,\mathrm{Tan}^{-1}x$.

   (k) $y = (a^2/2)\,\mathrm{Sin}^{-1}(x/a) + (x/2)\sqrt{a^2 - x^2}$.

   (l) $y = x/(\mathrm{Tan}^{-1}x)$.

   (m) $y = \sin^2 x\,\mathrm{Cos}^{-1}x$.

   (n) $y = \mathrm{Sin}^{-1}\left(\dfrac{x}{1 - x}\right)$.

   (o) $y = x^2\,\mathrm{Tan}^{-1}\left(\dfrac{x + 1}{x - 1}\right)$.

   (p) $y = \mathrm{Sin}^{-1}\sqrt{\dfrac{1 + x}{x}}$.

4. Derive formula (9.15).

5. Derive formula (9.17).

6. Find an equation of the line tangent to $y = 2 \operatorname{Sin}^{-1}(x/2)$ at $(1, \pi/3)$.

7. Show that the origin is a point of inflection of the curve $y = \operatorname{Tan}^{-1} x$.

8. Find the slope of the curve $y = \operatorname{Cos}^{-1} x$ at $(-1/2, 2\pi/3)$.

9. Draw the graphs of the functions defined by
    (a) $y = \operatorname{Sin}^{-1}(2x)$;   (d) $y = x \operatorname{Sin}^{-1} x$;
    (b) $y = 2 \operatorname{Cos}^{-1}(x/3)$;   (e) $y = x^2 \operatorname{Cos}^{-1} x$;
    (c) $y = 2 \operatorname{Tan}^{-1}(x + 1)$;   (f) $y = \operatorname{Sin}^{-1}\sqrt{4 - x^2}$.

10. Evaluate $\operatorname{Tan}^{-1} x + \operatorname{Tan}^{-1}(1/x)$.

11. Prove that $\pi/4 = 4 \operatorname{Tan}^{-1}(1/5) - \operatorname{Tan}^{-1}(1/239)$. This formula (due to Machin, 1680–1751) and certain generalizations of it played an important role in the computation of π to over 100,000 decimal places by digital computer.

12. A line passes through $(0, -1)$ and intersects the parabola $y = x^2$. Find the maximum angle such a line can make with the y-axis.

13. A rope extends from a boat to a point on a wharf 25 ft above the water level. If the rope is pulled in at the constant rate of 3 fps, how fast is the angle between the rope and the water changing when 40 ft of rope are out?

14. A searchlight, located 400 ft from a straight road, follows a car traveling along the road at the constant rate of 80 fps. How fast is the searchlight revolving when the car is 500 ft from the searchlight?

15. A direction indicator, located at the origin, follows a plane which is flying toward the y-axis along the line $y = 300$ ft. If the plane is approaching the origin at the constant rate of 400 fps, how fast is the indicator turning when it makes an angle of $\pi/4$ with the x-axis?

16. A man walks horizontally at the constant rate of 5 fps toward the base of an 80-ft tower. How fast is the angle of elevation of the top of the tower changing when he is 50 ft horizontally from the point directly under the top of the tower?

17. Locate point $P(x, 0)$ on the positive x-axis so that $\angle APB$ will be a maximum, A being the point $(0, 16)$ and B the point $(0, 25)$. Note that a picture extending from A to B would subtend the maximum viewing angle at the required point P.

18. Use differentials to find the approximate change in $\operatorname{Tan}^{-1} x$ as x changes from 1 to 1.04.

19. Establish the identity

$$\operatorname{Sin}^{-1} x + \operatorname{Cos}^{-1} x = \frac{\pi}{2}.$$

The logarithmic

and exponential functions

10.1 The Logarithmic Function

Since $y = x^n$, n an integer, is continuous on $0 < x < \infty$, it follows from Theorem 4-X that

$$F(x) = \int_1^x t^n \, dt$$

exists for $x > 0$.

If $n \neq -1$, the properties of the function F can be determined by examining $x^{n+1}/(n+1)$, since $x^{n+1}/(n+1)$ is a primitive or antiderivative of x^n and hence, by Theorem 4-XVI, must differ from $F(x)$ by a constant. If $n = -1$, the function F still exists, but we know of no antiderivative of x^{-1} which will enable us to determine the properties of F. Hence it is natural to investigate the properties of F when $n = -1$. This function, which we will denote by f and whose value at x is given by

$$f(x) = \log x = \int_1^x \frac{dt}{t} \quad (x > 0), \tag{10.1}$$

is called the logarithm of x. The reason for this designation will become apparent later when we discover the connection between $\log x$ and the logarithm of a number studied in secondary mathematics.

The shaded area in Fig. 10.1 furnishes a geometrical interpretation of $\log x$. It is clear that

$$f(1) = \log 1 = \int_1^1 \frac{dt}{t} = 0 \tag{10.2}$$

and that $\log x > 0$ for $x > 1$. If $0 < x < 1$,

$$\log x = \int_1^x \frac{dt}{t} = -\int_x^1 \frac{dt}{t},$$

and consequently log x is represented by the negative of the area under $y = 1/t$ from $t = x$ to $t = 1$. In other words

$$\log x < 0 \qquad \text{for} \qquad 0 < x < 1.$$

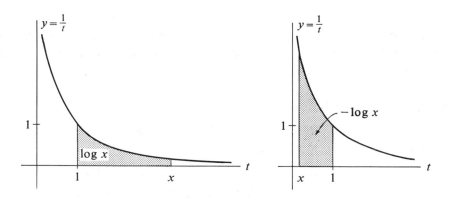

Figure 10.1

The function defined by $f(x) = \log x$ will be better understood if we can draw its graph. We first apply Theorem 4-XV (first fundamental theorem of calculus) to (10.1) to obtain

$$\frac{d}{dx} \log x = f'(x) = \frac{1}{x}. \qquad (10.3)$$

Thus log x is differentiable and hence continuous at all values of x in its domain of definition. Since $f'(x) > 0$ for $x > 0$, $f(x) = \log x$ defines an increasing function of x and the curve $y = \log x$ has no critical points. We also note that $f'(1) = 1$, $f'(x) > 1$ for $0 < x < 1$, and $f'(x) < 1$ for $x > 1$. In addition, it follows from (10.3) that

$$\lim_{x \to 0^+} f'(x) = \infty \qquad \text{and} \qquad \lim_{x \to \infty} f'(x) = 0.$$

From $f''(x) = -1/x^2$, we see that the curve $y = \log x$ is everywhere concave downward and has no points of inflection.

We know that log x increases as x increases, but this does not imply that $\log x \to \infty$ as $x \to \infty$. To decide this question we first derive the most important property of log x, namely,

$$\log(xy) = \log x + \log y \qquad (x > 0, y > 0). \qquad (10.4)$$

If u denotes a differentiable function of x, the chain rule and (10.3) yield

$$\frac{d}{dx} \log u = \frac{1}{u} \frac{du}{dx} \qquad (u > 0). \qquad (10.5)$$

Regarding $y > 0$ as fixed but arbitrary, we apply (10.5) to the left member of (10.4) to obtain

$$\frac{d}{dx} \log (xy) = \frac{1}{xy} \frac{d(xy)}{dx} = \frac{y}{xy} = \frac{1}{x}.$$

Since $\log (xy)$ and $\log x$ both have derivative $1/x$ with respect to x, it follows from Theorem 4-XVI that $\log (xy) - \log x$ is equal to a constant c. Setting $x = 1$ in

$$\log (xy) - \log x = c \tag{10.6}$$

yields

$$\log y - \log 1 = \log y - 0 = \log y = c.$$

Replacing c in (10.6) by $\log y$ and transposing $\log x$, we obtain (10.4). Property (10.4) is sometimes expressed by saying that $f(x) = \log x$ satisfies the functional equation

$$f(xy) = f(x) + f(y).$$

Setting $y = x$ in (10.4) yields

$$\log x^2 = \log x + \log x = 2 \log x.$$

Next, setting $y = x^2$ in (10.4) yields

$$\log x^3 = \log x + \log x^2 = \log x + 2 \log x = 3 \log x.$$

It is easily proved by mathematical induction (see Problem 2) that

$$\log x^n = n \log x \tag{10.7}$$

for every positive integer n.

For $x = 2$, (10.7) becomes

$$\log 2^n = n \log 2. \tag{10.8}$$

Now let M denote an arbitrarily large positive number. Then

$$\log 2^n = n \log 2 > M$$

whenever $n > M/\log 2$. Since the logarithm is an increasing function, it follows that $\log x > M$ whenever $n > M/\log 2$ and $x \geqslant 2^n$. This completes the proof that $\log x \to \infty$ as $x \to \infty$ and answers the question of what happens to the graph of $y = \log x$ as $x \to \infty$.

To determine the behavior of the graph as $x \to 0^+$, we set $y = 1/x$ in (10.4) to obtain

$$\log 1 = \log x + \log \left(\frac{1}{x}\right).$$

Then, since $\log 1 = 0$ by (10.2),

$$\log x = -\log \left(\frac{1}{x}\right). \tag{10.9}$$

Since $1/x \to \infty$ as $x \to 0^+$, it follows from (10.9) that

$$\log x \to -\infty \qquad \text{as } x \to 0^+.$$

Since $\log 1 = 0$ and $\log 2^n = n \log 2$, it follows from Theorem 4-VIII (intermediate-value theorem) that if $0 < k < n \log 2$, there exists at least one

$x = c$ satisfying $\log c = k$. Since $\log x$ defines an increasing function, there is exactly one such c. If $k = 1$, the value of c is denoted by e, after Euler who played a dominant role in introducing this important number into mathematics. A rough approximation to e could be obtained from Fig. 10.1. A frequently used approximation is

$$e \cong 2.718 \qquad (\log e = 1). \tag{10.10}$$

The number e, like π, is irrational and hence has a nonterminating decimal expansion. This expansion has been computed to over 60,000 decimal places by digital computer.

If $k < 0$, it is easy to show by using (10.9) that there exists exactly one $x = c$ such that $\log c = k$.

We now have sufficient information to enable us to draw the graph of $y = \log x$, except that we do not know the functional values for various values of x. The value of $\log 2$ can be approximated by using inscribed and circumscribed rectangles to approximate the area under $y = 1/t$ from $t = 1$ to $t = 2$ in Fig. 10.2. For a rough approximation we note that $\log 2$ is greater than the area of rectangle $ABCD$ but less than the area of trapezoid $AECD$. This yields the inequality

$$\frac{1}{2} < \log 2 < \frac{3}{4}.$$

The actual value of $\log 2$, correct to three decimal places, is 0.693.

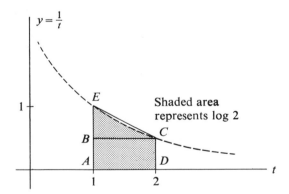

Figure 10.2

The height of the curve $y = \log x$ at $x = 2^n$, n an integer, can be found from (10.7) and (10.9). For example,

$$\log 4 = \log 2^2 = 2 \log 2 \cong 1.386,$$

$$\log 8 = \log 2^3 = 3 \log 2 \cong 2.079,$$

$$\log \frac{1}{2} = -\log 2 \cong -0.693,$$

$$\log \frac{1}{4} = -\log 4 \cong -1.386,$$

$$\log \frac{1}{8} = -\log 8 \cong -2.079,$$

and so forth.

Thus, several points on the curve $y = \log x$ can be plotted. The graph of $y = \log x$ is shown in Fig. 10.3.

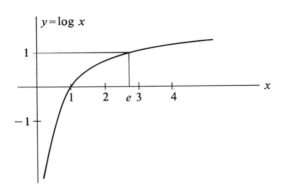

Figure 10.3

Values of $\log x$ can also be computed by the methods of infinite series to be discussed in Chapter 19. The function f has been extensively tabulated and a brief table of values is given in Appendix C.

We list two additional properties of the function defined by $y = \log x$, proofs of which will be left to the exercises:

$$\log \left(\frac{x}{y} \right) = \log x - \log y \tag{10.11}$$

$$\log x^{m/n} = \frac{m}{n} \log x \qquad (m \text{ and } n \text{ integers}, n \neq 0). \tag{10.12}$$

The following examples illustrate the use of formula (10.5).

Example 1

$$\frac{d}{dx} \log (x^2 - 1) = \frac{2x}{x^2 - 1} .$$

Example 2

$$\frac{d}{dx}(x^2 \log 3x) = x^2 \cdot \frac{3}{3x} + 2x \log 3x = x + 2x \log 3x.$$

Example 3. Find dy/dx if

$$y = \log \sqrt[3]{\frac{(x^2 - 4)^2}{(x^2 + 1)^5}} .$$

Solution. Before differentiating, we simplify the expression by applying the various properties of the logarithmic function:

$$y = \frac{1}{3}[\log (x^2 - 4)^2 - \log (x^2 + 1)^5]$$

$$= \frac{2}{3} \log (x^2 - 4) - \frac{5}{3} \log (x^2 + 1),$$

$$\frac{dy}{dx} = \frac{4x}{3(x^2 - 4)} - \frac{10x}{3(x^2 + 1)} = \frac{2x(-3x^2 + 22)}{3(x^2 - 4)(x^2 + 1)}.$$

Example 4.   Draw the graph of the function defined by $y = x^2 - 8 \log x$.

Solution.   The function has domain $x > 0$. From

$$y' = 2x - \frac{8}{x} = \frac{2(x + 2)(x - 2)}{x}$$

and

$$y'' = 2 + \frac{8}{x^2}$$

we find that $(2, 4 - 8 \log 2)$ is a minimum point and that the curve is everywhere concave upward. A few additional points may be plotted with the aid of Table II of Appendix C. The graph is shown in Fig. 10.4.

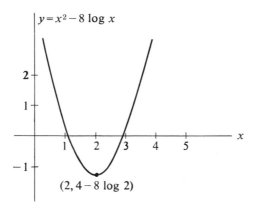

Figure 10.4

PROBLEM LIST 62

1. Replace y by $1/y$ in (10.4) to derive (10.11).
2. Prove (10.7) by mathematical induction.
3. Employ (10.7) and (10.9) to derive (10.12).
4. Write an equation of the line tangent to $y = 1/t$ at $(2, 1/2)$. Use this line in Fig. 10.2 to show that $\log 2 > 0.625$.
5. Show that $\log 1.5 \cong 5/12$ by approximating the area under $y = 1/t$ from $t = 2$ to $t = 3$ by the area of a trapezoid.

6. Use the identity $\log 1 = \log [x \cdot (1/x)]$ to prove that $\log (1/x) = -\log x$. Assume $x > 0$.

7. Prove that if n is a positive integer $\geqslant 2$ then

   (a) $\log n \leqslant \sum_{i=1}^{n-1} \dfrac{1}{i}$;

   (b) $\log n \geqslant \sum_{i=2}^{n} \dfrac{1}{i}$.

8. Find y':

   (a) $y = \log (3x + 2)$.

   (b) $y = \log x^2$.

   (c) $y = \log^2 x$.

   (d) $y = \log \tan x$.

   (e) $y = \log \sin x$.

   (f) $y = \log (\sec x + \tan x)$.

   (g) $y = x \log 3x$.

   (h) $y = x^2 \log x$.

   (i) $y = x \log (4 - x^2)$.

   (j) $y = x \log x - x$.

   (k) $y = x^3 \log^2 x$.

   (l) $y = \log (\log x)$.

9. Simplify each expression for y by applying the basic properties of logarithms. Then find y' and simplify.

   (a) $y = \log 3x$.

   (b) $y = \log\sqrt{x^2 - 1}$.

   (c) $y = \log \dfrac{x^2 - 1}{x^2 - 4}$.

   (d) $y = \log \sqrt[3]{\dfrac{x^2 - 1}{x - 2}}$.

   (e) $y - x \log \left[\dfrac{(x^2 - 1)^2}{x + 2}\right]$.

   (f) $y = \log \sqrt{\dfrac{1 + \sin x}{1 - \sin x}}$.

   (g) $y = \log\sqrt{ax^2 + bx + c}$.

   (h) $y = \log \left(\dfrac{\sqrt{4 - x^2}}{x}\right)$.

   (i) $y = \log \left(\dfrac{x\sqrt{x^2 + 1}}{x^2 - 1}\right)$.

   (j) $y = \log \left(\dfrac{\sqrt{x^2 + 1} - x}{\sqrt{x^2 + 1} + x}\right)$.

   (k) $y = \log \left[\dfrac{(x^3 - 1)^2}{(x^2 - 1)^3}\right]$.

   (l) $y = x \operatorname{Tan}^{-1} x - \log \sqrt{x^2 + 1}$.

10. Find y'':

   (a) $y = x \log x$.

   (b) $y = x^2 \log \sqrt{x}$.

   (c) $y = \log \cos x$.

   (d) $y = \log \sqrt{\dfrac{x^2 - 1}{x + 2}}$.

11. Given $y = x - 2 \log 3x$, find y' and y'' at $x = 4$.

12. Given $\log x + 2 \log y = 4$, find dy/dx.

13. Approximate $\log (1.02)$, using differentials.

14. Draw the graphs of the following equations:

   (a) $y = 2x - \log x$.

   (b) $y = \log (x + 2)$.

   (c) $y = \log (1 - x^2)$.

   (d) $y = \log kx$ for $k = 1, 2, 3, -2$.

   (e) $y = \log |x|$.

   (f) $y = \log (\log x)$.

15. Prove that $\lim_{n \to \infty} \log n = \infty$ by considering the area under $y = 1/t$ from $t = 1$ to $t = 2$, from $t = 2$ to $t = 4$, from $t = 4$ to $t = 8, \cdots$, and from $t = 2^{n-1}$ to $t = 2^n$.

10.2 *The Inverse Logarithmic or Exponential Function*

The function defined by $f(x) = \log x$ has domain $0 < x < \infty$ and range $-\infty < \log x < \infty$. Since to each value of $\log x$ in the range of f there corresponds one and only one value of x in the domain of f, the function f possesses an inverse function denoted by $f^{-1}(x) = \log^{-1} x$. The domain of f^{-1} is the range of f, and the range of f^{-1} is the domain of f. Since $\log x$ possesses a nonzero derivative at every $x > 0$, $\log^{-1} x$ is differentiable at every real x. The graphs of $y = \log x$ and $y = \log^{-1} x$, which are symmetric with respect to the line $y = x$, are displayed in Fig. 10.5. We will soon see why $\log^{-1} x$ is also written as e^x.

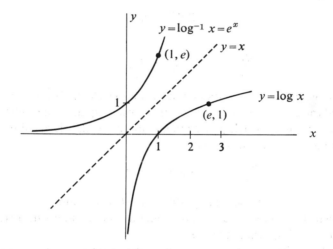

Figure 10.5

We note that if $y = \log^{-1} x$ then $\log y = x$, from which

$$\log 1 = 0 \quad \text{and} \quad \log e = 1.$$

or

$$\log^{-1} 0 = 1 \quad \text{and} \quad \log^{-1} 1 = e.$$

Setting $x = e$ in (10.12), we have

$$\log e^{m/n} = \frac{m}{n} \log e = \frac{m}{n}$$

or

$$e^{m/n} = \log^{-1}\left(\frac{m}{n}\right) \quad \text{for } m/n \text{ rational,} \quad (n \neq 0).$$

Now if α is irrational, e^α has not been defined, but since $\log^{-1} x$ is continuous, we know that

$$\lim_{x \to \alpha} \log^{-1} x = \log^{-1} \alpha.$$

If $x \longrightarrow \alpha$ along an arbitrary sequence $\{x_n\}$ of rational numbers, $\log^{-1} x_n = e^{x_n} \longrightarrow \log^{-1} \alpha$, and hence it is natural to define

$$e^\alpha = \log^{-1} \alpha. \tag{10.13}$$

With this definition we now have

$$e^x = \log^{-1} x \qquad \text{for all real } x. \tag{10.14}$$

This is why the inverse logarithm of x, sometimes called the antilogarithm of x, is also called the exponential function of x. The expression e^u is also written $\exp(u)$, particularly when u denotes a complicated function of x which would be difficult to write as an exponent.

To differentiate $y = \log^{-1} x = e^x$ we write $\log y = x$ and differentiate implicitly to obtain

$$\frac{1}{y}\frac{dy}{dx} = 1,$$

from which

$$\frac{dy}{dx} = y \qquad \text{or} \qquad \frac{de^x}{dx} = e^x. \tag{10.15}$$

The importance of the exponential function stems from this remarkable property, that the derivative of the function is always equal to the value of the function. That is, the rate at which e^x is changing at any instant is equal to the value of e^x at that instant. We note also that

$$\frac{d^n y}{dx^n} = e^x \quad \text{for } n = 1, 2, 3, \cdots.$$

From $y' = y'' = e^x$ we see that $y'(0) = 1$, $y'(1) = e$, $\lim_{x \to -\infty} y' = 0$, $\lim_{x \to \infty} y' = \infty$, and that the curve $y = e^x$ is everywhere concave upward. These facts are evident in the very important Fig. 10.5.

The function whose value at x is e^x has been extensively tabulated and a brief table of its values is given in Table III of Appendix C.

If $y = e^u$, where u denotes a differentiable function of x, the chain rule and (10.15) yield

$$\frac{d}{dx}e^u = e^u\frac{du}{dx}. \tag{10.16}$$

Example 1

$$\frac{d}{dx}e^{x^2-1} = 2xe^{x^2-1}.$$

Example 2

$$\frac{d}{dx}(x^2 e^{-3x}) = x^2(-3e^{-3x}) + e^{-3x}(2x)$$
$$= xe^{-3x}(2 - 3x).$$

Example 3

$$\frac{d}{dx}\exp(\sin x^3) = 2x\cos x^3 \exp(\sin x^3).$$

PROBLEM LIST 63

1. Show that $g(x) = e^x$ satisfies the functional equation $g(x)\, g(y) = g(x + y)$. That is, show that $e^x e^y = e^{x+y}$. *Hint:* Let $u = e^x$ and $v = e^y$; then $x = \log u$ and $y = \log v$.

2. Derive the following properties of e^x:
   (a) $e^x / e^y = e^{x-y}$.
   (b) $(e^x)^y = e^{xy}$ (x real and y rational).

3. Evaluate (a) $e^{-\log 3}$, (b) $e^{5 \log 3}$, (c) $e^{-\log 2}$.

4. Find dy/dx:
   (a) $y = e^{3x}$.
   (b) $y = e^{x^2-4}$.
   (c) $y = xe^{2x}$.
   (d) $y = (x - 1)\, e^{4x}$.
   (e) $y = x^2\, e^{-x^2}$.
   (f) $y = e^{\sin 2x}$.
   (g) $y = 4e^{-2x} + 3 \log x$.
   (h) $y = \text{Sin}^{-1}(e^{-x})$.
   (i) $y = e^{-2x} \sin 3x$.
   (j) $y = e^{-x}(x^2 - 2x + 3)$
   (k) $y = e^{2x}\sqrt{1 + \log x}$.
   (l) $y = \dfrac{e^{2x} - 1}{e^{2x} + 1}$.

5. Find y' and y'':
   (a) $y = e^{5x}$.
   (b) $y = e^x - e^{-x}$.
   (c) $y = xe^x$.
   (d) $y = x^2 e^{-2x}$.
   (e) $y = x\, e^{1/x}$.
   (f) $y = e^{-3x}(x^2 - 4x + 2)$.

6. Given $y = e^{kx}$, find $d^n y/dx^n$.

7. Solve the equation $e^{2x} - 7e^x + 10 = 0$.

8. Find the minimum value of $y = e^{2x} - 2e^x - 12x$.

9. Draw the graphs of the following equations:
   (a) $y = e^{2x}$.
   (b) $y = e^{-x}$.
   (c) $y = e^x + e^{-x}$.
   (d) $y = e^x - e^{-x}$.
   (e) $y = e^{x/2}$.
   (f) $y = e^{-x^2}$.
   (g) $y = e^{x-1}$.
   (h) $y = e^{x^2}$.
   (i) $y = e^{1/x}$.
   (j) $y = e^{-x} \sin x$.
   (k) $y = e^{-x} \cos 2x$.
   (l) $y = e^{\sin x}$.

10. Show the $y = e^x \cos x$ satisfies the differential equation $y'' - 2y' + 2y = 0$.

11. Prove that the rectangle of maximum area having its base on the x-axis and two corners on the curve $y = e^{-x^2}$ must have the two latter corners at the points of inflection of $y = e^{-x^2}$.

12. The reliability R of a component is the probability that it will not fail during the first t hours it is in use. Find the probability that a certain electrical component will not fail during the first 20 hr of operation if R is given by

$$R = e^{-0.02t}.$$

13. The function defined by

$$f(x) = \frac{1}{\sqrt{2\pi}\,\sigma} exp\left[-\frac{1}{2}\left(\frac{x - \mu}{\sigma}\right)^2\right],$$

known as the normal probability density function, plays an important role in probability and statistics. Find the maximum point and the points of inflection on its graph, known as the normal curve.

14. The temperature τ in degrees centigrade of a certain liquid is given by $\tau = 100\, e^{-t/10}$, where t is in minutes. Find τ and $d\tau/dt$ when $t = 5$ min. Show graphically how τ varies with t.

15. Draw the graph of $y = xe^{-x}$. Assume that $y \longrightarrow 0$ as $x \longrightarrow \infty$.

16. A cable hangs in a curve which is symmetric with respect to the y-axis. The tension T in pounds at a point x feet from the y-axis is given by $T = 100\,(e^{x/10} + e^{-x/10})$. Find T and dT/dx at $x = 5$ ft. Also find the maximum and minimum tensions if the cable extends from $x = -10$ to $x = 10$.

17. Approximate $e^{0.002}$, using differentials.

18. Given $M(s) = e^{as + (b^2 s^2/2)}$, find **(a)** $M'(0)$, **(b)**, $M''(0)$, **(c)** $M''(0) - [M'(0)]^2$.

10.3   The General Exponential Function

If $a > 0$, and $k = \log a$,
then
$$a = e^k \quad \text{or} \quad a = e^{\log a}. \tag{10.17}$$
Therefore
$$a^r = (e^{\log a})^r = e^{r \log a} \tag{10.18}$$
for r rational. If α is irrational and if $\{x_n\}$ is an arbitrary sequence of rational numbers approaching α as a limit,
$$\lim_{x_n \to \alpha} e^{x_n \log a} = e^{\alpha \log a},$$
since the exponential function and the function whose value at x is $x \log a$ are both continuous. This prompts us to define, for $a > 0$, and α irrational,
$$a^\alpha = e^{\alpha \log a}.$$

With this definition we now have defined the general exponential function given by
$$a^x = e^{x \log a} \quad \text{for all real } x\ (a > 0). \tag{10.19}$$

Example 1
$$2^x = e^{x \log 2}.$$

Example 2
$$(\sqrt{3})^x = e^{x \log \sqrt{3}} = e^{(x \log 3)/2}.$$

Example 3
$$\pi^x = e^{x \log \pi}.$$

Example 4
$$e^x = e^{x \log e}.$$

Example 5.   Evaluate $(d/dx)(2^x)$.

   Solution

$$\frac{d}{dx}(2^x) = \frac{d}{dx}(e^{x \log 2}) = (e^{x \log 2})(\log 2)$$
$$= 2^x \log 2.$$

Example 6.   Evaluate $(d/dx)(3^{x^2-1})$.

   Solution

$$\frac{d}{dx}(3^{x^2-1}) = \frac{d}{dx}[e^{(x^2-1) \log 3}] = e^{(x^2-1) \log 3}(2x \log 3)$$
$$= 3^{x^2-1}2x \log 3.$$

Example 7.   Evaluate $(d/dx)(u^n)$ where u denotes a positive differentiable function of x.

   Solution

$$\frac{d}{dx}(u^n) = \frac{d}{dx}(e^{n \log u}) = e^{n \log u}\left(\frac{n}{u}\right)\frac{du}{dx}$$
$$= \left(\frac{n}{u}\right) \cdot u^n \frac{du}{dx} = nu^{n-1}\frac{du}{dx} \cdot$$

Previously we were able to establish this important differentiation formula only for rational values of n.

10.4   *The Number e Expressed as a Limit*

Although we know that the derivative of $\log x$ with respect to x has the value 1 at $x = 1$, we now obtain an important relationship by applying the definition of a derivative to $y = \log x$ at $x = 1$.

Given $y = f(x) = \log x$, we have

$$f'(1) = \lim_{h \to 0} \left[\frac{\log(1+h) - \log 1}{h}\right]$$
$$= \lim_{h \to 0} \left[\frac{1}{h} \log(1+h)\right]$$
$$= \lim_{h \to 0} [\log(1+h)^{1/h}] = 1.$$

Since the logarithmic function is continuous at all points of its domain,

$$\log\left[\lim_{h \to 0}(1+h)^{1/h}\right] = 1$$

or

$$\lim_{h \to 0}(1+h)^{1/h} = e. \qquad (10.20)$$

If we set $h = 1/k$, we obtain the following equivalent form:

$$\lim_{k \to \infty}\left(1 + \frac{1}{k}\right)^k = e. \qquad (10.21)$$

10.5   The General Logarithmic Function

If $a > 1$, it is easy to show that $y = a^x$ defines an increasing function of x possessing a positive derivative at every x, while if $0 < a < 1$, $y = a^x$ defines a decreasing function of x possessing a negative derivative at every x. (See Problem 3.) Therefore the function defined by $y = f(x) = a^x$ possesses an inverse having domain $x > 0$ and range $-\infty < y < \infty$. Following the custom of secondary school mathematics, we will write

$$y = f^{-1}(x) = \log_a x, \qquad (a > 0, a \neq 1), \qquad (10.22)$$

read as "y is the logarithm of x to the base a." This defines the general logarithmic function and reduces to $\log x$ when $a = e$.

Writing (10.22) in the corresponding exponential form $a^y = x$, we have

$$\log a^y = y \log a = \log x$$

or

$$y = \log_a x = \frac{\log x}{\log a}. \qquad (10.23)$$

Formula (10.23) furnishes the means of finding the logarithm of a number x to the base a in terms of the logarithms of x and a to the base e. We say that $\log x$ is the logarithm of x to the base e because if $x = e^y$, then $y = \log x = \log_e x$. Logarithms to the base e were invented by John Napier (1550–1617), and are called Naperian or natural logarithms. Many books use the symbol $\ln x$ for $\log_e x$. We prefer to use $\log x$ with no subscript, since bases other than e are seldom used in the calculus. If a base other than e should appear, it is preferable to remove it by use of (10.23).

The graphs of $y - a^x$ and $y - \log_a x$ are similar to those of $y = e^x$ and $y = \log x$ shown in Fig. 10.5. The truth of this statement is evident from (10.23) and (10.19).

The student is undoubtedly familiar with logarithms to the base 10, referred to as common logarithms. They are useful in computing because 10 is also the base of our number system, but they have almost no importance in calculus and its applications.

Example 8

$$\frac{d}{dx} \log_2 x = \frac{d}{dx} \frac{\log x}{\log 2} = \frac{1}{x \log 2}.$$

Example 9

$$\frac{d}{dx} \log_{10}(x^2 - 1) = \frac{d}{dx} \frac{\log(x^2 - 1)}{\log 10} = \frac{2x}{(x^2 - 1)\log 10}.$$

An alternate approach is to begin with the general exponential function given by $y = a^x$ and then to define the general logarithmic function as the inverse of the function given by $y = a^x$. The course we have followed has several advantages over this approach. The problem of defining a^x for $a > 0$ and x irrational is greatly simplified. Also, the differentiability and hence the continuity of log x are readily obtained from the first fundamental theorem. Our knowledge of inverse functions yields the differentiability and continuity of $\log^{-1} x = e^x$. Finally, the important limit (10.20) exists because log x is differentiable at $x = 1$, whereas in the alternate approach it is difficult to establish that the limit actually exists.

As in the case of the trigonometric and inverse trigonometric functions, the importance of the logarithmic and exponential functions is due to the fact that they enable us to solve many important differential equations. This will be possible after we have studied the integral formulas that are immediate consequences of the formulas for differentiating these functions.

PROBLEM LIST 64

(Assume that $a > 0$ and $a \neq 1$.)

1. Write each of the following numbers as a power of e: **(a)** 3, **(b)** π, **(c)** $\sqrt{2}$, **(d)** $1/2$, **(e)** e.

2. Write 2^{3x+4} as a power of e.

3. Prove that $f(x) = a^x$ defines an increasing function for $a > 1$ and a decreasing function for $0 < a < 1$.

4. State the domain and range of the function defined by **(a)** $f(x) = 3^x$, **(b)** $f(x) = \log_3 x$.

5. Derive the following properties of the function defined by $f(x) = a^x$:

    (a) $a^x a^y = a^{x+y}$.   **(c)** $(a^x)^y = a^{xy}$.

    (b) $a^x/a^y = a^{x-y}$.   **(d)** $a^0 = 1$.

6. Find y':

    (a) $y = 5^x$.   **(c)** $y = 10^{-2x^2}$.

    (b) $y = 2^{3x}$.   **(d)** $y = \pi^{1-x^2}$.

7. Show that the curve $y = 2^x$ is everywhere concave upward.

8. Derive the formula

$$\frac{d}{dx} a^u = a^u \log a \frac{du}{dx},$$

where u denotes a differentiable function of x. This formula is seldom used and should not be memorized. It is preferable to employ the technique of Example 6.

9. Draw the graph of $y = a^x$ for a equal to

    (a) e;   **(e)** $\dfrac{1}{2}$;

    (b) 3;   **(f)** $\dfrac{1}{e}$;

    (c) 4;   **(g)** $\dfrac{1}{4}$.

    (d) 2;

10. Follow the instructions of Problem 9 for $y = \log_a x$.

11. Write the equation $y = 2^{x^2}$ in the corresponding logarithmic form.

12. Write the equation $y = \log_2 (5x)$ in the corresponding exponential form.

13. Prove that $f(x) = \log_a x$ defines an increasing function for $a > 1$ and a decreasing function for $0 < a < 1$.

14. Derive the following properties of the function defined by $f(x) = \log_a x$:

    (a) $\log_a (xy) = \log_a x + \log_a y$.

    (b) $\log_a (x/y) = \log_a x - \log_a y$.

    (c) $\log_a x^y = y \log_a x$.

    (d) $\log_a 1 = 0$.

15. Find y':

    (a) $y = \log_2 (x^2 - 4)$.

    (b) $y = \log_{10} \sin x$.

16. Derive the formula

$$\frac{d}{dx} \log_a u = \frac{1}{u \log a} \frac{du}{dx},$$

where u denotes a positive differentiable function of x. This is another seldom used formula which should not be memorized. It is preferable to employ the technique of Example 9.

17. Prove that the curve $y = \log_a x$ is concave downward for $a > 1$ and concave upward for $0 < a < 1$.

18. Prove that $\log_a a = 1$.

19. Prove that $\log_a e = 1/\log a$.

20. Evaluate $\log_{10} e$ to three decimal places.

21. Evaluate

    (a) $\lim_{h \to 0} (1 - h)^{2/h}$;

    (b) $\lim_{k \to \infty} \left(1 + \frac{1}{2k}\right)^k$;

    (c) $\lim_{k \to \infty} \left(\frac{k + x}{k}\right)^k$;

    (d) $\lim_{h \to 0} \left(\frac{a^h - 1}{h}\right)$.

22. If P dollars is invested at r percent, with interest compounded n times each year, the amount y accumulated after x years is given by

$$y(x) = P\left(1 + \frac{r}{n}\right)^{nx} \quad \text{dollars.}$$

Show that $\lim_{n \to \infty} y(x) = Pe^{rx}$. If y is given by $y = Pe^{rx}$, we say that interest is compounded continuously. For example, \$1.00 at 4% compounded continuously for 10 years would amount to $e^{0.4} \cong 1.49$ dollars.

10.6   Logarithmic Differentiation

The function defined by $y = \log \sqrt{x^2} = \log |x|$ has derivative

$$\frac{dy}{dx} = \frac{1}{\sqrt{x^2}} \cdot \frac{2x}{2\sqrt{x^2}} = \frac{1}{x}. \qquad (10.24)$$

That (10.24) is correct is easy to see by examining the graph of $y = \log |x|$, shown in Fig. 10.6.

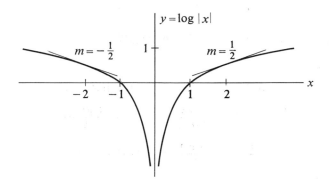

Figure 10.6

Since $\log |-x| = \log |x|$, the graph is symmetric with respect to the y-axis. For $x > 0$, the graph coincides with that of $y = \log x$ and for $x = 0$, $\log |x|$ is undefined. The slope at a point on the left branch of $y = \log |x|$ is the negative of the slope at the corresponding point on the right branch. For example, the slope at $(2, \log 2)$ is $1/2$, while the slope at $(-2, \log 2)$ is $-1/2 = 1/(-2)$.

By (10.24) and the chain rule,

$$\frac{d}{dx} \log |u| = \frac{1}{u} \cdot \frac{du}{dx}, \tag{10.25}$$

where u denotes a differentiable function of x. The right member of (10.25) is called the logarithmic derivative of u.

We now employ (10.25) in a method known as logarithmic differentiation. Assume that we wish to differentiate $y = u$, where u denotes a differentiable function of x. If u is a complicated expression, we first form $|y| = |u|$, from which we obtain $\log |y| = \log |u|$. Then by (10.25),

$$\frac{1}{y} \frac{dy}{dx} = \frac{d}{dx} \log |u|. \tag{10.26}$$

In the right member of (10.26), $\log |u|$ is now simplified by employing the basic properties of logarithms. The result is differentiated with respect to x, after which both sides of (10.26) are multiplied by y to obtain dy/dx.

Example 1.   Given $y = (x + 2)(x + 1)(x - 1)^2$, find dy/dx.

   Solution

$$\log |y| = \log |x + 2| + \log |x + 1| + 2 \log |x - 1|,$$

$$\frac{1}{y} \frac{dy}{dx} = \frac{1}{x + 2} + \frac{1}{x + 1} + \frac{2}{x - 1}.$$

Multiplying both sides by $y = (x + 2)(x + 1)(x - 1)^2$, we obtain

$$\frac{dy}{dx} = (x + 1)(x - 1)^2 + (x + 2)(x - 1)^2$$
$$+ 2(x + 2)(x + 1)(x - 1)$$
$$= (x - 1)(4x^2 + 7x + 1).$$

Example 2.   Given $y = (x^3 \sin x)/e^x$, find dy/dx.

Solution

$$\log |y| = 3 \log |x| + \log |\sin x| - x.$$

$$\frac{1}{y}\frac{dy}{dx} = \frac{3}{x} + \frac{\cos x}{\sin x} - 1 = \frac{3 + x \cot x - x}{x}.$$

$$\frac{dy}{dx} = \frac{x^2 \sin x}{e^x}(3 + x \cot x - x).$$

Example 3.   Given $y = x^x$ $(x > 0)$, find dy/dx.

Solution

$$\log |y| = x \log |x|.$$

$$\frac{1}{y}\frac{dy}{dx} = x \cdot \frac{1}{x} + \log x.$$

$$\frac{dy}{dx} = x^x(1 + \log x).$$

Example 4.   The relative error in a quantity u is the ratio of the error Δu to the quantity u. The relative error $\Delta u/u$ can be approximated by du/u. The percentage error is 100 times the relative error. For example, if dr is the approximate error in measuring the radius of a sphere, then from $V = (4/3)\pi r^3$,

$$\log |V| = \log \left(\frac{4\pi}{3}\right) + 3 \log r$$

and

$$\frac{1}{V}\frac{dV}{dr} = \frac{3}{r} \qquad \text{or} \qquad \frac{dV}{V} = 3\frac{dr}{r}.$$

Thus the approximate relative error in the volume is three times the approximate relative error in the radius.

Note: If $y = u(x)$ and $u(a) = 0$, then $u'(a)$ cannot be found by logarithmic differentiation, since log 0 is not defined. However, if u has a continuous derivative at $x = a$, $u'(a)$ can be found from $\lim_{x \to a} u'(x) = u'(a)$. See Problem 8.

PROBLEM LIST 65

1. Find dy/dx
    (i) without using logarithmic differentiation;
    (ii) using logarithmic differentiation.
    Verify that the results agree.

(a) $y = (x + 1)(x - 3)^2$.

(c) $y = (x^2 - 4)(x + 3)$.

(b) $y = xe^{-2x}$.

(d) $y = \dfrac{e^{-x} \cos x}{x^3}$.

2. Find dy/dx by logarithmic differentiation.

(a) $y = \sqrt{(x + 2)(x^2 - 1)}$.

(g) $y = \dfrac{x^3 \sin x}{1 + e^x}$.

(b) $y = e^{-x^2}(x^3 + 3x - 5)$.

(h) $y = \dfrac{(x - 1)^{2/3}(x + 4)^{3/4}}{(x + 2)^{1/2}}$.

(c) $y = \dfrac{(x - 1)(x + 2)^2}{(x - 3)^3}$.

(i) $y = x^{2x}$.

(d) $y = \dfrac{x\sqrt{x^2 + 4}}{x^2 - 1}$.

(j) $y = (\sin x)^{\sin x}$.

(e) $y = (x + 1)^3(x - 3)(x - 1)$.

(k) $y = x^{\log x}$.

(f) $y = \sqrt[3]{\dfrac{x - 3}{x^2 - 1}}$.

(l) $y = x(2^x)$.

3. Show that $y = x^x$ $(x > 0)$ is everywhere concave upward.

4. Given that u and v denote differentiable functions of x, derive the formulas for the derivative of a product and a quotient by logarithmic differentiation.

5. If u and v denote differentiable functions of x, show that

$$\frac{d}{dx} u^v = vu^{v-1}\frac{du}{dx} + u^v \log u \frac{dv}{dx}.$$

6. Show that the approximate relative error in x^n is n times the approximate relative error in x.

7. If the maximum allowable percentage error in the surface of a sphere is 4%, find the maximum allowable percentage error in the radius.

8. Given $f(x) = x^2 + 3x$, find $f'(x)$ for $x \neq 0$ by logarithmic differentiation. Use the result to compute $f'(0)$. Assume that $x^2 + 3x$ has a continuous derivative at $x = 0$.

9. The function f is defined by

$$L = f(\theta) = \prod_{i=1}^{n} \theta^{x_i}(1 - \theta)^{1-x_i} = \theta^{x_1}(1 - \theta)^{1-x_1}\theta^{x_2}(1 - \theta)^{1-x_2} \cdots \theta^{x_n}(1 - \theta)^{1-x_n}.$$

Show that L is maximum when

$$\theta = \frac{\sum_{i=1}^{n} x_i}{n}.$$

(The function f plays an important role in the theory of statistics.)

Chapter

11

Techniques of integration

11.1 Basic Formulas

In Sec. 4.16 we learned that if

$$\frac{dF(x)}{dx} = f(x)$$

[or $dF(x) = f(x)\, dx$], $F(x) + C$ is called the general antiderivative of $f(x)$. This general antiderivative is denoted by $D_x^{-1} f(x)$ or by $\int f(x)\, dx$. We now use the latter symbol, read as "the integral of $f(x)$ with respect to x." Our objective in this chapter is to develop formulas and methods which, in a large number of cases, will enable us to find $\int f(x)\, dx = F(x) + C$ when we are given $f(x)$. If we are given $F(x)$ it is easy to verify that the formula

$$\int f(x)\, dx = F(x) + C \tag{11.1}$$

is correct. We merely verify that $dF(x) = f(x)\, dx$. The real problem is that of finding $F(x)$ when $f(x)$ is given.

Instead of writing our integral formulas in the form (11.1), we will use the more general form

$$\int f(u)\, du = F(u) + C, \tag{11.2}$$

where $u = u(x)$ denotes a differentiable function of x. Since $f(u)\, du = f(u)\, (du/dx)\, dx$, we see that (11.2) is correct if $dF/dx = f(u)\, (du/dx)$. By the chain rule, $dF/dx = dF/du \cdot du/dx$, and therefore (11.2) is a correct formula if

$$dF = \frac{dF}{du} \cdot du = f(u)\, du.$$

The following list of important integral formulas should be memorized. The

best way to effect this memorization is to work problems with the list in sight
until eventually reference to the list is unnecessary.

$$\int u^n \, du = \frac{u^{n+1}}{n+1} + C \qquad (n \neq -1). \tag{11.3}$$

$$\int \frac{du}{u} = \log |u| + C. \tag{11.4}$$

$$\int e^u \, du = e^u + C. \tag{11.5}$$

$$\int \sin u \, du = -\cos u + C. \tag{11.6}$$

$$\int \cos u \, du = \sin u + C. \tag{11.7}$$

$$\int \tan u \, du = -\log |\cos u| + C. \tag{11.8}$$

$$\int \cot u \, du = \log |\sin u| + C. \tag{11.9}$$

$$\int \sec u \, du = \log |\sec u + \tan u| + C. \tag{11.10}$$

$$\int \csc u \, du = \log |\csc u - \cot u| + C. \tag{11.11}$$

$$\int \sec^2 u \, du = \tan u + C. \tag{11.12}$$

$$\int \csc^2 u \, du = -\cot u + C. \tag{11.13}$$

$$\int \sec u \tan u \, du = \sec u + C. \tag{11.14}$$

$$\int \csc u \cot u \, du = -\csc u + C. \tag{11.15}$$

$$\int \frac{du}{\sqrt{a^2 - u^2}} = \operatorname{Sin}^{-1} \frac{u}{a} + C. \tag{11.16}$$

$$\int \frac{du}{a^2 + u^2} = \frac{1}{a} \operatorname{Tan}^{-1} \frac{u}{a} + C. \tag{11.17}$$

It is easy to verify that each of these formulas is correct. For example, (11.12)
is correct since

$$d \tan u = \sec^2 u \, du,$$

and (11.9) is correct since

$$d \log |\sin u| = \frac{d \sin u}{\sin u} = \frac{\cos u \, du}{\sin u} = \cot u \, du.$$

It is also interesting to see how the formulas are derived. Most of them are
immediate consequences of the corresponding differentiation formulas. Formula
(11.4) follows from formula (10.25). Formula (11.8) is derived by writing

$$\int \tan u\, du = \int \frac{\sin u\, du}{\cos u} = -\int \frac{-\sin u\, du}{\cos u}$$
$$= -\log |\cos u| + C,$$

the last equality holding by virtue of (11.4). The derivation of (11.9) is similar. To obtain (11.10) we write

$$\int \sec u\, du = \int \frac{\sec u(\sec u + \tan u)\, du}{\sec u + \tan u}$$
$$= \int \frac{(\sec^2 u + \sec u \tan u)\, du}{\sec u + \tan u}.$$

Since the numerator is the differential of the denominator, (11.10) follows from (11.4). Formula (11.11) is obtained similarly.

To obtain (11.17) we write

$$\int \frac{du}{a^2 + u^2} = \frac{1}{a} \int \frac{(1/a)\, du}{1 + (u/a)^2}$$

and then apply formula (9.16).

The basic technique for evaluating $\int f(u)\, du$ is to identify $f(u)\, du$ with the corresponding expression in an integral formula. Once this has been accomplished, the answer is obtained immediately by looking at the right member of the formula. Skill in recognizing what formula to employ is acquired through practice.

Example 1

$$\int \sin 2x\, dx = \frac{1}{2} \int \sin 2x(2dx) = \frac{-1}{2} \cos 2x + C.$$

The integrand was written in the form $\sin u\, du$ and (11.6) employed.

Example 2

$$\int xe^{-x^2}\, dx = \frac{-1}{2} \int e^{-x^2}(-2x\, dx) = \frac{-e^{-x^2}}{2} + C.$$

The integrand was written in the form $e^u\, du$ and (11.5) employed.

Example 3

$$\int \sec^2 \frac{x}{2}\, dx = 2 \int \sec^2 \frac{x}{2} \left(\frac{dx}{2}\right) = 2 \tan \frac{x}{2} + C.$$

Example 4

$$\int \frac{x\, dx}{1 + x^2} = \frac{1}{2} \int \frac{2x\, dx}{1 + x^2} = \frac{1}{2} \log (1 + x^2) + C,$$

by (11.4). The absolute value bars are omitted, since $1 + x^2 > 0$.

Example 5

$$\int \frac{dx}{1 + 9x^2} = \frac{1}{3} \int \frac{3dx}{1 + (3x)^2} = \frac{1}{3} \operatorname{Tan}^{-1}(3x) + C.$$

Example 6

$$\int \frac{\cos x \, dx}{\sqrt{1 + \sin x}} = \int (1 + \sin x)^{-1/2} (\cos x \, dx)$$

$$= \frac{(1 + \sin x)^{1/2}}{1/2} + C = 2\sqrt{1 + \sin x} + C$$

by (11.3).

Example 7

$$\int \frac{8dx}{\sqrt{1 - 4x^2}} = 4 \int \frac{2dx}{\sqrt{1 - (2x)^2}} = 4 \, \mathrm{Sin}^{-1}(2x) + C.$$

Example 8

$$\int \sec^2 x \tan x \, dx = \int (\tan x)^1 (\sec^2 x \, dx)$$

$$= \frac{\tan^2 x}{2} + C$$

by (11.3) or

$$\int \sec^2 x \tan x \, dx = \int (\sec x)^1 (\sec x \tan x \, dx)$$

$$= \frac{\sec^2 x}{2} + C,$$

again by (11.3). Note that $(\tan^2 x)/2$ and $(\sec^2 x)/2$ differ by a constant, since $1 + \tan^2 x \equiv \sec^2 x$.

Example 9

$$\int \frac{\log x \, dx}{x} = \int (\log x)^1 \left(\frac{dx}{x}\right)$$

$$= \frac{(\log x)^2}{2} + C = \frac{\log^2 x}{2} + C.$$

Example 10

$$\int \frac{dx}{x \log x} = \int \frac{dx/x}{\log x} = \log |\log x| + C.$$

Example 11

$$\int e^x \tan e^x \, dx = \int \tan e^x (e^x \, dx)$$

$$= -\log |\cos e^x| + C.$$

Example 12

$$\int 2^x \, dx = \int e^{x \log 2} \, dx = \frac{1}{\log 2} \int e^{x \log 2} [(\log 2) \, dx]$$

$$= \frac{e^{x \log 2}}{\log 2} + C = \frac{2^x}{\log 2} + C.$$

Observe that the base e was introduced by applying formula (10.19). Then the integration was carried out by (11.5).

PROBLEM LIST 66

Evaluate the integrals in Problems 1–44. Several should be checked by differentiation.

1. $\displaystyle\int (x^2 + 2)x \, dx.$

2. $\displaystyle\int \frac{dx}{x - 1}.$

3. $\displaystyle\int \frac{x \, dx}{x^2 - 1}.$

4. $\displaystyle\int \sin 5x \, dx.$

5. $\displaystyle\int \csc (x/3) \, dx.$

6. $\displaystyle\int \sin^3 x \cos x \, dx.$

7. $\displaystyle\int \sin 2x \cos x \, dx.$

8. $\displaystyle\int (1 - \sin x)^4 \cos x \, dx.$

9. $\displaystyle\int x e^{4x^2} \, dx.$

10. $\displaystyle\int (x - e^{-x}) \, dx.$

11. $\displaystyle\int \frac{\sin 2x \, dx}{\cos^3 2x}.$

12. $\displaystyle\int \frac{3x \, dx}{5x^2 - 1}.$

13. $\displaystyle\int \frac{x + 2}{x + 1} dx.$

14. $\displaystyle\int \frac{dx}{4x^2 + 1}.$

15. $\displaystyle\int \csc^2 2x \cot 2x \, dx.$

16. $\displaystyle\int \frac{dx}{x \log^3 x}.$

17. $\displaystyle\int (e^x - e^{-x})^2 \, dx.$

18. $\displaystyle\int (x^2 + 1)^2 \, dx.$

19. $\displaystyle\int \frac{x^2 \, dx}{x^2 + 1}.$

20. $\displaystyle\int \frac{3e^{-x} \, dx}{1 - e^{-x}}.$

21. $\displaystyle\int \frac{\sqrt[3]{1 + \log x} \, dx}{x}.$

22. $\displaystyle\int \frac{\sin 3x \, dx}{\cos^2 3x}.$

23. $\displaystyle\int \frac{\cot (x/3) \, dx}{\sin (x/3)}.$

24. $\displaystyle\int \frac{du}{2e^u}.$

25. $\displaystyle\int \frac{dx}{x^{3/2}\sqrt{x + 1}}.$

26. $\displaystyle\int \frac{(-1 + \sin x) \, dx}{x + \cos x}.$

27. $\displaystyle\int \frac{dx}{e^x + e^{-x}}.$

28. $\displaystyle\int \frac{(x + 1)^2 \, dx}{x^2 + 1}.$

29. $\displaystyle\int \frac{e^x \, dx}{\sqrt{e^x - 2}}.$

30. $\displaystyle\int 3^x \, dx.$

31. $\displaystyle\int \frac{dx}{\sqrt{x} (1 + \sqrt{x})}.$

32. $\displaystyle\int \frac{(e^{2x} - e^{-2x}) \, dx}{e^{2x} + e^{-2x}}.$

33. $\displaystyle\int \frac{(x^2 + 2) \, dx}{x^2 + 1}.$

34. $\displaystyle\int \frac{(1 - \cos 2x) \, dx}{1 + \cos 2x}.$

35. $\displaystyle\int \frac{\operatorname{Tan}^{-1} x \, dx}{1 + x^2}.$

36. $\displaystyle\int \frac{x^2 \, dx}{4x^3 - 1}.$

37. $\displaystyle\int \frac{dx}{\sqrt{e^{2x} - 1}}.$

38. $\displaystyle\int \frac{x \, dx}{x^4 + 1}.$

39. $\int (\cos^4 2x - \sin^4 2x)\, dx.$

40. $\int \dfrac{\sin x\, dx}{4 + \cos^2 x}.$

41. $\int \dfrac{dx}{e^x + 1}.$

42. $\int [x^2 - (10)^x]\, dx.$

43. $\int x(1 + x^3)^2\, dx.$

44. $\int \dfrac{e^x - e^{-x}}{e^x + e^{-x}}\, dx.$

45. Find the area under one arch of the curve $y = \sin x$. What is the average height, with respect to x, of the curve over this interval?

46. Find the first-quadrant area bounded by $y = \sin x$, $y = \cos x$, and the y-axis $(0 \leqslant x \leqslant \pi/4)$.

47. Find the volume generated by revolving $y = e^x$ from $x = 0$ to $x = 2$ about the x-axis.

48. The arc of $y - x^2$ from $(0, 0)$ to $(2, 4)$ is revolved about the y-axis. Find the surface area generated by the arc.

49. Find the area bounded by the curve $y = 1/(1 + x^2)$ and the line through the points of inflection of the curve.

50. Find the area bounded by $xy = 1$ and $x + 4y + 5 = 0$.

51. Find the length of $y = \log \cos x$ from $(0, 0)$ to $(\pi/3, -\log 2)$.

52. Derive (11.9).

53. Derive (11.11).

54. Show that (11.8) can also be written $\int \tan u\, du = \log |\sec u| + C.$

55. Show that (11.10) can also be written

$$\int \sec u\, du = \log \left| \tan \left(\frac{u}{2} + \frac{\pi}{4} \right) \right| + C.$$

56. Evaluate $\int \sin x \cos x\, dx$ three ways and verify that the members of each pair of answers differ only by a constant.

57. Derive (11.5) by means of (11.3).

58. Show that $\int_k^{k+2\pi} \sin mx \cos nx\, dx = 0$, where k is an arbitrary constant and m and n are positive integers. Use the formula

$$\sin A \cos B = \frac{1}{2}[\sin (A + B) + \sin (A - B)].$$

59. Derive formulas (11.10) and (11.11) by employing the identities

$$\sec x = \tan x + \frac{\cos x}{1 + \sin x}; \qquad \csc x = \cot x + \frac{\sin x}{1 + \cos x}.$$

60. Evaluate

$$\int \frac{(x^2 - 1)\, dx}{x^4 + 3x^2 + 1}.$$

61. Add the equations $d(\sec u) = \sec u \tan u\, du$ and $d(\tan u) = \sec^2 u\, du$. Use the result to evaluate $\int \sec u\, du$.

11.2   *Trigonometric Integrals*

To evaluate $\int \sin^m x \cos^n x \, dx$ when either m or n is an odd positive integer, we rewrite the integrand as a sum of terms of the form $\sin^k x \cos x$ or $\cos^k x \, (-\sin x)$. Each term is then integrated by the power formula (11.3).

Example 1

$$\int \sin^2 x \cos^3 x \, dx = \int \sin^2 x \, (1 - \sin^2 x) \cos x \, dx$$

$$= \int \sin^2 x (\cos x \, dx) - \int \sin^4 x (\cos x \, dx)$$

$$= \frac{\sin^3 x}{3} - \frac{\sin^5 x}{5} + C.$$

Example 2

$$\int (\sin^3 x) \sqrt{\cos x} \, dx = \int (1 - \cos^2 x) \cos^{1/2} x \sin x \, dx$$

$$= \int \cos^{5/2} x (-\sin x \, dx) - \int \cos^{1/2} x (-\sin x \, dx)$$

$$= \frac{2}{7} \cos^{7/2} x - \frac{2}{3} \cos^{3/2} x + C.$$

To evaluate $\int \tan^n x \, dx$ when n is any integer greater than 2, we rewrite the integrand as a sum of terms of the form $\tan^k x \sec^2 x$, minus $\tan x$ or $\tan^2 x$.

Example 3

$$\int \tan^3 x \, dx = \int \tan x (\sec^2 x - 1) \, dx$$

$$= \int (\tan x)^1 (\sec^2 x \, dx) - \int \tan x \, dx$$

$$= \frac{\tan^2 x}{2} + \log |\cos x| + C.$$

Example 4

$$\int \tan^4 x \, dx = \int \tan^2 x (\sec^2 x - 1) \, dx$$

$$= \int (\tan x)^2 (\sec^2 x \, dx) - \int (\sec^2 x - 1) \, dx$$

$$= \frac{\tan^3 x}{3} - \tan x + x + C.$$

Integrals of the form $\int \cot^n x \, dx$, n an integer, are handled similarly, employing the identity $\cot^2 x \equiv \csc^2 x - 1$. If m is even, the forms $\int \tan^n x \sec^m x \, dx$ and $\int \cot^n x \csc^m x \, dx$ are treated in similar fashion.

Example 5

$$\int \tan^2 2x \sec^4 2x \, dx = \int \tan^2 2x (1 + \tan^2 2x) \sec^2 2x \, dx$$

$$= \frac{1}{2} \int \tan^2 2x (2 \sec^2 2x \, dx) + \frac{1}{2} \int \tan^4 2x (2 \sec^2 2x \, dx)$$

$$= \frac{\tan^3 2x}{6} + \frac{\tan^5 2x}{10} + C.$$

Even powers of sec x or csc x can be integrated by rewriting the integrand in terms of tan x or cot x, or by the technique in Example 6.

Example 6

$$\int \sec^4 x \, dx = \int (1 + \tan^2 x) \sec^2 x \, dx$$

$$= \int \sec^2 x \, dx + \int \tan^2 x \sec^2 x \, dx$$

$$= \tan x + \frac{\tan^3 x}{3} + C.$$

To evaluate $\int \sin^m x \cos^n x \, dx$ when both m and n are positive integers, we employ the formulas

$$\sin^2 x = \frac{1}{2}(1 - \cos 2x); \qquad \cos^2 x = \frac{1}{2}(1 + \cos 2x);$$

$$\sin x \cos x = \frac{1}{2} \sin 2x.$$

Example 7

$$\int \sin^2 x \, dx = \int \frac{1}{2}(1 - \cos 2x) \, dx$$

$$= \frac{1}{2} \int dx - \frac{1}{4} \int \cos 2x (2dx) = \frac{x}{2} - \frac{\sin 2x}{4} + C.$$

Example 8

$$\int \cos^4 x \, dx = \int \frac{1}{4}(1 + \cos 2x)^2 \, dx$$

$$= \frac{1}{4} \int (1 + 2 \cos 2x + \cos^2 2x) \, dx$$

$$= \frac{1}{4} \int dx + \frac{1}{4} \int \cos 2x (2dx) + \frac{1}{4} \int \frac{1}{2}(1 + \cos 4x) \, dx$$

$$= \frac{x}{4} + \frac{\sin 2x}{4} + \frac{x}{8} + \frac{1}{32} \int \cos 4x \, (4dx)$$

$$= \frac{3x}{8} + \frac{\sin 2x}{4} + \frac{\sin 4x}{32} + C.$$

Example 9

$$\int \sin^2 x \cos^4 x \, dx = \int (\sin x \cos x)^2 \cos^2 x \, dx$$

$$= \int \left(\frac{1}{4} \sin^2 2x\right) \frac{1}{2} (1 + \cos 2x) \, dx$$

$$= \frac{1}{8} \int \sin^2 2x \, dx + \frac{1}{8} \int \sin^2 2x \cos 2x \, dx$$

$$= \frac{1}{16} \int (1 - \cos 4x) \, dx + \frac{1}{16} \int \sin^2 2x(2 \cos 2x \, dx)$$

$$= \frac{x}{16} - \frac{\sin 4x}{64} + \frac{\sin^3 2x}{48} + C.$$

PROBLEM LIST 67

Evaluate the integrals in Problems 1–39.

1. $\int \sin^3 x \, dx.$

2. $\int \cos^3 2x \, dx.$

3. $\int \sin^3 x \cos^2 x \, dx.$

4. $\int \sin^5 x \cos^2 x \, dx.$

5. $\int \sqrt{\sin x} \cos^3 x \, dx.$

6. $\int \frac{\cos^3 x \, dx}{\sin^2 x}.$

7. $\int \sec^2 x \sin x \, dx.$

8. $\int \sin 2x \cos x \, dx.$

9. $\int \sin^2 2x \cos x \, dx.$

10. $\int \sin^{2/3} x \cos^3 x \, dx.$

11. $\int \sin^5 3x \, dx.$

12. $\int \sqrt{1 + \cos 2x} \, dx, \left(-\frac{\pi}{2} \leqslant x \leqslant \frac{\pi}{2}\right).$

13. $\int (1 + \cos 2x)^3 \, dx.$

14. $\int \sqrt{1 - \cos(x/2)} \, dx, (0 \leqslant x \leqslant 4\pi).$

15. $\int (\sin^4 x - \cos^4 x)^3 \, dx.$

16. $\int \tan^2 x \cos x \, dx.$

17. $\int \frac{\tan^3 x \, dx}{\sec^4 x}.$

18. $\int \frac{dx}{\tan^4 x}.$

19. $\int \tan^5 x \, dx.$

20. $\int \tan^6 x \, dx.$

21. $\int \cot^3 2x \, dx.$

22. $\int \tan^4 (x/2) \sec^2 (x/2) \, dx.$

23. $\int \csc^4 2x \, dx.$

24. $\int \tan^2 3x \, dx.$

25. $\int \cos^2 2x \, dx.$

26. $\int \sin^4 x \, dx.$

27. $\int \sin^4 x \cos^2 x \, dx.$

28. $\int \sin^2 (x/2) \cos^2 (x/2) \, dx.$

29. $\int \cot^2 x \csc^2 x \, dx.$

30. $\int \frac{dx}{1 - \sin x}$

31. $\int \dfrac{\sin^4 x \, dx}{\cos^2 x}.$

34. $\int \sin x \sin 2x \, dx.$

32. $\int \dfrac{dx}{(\sqrt{3} \sin x + \cos x)^2}.$

35. $\int \sin x \sin 2x \sin 3x \, dx.$

33. $\int_0^{2\pi/3} \sin^3 (x/2) \cos^2 (x/2) \, dx.$

36. $\int_k^{k+2\pi} \cos^2 nx \, dx, \ (n = 1, 2, \cdots).$

37. $\int \sin 4x \cos 3x \, dx.$

Use $\sin A \cos B = \frac{1}{2}[\sin (A - B) + \sin (A + B)].$

38. $\int \sin 6x \sin 4x \, dx.$

Use $\sin A \sin B = \frac{1}{2}[\cos (A - B) - \cos (A + B)].$

39. $\int \cos 2x \cos 3x \, dx.$

Use $\cos A \cos B = \frac{1}{2}[\cos (A - B) + \cos (A + B)].$

40. Find the area under one arch of the curve $y = \sin^2 x$.

41. Find the volume generated by revolving one arch of the curve $y = \sin x$ about the x-axis.

42. Explain why the technique of Example 1 cannot be used to evaluate $\int \sin^4 x \cos^4 x \, dx$.

43. Explain why the technique of Example 6 cannot be used to evaluate $\int \sec^3 x \, dx$.

44. Verify by differentiation that the integrations in the illustrative examples in this section are correct.

11.3   *Integration by Parts*

If $u = u(x)$ and $v = v(x)$ define differentiable functions of x, then
$$d[u(x)v(x)] = u(x)v'(x) \, dx + v(x)u'(x) \, dx$$
or
$$u(x)v'(x) \, dx = d[u(x)v(x)] - v(x)u'(x) \, dx.$$
Integrating both sides with respect to x, we obtain
$$\int u(x)v'(x) \, dx = u(x)v(x) - \int v(x)u'(x) \, dx. \qquad \textbf{(11.18)}$$

This is known as the formula for integrating by parts. It is one of the most important of all integration formulas and should be memorized. Usually it is written in the abbreviated form
$$\int u \, dv = uv - \int v \, du. \qquad \textbf{(11.19)}$$

The formula suggests itself when the integrand $f(x)$ in $\int f(x) \, dx$ involves a product. The idea is to separate $f(x)$ into two factors, one to play the role of $u(x)$ and the other that of $v'(x)$. The method succeeds when $u = u(x)$ and $dv = v'(x) \, dx$ are so chosen that it is possible to evaluate the integral on the right side of (11.18).

There is no general rule for choosing $u(x)$ and $v'(x)$, but clearly $v'(x)$ must be an expression which can be integrated, since $v(x)$ must be found from $v'(x)$. As a first trial, one usually chooses for $v'(x)$ the most complicated factor of $f(x)$ one knows how to integrate. With practice one learns to look ahead and ask what form $v \, du$ will assume for a particular choice of u and dv.

Example 1.   Evaluate $\int x \cos x \, dx$.

Solution.   Let $u = x$ and $dv = \cos x \, dx$. Then $du = dx$ and $v = \sin x + C'$. Hence, by (11.19),

$$\int x \cos x \, dx = x(\sin x + C') - \int (\sin x + C') \, dx$$

$$= x \sin x + C'x + \cos x - C'x + C$$

$$= x \sin x + \cos x + C.$$

It is easily seen that the constant C', introduced in the passage from dv to v, will always cancel out, as in this example. Hence we will no longer add C' when v is obtained from dv.

Example 2.   Evaluate $\int x^2 \sin x \, dx$.

Solution.   Let $u = x^2$ and $dv = \sin x \, dx$. Then $du = 2x \, dx$ and $v = -\cos x$. This yields

$$\int x^2 \sin x \, dx = -x^2 \cos x + 2 \int x \cos x \, dx.$$

This example shows that it is often necessary to apply the parts formula more than once. Since we have already found in Example 1 that $\int x \cos x \, dx = x \sin x + \cos x + C$, we easily obtain

$$\int x^2 \sin x \, dx = -x^2 \cos x + 2x \sin x + 2 \cos x + C'.$$

Example 3.   Evaluate $I = \int \sec^3 x \, dx$.

Solution.   Let $u = \sec x$ and $dv = \sec^2 x \, dx$. Then $du = \sec x \tan x \, dx$ and $v = \tan x$. Hence

$$I = \int \sec^3 x \, dx$$

$$= \sec x \tan x - \int \sec x \tan^2 x \, dx$$

$$= \sec x \tan x - \int \sec x \, (\sec^2 x - 1) \, dx$$

$$= \sec x \tan x - I + \int \sec x \, dx,$$

and

$$2I = \sec x \tan x + \log |\sec x + \tan x| + C,$$

or

$$I = \frac{1}{2} \sec x \tan x + \frac{1}{2} \log |\sec x + \tan x| + C'.$$

This example shows that the required integral sometimes reappears when the parts formula is applied. We then solve for the required integral.

Example 4.   Evaluate $I = \int e^{ax} \cos bx \, dx$.

Solution.   Let $u = e^{ax}$ and $dv = \cos bx \, dx$. Then $du = ae^{ax}$ and $v = (1/b) \sin bx$. Therefore

$$I = \int e^{ax} \cos bx \, dx$$

$$= \frac{1}{b} e^{ax} \sin bx - \frac{a}{b} \int e^{ax} \sin bx \, dx. \tag{11.20}$$

We now obtain a second expression for I by letting $u = \cos bx$ and $dv = e^{ax} \, dx$. Then $du = -b \sin bx$ and $v = (1/a) e^{ax}$, and hence

$$I = \frac{1}{a} e^{ax} \cos bx + \frac{b}{a} \int e^{ax} \sin bx \, dx. \tag{11.21}$$

Multiplying (11.20) by b/a and (11.21) by a/b and adding, we obtain

$$\left(\frac{b}{a} + \frac{a}{b} \right) I = \left(\frac{a^2 + b^2}{ab} \right) I = \frac{1}{a} e^{ax} \sin bx + \frac{1}{b} e^{ax} \cos bx$$

or

$$I = e^{ax} \frac{(b \sin bx + a \cos bx)}{a^2 + b^2} + C.$$

After obtaining (11.20), an alternate procedure is to apply the parts formula to $\int e^{ax} \sin bx \, dx$. The required integral I then reappears and the method of Example 3 succeeds. Integrals of this type are important in applications to physics and electronics. The trigonometric factor in the integrand represents a wave, and the exponential factor represents a damping or amplification of the wave.

Example 5.   Derive the formula

$$\int x^n e^{ax} \, dx = \frac{1}{a} x^n e^{ax} - \frac{n}{a} \int x^{n-1} e^{ax} \, dx. \tag{11.22}$$

Solution.   Let $u = x^n$ and $dv = e^{ax} \, dx$. Then

$$du = nx^{n-1} \, dx \qquad \text{and} \qquad v = \frac{1}{a} e^{ax}.$$

The required formula follows immediately from the parts formula. Formula (11.22) is known as a reduction formula, since it expresses an integral in terms of a similar integral in which an exponent has been reduced. In this case the exponent of x has been reduced from n to $n - 1$.

Example 6.   Find the area bounded by $y = \log x$, $y = 0$, and $x = 2$.

Solution

$$A = \int_1^2 \log x \, dx$$

Let

$$u = \log x \qquad \text{and} \qquad dv = dx.$$

Then

$$du = \frac{dx}{x} \qquad \text{and} \quad v = x.$$

Therefore

$$A = x \log x]_1^2 - \int_1^2 dx$$
$$= x \log x - x]_1^2$$
$$= 2 \log 2 - 1 \cong 0.386.$$

Here $v'(x)$ was chosen to be the constant 1. This choice is also successful in integrals like $\int \mathrm{Tan}^{-1} x \, dx$ or $\int \mathrm{Sin}^{-1} x \, dx$.

PROBLEM LIST 68

In Problems 1–40 evaluate the integrals, using integration by parts.

1. $\int x \sin x \, dx$.

2. $\int x e^{-x} \, dx$.

3. $\int x \cos 2x \, dx$.

4. $\int x \sec^2 x \, dx$.

5. $\int x^2 e^x \, dx$.

6. $\int x \log x \, dx$.

7. $\int x \tan^2 x \, dx$.

8. $\int \csc^3 x \, dx$.

9. $\int \mathrm{Tan}^{-1} x \, dx$.

10. $\int \mathrm{Sin}^{-1} x \, dx$.

11. $\int x \, \mathrm{Tan}^{-1} x \, dx$.

12. $\int x e^{-3x} \, dx$.

13. $\int \sin x \cos x \, dx$.

14. $\int x^3 \sqrt{1 - x^2} \, dx$.

15. $\int \log (1 + x^2) \, dx$.

16. $\int x \sin^2 x \, dx$.

17. $\int \sin x \sin 3x \, dx$.

18. $\int \frac{x^3 \, dx}{\sqrt{4 - x^2}}$.

19. $\int x^2 \cos x \, dx$.

20. $\int \sec^5 x \, dx$.

21. $\int \sqrt{x} \log x \, dx$.

22. $\int x \sin 5x \, dx$.

23. $\int x \sqrt{x + 1} \, dx$.

24. $\int \log^2 x \, dx$.

25. $\displaystyle\int \frac{\log x \, dx}{x}.$

33. $\displaystyle\int xe^{3x} \, dx.$

26. $\displaystyle\int \frac{x^3 \, dx}{\sqrt{1 + x^2}}.$

34. $\displaystyle\int e^{-3x} \cos 2x \, dx.$

27. $\displaystyle\int x \sin^3 x \, dx.$

35. $\displaystyle\int e^{ax} \sin bx \, dx.$

28. $\displaystyle\int x^2 e^{-x} \, dx.$

36. $\displaystyle\int_0^2 xe^{-2x} \, dx.$

29. $\displaystyle\int x^2 \sin x \, dx.$

37. $\displaystyle\int_0^{\pi/2} x \sin 2x \, dx.$

30. $\displaystyle\int x^2 \log x \, dx.$

38. $\displaystyle\int_1^2 \log 3x \, dx.$

31. $\displaystyle\int x \sin^2 x \cos x \, dx.$

39. $\displaystyle\int_0^1 \mathrm{Tan}^{-1} 3x \, dx.$

32. $\displaystyle\int xe^x \cos x \, dx.$

40. $\displaystyle\int_0^{\pi} e^{-2x} \sin x \, dx.$

Derive the reduction formulas in Problems 41–45.

41. $\displaystyle\int \sin^n x \, dx = -\frac{\sin^{n-1} x \cos x}{n} + \frac{n-1}{n} \int \sin^{n-2} x \, dx.$

42. $\displaystyle\int \cos^n x \, dx = \frac{\cos^{n-1} x \sin x}{n} + \frac{n-1}{n} \int \cos^{n-2} x \, dx.$

43. $\displaystyle\int x^n \sin ax \, dx = -\frac{1}{a} x^n \cos ax + \frac{n}{a} \int x^{n-1} \cos ax \, dx.$

44. $\displaystyle\int x^n \cos ax \, dx = \frac{1}{a} x^n \sin ax - \frac{n}{a} \int x^{n-1} \sin ax \, dx.$

45. $\displaystyle\int \sec^n x \, dx = \frac{\sec^{n-2} x \tan x}{n-1} + \frac{n-2}{n-1} \int \sec^{n-2} x \, dx.$

46. Evaluate $\int x^3 e^{2x} \, dx$ by means of the reduction formula (11.22).

47. Evaluate $\int_0^{\pi/2} \sin^6 x \, dx$ by means of the reduction formula of Problem 41.

48. Evaluate $\int_0^{\pi/2} \sin^5 x \, dx$ by means of the reduction formula of Problem 41.

49. Find the volume generated by revolving about the y-axis the arc of $y = \sin x$ from $(0, 0)$ to $(\pi, 0)$.

50. Find the area bounded by the curve $y = xe^{-x}$, the vertical line through the point of inflection of the curve, and the x-axis.

51. Verify by differentiation that the answers to the illustrative examples in this section are correct.

52. Evaluate $\int x \, \mathrm{Tan}^{-1} x \, dx$ by letting $u = \mathrm{Tan}^{-1} x$ and $dv = x \, dx$. Write $v = (x^2/2) + C'$ and choose $C' = 1/2$. This problem shows that it is occasionally advantageous to retain the constant of integration when finding v from dv.

53. Evaluate $\int \ln (x + 3) \, dx$ by the method of Problem 52.

54. Evaluate $\int \csc^3 x \, dx$ by employing the identity

$$\csc^3 x \equiv \frac{\sec^6 (x/2)}{8 \sin^3 (x/2) \cos^3 (x/2) \sec^6 (x/2)}$$
$$\equiv \frac{[1 + \tan^2 (x/2)]^2 \sec^2 (x/2)}{8 \tan^3 (x/2)}.$$

11.4 Integration by Change of Variable

It is often possible to evaluate $\int f(x)\, dx$ by introducing a new variable t. We assume that f is continuous on an interval I and that the function g defined by $x = g(t)$ has range I. We also assume that g has a continuous derivative and that an inverse function g^{-1} given by $t = g^{-1}(x)$ exists. Then

$$\int f(x)\, dx = \int f(g(t))g'(t)\, dt. \tag{11.23}$$

After the integral on the right has been evaluated, t is replaced by $g^{-1}(x)$, thereby furnishing the answer in terms of x. In the case of a definite integral, it is unnecessary to return to the original variable x, and we have

$$\int_{x_1}^{x_2} f(x)\, dx = \int_{t_1}^{t_2} f(g(t))g'(t)\, dt.$$

It is important to remember that $t_1 = g^{-1}(x_1)$ and $t_2 = g^{-1}(x_2)$. That is, the new limits are obtained from the original limits by using the relationship between the new variable t and the original variable x.

A proof of the validity of a change of variable under the stated conditions is given in Ref. 11.1. A change of variable of this type is commonly referred to as a substitution.

The question of how to choose the function g defined by $x = g(t)$ is not easy to answer. The object is to arrive at an integral which will be simpler to evaluate than the given integral. The illustrative examples make use of certain frequently employed substitutions.

Example 1. *Note:* This example is inserted so that the technique involved will be available in the problems. Evaluate

$$I = \int \frac{x^3 + 1}{x^2 + 1}\, dx.$$

Solution. Whenever the integrand is the quotient of two polynomials and the degree of the numerator is equal to or greater than the degree of the denominator, elementary division is employed to obtain a polynomial plus a quotient of two polynomials in which the degree of the numerator is less than the degree of the denominator. This process yields

$$I = \int \left(x + \frac{-x + 1}{x^2 + 1} \right) dx = \int x\, dx - \frac{1}{2} \int \frac{2x\, dx}{x^2 + 1} + \int \frac{dx}{x^2 + 1}$$
$$= \frac{x^2}{2} - \frac{1}{2} \log (x^2 + 1) + \mathrm{Tan}^{-1} x + C.$$

Example 2. Evaluate

$$\int \frac{dx}{1 + \sqrt{x}}.$$

Solution.   The integrand will be simplified if $\sqrt{x}$ is replaced by t. This suggests the substitution $x = t^2$. Therefore $dx = 2t\, dt$ and

$$\int \frac{dx}{1 + \sqrt{x}} = \int \frac{2t\, dt}{1 + t} = \int \left(2 - \frac{2}{1 + t}\right) dt$$

$$= 2t - 2 \log (1 + t) + C.$$

Note that $1 + t > 0$, since $t = \sqrt{x}$ and $x \geqslant 0$. We now substitute $t = \sqrt{x}$ to obtain

$$\int \frac{dx}{1 + \sqrt{x}} = 2\sqrt{x} - 2 \log (1 + \sqrt{x}) + C.$$

It is important to note not only that x is replaced by $g(t) = t^2$, but also that dx is replaced by $g'(t)\, dt = 2t\, dt$.

Example 3.   Evaluate

$$\int_4^9 \frac{dx}{1 + \sqrt{x}}.$$

Solution.   From Example 2 we have $t = \sqrt{x}$. Hence when $x = x_1 = 4$,

$$t = t_1 = \sqrt{x_1} = 2$$

and when $x = x_2 = 9$,

$$t = t_2 = \sqrt{x_2} = 3.$$

Thus

$$\int_4^9 \frac{dx}{1 + \sqrt{x}} = \int_2^3 \frac{2t\, dt}{1 + t} = 2t - 2 \log (1 + t)]_2^3$$

$$= (6 - 2 \log 4) - (4 - 2 \log 3) = 2 - 2 \log \left(\frac{4}{3}\right).$$

Example 4.   Evaluate

$$\int x(1 + x)^{1/3}\, dx.$$

Solution.   The integrand is simplified if $(1 + x)^{1/3}$ is replaced by t. This suggests the substitution $x = t^3 - 1$. Hence $dx = 3t^2\, dt$ and

$$\int x(1 + x)^{1/3}\, dx = \int (t^3 - 1)t\, 3t^2\, dt$$

$$= \int (3t^6 - 3t^3)\, dt$$

$$= \frac{3t^7}{7} - \frac{3t^4}{4} + C$$

$$= \frac{3t^4}{28} (4t^3 - 7) + C$$

$$= \frac{3(1 + x)^{4/3}}{28} (4x - 3) + C.$$

Example 5.   Evaluate

$$\int \frac{dx}{x^2\sqrt{1 - x^2}} \qquad (0 < x < 1).$$

Solution.   Let $x = 1/t$. Then $dx = -dt/t^2$ and

$$\int \frac{dx}{x^2\sqrt{1-x^2}} = \int (t^2)\frac{1}{\sqrt{1-(1/t^2)}}\left(\frac{-dt}{t^2}\right)$$

$$= -\int \frac{t\,dt}{\sqrt{t^2-1}} = -\frac{1}{2}\int (t^2-1)^{-1/2}(2t\,dt)$$

$$= -\frac{1}{2}\frac{(t^2-1)^{1/2}}{1/2} + C$$

$$= -\sqrt{t^2-1} + C = -\sqrt{(1/x^2)-1} + C$$

$$= -\frac{\sqrt{1-x^2}}{x} + C.$$

Example 6.   Evaluate

$$\int \frac{dx}{1+\cos x}.$$

Solution.   Let $x = 2\,\mathrm{Tan}^{-1}\,t$. This substitution, introduced by the distinguished German mathematician Karl Weierstrass (1815–1897), transforms an expression defining a rational function of $\sin x$ and $\cos x$ into an expression defining a rational function of t. Since $\tan (x/2) = t$, the trigonometric functions of x can be computed from Fig. 11.1 and the formulas

$$\sin x = 2\sin\frac{x}{2}\cos\frac{x}{2}; \qquad \cos x = 2\cos^2\frac{x}{2} - 1;$$

$$\tan x = \frac{2\tan(x/2)}{1-\tan^2(x/2)}.$$

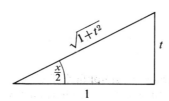

Figure 11.1

From

$$dx = \frac{2dt}{1+t^2}$$

and

$$\cos x = 2\cos^2\frac{x}{2} - 1$$

$$= \frac{2}{1+t^2} - 1,$$

we obtain

$$\int \frac{dx}{1 + \cos x} = \int \frac{1}{2/(1 + t^2)} \cdot \frac{2dt}{1 + t^2} = \int dt$$

$$= t + C = \tan \frac{x}{2} + C.$$

PROBLEM LIST 69

Evaluate the integrals in Problems 1–18.

1. $\int \dfrac{dx}{1 + 2\sqrt{x}}.$

2. $\int x\sqrt{1 + x}\, dx.$

3. $\int x^2 \sqrt[3]{1 + x}\, dx.$

4. $\int \dfrac{dx}{1 - x^{1/3}}.$

5. $\int \dfrac{dx}{x^{1/2} + x^{1/3}}.$

6. $\dfrac{\sqrt{x + 1}\, dx}{x + 2}.$

7. $\int (1 - x^{1/3})^{3/2}\, dx.$

8. $\int \dfrac{x\, dx}{\sqrt{x + 2}}.$

9. $\int \dfrac{(x + 3)\, dx}{\sqrt{x + 2}}.$

10. $\int \dfrac{x^5\, dx}{\sqrt[3]{1 + x^3}}.$

11. $\int \dfrac{dx}{\sqrt{x + 1} - \sqrt{x}}.$

12. $\int \dfrac{dx}{1 - \sin x}.$

13. $\int \sqrt{1 + \sqrt{x}}\, dx.$

14. $\int_4^9 \dfrac{dx}{2 + \sqrt{x}}.$

15. $\int_{-1}^{15} x(1 + x)^{1/4}\, dx.$

16. $\int_2^7 x^2 \sqrt{2 + x}\, dx.$

17. $\int_0^1 \dfrac{x^{1/2}\, dx}{1 + x}.$

18. $\int_{\pi/2}^{2\pi/3} \dfrac{dx}{1 - \cos x}.$

19. Show that $\int_0^a f(x)\, dx = \int_0^a f(a - x)\, dx.$

20. Show that $\int_{\pi/2}^{\pi} \sin^n x\, dx = \int_0^{\pi/2} \cos^n x\, dx,\ (n = 1, 2, \cdots).$

21. Evaluate $\int x\,(1 - x)^n\, dx,\ (n = 1, 2, \cdots)$ by (a) the substitution $x = 1 - t$, (b) parts.

22. Show that

$$\int \frac{\cos x\, dx}{1 + \cos x} = 2 \operatorname{Tan}^{-1}\left(\tan \frac{x}{2}\right) - \tan \frac{x}{2} + C.$$

23. Given that m, n, p, and q are integers $(n \neq 0)$, show that whenever $(m + 1)/n$ is an integer, $\int x^m (a + bx^n)^{p/q}\, dx$ is transformed into an integral without fractional exponents by the substitution

$$x = \left(\frac{z^q - a}{b}\right)^{1/n}.$$

24. Find the volume generated by revolving about the y-axis the first-quadrant area bounded by $y = \sqrt{3 + x}$, the line $x = 1$, and the coordinate axes.

25. Use the substitution $u = -t$ to show that

$$\int \frac{du}{u} = \log |u| + C \qquad \text{when } u < 0.$$

26. Prove the relationship $\log (xy) = \log x + \log y$ from the definition

$$\log x = \int_1^x \frac{dt}{t}.$$

27. Find the area inside the loop of $y^2 = x^2(4 - x)$.

28. Verify by differentiation that the answers to the illustrative examples in this section are correct.

11.5 *Trigonometric Substitution*

When an integrand $f(x)$ involves $(a^2 - x^2)^{1/2}$, the substitution $x = g(\theta) = a \sin \theta$ is often effective. This transforms $(a^2 - x^2)^{1/2}$ into

$$(a^2 - a^2 \sin^2 \theta)^{1/2} = [a^2(1 - \sin^2 \theta)]^{1/2}$$
$$= (a^2 \cos^2 \theta)^{1/2} = a \cos \theta,$$

thereby removing the fractional exponent. The domain of f includes at most values of x satisfying $-a \leqslant x \leqslant a$. (In this section a is assumed to be positive.) The inverse g^{-1} of g is given by

$$\theta = g^{-1}(x) = \operatorname{Sin}^{-1} \frac{x}{a}$$

and hence θ satisfies $-\pi/2 \leqslant \theta \leqslant \pi/2$. Note that

$$(\cos^2 \theta)^{1/2} = \cos \theta \qquad \text{since } \cos \theta \geqslant 0.$$

After the integral is found in terms of θ, the trigonometric functions of θ are often required to obtain the integral in terms of x. These are easily read from Fig. 11.2. The right diagram is unnecessary and merely emphasizes that $-\pi/2 \leqslant \theta \leqslant \pi/2$.

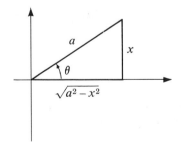
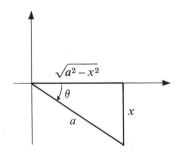

Figure 11.2

Example 1.   Evaluate

$$\int \frac{dx}{x^2 \sqrt{4 - x^2}}.$$

Solution.   Let $x = 2 \sin \theta$. Then $dx = 2 \cos \theta \, d\theta$, and

$$\int \frac{dx}{x^2 \sqrt{4 - x^2}} = \int \frac{2 \cos \theta \, d\theta}{4 \sin^2 \theta \sqrt{4 - 4 \sin^2 \theta}}$$

$$= \frac{1}{4} \int \csc^2 \theta \, d\theta$$

$$= \frac{-\cot \theta}{4} + C = \frac{-\sqrt{4 - x^2}}{4x} + C.$$

When $f(x)$ involves $(a^2 + x^2)^{1/2}$, the substitution $x = g(\theta) = a \tan \theta$ is often effective. This transforms $(a^2 + x^2)^{1/2}$ into

$$(a^2 + a^2 \tan^2 \theta)^{1/2} = [a^2(1 + \tan^2 \theta)]^{1/2}$$
$$= (a^2 \sec^2 \theta)^{1/2} = a \sec \theta.$$

The inverse g^{-1} of g is given by

$$\theta = g^{-1}(x) = \mathrm{Tan}^{-1} \frac{x}{a}$$

and hence $-\pi/2 < \theta < \pi/2$. Note that $(\sec^2 \theta)^{1/2} = \sec \theta$, since $\sec \theta > 0$.
The trigonometric functions of θ are easily read from Fig. 11.3.

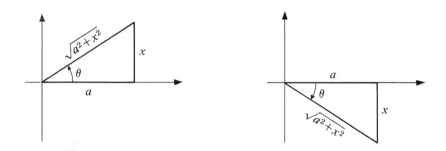

Figure 11.3

Example 2.   Evaluate $\int \sqrt{a^2 + x^2} \, dx$.

Solution.   Let $x = a \tan \theta$. Then $dx = a \sec^2 \theta \, d\theta$, and

$$\int \sqrt{a^2 + x^2} \, dx = \int \sqrt{a^2 + a^2 \tan^2 \theta} \; a \sec^2 \theta \, d\theta$$

$$= a^2 \int \sec^3 \theta \, d\theta$$

$$= \frac{a^2}{2} \sec \theta \tan \theta + \frac{a^2}{2} \log |\sec \theta + \tan \theta| + C'$$

as shown in Example 3 of Sec. 11.3. In terms of x we have

$$\int \sqrt{a^2 + x^2}\, dx = \frac{a^2}{2} \cdot \frac{\sqrt{a^2 + x^2}}{a} \cdot \frac{x}{a} + \frac{a^2}{2} \log \left| \frac{\sqrt{a^2 + x^2}}{a} + \frac{x}{a} \right| + C'$$

$$= \frac{x}{2}\sqrt{a^2 + x^2} + \frac{a^2}{2} \log (x + \sqrt{a^2 + x^2}) - \frac{a^2}{2} \log a + C'$$

$$= \frac{x}{2}\sqrt{a^2 + x^2} + \frac{a^2}{2} \log (x + \sqrt{a^2 + x^2}) + C.$$

Note that $(\sec^2 \theta)^{1/2} = \sec \theta$, since $\sec \theta > 0$, and that $x + \sqrt{a^2 + x^2} > 0$ even if $x \leqslant 0$.

_____

When $f(x)$ involves $(x^2 - a^2)^{1/2}$, the substitution $x = g(\theta) = a \sec \theta$ is employed. This reduces $(x^2 - a^2)^{1/2}$ to

$$(a^2 \sec^2 \theta - a^2)^{1/2} = [a^2 (\sec^2 \theta - 1)]^{1/2}$$
$$= (a^2 \tan^2 \theta)^{1/2} = a \tan \theta.$$

The domain of f includes at most values of x for which $|x| \geqslant a$. The inverse g^{-1} of g is given by

$$\theta = g^{-1}(x) = \operatorname{Sec}^{-1} \frac{x}{a}$$

and hence θ satisfies $0 \leqslant \theta < \pi/2$ when $x \geqslant a$ and $\pi \leqslant \theta < 3\pi/2$ when $x \leqslant -a$.

The graph of $\operatorname{Sec}^{-1} x$ is shown in Fig. 9.13. Note that $(\tan^2 \theta)^{1/2} = \tan \theta$, since $\tan \theta \geqslant 0$.

The trigonometric functions of θ are read from Fig. 11.4.

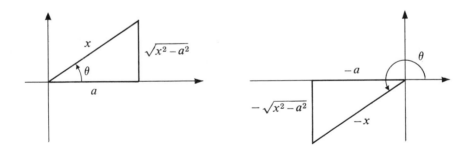

Figure 11.4

Example 3.   Evaluate

$$\int_{-2}^{-1} \frac{\sqrt{x^2 - 1}}{x}\, dx.$$

Solution.   Let $x = \sec \theta$. Then $dx = \sec \theta \tan \theta\, d\theta$ and

$$\int_{-2}^{-1} \frac{\sqrt{x^2 - 1}}{x} \, dx = \int_{4\pi/3}^{\pi} \frac{\sqrt{\sec^2 \theta - 1}}{\sec \theta} \sec \theta \tan \theta \, d\theta$$

$$= \int_{4\pi/3}^{\pi} \tan^2 \theta \, d\theta = \int_{4\pi/3}^{\pi} (\sec^2 \theta - 1) \, d\theta$$

$$= \tan \theta - \theta]_{4\pi/3}^{\pi}$$

$$= -\pi - \tan \frac{4\pi}{3} + \frac{4\pi}{3} = \frac{\pi}{3} - \sqrt{3}.$$

Example 4.   Derive the formula for the area of a circle.

Solution.   Let the circle have equation $x^2 + y^2 = a^2$. From Fig. 11.5 it is clear that the area A is given by

$$A = 4 \int_0^a \sqrt{a^2 - x^2} \, dx.$$

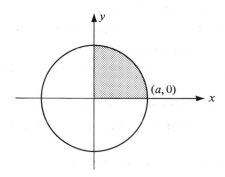

Figure 11.5

Let $x = a \sin \theta$. Then $dx = a \cos \theta \, d\theta$ and

$$A = 4 \int_0^{\pi/2} \sqrt{a^2 - a^2 \sin^2 \theta} \, a \cos \theta \, d\theta$$

$$= 4a^2 \int_0^{\pi/2} \cos^2 \theta \, d\theta = 2a^2 \int_0^{\pi/2} (1 + \cos 2\theta) \, d\theta$$

$$= 2a^2 \left[\theta + \frac{1}{2} \sin 2\theta \right]_0^{\pi/2} = 2a^2 \frac{\pi}{2} = \pi a^2.$$

PROBLEM LIST 70

In Problems 1–18 evaluate the integrals by a trigonometric substitution.

1. $\displaystyle \int \frac{dx}{\sqrt{9 + x^2}}$.

2. $\displaystyle \int \frac{x^2 \, dx}{\sqrt{1 - x^2}}$.

3. $\displaystyle \int \frac{dx}{\sqrt{x^2 - 4}}$.

4. $\displaystyle \int \frac{dx}{(4 - x^2)^{3/2}}$.

5. $\displaystyle\int \frac{dx}{a^2 + x^2}.$

12. $\displaystyle\int \frac{dx}{x^2\sqrt{x^2 + a^2}}.$

6. $\displaystyle\int \frac{dx}{\sqrt{a^2 - x^2}}.$

13. $\displaystyle\int \frac{dx}{\sqrt{1 - x^2}}.$

7. $\displaystyle\int \sqrt{x^2 - a^2}\, dx.$

14. $\displaystyle\int \frac{dx}{(9 + x^2)^{3/2}}.$

8. $\displaystyle\int \frac{dx}{x(1 + x^2)}.$

15. $\displaystyle\int_1^2 \sqrt{x^2 - 1}\, dx.$

9. $\displaystyle\int \frac{\sqrt{x^2 - a^2}}{x^2}\, dx.$

16. $\displaystyle\int_0^2 x^3 \sqrt{4 - x^2}\, dx.$

10. $\displaystyle\int \frac{x^2\, dx}{(16 + x^2)^2}.$

17. $\displaystyle\int_0^1 \sqrt{4 + x^2}\, dx.$

11. $\displaystyle\int \frac{dx}{x\sqrt{4x^2 + 9}}.$

18. $\displaystyle\int_{-\sqrt{2}/2}^{-1/2} \frac{dx}{x(1 - x^2)}.$

19. Derive the formula for the area of an ellipse.

20. Find the area bounded by $x^2 - y^2 = 4$ and the line $x = 4$.

21. Find the length of $y = x^2/2$ from $(0, 0)$ to $(4, 8)$.

22. The area bounded by $y = x^2\sqrt{x^2 + 1}$, $x = 1$, and the x-axis is revolved about the y-axis. Find the volume generated.

23. Find the area inside one loop of $y^2 = x^4 - x^6$.

24. Verify by differentiation that the answers to the illustrative examples in this section are correct.

25. Find the area inside the loop of the strophoid

$$y^2 = x^2 \frac{a - x}{a + x}.$$

26. Evaluate

$$\int \frac{\mathrm{Tan}^{-1}(x)\, dx}{x^2}.$$

11.6   *Integration by Partial Fractions*

In elementary algebra one learns the following technique for adding fractions:

$$\frac{3}{x - 2} + \frac{2}{x + 4} = \frac{3(x + 4) + 2(x - 2)}{(x - 2)(x + 4)}$$

$$= \frac{5x + 8}{x^2 + 2x - 8}. \tag{11.24}$$

The left member of (11.24) is simpler to integrate than the right member and hence it is advantageous to know how to reverse the process shown and to find the fractions on the left when the expression

$$\frac{5x + 8}{x^2 + 2x - 8}$$

is given. This reverse process is known as the resolution of an expression defining a rational function into its partial fractions.

Let us assume that there exist numbers A and B such that

$$\frac{5x + 8}{x^2 + 2x - 8} \equiv \frac{A}{x - 2} + \frac{B}{x + 4} \tag{11.25}$$

for all values of x except 2 and -4. Then

$$5x + 8 \equiv A(x + 4) + B(x - 2) \tag{11.26}$$

for all values of x except possibly 2 and -4. But (11.26) is a linear equation and must hold for all values of x if it holds for more than one value of x. Hence (11.26) also holds for $x = 2$ and $x = -4$. Substituting $x = 2$ and $x = -4$ into (11.26), we obtain

$$18 = 6A \qquad \text{and} \qquad -12 = -6B$$

and hence $A = 3$ and $B = 2$.

With this process available we would now be able to obtain

$$\int \frac{(5x + 8)\, dx}{x^2 + 2x - 8} = \int \left(\frac{3}{x - 2} + \frac{2}{x + 4} \right) dx$$
$$= 3 \log |x - 2| + 2 \log |x + 4| + C$$
$$= \log |(x - 2)^3 (x + 4)^2| + C.$$

Now let $N(x)$ and $D(x)$ denote polynomials and consider the problem of resolving $N(x)/D(x)$ into its partial fractions.

We first assume that the degree of $D(x)$ is greater than the degree of $N(x)$, since otherwise we would apply the technique of Example 1 of Sec. 11.4.

If $(x - a)^n$ is a factor of $D(x)$ we assume that there exist terms

$$\frac{A_1}{(x - a)}, \frac{A_2}{(x - a)^2}, \ldots, \frac{A_n}{(x - a)^n}$$

in the partial fractions resolution of N/D. If $(x^2 + bx + c)^m$ is a factor of $D(x)$, we assume that there exist terms

$$\frac{B_1 x + C_1}{x^2 + bx + c}, \frac{B_2 x + C_2}{(x^2 + bx + c)^2}, \ldots, \frac{B_m x + C_m}{(x^2 + bx + c)^m}$$

in the required resolution. A justification for these assumptions is given in Ref. 11.3.

Example 1. Resolve

$$\frac{5x^2 - 9x - 2}{(x + 2)(x - 1)^2}$$

into partial fractions.

Solution. Let

$$\frac{5x^2 - 9x - 2}{(x + 2)(x - 1)^2} \equiv \frac{A}{x + 2} + \frac{B}{x - 1} + \frac{C}{(x - 1)^2}.$$

Then

$$5x^2 - 9x - 2 \equiv A(x - 1)^2 + B(x + 2)(x - 1) + C(x + 2).$$

Substituting 1, -2, and 0 for x yields

$$-6 = 3C; \qquad 36 = 9A; \qquad -2 = A - 2B + 2C,$$

from which we obtain

$$C = -2; \qquad A = 4; \qquad B = 1.$$

Example 2.   Resolve

$$\frac{7x^3 - 29x^2 + 46x - 55}{(x - 3)^2(x^2 + 2)}$$

into partial fractions.

Solution.   Let

$$\frac{7x^3 - 29x^2 + 46x - 55}{(x - 3)^2(x^2 + 2)} \equiv \frac{A}{x - 3} + \frac{B}{(x - 3)^2} + \frac{Cx + D}{x^2 + 2}.$$

Then

$$7x^3 - 29x^2 + 46x - 55 \equiv A(x - 3)(x^2 + 2) + B(x^2 + 2) + (Cx + D)(x - 3)^2.$$

The values of A, B, and C can be found by the method of Example 1. Although this method is preferable, we present an alternate method known as the method of undetermined coefficients. This powerful method has many applications and we present it for this reason. We first write

$$7x^3 - 29x^2 + 46x - 55 \equiv (A + C)x^3 + (-3A + B - 6C + D)x^2$$
$$+ (2A + 9C - 6D)x$$
$$+ (-6A + 2B + 9D). \qquad \textbf{(11.27)}$$

In order that (11.27) hold, the coefficients of like powers of x must be equal. Otherwise (11.27) would be a polynomial equation of degree 3 or less possessing more than three distinct roots, a condition known in algebra to be impossible. By equating coefficients of like powers of x, we obtain the system of linear equations

$$A \qquad + C \qquad = 7,$$
$$-3A + B - 6C + D = -29,$$
$$2A \qquad + 9C - 6D = 46,$$
$$-6A + 2B \qquad + 9D = -55,$$

having solution

$$A = 5; \qquad B = 1; \qquad C = 2; \qquad D = -3.$$

Example 3.   Evaluate

$$\int \frac{4x^4 + 3x^3 + 4x^2 - x - 2}{(x - 2)(x^2 + 1)^2}\, dx.$$

Solution.   We first resolve the integrand into its partial fractions:

$$\frac{4x^4 + 3x^3 + 4x^2 - x - 2}{(x - 2)(x^2 + 1)^2} = \frac{A}{x - 2} + \frac{Bx + C}{x^2 + 1} + \frac{Dx + E}{(x^2 + 1)^2},$$

$$4x^4 + 3x^3 + 4x^2 - x - 2 \equiv A(x^2 + 1)^2 + (Bx + C)(x - 2)(x^2 + 1)$$
$$+ (Dx + E)(x - 2).$$

By substituting $x = 2, 0, 1, -1$, and -2, we obtain

$$100 = 25A$$
$$-2 = \quad A \qquad - \quad 2C \qquad - 2E,$$
$$8 = \quad 4A - \quad 2B - \quad 2C - \quad D - \quad E,$$
$$4 = \quad 4A + \quad 6B - \quad 6C + 3D - 3E,$$
$$56 = 25A + 40B - 20C + 8D - 4E.$$

Solving this system of linear equations yields $A = 4$, $B = 0$, $C = 3$, $D = 2$, and $E = 0$. The algebra can sometimes be simplified by combining methods of Examples 1 and 2. For example, it is seen by inspection that $A + B = 4$, since these are the coefficients of x^4 in the two members. But $A = 4$ by our first equation, and hence $B = 0$.

We next obtain

$$\int \left(\frac{4}{x - 2} + \frac{3}{x^2 + 1} + \frac{2x}{(x^2 + 1)^2} \right) dx = 4 \int \frac{dx}{x - 2} + 3 \int \frac{dx}{x^2 + 1}$$
$$+ \int (x^2 + 1)^{-2} 2x \, dx$$
$$= 4 \log |x - 2| + 3 \operatorname{Tan}^{-1} x$$
$$- (x^2 + 1)^{-1} + C.$$

PROBLEM LIST 71

Evaluate the integrals in Problems 1–29.

1. $\int \dfrac{(5x + 2) \, dx}{(x - 1)(x + 4)}$.

2. $\int \dfrac{(2x - 19) \, dx}{(x + 3)(x - 2)}$.

3. $\int \dfrac{(7x + 2) \, dx}{x^2 - 4}$.

4. $\int \dfrac{(4x + 11) \, dx}{x^2 + 5x + 6}$.

5. $\int \dfrac{(38 - 3x) \, dx}{x^2 - 9x + 8}$.

6. $\int \dfrac{(x + 4) \, dx}{(x + 1)^2}$.

7. $\int \dfrac{(2x - 7) \, dx}{(x - 2)^2}$.

8. $\int \dfrac{(x^3 - 5) \, dx}{x^2 - 1}$.

9. $\int \dfrac{(x^4 - x^3 - 2x^2 + x - 14) \, dx}{x^2 - x - 2}$.

10. $\int \dfrac{(7x^2 + 2x - 80) \, dx}{(x + 1)(x - 2)(x + 6)}$.

11. $\int \dfrac{(6x^2 + 5x - 5) \, dx}{(x^2 - 1)(x + 2)}$.

12. $\int \dfrac{dx}{(x - a)(x + b)}$.

13. $\int \dfrac{dx}{a^2 - x^2}$, $(x^2 < a^2)$.

14. $\int \dfrac{dx}{x^2 - a^2}$, $(x^2 > a^2)$.

15. $\int \dfrac{(x^2 - x + 1) \, dx}{(x - 1)(x - 2)^2}$.

16. $\int \dfrac{(2x^2 + x - 4) \, dx}{(x + 2)(x + 1)^2}$.

17. $\int \dfrac{(3x^3 - 6x^2 + 3x + 4) \, dx}{(x - 1)^2}$.

18. $\int \dfrac{(-x^3 - 3x^2 + 2x + 9) \, dx}{(x + 2)(x + 1)^3}$.

19. $\int \dfrac{(x^2 + 3x - 2)\, dx}{(x-1)(x^2+1)}$.

20. $\int \dfrac{(3x^2 + 5x - 8)\, dx}{(x+4)(x^2+4)}$.

21. $\int \dfrac{(5x^2 + 2x + 2)\, dx}{x^3 - 1}$.

22. $\int \dfrac{(2x^3 - x^2 + 8x)\, dx}{(x^2+4)^2}$.

23. $\int_0^1 \dfrac{(x-8)\, dx}{(x+5)(x-6)}$.

24. $\int_0^1 \dfrac{(4x^2 - x + 4)\, dx}{(x+1)(x-2)^2}$.

25. $\int_0^3 \dfrac{(-2x^2 + 5x - 3)\, dx}{(x+3)(x^2+9)}$.

26. $\int_1^2 \dfrac{(2x+1)\, dx}{(x+1)^2}$.

27. $\int \dfrac{dx}{e^{2x} + 5e^x + 6}$.

28. $\int \dfrac{dx}{x^{3/2}(x+1)}$.

29. $\int \dfrac{d\theta}{3 + 5\cos\theta}$.

30. Find the area bounded by $y = 1/(x^2 - 1)$, $x = 1/2$, and the coordinate axes.

31. Find the volume generated by revolving about the x-axis the curve $y = (x+1)/(x^2+1)$ from $x = 0$ to $x = 1$.

32. Verify by differentiation that the answers to the illustrative examples in this section are correct.

11.7   Integrals Involving Quadratic Polynomials

When an integrand involves $ax^2 + bx + c$, $(a \neq 0)$, it is generally preferable to factor a from each term. The expression $x^2 + dx + e$ is then written in the form $f^2 + (x+g)^2$, $f^2 - (x+g)^2$, or $(x+g)^2 - f^2$ by the process of completing the square.

Example 1

$$x^2 + 2x + 5 = x^2 + 2x + 1 + 4$$
$$= (x+1)^2 + (2)^2.$$

Example 2

$$-x^2 + 6x + 7 = -(x^2 - 6x + 9 - 16)$$
$$= -[(x-3)^2 - (4)^2]$$
$$= (4)^2 - (x-3)^2.$$

Example 3

$$4x^2 + 8x + 3 = 4\left(x^2 + 2x + \frac{3}{4}\right)$$
$$= 4\left(x^2 + 2x + 1 - \frac{1}{4}\right)$$
$$= 4\left[(x+1)^2 - \left(\frac{1}{2}\right)^2\right].$$

Example 4

$$\int \frac{dx}{\sqrt{-x^2 - 10x - 9}} = \int \frac{dx}{\sqrt{(4)^2 - (x + 5)^2}} = \text{Sin}^{-1} \frac{x + 5}{4} + C.$$

Example 5

$$\int \frac{(x - 2)\,dx}{x^2 + 4x + 5} = \frac{1}{2} \int \frac{(2x + 4 - 8)\,dx}{x^2 + 4x + 5}$$

$$= \frac{1}{2} \int \frac{(2x + 4)\,dx}{x^2 + 4x + 5} - 4 \int \frac{dx}{(x + 2)^2 + (1)^2}$$

$$= \frac{1}{2} \log (x^2 + 4x + 5) - 4\,\text{Tan}^{-1}(x + 2) + C.$$

Example 6

$$\int \frac{(x - 3)\,dx}{\sqrt{5 + 4x - x^2}} = -\frac{1}{2} \int \frac{(4 - 2x + 2)\,dx}{\sqrt{5 + 4x - x^2}}$$

$$= -\frac{1}{2} \int (5 + 4x - x^2)^{-1/2}(4 - 2x)\,dx - \int \frac{dx}{\sqrt{(3)^2 - (x - 2)^2}}$$

$$= -(5 + 4x - x^2)^{1/2} - \text{Sin}^{-1} \frac{x - 2}{3} + C.$$

Integrals such as

$$\int \frac{dx}{\sqrt{(x + 1)^2 - 1}}$$

can be evaluated by a trigonometric substitution, but it is usually simpler to refer to a table of integrals. This method will be discussed in Sec. 11.9.

PROBLEM LIST 72

Evaluate the integrals in Problems 1–15.

1. $\int \dfrac{dx}{x^2 + 4x + 13}.$

2. $\int \dfrac{dx}{4x^2 - 8x + 5}.$

3. $\int \dfrac{dx}{\sqrt{8 - 2x - x^2}}.$

4. $\int \dfrac{dx}{\sqrt{-x^2 + 10x - 16}}.$

5. $\int \dfrac{(x + 1)\,dx}{1 + x^2}.$

6. $\int \dfrac{(4x + 9)\,dx}{x^2 + 4x + 5}.$

7. $\int \dfrac{(4 - 2x)\,dx}{x^2 - 2x + 5}.$

8. $\int \dfrac{dx}{\sqrt{12x - x^2}}.$

9. $\int \dfrac{4x\,dx}{\sqrt{9x - x^2}}.$

10. $\int \dfrac{(x + 4)\,dx}{\sqrt{26 - 2x - x^2}}.$

11. $\int \dfrac{(x^2 + 3x + 2)\,dx}{x(x^2 + 2x + 2)}.$

12. $\int \dfrac{(5 - 2x)\,dx}{\sqrt{-x^2 + 4x - 3}}.$

13. $\int \dfrac{(3x + 2)\,dx}{\sqrt{10 - 4x - 4x^2}}.$

14. $\int \dfrac{(1 - 2x)\,dx}{4 - x^2}.$

15. $\int \dfrac{(2x^3 + 7x^2 + 12x + 8)\,dx}{(x^2 + 2x + 2)^2}.$

16. Verify by differentiation that the integrals in the illustrative examples in this section are correct.

11.8   Wallis's Formulas

The following useful formulas are due to the English mathematician John Wallis (1616–1703). The exponents m and n denote positive integers.

$$\int_0^{\pi/2} \sin^m x \, dx = \int_0^{\pi/2} \cos^m x \, dx = \frac{(m-1)(m-3)\cdots(3 \text{ or } 2)}{m(m-2)\cdots(3 \text{ or } 2)} k, \quad \textbf{(11.28)}$$

where $k = 1$ if m is odd, and $k = \pi/2$ if m is even.

$$\int_0^{\pi/2} \sin^m x \cos^n x \, dx = \frac{(m-1)(m-3)\cdots(3 \text{ or } 2)(n-1)(n-3)\cdots(3 \text{ or } 2)}{(m+n)(m+n-2)\cdots(3 \text{ or } 2)} k,$$
$$\textbf{(11.29)}$$

where $k = 1$ unless both m and n are even, and $k = \pi/2$ if both m and n are even.

To obtain (11.28) we apply integration by parts to $\int \sin^m x \, dx$, with $u = \sin^{m-1} x$ and $dv = \sin x \, dx$. This leads to the reduction formula

$$\int \sin^m x \, dx = \frac{-\cos x \sin^{m-1} x}{m} + \frac{m-1}{m} \int \sin^{m-2} x \, dx. \quad \textbf{(11.30)}$$

Applying the limits 0 to $\pi/2$ to (11.30), and noting that the first term on the right is zero at both limits, we obtain

$$\int_0^{\pi/2} \sin^m x \, dx = \frac{m-1}{m} \int_0^{\pi/2} \sin^{m-2} x \, dx$$
$$= \frac{m-1}{m} \left[\frac{m-3}{m-2} \int_0^{\pi/2} \sin^{m-4} x \, dx \right]$$
$$= \frac{m-1}{m} \cdot \frac{m-3}{m-2} \left[\frac{m-5}{m-4} \int_0^{\pi/2} \sin^{m-6} x \, dx \right], \quad \textbf{(11.31)}$$

and so forth.

Repeated application of (11.31) eventually reduces the integral on the right to $\int_0^{\pi/2} \sin x \, dx = 1$ when m is odd, and to $\int_0^{\pi/2} dx = \pi/2$ when m is even.

The identity

$$\int_0^{\pi/2} \sin^m x \, dx = \int_0^{\pi/2} \cos^m x \, dx$$

is established by making the change of variable $x = \pi/2 - t$. This completes the proof of (11.28). The proof of (11.29) is similar and is left to the exercises.

Example 1

$$\int_0^{\pi/2} \sin^7 x \, dx = \frac{6 \cdot 4 \cdot 2}{7 \cdot 5 \cdot 3} = \frac{16}{35}.$$

Example 2

$$\int_0^{\pi/2} \cos^8 x \, dx = \frac{7 \cdot 5 \cdot 3}{8 \cdot 6 \cdot 4 \cdot 2} \cdot \frac{\pi}{2} = \frac{35\pi}{256}.$$

Example 3

$$\int_0^{\pi/2} \sin^6 x \cos^5 x \, dx = \frac{5 \cdot 3 \cdot 4 \cdot 2}{11 \cdot 9 \cdot 7 \cdot 5 \cdot 3} = \frac{8}{693}.$$

Example 4

$$\int_0^{\pi/2} \sin^6 x \cos^4 x \, dx = \frac{5 \cdot 3 \cdot 3}{10 \cdot 8 \cdot 6 \cdot 4 \cdot 2} \cdot \frac{\pi}{2} = \frac{3\pi}{512}.$$

Example 5

$$\int_0^{\pi/2} \sin^5 x \cos x \, dx = \frac{4 \cdot 2}{6 \cdot 4 \cdot 2} = \frac{1}{6}.$$

In this example $n = 1$ and hence no factors corresponding to n appear in the numerator.

At this point the reader may have gained the impression that Wallis's formulas are too special to be of great value, since the integrations cover only the first quadrant from 0 to $\pi/2$. However, in the applications of calculus to geometry, mechanics, physics, and similar fields, these limits occur with great frequency. Furthermore, the integrations are easily extended to cover other quadrants. By employing the substitution $x = t + (k\pi/2)$, it can be shown (see Problem 30) that

$$\left| \int_{k\pi/2}^{(k+1)(\pi/2)} \sin^m x \cos^n x \, dx \right| = \left| \int_0^{\pi/2} \sin^m t \cos^n t \, dt \right|.$$

(In this equation m or n may be zero.)

Since the sign of the integrand in any particular quadrant can be determined by inspection, the formulas are readily applied over several quadrants.

Example 6

$$\int_0^{3\pi/2} \sin^4 x \cos^2 x \, dx = 3 \int_0^{\pi/2} \sin^4 x \cos^2 x \, dx$$

$$= 3 \cdot \frac{3}{6 \cdot 4 \cdot 2} \cdot \frac{\pi}{2} = \frac{3\pi}{32}.$$

The integrand is clearly positive in all three quadrants.

Example 7

$$\int_0^{3\pi/2} \sin^3 x \cos^3 x \, dx = (1 - 1 + 1) \int_0^{\pi/2} \sin^3 x \cos^3 x \, dx$$

$$= \frac{2 \cdot 2}{6 \cdot 4 \cdot 2} = \frac{1}{12}.$$

The integrand is positive in quadrants I and III and negative in quadrant II.

A change of variable often reduces an integral to one which can be evaluated by Wallis's formulas.

Example 8.   Evaluate $\int_0^{\pi} \sin^6 (x/2) \cos^2 (x/2) \, dx$.

Solution.   Let $x = 2\theta$. Then $dx = 2d\theta$ and the integral becomes

$$2 \int_0^{\pi/2} \sin^6 \theta \cos^2 \theta \, d\theta = 2 \cdot \frac{5 \cdot 3}{8 \cdot 6 \cdot 4 \cdot 2} \cdot \frac{\pi}{2} = \frac{5\pi}{128}.$$

Example 9.   Evaluate $\int_0^a (a^2 - x^2)^{5/2} \, dx$.

Solution.   Let $x = a \sin \theta$. Then $dx = a \cos \theta \, d\theta$ and the integral becomes

$$\int_0^{\pi/2} (a^2 - a^2 \sin^2 \theta)^{5/2} a \cos \theta \, d\theta = a^6 \int_0^{\pi/2} \cos^6 \theta \, d\theta$$

$$= a^6 \cdot \frac{5 \cdot 3}{6 \cdot 4 \cdot 2} \cdot \frac{\pi}{2}$$

$$= \frac{5\pi a^6}{32}.$$

PROBLEM LIST 73

Evaluate the integrals in Problems 1–28.

1. $\int_0^{\pi/2} \sin^5 x \, dx.$

15. $\int_\pi^{3\pi} \sin^4 x \cos^7 x \, dx.$

2. $\int_0^{\pi/2} \sin^6 x \, dx.$

16. $\int_{-\pi/2}^\pi \sin^2 x \cos^5 x \, dx.$

3. $\int_0^{\pi/2} \cos^6 x \, dx.$

17. $\int_0^{6\pi} \sin^5 x \cos^5 x \, dx.$

4. $\int_0^{\pi/2} \cos^7 x \, dx.$

18. $\int_0^\pi \sin^2 (x/2) \cos^2 (x/2) \, dx.$

5. $\int_0^{\pi/2} \sin^6 x \cos^2 x \, dx.$

19. $\int_0^{\pi/3} \sin^3 3x \, dx.$

6. $\int_0^{\pi/2} \sin^5 x \cos^4 x \, dx.$

20. $\int_{-\pi/6}^{\pi/6} \cos^5 3x \, dx.$

7. $\int_0^{\pi/2} \sin^3 x \cos^6 x \, dx.$

21. $\int_0^{\pi/4} \sin^4 4x \cos^4 4x \, dx.$

8. $\int_0^{\pi/2} \sin^2 x \cos^6 x \, dx.$

22. $\int_0^{2\pi} \cos^4 2x \, dx.$

9. $\int_0^{\pi/2} \sin^4 x \cos x \, dx.$

23. $\int_0^{6\pi} \sin^2 (x/3) \cos^8 (x/3) \, dx.$

10. $\int_0^{\pi/2} \sin x \cos^6 x \, dx.$

24. $\int_0^\pi \sin^3 x \cos^4 (x/2) \, dx.$

11. $\int_0^\pi \sin^9 x \, dx.$

25. $\int_0^1 \sqrt{1 - x^2} \, dx.$

12. $\int_0^{3\pi/2} \cos^5 x \, dx.$

26. $\int_0^a (a^2 - x^2)^6 \, dx.$

13. $\int_\pi^{2\pi} \sin^3 x \cos^3 x \, dx.$

27. $\int_0^2 (4 - x^2)^{3/2} \, dx.$

14. $\int_{\pi/2}^{2\pi} | \sin^5 x | \, dx.$

28. $\int_0^1 x^2 \sqrt{1 - x^2} \, dx.$

29. Derive the reduction formula

$$\int_0^{\pi/2} \sin^m x \cos^n x \, dx = \frac{m-1}{m+n} \int_0^{\pi/2} \sin^{m-2}x \cos^n x \, dx.$$

Then derive (11.29).

30. Prove the formula given in Example 5.

31. Find the area under $y = \sin^5 x$ from $x = 0$ to $x = \pi$.

32. Find the area in quadrants I and IV enclosed by the curve $y^2 = x^4(4 - x^2)$.

33. Find the area enclosed by one loop of the curve $y^2 = x^2(9 - x)^3$.

34. Derive the formula for the area of a circle.

35. Prove that

$$\int_0^{\pi/2} \sin^{2m} x \, dx = \frac{\pi(2m)!}{2^{2m+1}(m!)^2}.$$

11.9   Use of a Table of Integrals

An understanding of the basic techniques of integration is essential for one who uses the calculus. However, many integrals can be evaluated by using a table of integrals such as the table given in Appendix B. For example, to evaluate

$$I = \int \frac{x^2 \, dx}{\sqrt{25 - 9x^2}}$$

we rewrite I in the form

$$\frac{1}{27} \int \frac{(3x)^2 \, 3dx}{\sqrt{(5)^2 - (3x)^2}}$$

and employ formula (70) of Appendix B to obtain

$$I = -\frac{x}{18}\sqrt{25 - 9x^2} + \frac{25}{54} \operatorname{Sin}^{-1} \frac{3x}{5} + C.$$

In this problem $a = 5$, $u = 3x$, and $du = 3dx$.
    More extensive tables are to be found in Refs. 11.2 and 11.4.

PROBLEM LIST 74

Evaluate the integrals by means of Appendix B.

1. $\displaystyle \int \frac{x \, dx}{2x + 3}.$

2. $\displaystyle \int x\sqrt{5x - 2} \, dx.$

3. $\displaystyle \int \frac{x \, dx}{\sqrt{2x - 1}}.$

4. $\displaystyle \int \frac{dx}{4x^2 - 9}.$

5. $\displaystyle \int \frac{x^2 \, dx}{16x^2 - 1}.$

6. $\displaystyle \int \frac{x^2 \, dx}{x^2 + 4}.$

7. $\displaystyle \int \sqrt{x^2 + 4} \, dx.$

8. $\displaystyle \int \sqrt{3 - x^2} \, dx.$

9. $\displaystyle \int \frac{\sqrt{4 - 9x^2}}{x^2} \, dx.$

10. $\displaystyle \int \tan^2 2x \, dx.$

11. $\int \sin^2 5x \, dx.$ **15.** $\int e^{2x} \cos 3x \, dx.$

12. $\int x^2 \sin 3x \, dx.$ **16.** $\int \text{Tan}^{-1} 4x \, dx.$

13. $\int xe^{6x} \, dx.$ **17.** $\int \log 4x \, dx.$

14. $\int x^2 e^{-3x} \, dx.$

11.10   Improper Integrals

At this stage of our development the integral $I = \int_a^b f(x) \, dx$ has no meaning unless f is defined on $a \leqslant x \leqslant b$. We now define certain extensions of I known as improper integrals.

The symbol $\int_a^\infty f(x) \, dx$ is defined by

$$\int_a^\infty f(x) \, dx = \lim_{t \to \infty} \int_a^t f(x) \, dx.$$

If the limit on the right exists, the improper integral is said to converge to that limit. If the limit does not exist, the integral is said to diverge, and no value is assigned to it.

Example 1

$$\int_1^\infty \frac{dx}{x^2} = \lim_{t \to \infty} \int_1^t x^{-2} \, dx$$
$$= \lim_{t \to \infty} [-x^{-1}]_1^t$$
$$= \lim_{t \to \infty} \left[-\frac{1}{t} + 1 \right] = 1.$$

Example 2

$$\int_1^\infty \frac{dx}{x} = \lim_{t \to \infty} \int_1^t \frac{dx}{x}$$
$$= \lim_{t \to \infty} [\log x]_1^t$$
$$= \lim_{t \to \infty} \log t.$$

This limit does not exist, since $\log t \to \infty$ as $t \to \infty$. Hence the integral diverges.

The geometric interpretation of Examples 1 and 2 is given in Fig. 11.6. As $t \to \infty$, the shaded area on the left approaches one square unit and we say that the area bounded by $y = 0$, $y = 1/x^2$, and $x = 1$ is one square unit even through the region in question is not finite in extent. On the other hand, as $t \to \infty$ the shaded area on the right becomes large without limit. It should be noted that the marked difference between the results in these two examples is not intuitively evident.

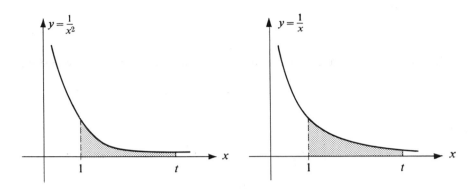

Figure 11.6

Example 3

$$\int_0^\infty \cos x \, dx = \lim_{t \to \infty} \int_0^t \cos x \, dx$$

$$= \lim_{t \to \infty} [\sin x]_0^t$$

$$= \lim_{t \to \infty} \sin t.$$

The integral diverges, since $\sin t$ oscillates between -1 and $+1$ as $t \to \infty$.

The symbol $\int_{-\infty}^a f(x) \, dx$ is defined by

$$\int_{-\infty}^a f(x) \, dx = \lim_{t \to -\infty} \int_t^a f(x) \, dx.$$

Example 4

$$\int_{-\infty}^0 e^x \, dx = \lim_{t \to -\infty} \int_t^0 e^x \, dx$$

$$= \lim_{t \to -\infty} [e^x]_t^0$$

$$= \lim_{t \to -\infty} [1 - e^t] = 1.$$

The symbol $\int_{-\infty}^\infty f(x) \, dx$ is defined by

$$\int_{-\infty}^\infty f(x) \, dx = \int_{-\infty}^a f(x) \, dx + \int_a^\infty f(x) \, dx,$$

where a denotes an arbitrary real number.

If either of the improper integrals on the right diverges, the integral on the left is classified as divergent. It is easily shown that the choice of the number a is immaterial.

Example 5. $\int_{-\infty}^{\infty} \cos x \, dx$ diverges, since $\int_{0}^{\infty} \cos x \, dx$ was shown in Example 3 to be divergent.

_____

If f is not defined at $x = a$, and $a < b$, the symbol $\int_{a}^{b} f(x) \, dx$ is defined by

$$\int_{a}^{b} f(x) \, dx = \lim_{t \to a^+} \int_{t}^{b} f(x) \, dx.$$

Example 6

$$\int_{0}^{4} \frac{dx}{\sqrt{x}} = \lim_{t \to 0^+} \int_{t}^{4} x^{-1/2} \, dx$$

$$= \lim_{t \to 0^+} [2x^{1/2}]_{t}^{4}$$

$$= \lim_{t \to 0^+} (4 - 2\sqrt{t}) = 4.$$

The shaded area in Fig. 11.7 approaches 4 square units as $t \to 0^+$.

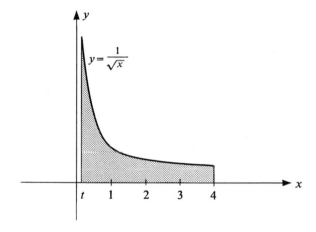

Figure 11.7

Similarly, if f is not defined at $x = b$, and $a < b$, the symbol $\int_{a}^{b} f(x) \, dx$ is defined by

$$\int_{a}^{b} f(x) \, dx = \lim_{t \to b^-} \int_{a}^{t} f(x) \, dx.$$

It f is not defined at $x = c$ where $a < c < b$, the symbol $\int_{a}^{b} f(x) \, dx$ is defined by

$$\int_{a}^{b} f(x) \, dx = \int_{a}^{c} f(x) \, dx + \int_{c}^{b} f(x) \, dx.$$

Example 7

$$\int_{-1}^{1} \frac{dx}{x^2} = \lim_{t \to 0^-} \int_{-1}^{t} x^{-2} \, dx \mid \lim_{t \to 0^+} \int_{t}^{1} x^{-2} \, dx$$

The integral diverges, since

$$\lim_{t \to 0^+} \int_t^1 x^{-2}\, dx = \lim_{t \to 0^+} [-x^{-1}]_t^1$$

$$= \lim_{t \to 0^+} \left[-1 + \frac{1}{t} \right],$$

and the latter limit does not exist.

Note that the computation

$$\int_{-1}^1 \frac{dx}{x^2} = -x^{-1}]_{-1}^1 = (-1) - (1) = -2$$

is invalid. The second fundamental theorem does not apply because $-x^{-1}$ is not an antiderivative of x^{-2} for every x in $-1 \leqslant x \leqslant 1$. The function given by $F(x) = -x^{-1}$ is not defined at $x = 0$, and hence could not possibly possess a derivative at $x = 0$.

We will make use of improper integrals in the chapter on infinite series. These integrals have many other important applications. In probability and statistics the integral $\int_{-\infty}^{\infty} e^{-x^2}\, dx$ is extremely important. The gamma function, defined by

$$\Gamma(x) = \int_0^{\infty} e^{-t} t^{x-1}\, dt \qquad (x > 0),$$

plays an important role in advanced calculus and applied mathematics.

PROBLEM LIST 75

In Problems 1–22 determine the value of each integral or show that it diverges.

1. $\int_2^{\infty} \frac{dx}{x^3}$.

2. $\int_3^{\infty} \frac{dx}{x^4}$.

3. $\int_1^{\infty} \frac{dx}{x^{1/3}}$.

4. $\int_{-\infty}^0 e^{2x}\, dx$.

5. $\int_0^{\infty} \frac{dx}{x+1}$.

6. $\int_{\pi}^{\infty} \sin x\, dx$.

7. $\int_0^1 x^{-1/3}\, dx$.

8. $\int_0^1 \frac{dx}{2\sqrt{x}}$.

9. $\int_0^{\infty} xe^{-x^2}\, dx$.

10. $\int_0^{\infty} \frac{dx}{1+x^2}$.

11. $\int_0^{\infty} \frac{x\, dx}{(x^2+1)^2}$.

12. $\int_2^3 \frac{dx}{\sqrt{x-2}}$.

13. $\int_{\pi/3}^{\pi/2} \sec x\, dx$.

14. $\int_{-1}^1 \frac{dx}{x}$.

15. $\int_0^2 \frac{dx}{\sqrt{4-x^2}}$.

16. $\int_0^2 \frac{x\, dx}{x}$.

17. $\int_1^3 \frac{dx}{(x-2)^2}$.

18. $\int_0^4 \frac{x\, dx}{\sqrt{16-x^2}}$.

19. $\int_{-\infty}^{\infty} x^{-2/3}\, dx$.

20. $\int_0^{\infty} e^{-x} \cos x\, dx$.

21. $\int_0^\infty xe^{-x}\,dx$. (Assume $\lim\limits_{t\to\infty}(t/e^t)=0$.)   **22.** $\int_0^\infty \dfrac{dx}{x^2}$.

23. Find the area bounded by the curve $y=(x^2-1)/(x^2+1)$ and its asymptote.

24. Show that $\int_1^\infty dx/x^k$ exists if $k>1$.

25. Find the length of the first-quadrant arc of the circle $x^2+y^2=a^2$.

26. Compare the area bounded by $y=0$, $y=1/x$, and $x=1$ with the volume generated by revolving the same area about the x-axis. In what respect is the result paradoxical?

27. Find the area between the cissoid $(2a-x)y^2=x^3$ and its vertical asymptote.

28. Show that $\int_0^\infty e^{-x^2}\,dx$ exists.

29. Find the perimeter of the loop of the curve $9y^2=x(3-x)^2$.

30. Set up, but do not evaluate, an integral for the length of the ellipse
$$b^2x^2+a^2y^2=a^2b^2.$$

31. Find the surface area generated when the arc of the curve $x^{2/3}+y^{2/3}=a^{2/3}$ from $(0,a)$ to $(a,0)$ is revolved about the x-axis.

32. Find the surface area of a sphere of radius a.

33. The probability p that a certain satellite will fail during the first t years it is in orbit is given approximately by $p=\int_0^t 2e^{-2x}\,dx$.

   (a) Find the probability that the satellite will fail within 3 years after it is launched.

   (b) Show that $\int_0^\infty 2e^{-2x}\,dx=1$. What is the significance of this result?

   (c) Express as an improper integral the probability that the satellite will be in orbit 6 months after it is launched. Compute this probability.

11.11   Approximate Integration

Given $y=f(x)$, our basic method for evaluating $\int_a^b f(x)\,dx$ is to produce a function F such that $F'(x)=f(x)$ on $a\leqslant x\leqslant b$, and then to employ the second fundamental theorem. Unfortunately, there exist many functions f for which no antiderivative F can be expressed in terms of the functions with which we are familiar, the so-called elementary functions. For example, it is easy to show that the perimeter of the ellipse $b^2x^2+a^2y^2=a^2b^2$ is given by

$$4a\int_0^{\pi/2}\sqrt{1-e^2\cos^2\theta}\,d\theta,$$

where e denotes the eccentricity of the ellipse. Yet there exists no elementary function of θ whose derivative is $\sqrt{1-e^2\cos^2\theta}$. Other examples of integrals which cannot be evaluated in terms of elementary functions are

$$\int e^{-x^2}\,dx;\qquad \int \sqrt{1-\sin^2 x}\,dx;\qquad \int \frac{\sin x\,dx}{x}.$$

Approximate methods of evaluating such integrals are based upon the fact that $\int_a^b f(x)\,dx$ can always be interpreted as representing the area under the curve

$y = f(x)$ from $x = a$ to $x = b$. Thus a method of approximating the area is also a method of approximating the corresponding integral. If the curve $y = f(x)$ is drawn on graph paper, the area can be approximated by counting the number of unit squares in the area under the curve. Another method is to cut out the area from a piece of homogeneous cardboard, weigh it, and compare the result with the weight of a unit square. Engineers often employ an instrument known as a planimeter to approximate areas.

For more accurate results, many numerical methods are known, and we will discuss two of these. For more detailed descriptions, books on numerical analysis (such as Ref. 11.5) should be consulted.

Trapezoidal Rule

In Fig. 11.8 the interval from a to b is divided into n equal parts by the points $x_0 = a$, x_1, $x_2, \cdots$, $x_n = b$. The area under $y = f(x)$ from $x = a$ to $x = b$ is approximated by the sum of the areas of the n trapezoids having bases y_0, y_1, $y_2, \cdots$, y_n. Since each trapezoid has height $h = (b - a)/n$, the sum of the areas of the n trapezoids is given by

$$\frac{h}{2}(y_0 + y_1) + \frac{h}{2}(y_1 + y_2) + \frac{h}{2}(y_2 + y_3)$$

$$+ \cdots + \frac{h}{2}(y_{n-2} + y_{n-1}) + \frac{h}{2}(y_{n-1} + y_n).$$

Simplification leads to the trapezoidal rule:

$$\int_a^b f(x)\, dx \cong h\left(\frac{y_0}{2} + y_1 + y_2 + \cdots + y_{n-1} + \frac{y_n}{2}\right). \qquad (11.32)$$

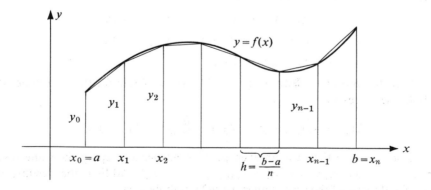

Figure 11.8

Example 1.   Approximate $\int_1^9 dx/x$ by the trapezoidal rule, using $n = 8$.

Solution.   Since $h = (9 - 1)/8 = 1$, we have

$$\int_1^9 \frac{dx}{x} \cong 1\left(\frac{1}{2} + \frac{1}{2} + \frac{1}{3} + \frac{1}{4} + \frac{1}{5} + \frac{1}{6} + \frac{1}{7} + \frac{1}{8} + \frac{1}{18}\right) = 2.27$$

to two decimal places.

The exact answer is

$$\int_1^9 \frac{dx}{x} = \log 9 = 2.20$$

to two decimal places. The trapezoidal rule overestimates the integral, since the curve $y = 1/x$ is concave upward from $x = 1$ to $x = 9$.

Simpson's Rule

In Fig. 11.8 let us approximate the area under $y = f(x)$ from $x = x_0$ to $x = x_2$ by the area under the parabola passing through (x_0, y_0), (x_1, y_1), and (x_2, y_2). Let the equation of the parabola be written in the form

$$y = y_1 + r(x - x_1) + s(x - x_1)^2. \tag{11.33}$$

It is seen by inspection that the parabola passes through (x_1, y_1); r and s are constants such that the parabola also passes through (x_0, y_0) and (x_2, y_2). The area under the parabola is given by

$$\int_{x_0}^{x_2} [y_1 + r(x - x_1) + s(x - x_1)^2]\, dx = \left[y_1 x + \frac{r(x - x_1)^2}{2} + \frac{s}{3}(x - x_1)^3\right]_{x_0}^{x_2}$$

$$= 2y_1 h + \frac{2sh^3}{3}. \tag{11.34}$$

We now substitute $x = x_0$ and $x = x_2$ into (11.33) and add the results, remembering that $x_0 - x_1 = -h$ and $x_2 - x_1 = h$.

$$y_0 = y_1 + r(x_0 - x_1) + s(x_0 - x_1)^2,$$

$$y_2 = y_1 + r(x_2 - x_1) + s(x_2 - x_1)^2,$$

$$y_0 + y_2 = 2y_1 + 2sh^2.$$

Solving for $2sh^2$ and substituting into (11.34), we obtain for the area under the parabola the expression

$$2y_1 h + \frac{h}{3}(y_0 + y_2 - 2y_1) = \frac{h}{3}(y_0 + 4y_1 + y_2).$$

We now assume that n is an even positive integer and apply the same result over $x_2 \leqslant x \leqslant x_4$, $x_4 \leqslant x \leqslant x_6, \cdots, (x_{n-2} \leqslant x \leqslant x_n)$. Adding the results, we obtain, for the sum of the areas under the $n/2$ parabolic arcs,

$$\frac{h}{3}(y_0 + 4y_1 + y_2) + \frac{h}{3}(y_2 + 4y_3 + y_4) + \frac{h}{3}(y_4 + 4y_5 + y_6)$$

$$+ \cdots + \frac{h}{3}(y_{n-4} + 4y_{n-3} + y_{n-2}) + \frac{h}{3}(y_{n-2} + 4y_{n-1} + y_n).$$

Simplification leads to Simpson's rule:

$$\int_a^b f(x)\, dx \cong \frac{h}{3}(y_0 + 4y_1 + 2y_2 + 4y_3 + 2y_4 + \cdots + 2y_{n-2} + 4y_{n-1} + y_n).$$

$$(11.35)$$

Example 2. Approximate $\int_0^6 e^{-x^2}\, dx$ by Simpson's rule, using $n = 6$.

Solution. Since $h = (6 - 0)/6 = 1$, we have

$$\int_0^6 e^{-x^2}\, dx \cong \frac{1}{3}(e^0 + 4e^{-1} + 2e^{-4} + 4e^{-9} + 2e^{-16} + 4e^{-25} + e^{-36}).$$

The last four terms are negligible.
Table III of Appendix C yields

$$\int_0^6 e^{-x^2}\, dx \cong \frac{1}{3}[1 + 4(0.3679) + 2(0.0183)] = 0.836$$

to three decimal places.

PROBLEM LIST 76

1. Approximate each of the following integrals to two decimal places by the trapezoidal rule, using the given value of n. Compare each answer with the exact answer.

   (a) $\int_2^8 x^2\, dx,\ n = 6.$ (d) $\int_0^1 4x^3\, dx,\ n = 5.$

   (b) $\int_1^{11} \frac{dx}{x},\ n = 5.$ (e) $\int_1^2 e^x\, dx,\ n = 10.$

   (c) $\int_0^{\pi/2} \cos x\, dx,\ n = 3.$

2. Approximate each of the following integrals to two decimal places by Simpson's rule, using the given value of n. Compare each answer with the exact answer.

   (a) $\int_1^3 x^2\, dx,\ n = 2.$ (d) $\int_0^{10} \sqrt{x}\, dx,\ n = 10.$

   (b) $\int_0^1 e^{-x}\, dx,\ n = 2.$ (e) $\int_1^7 \log x\, dx,\ n = 6.$

   (c) $\int_1^5 \frac{dx}{x^2},\ n = 4.$ (f) $\int_0^1 \frac{dx}{1 + x^2},\ n = 10.$

3. Approximate each of the following integrals to two decimal places (i) by the trapezoidal rule, (ii) by Simpson's rule. Use the given value of n in both methods.

   (a) $\int_0^1 \frac{dx}{1 + x^3},\ n = 2.$ (d) $\int_1^9 \sqrt{3 + x^3}\, dx,\ n = 4.$

   (b) $\int_0^2 e^{-x^2}\, dx,\ n = 4.$ (e) $\int_1^9 \sqrt{x^3 - 1}\, dx,\ n = 8.$

   (c) $\int_0^\pi \sqrt{\sin x}\, dx,\ n = 4.$ (f) $\int_0^\pi f(x)\, dx,\ n = 6,$

   where $f(x) = \sin x/x$ for $x \neq 0$ and $f(0) = 1.$

4. Find the approximate length of one arch of the curve $y = \sin x$.

5. Approximate $\text{Tan}^{-1} 2$ by expressing $\text{Tan}^{-1} x$ as an integral and using Simpson's rule.

6. Find the approximate perimeter of the ellipse $x^2 + 4y^2 = 4$.

7. Show that Simpson's rule gives the exact answer to $\int_a^b f(x)\,dx$ when $f(x)$ is a polynomial of degree $\leqslant 3$.

REFERENCES

11.1 L. BRAND, *Advanced Calculus*, John Wiley, New York, 1962.

11.2 H. B. DWIGHT, *Mathematical Tables*, McGraw-Hill, New York, 1941.

11.3 W. F. OSGOOD, *Advanced Calculus*, Macmillan, New York, 1929.

11.4 B. O. PIERCE, *A Short Table of Integrals*, Ginn, Boston, 1929.

11.5 J. B. SCARBOROUGH, *Numerical Mathematical Analysis*, The Johns Hopkins Press, Baltimore, 1962.

Parametric equations

12.1 Parametric Representation of a Curve

A rectangular or cartesian (after Descartes) equation of a curve has the form $y = f(x)$ or $g(x, y) = 0$. An alternate method of representing the curve is to employ two equations, one expressing the abscissa x in terms of a parameter t and the other expressing the ordinate y in terms of t. The equations

$$x - f(t); \qquad y = g(t) \qquad \qquad (12.1)$$

are termed a parametric representation of the curve. The parameter t may take on certain specified values, but if no restriction is placed on t, it is understood that t may assume any real value for which both $f(t)$ and $g(t)$ are defined.

It is often easier to study the properties of a curve by employing a parametric representation than by studying a rectangular equation of the curve. A rectangular equation of the curve may be found by eliminating the parameter from (12.1), but this may be difficult because of algebraic complications.

Example 1. The equations

$$x = t; \qquad y = t^2$$

represent the parabola $y = x^2$, the latter equation being obtained by eliminating the parameter t.

Example 2. The equations

$$x = \cos^2 t; \qquad y = \sin^2 t \qquad \qquad (12.2)$$

yield $x + y = 1$ when t is eliminated by adding the two equations. Although $x + y = 1$ is an equation of a line, the parametric equations represent only the segment of the line shown in Fig. 12.1. Since $0 \leqslant \cos^2 t \leqslant 1$ and

$0 \leqslant \sin^2 t \leqslant 1$ for all t, only part of the line is represented by (12.2). The parameter t could be restricted to the interval $0 \leqslant t \leqslant \pi/2$, since the entire segment in Fig. 12.1 is obtained when t varies over this interval. When t varies over $\pi/2 \leqslant t \leqslant \pi$, the same graph is obtained.

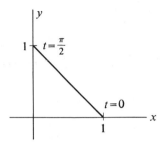

Figure 12.1

Example 3. Obtain a parametric representation of the hyperbola $(x^2/a^2) - (y^2/b^2) = 1$.

Solution. Since $y = \pm(b/a)\sqrt{x^2 - a^2}$, we try $x = f(t) = a \sec t$ because this leads to a simple expression for y in terms of t. Either $y = b \tan t$ or $y = -b \tan t$ can be employed for $y = g(t)$.

To draw the graph of (12.1) we can make up a table of values by assigning values to t and computing the corresponding values of x and y. We can also obtain information by determining the values of t for which x (or y) increases or decreases. With experience, one learns to visualize graphically the positions taken on by (x, y) as t varies over different intervals.

Critical points and points of inflection are obtained by computing dy/dx and d^2y/dx^2. To obtain dy/dx, we divide dy/dt by dx/dt. This yields

$$\frac{dy}{dx} = y'(t),$$

where y' is a function of t. To obtain $d^2y/dx^2 = dy'/dx$, we divide dy'/dt by dx/dt.

Example 4. Draw the graph of the equations

$$x = \frac{3t + t^3}{54}; \qquad y = \frac{t^3 - 9t^2}{9}.$$

Solution. From

$$\frac{dx}{dt} = \frac{1 + t^2}{18}$$

we see that x increases for $-\infty < t < \infty$. From

$$\frac{dy}{dt} = \frac{t^2 - 6t}{3} = \frac{t(t - 6)}{3},$$

we see that y increases for $-\infty < t < 0$ and $6 < t < \infty$, and decreases for $0 < t < 6$.

From
$$y' = \frac{dy}{dx} = \frac{t(t-6)/3}{(1+t^2)/18} = \frac{6t(t-6)}{1+t^2} = \frac{6t^2 - 36t}{1+t^2},$$
we see that $(0, 0)$, corresponding to $t = 0$, and $(13/3, -12)$, corresponding to $t = 6$, are critical points.

From
$$\frac{d^2y}{dx^2} = \frac{(1+t^2)(12t-36) - (6t^2 - 36t)(2t)}{(1+t^2)^2} \div \frac{1+t^2}{18}$$
$$= \frac{(18)(12)(3t^2 + t - 3)}{(1+t^2)^3},$$

we find that 0 is a relative maximum and -12 a relative minimum. The curve is concave downward for
$$\frac{-1 - \sqrt{37}}{6} < t < \frac{-1 + \sqrt{37}}{6},$$

and concave upward elsewhere except at the two points of inflection, which are both close to the origin. After computing the slope at a few points and making out a small table of values, the curve is drawn in Fig. 12.2.

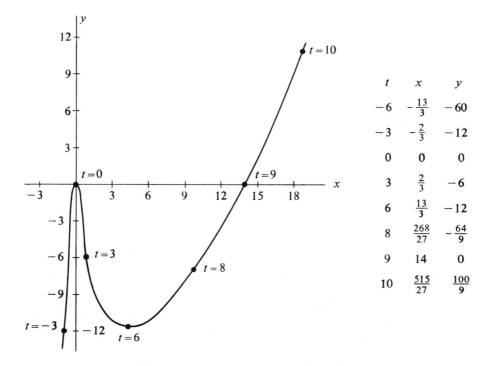

t	x	y
-6	$-\frac{13}{3}$	-60
-3	$-\frac{2}{3}$	-12
0	0	0
3	$\frac{2}{3}$	-6
6	$\frac{13}{3}$	-12
8	$\frac{268}{27}$	$-\frac{64}{9}$
9	14	0
10	$\frac{515}{27}$	$\frac{100}{9}$

Figure 12.2

12.2   Derivation of Parametric Equations

In deriving an equation of a curve, it is often advantageous to obtain parametric equations rather than a cartesian equation.

Example 1.   To derive parametric equations of a circle of radius a with center at the origin, we employ the parameter θ shown in Fig. 12.3. It is easy to see that

$$x = a \cos \theta; \qquad y = a \sin \theta.$$

The cartesian equation $x^2 + y^2 = a^2$ is readily obtained by eliminating θ.

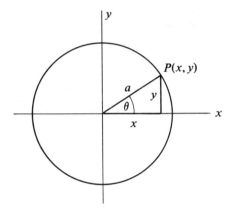

Figure 12.3

The circle can also be represented by the equations $x = a \sin \theta$; $y = a \cos \theta$. This illustrates the fact that a curve does not have a unique parametric representation.

Example 2.   The curve traced out by a point P on the circumference of a circle as the circle rolls along a straight line without slipping is called a cycloid. In Fig. 12.4, $P(x, y)$ is the point on the circle which coincided with the origin before the circle of radius a turned through the angle θ.
Since $OA = PA = a\theta$,

$$x = OA - PB = a\theta - a \sin \theta = a(\theta - \sin \theta)$$

and

$$y = AC - BC = a - a \cos \theta = a(1 - \cos \theta).$$

The cycloid, which was known to Galileo, has many interesting properties and applications. It is used in architecture, in gear theory, in the cycloidal pendulum in physics, and in many problems in pure mathematics. Its properties are best studied by employing parametric equations, since a cartesian equation of the cycloid is quite complicated.

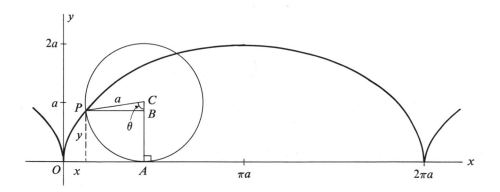

Figure 12.4

12.3   *Parametric Equations and Integrals*

Integrals of the form $\int_{a}^{b} F(x, y)\, dx$ can be evaluated, provided $x = f(t), y = g(t),$ and $F(f(t), g(t))$ define functions of t satisfying the conditions for a change of variable given in Sec. 11.4.

Example 1.   Find the area under one arch of the cycloid.

Solution.   The required area is given by

$$A = \int_{0}^{2\pi a} y\, dx.$$

(See Fig. 12.4.)
    Substituting $y = a(1 - \cos\theta)$ and $dx = (a - a\cos\theta)\, d\theta$ yields

$$A = \int_{0}^{2\pi} a(1 - \cos\theta)(a - a\cos\theta)d\theta$$

$$= a^2 \int_{0}^{2\pi} (1 - \cos\theta)^2 d\theta$$

$$= 4a^2 \int_{0}^{2\pi} \sin^4 \frac{\theta}{2}\, d\theta.$$

Letting $\theta/2 = t$ and applying Wallis's rule, we obtain

$$A = 4a^2 \int_{0}^{\pi} \sin^4 t\, (2dt)$$

$$= 16a^2 \int_{0}^{\pi/2} \sin^4 t\, dt$$

$$= 16a^2 \cdot \frac{3}{4 \cdot 2} \cdot \frac{\pi}{2} = 3\pi a^2.$$

If dx is replaced by $(dx/dt)\cdot(dt)$ and dy/dx by $(dy/dt) \div (dx/dt)$, formula (8.9),

$$L = \int_a^b \sqrt{1 + \left(\frac{dy}{dx}\right)^2}\, dx,$$

becomes

$$L = \int_{t_1}^{t_2} \sqrt{\left(\frac{dx}{dt}\right)^2 + \left(\frac{dy}{dt}\right)^2}\, dt. \qquad (12.3)$$

This important formula is used to find the length of the curve $x = f(t); y = g(t)$, from the point where $t = t_1$ to the point where $t = t_2$.

Example 2.   Find the length of the hypocycloid of four cusps:

$$x = a \cos^3 t; \qquad y = a \sin^3 t.$$

Solution.   The graph of a hypocycloid of four cusps is shown in Fig. 12.5. By symmetry, the length of the curve is four times the length of the arc in the first quadrant. This arc is generated as t varies from 0 at $(a, 0)$ to $\pi/2$ at $(0, a)$. Substituting

$$\frac{dx}{dt} = -3a \cos^2 t \sin t$$

and

$$\frac{dy}{dt} = 3a \sin^2 t \cos t$$

into (12.3) we obtain

$$L = 4\int_0^{\pi/2} (9a^2 \cos^4 t \sin^2 t + 9a^2 \sin^4 t \cos^2 t)^{1/2}\, dt$$

$$= 12a\int_0^{\pi/2} \cos t \sin t\, dt = 6a.$$

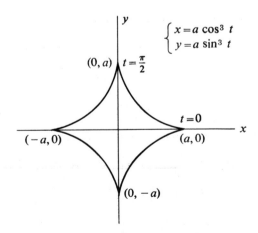

$$\begin{cases} x = a \cos^3 t \\ y = a \sin^3 t \end{cases}$$

Figure 12.5

PROBLEM LIST 77

1. Draw the graphs of the curves represented by the following parametric equations. After a graph has been drawn, eliminate the parameter and verify that the graph is correct.
   (a) $x = 3 + 4t; y = 2 + 5t$.
   (b) $x = 4 - 3t; y = -6 + 2t$.
   (c) $x = 3 \sin t; y = 3 \cos t$.
   (d) $x = t + 3; y = t^2 + 6t + 8$.
   (e) $x = 4t^2 - 1; y = 2t + 1$.
   (f) $x = 4 \cos t; y = 3 \sin t$.
   (g) $x = 2 \sec t; y = 4 \tan t$.
   (h) $x = \cos t; y = 9 - \cos^2 t$.

2. Obtain a parametric representation for each of the following curves:
   (a) $x^2 + y^2 = 9$.   (c) $y = x^2 - 3x$.
   (b) $2x + 3y = 5$.   (d) $9x^2 + 4y^2 = 36$.

3. Determine the center and radius of the circle represented by
   $$x = a \cos t + b \sin t; \qquad y = a \sin t - b \cos t.$$

4. Find dy/dx and d^2y/dx^2 for the following equations:
   (a) $x = 4 - 2t^2; y = t^3 + 2t$.
   (b) $x = t^2 + 1; y = t^2 - t$.
   (c) $x = \sqrt{t}; y = 2t + t^2$.
   (d) $x = 1 + \cos t; y = \sin^2 t$.

5. Draw the graphs of the curves represented by the following equations. When convenient, determine critical points and points of inflection.
   (a) $x = t^2 + t; y = t^2 - t$.
   (b) $x = \dfrac{1 - t^2}{1 + t^2}; y = \dfrac{2t}{1 + t^2}$.
   (c) $x = \cos 2t; y = \cos t$.
   (d) $x = t^3 + t; y = t^2 - 4t$.
   (e) $x = \dfrac{4t}{1 + t^3}; y = \dfrac{t^2}{1 + t^3}$.
   (f) $x = t^2 + \sqrt{t}; y = t^3 - 6t^2$.

6. Draw the circles $x^2 + y^2 = a^2$ and $x^2 + y^2 = b^2$, $(a > b > 0)$, on the same set of axes. Let A denote the intersection of the line $y = x \tan \theta$ with the smaller circle and B its intersection with the larger circle. Let $P(x, y)$ denote the intersection of the line through A parallel to the x-axis and the line through B parallel to the y-axis. Find x and y in terms of the parameter θ and show that P traces out an ellipse as θ varies over $0 \leqslant \theta < 2\pi$. See Fig. 12.6.

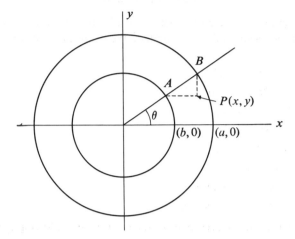

Figure 12.6

7.   Draw the circle $x^2 + (y - a)^2 = a^2$. Let A denote the intersection of the line
     $y = x \tan \theta$ and the circle and let B denote the intersection of $y = x \tan \theta$ and the
     line $y = 2a$. Let $P(x, y)$ denote the intersection of the line through A parallel to
     the x-axis and the line through B parallel to the y-axis. Find x and y in terms of the
     parameter θ and draw the curve traced out by P as θ varies over $0 < \theta < \pi$. This
     curve is known as the *witch of Agnesi*. See Fig. 12.7.

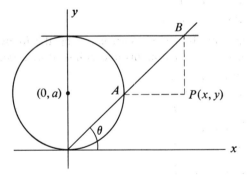

Figure 12.7

8.   The curve having parametric equations

$$x = \frac{3at}{1 + t^3}; \qquad y = \frac{3at^2}{1 + t^3}$$

   is known as the *folium of Descartes*. Draw the curve and find its corresponding
   cartesian equation. Show that the line $x + y + a = 0$ is an asymptote of the curve.

9.   Find the area of an ellipse from the parametric equations $x = a \cos \theta$ and $y = b \sin \theta$.

10. Find the length of one arch of the cycloid.

11. Find the area of the surface generated by revolving one arch of the cycloid about its base.

12. Find the area enclosed by the hypocycloid $x = a \cos^3 \theta$ and $y = a \sin^3 \theta$.

13. Find the volume and the surface area generated by revolving the upper half of the hypocycloid $x = a \cos^3 \theta$ and $y = a \sin^3 \theta$ about the x-axis.

14. Draw the circles $x^2 + y^2 = a^2$ and $(x - (3a/4))^2 + y^2 = (a/4)^2$. Let the smaller circle roll without slipping around the inside of the larger circle and let $P(x, y)$ denote the point of the smaller circle which originally coincided with $(a, 0)$. If θ denotes the inclination of the line through the origin and the center of the smaller circle, show that x and y satisfy

$$x = a \cos^3 \theta \quad \text{and} \quad y = a \sin^3 \theta.$$

The curve traced out by P is called a hypocycloid of four cusps and is shown in Fig. 12.5. It is easily seen that the curve has cartesian equation $x^{2/3} + y^{2/3} = a^{2/3}$. The curve is also called an astroid.

Chapter

13

Polar coordinates

13.1 *Definition of Polar Coordinates*

Rectangular coordinates furnish only one method of locating a point in a plane. We now consider a second system of coordinates in a plane, known as polar coordinates, which is useful in many problems.

In Fig. 13.1 point O, called the pole, is the endpoint of the half-line or ray Ox, called the polar axis. Let P be any point in the plane other than O, and let θ denote any angle, positive or negative, between Ox and OP. Angle θ is called a polar angle of point P. Let $r > 0$ denote the distance from O to P. Then r is called a radius vector of P. The numbers r and θ are called a set of polar coordinates of P.

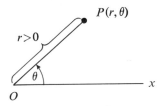

Figure 13.1

In Fig. 13.2, θ denotes any angle between Ox and OQ, the extension of OP. Such an angle θ is also a polar angle of P, but the corresponding radius vector r is negative.

The pole is assigned radius vector 0 and arbitrary polar angle θ, and is denoted by $(0, \theta)$. Thus, every point P has infinitely many sets of polar coordinates, but one and only one set of rectangular coordinates.

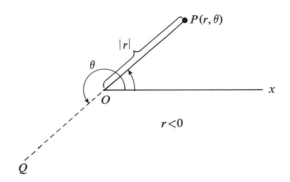

Figure 13.2

Example 1.   The point P shown in Fig. 13.3 has polar coordinates $(2, \pi/3 + 2n\pi)$ or $(-2, 4\pi/3 + 2n\pi)$, where n is any integer.

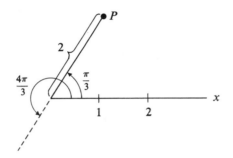

Figure 13.3

Although the polar representation of a point P is not unique, it is easily seen that a set of polar coordinates r and θ determines a unique point.

13.2   Relations Between Polar and Rectangular Coordinates

In many applications it is advantageous to employ both polar and rectangular coordinates. For this reason we will assume that the pole coincides with the origin and that the polar axis coincides with the origin and the positive x-axis. From Fig. 13.4 we see that if r and θ are polar coordinates of P, the corresponding rectangular coordinates of P are given by

$$x = r \cos \theta; \qquad y = r \sin \theta. \tag{13.1}$$

If x and y are the rectangular coordinates of P, corresponding polar coordinates of P are determined from

$$r = \pm\sqrt{x^2 + y^2}; \qquad \sin \theta = \frac{y}{\pm\sqrt{x^2 + y^2}};$$

$$\cos \theta = \frac{x}{\pm\sqrt{x^2 + y^2}} \quad (x^2 + y^2 \neq 0). \tag{13.2}$$

If r is chosen negative in (13.2), the denominators in the formulas for $\sin \theta$ and $\cos \theta$ must also be negative.

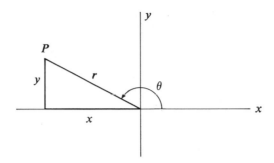

Figure 13.4

Example 1.   If P has polar coordinates $r = 6$ and $\theta = 5\pi/6$, the rectangular coordinates of P are $x = 6 \cos (5\pi/6) = -3\sqrt{3}$ and $y = 6 \sin (5\pi/6) = 3$.

Example 2.   If P has rectangular coordinates $(4, -4)$, a set of polar coordinates of P are $r = \sqrt{(4)^2 + (-4)^2} = 4\sqrt{2}$ and $\theta = -\pi/4$. Another set are $r = -4\sqrt{2}$ and $\theta = 3\pi/4$.

13.3   Graph of a Polar Equation

The graph of a polar equation $g(r, \theta) = 0$ is the set of all points for which some pair of polar coordinates satisfies the equation. We will deal almost exclusively with polar equations of the form $r = f(\theta)$.

Example 1.   If c is a positive constant, the graph of the equation $r = c$ is a circle with center at the pole and radius c. The graph of $r = -c$ is the same circle. The graph of $r = 0$ consists of the pole alone.

Example 2.   The graph of the equation $\theta = c$, where c is a constant, is a straight line through the pole. Since negative values of r are permissible, the graph is a line rather than a half-line.

Example 3.   Draw the graph of $r = 2 \sin \theta$.

    Solution.   We first observe that r is unchanged if θ is replaced by $\pi - \theta$. Consequently, the graph is symmetric with respect to the line $\theta = \pi/2$. As θ varies from 0 to $\pi/2$, r increases from 0 to 2. The graph in Fig. 13.5 is easily drawn after plotting the points $(0, 0)$, $(1, \pi/6)$, $(\sqrt{2}, \pi/4)$, $(\sqrt{3}, \pi/3)$, and $(2, \pi/2)$.
    As θ varies from $\pi/2$ to π, r decreases from 2 to 0 and the portion of the curve obtained is a reflection in the line $\theta = \pi/2$ of the portion of the curve obtained for $0 \leqslant \theta \leqslant \pi/2$. As θ varies from π to 2π, no new points are

obtained and the points corresponding to $0 \leqslant \theta \leqslant \pi$ are obtained a second time.

If r is replaced by $\sqrt{x^2 + y^2}$ and $\sin \theta$ by $y/\sqrt{x^2 + y^2}$, the equation becomes

$$\sqrt{x^2 + y^2} = \frac{2y}{\sqrt{x^2 + y^2}} \qquad (x^2 + y^2 \neq 0). \qquad \textbf{(13.3)}$$

Upon simplification, equation (13.3) becomes $x^2 + (y - 1)^2 = 1$. It is easily verified that the pole is a point of $r = 2 \sin \theta$ and that the origin is a point of $x^2 + (y - 1)^2 = 1$. Thus the graph is a circle of radius 1 with center at $x = 0, y = 1$.

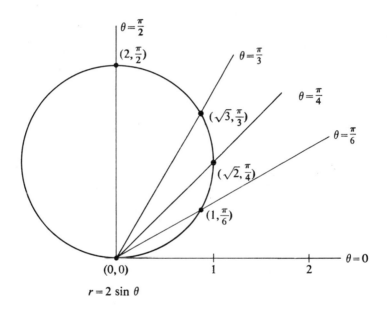

$r = 2 \sin \theta$

Figure 13.5

Example 4.   Draw the graph of $r = 1 + \cos \theta$.

Solution.   Since r is unchanged when θ is replaced by $(-\theta)$, the curve is symmetric with respect to the polar axis. As θ varies from 0 to $\pi/2$, r decreases from 2 to 1, and as θ varies from $\pi/2$ to π, r decreases from 1 to 0.

After plotting the points $(2, 0)$, $(1 + \sqrt{3}/2, \pi/6)$, $(1 + \sqrt{2}/2, \pi/4)$, $(3/2, \pi/3)$, $(1, \pi/2)$, $(1/2, 2\pi/3)$, $(1 - \sqrt{2}/2, 3\pi/4)$, $(1 - \sqrt{3}/2, 5\pi/6)$, and $(0, \pi)$, the curve, known as a cardioid because of its heartlike shape, is drawn in Fig. 13.6.

Points where the curve has a horizontal tangent are located by solving $dy/d\theta = 0$; those with vertical tangents, by solving $dx/d\theta = 0$.

For example, the height y of the cardioid $r = 1 + \cos \theta$ is given by $y = r \sin \theta = (1 + \cos \theta) \sin \theta$. From

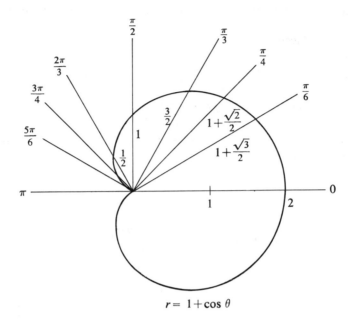

$$r = 1 + \cos \theta$$

Figure 13.6

$$\frac{dy}{d\theta} = (1 + \cos \theta) \cos \theta + \sin \theta \, (-\sin \theta)$$
$$= \cos \theta + \cos^2 \theta - \sin^2 \theta$$
$$= 2 \cos^2 \theta + \cos \theta - 1$$
$$= (2 \cos \theta - 1)(\cos \theta + 1) = 0,$$

we find that at $(3/2, \pi/3)$, y takes on its maximum value $3\sqrt{3}/4$.

Similarly, using $x = r \cos \theta = (1 + \cos \theta) \cos \theta$, we can show that x takes on its minimum value, $-(1/4)$, at $(1/2, 2\pi/3)$ and at $(1/2, 4\pi/3)$.

Extreme values of r can be determined from the equation $dr/d\theta = 0$, although in many cases these extrema can be determined by inspection. For example, the cardioid $r = 1 + \cos \theta$ has maximum $r = 2$ and minimum $r = 0$.

Example 5.   Draw the graph of $r^2 = a^2 \cos 2\theta$.

    Solution.   The curve is symmetric with respect to the pole, since the equation is unchanged when r is replaced by $-r$. The curve is also symmetric with respect to the line $\theta = 0$ and the line $\theta = \pi/2$.

    From $r = \pm a \sqrt{\cos 2\theta}$, we see that r is real only when $\cos 2\theta \geqslant 0$, or 2θ is coterminal with a first- or fourth-quadrant angle. Hence θ (or $\pi + \theta$) must be coterminal with some angle in the interval $-\pi/4 \leqslant \theta \leqslant \pi/4$.

    As θ varies from 0 to $\pi/4$, r decreases from a to 0 (and increases from $-a$ to 0).

    By solving the equation $d(y^2)/d\theta = 0$, where

$$y^2 = a^2 \cos 2\theta \sin^2 \theta = a^2 \, (\sin^2 \theta - 2 \sin^4 \theta),$$

it can be shown that y^2, and hence y, is a maximum when $\theta = \pi/6$ or $5\pi/6$.

The height y assumes its maximum value $a\sqrt{2}/4$ at $(a\sqrt{2}/2, \pi/6)$ and at $(a\sqrt{2}/2, 5\pi/6)$. The curve, known as a lemniscate, is shown in Fig. 13.7.

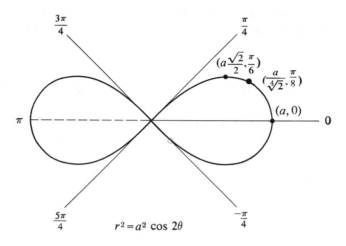

Figure 13.7

Example 6.   Draw the graph of $r = a\theta$ $(a > 0)$.

Solution.   Since $dr/d\theta = a > 0$, r increases as θ increases. The curve, known as a spiral of Archimedes, is shown in Fig. 13.8. The dotted portion of the curve corresponds to negative values of θ.

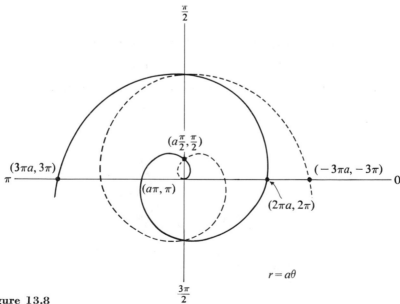

Figure 13.8

13.4   Tangents to Polar Curves

Let $r = f(\theta)$ be an equation of the curve shown in Fig. 13.9. We assume that f is a differentiable function of θ. Then x and y define differentiable functions of θ given by

$$x = f(\theta) \cos \theta; \qquad y = f(\theta)\sin \theta. \tag{13.4}$$

Equations (13.4) may be regarded as parametric equations of the curve with θ serving as the parameter.

The slope of the curve is given by

$$\frac{dy}{dx} = \tan \phi = \frac{f(\theta) \cos \theta + f'(\theta) \sin \theta}{-f(\theta) \sin \theta + f'(\theta) \cos \theta} \tag{13.5}$$

or, if $\cos \theta \neq 0$,

$$\tan \phi = \frac{f(\theta) + f'(\theta) \tan \theta}{-f(\theta) \tan \theta + f'(\theta)}. \tag{13.6}$$

Clearing fractions in (13.6) and solving for $f'(\theta)$, we find that if $\tan \phi \neq \tan \theta$, then

$$f'(\theta) = f(\theta)\left[\frac{1 + \tan \phi \tan \theta}{\tan \phi - \tan \theta}\right] = f(\theta) \cot (\phi - \theta).$$

We see from Fig. 13.9 that

$$\cot(\phi - \theta) = \cot \psi,$$

where ψ is the angle between radius vector OP and the tangent at P, measured counterclockwise from OP. Hence

$$\tan \psi = \frac{f(\theta)}{f'(\theta)} \qquad (f'(\theta) \neq 0). \tag{13.7}$$

If $\cos \theta = 0$, ϕ is easily found from (13.5), which reduces to

$$\tan \phi = -f'(\theta)/f(\theta).$$

If $\cos \theta \neq 0$, it is simpler to find ψ from (13.7) and then to determine ϕ from ψ.

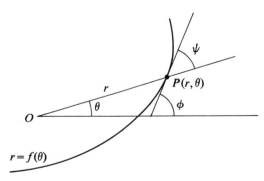

$r = f(\theta)$

Figure 13.9

Example 1. For the cardioid, $r = f(\theta) = 1 + \cos \theta$ of Example 4 of Sec. 13.3,

$$f'(\theta) = -\sin \theta,$$

and from (13.7),

$$\tan \psi = \frac{f(\theta)}{f'(\theta)} = \frac{1 + \cos \theta}{-\sin \theta}.$$

If $\theta = \pi/6$,

$$\tan \psi = \frac{1 + \sqrt{3}/2}{-(1/2)} = -2 - \sqrt{3},$$

$$\psi = \pi - \text{Tan}^{-1} (2 + \sqrt{3}),$$

and

$$\phi = \theta + \psi = \frac{7\pi}{6} - \text{Tan}^{-1} (2 + \sqrt{3}).$$

If $\theta = \pi/2$, $\tan \phi = 1$, $\phi = \pi/4$, and $\psi = \pi/2 + \phi = 3\pi/4$.

These results are illustrated in Fig. 13.10.

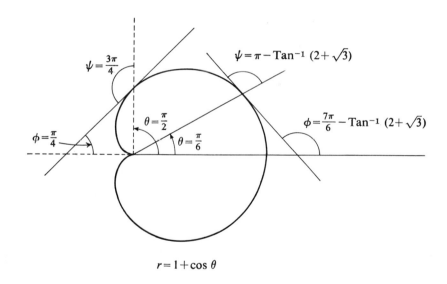

$r = 1 + \cos \theta$

Figure 13.10

PROBLEM LIST 78

1. Plot the points having polar representation

(a) $(5, 0)$, (e) $(4, 3\pi/4)$,

(b) $(4, \pi/6)$, (f) $(7, 3\pi/2)$,

(c) $(-3, -\pi)$, (g) $(2, -\pi)$,

(d) $(-6, 4\pi)$, (h) $(0, \pi/2)$.

2. Give the rectangular coordinates of each of the points in Problem 1.

3. Give two polar representations of the point having rectangular representation
   (a) $(4, 4)$,   (d) $(0, -6)$,
   (b) $(-2, \sqrt{3})$,   (e) $(-\sqrt{3}, -1)$,
   (c) $(0, 6)$,   (f) $(5, -5)$.

4. Find a polar equation of the curve having rectangular equation
   (a) $x = 5$;   (f) $x^2 + y^2 = by$;
   (b) $x^2 + y^2 = 9$;   (g) $xy = 4$;
   (c) $x^2 - y^2 = 4$;   (h) $(x^2 + y^2)^3 = 4a^2x^2y^2$;
   (d) $y^2 = 1 - 4x$;   (i) $y^2 = \dfrac{x^3}{2a - x}$;
   (e) $x^2 - 8x + y^2 + 7 = 0$;   (j) $(x^2 + y^2)^2 = 2a^2xy$.

5. Find a rectangular equation of the curve having polar equation
   (a) $r = -3$;   (f) $\theta = \pi/4$;
   (b) $r = 2 \cos \theta$;   (g) $r = a(1 - \cos \theta)$;
   (c) $r = 4 \cos 2\theta$;   (h) $r = 2 - \cos \theta$;
   (d) $r = a \sec^2(\theta/2)$;   (i) $r = 2a \sin \theta \tan \theta$;
   (e) $r^2 = a^2 \sin 2\theta$;   (j) $r = \dfrac{8}{2 - \cos \theta}$.

6. Draw the graphs of the following equations:
   (a) $r = 4$.   (k) $r = e^{a\theta}$ (logarithmic spiral).
   (b) $\theta = 3\pi/2$.   (l) $r = 2a \sin \theta \tan \theta$ (cissoid).
   (c) $r = 6 \sin \theta$.   (m) $r = a/\theta$ (hyperbolic spiral).
   (d) $r = -4 \cos \theta$.   (n) $r = a(4 \cos \theta - \sec \theta)$ (trisectrix).
   (e) $r = 1 - \cos \theta$.   (o) $r = 2a \csc 2\theta$ (cruciform).
   (f) $r = 1 + 2 \sin \theta$ (limaçon).   (p) $r = 2 + \sin (3\theta/2)$.
   (g) $r^2 = a^2 \sin 2\theta$ (lemniscate).   (q) $r = \sqrt{\sin \theta}$.
   (h) $r = \pi\theta$ (spiral of Archimedes).   (r) $r^2\theta = a$ (lituus).
   (i) $r = a \cos 2\theta$ (four-leaved rose).   (s) $r = 3 + \cos 5\theta$.
   (j) $r = a \sin 3\theta$ (three-leaved rose).

7. Draw the circles $r = a$ and $r = a \cos \theta$ on the same figure. Use these two circles to draw the curve $r = a + a \cos \theta$.

8. Show that the distance between (r_1, θ_1) and (r_2, θ_2) is given by
$$d = \sqrt{r_1^2 + r_2^2 - 2r_1 r_2 \cos (\theta_2 - \theta_1)}.$$

9. What effect does the transformation $\theta = \theta_0 + \alpha$ have upon the curve $r = f(\theta)$? Apply this transformation to $r = 2 \cos \theta$ with $\theta_0 = \pi/2$.

10. Find ψ and ϕ at the indicated point of each of the following curves. Illustrate graphically.
   (a) $r = 1 + \cos \theta$; $(1 + \sqrt{2}/2, \pi/4)$.

(b) $r = 1 + \cos \theta$; $(3/2, \pi/3)$.

(c) $r = \theta/\pi$; $(1/\pi, 1)$.

(d) $r = 4 \sin \theta$; $(2, \pi/6)$.

(e) $r = 1 + \sin \theta$; $(3/2, \pi/6)$.

(f) $r^2 = a^2 \cos 2\theta$; $(a/\sqrt{2}, \pi/6)$.

(g) $r = a \sin 2\theta$; $(a/\sqrt{2}, \pi/8)$.

(h) $r = a \sin 2\theta$; $(a, \pi/4)$.

11. Show that ψ is constant for the equiangular spiral $r = ae^{b\theta}$.

12. Find the points on $r = 1 + \sin \theta$ where the tangent is vertical.

13.5   Polar Equation of a Conic

The procedure for deriving a polar equation of a graph is essentially the one employed in Chapter 6 for rectangular equations. As an example we will derive a polar equation of a conic, defined in Sec. 6.6 as the set of points P such that the ratio r of the distance from the focus F to P to the distance from the directrix to P is a positive constant e. The applications of conics to space mechanics, referred to in Sec. 6.6, are often simplified when a polar equation of a conic is employed.

Let a focus F of the conic coincide with the pole, and let the corresponding directrix d of the conic be perpendicular to the polar axis extended at (p, π). If $P(r, \theta)$ is an arbitrary point on the conic, from Fig. 13.11 we have

$$\frac{FP}{DP} = e \qquad \text{or} \qquad \frac{r}{p + r \cos \theta} = e.$$

Solving for r, we obtain

$$r = \frac{ep}{1 - e \cos \theta}. \tag{13.8}$$

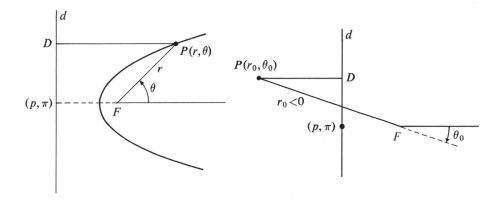

Figure 13.11   Figure 13.12

Conversely, if $r = r_0$ and $\theta = \theta_0$ satisfy (13.8), then, as is easily shown by reversing the steps by which (13.8) was obtained, $FP_0/DP_0 = e$, and hence $P_0(r_0, \theta_0)$ lies on the conic. Therefore (13.8) is a polar equation of the conic.

If $r_0 < 0$, then $e > 1$ and the conic is a hyperbola. The point $P_0(r_0, \theta_0)$ then lies on the branch of the hyperbola which is to the left of d. See Fig. 13.12.

For example, the left branch of the hyperbola

$$r = \frac{3}{1 - 2 \cos \theta}$$

corresponds to the interval $-\pi/3 < \theta < \pi/3$, while the right branch corresponds to the interval $\pi/3 < \theta < 5\pi/3$. The asymptotes pass through the center of the hyperbola and are parallel to the lines $\theta = \pm\pi/3$.

If d is perpendicular to the polar axis at $(p, 0)$, the conic has equation

$$r = \frac{ep}{1 + e \cos \theta},$$

and if d is parallel to the polar axis, the conic has equation

$$r = \frac{ep}{1 \pm e \sin \theta},$$

according to whether d is above or below F.

If $e < 1$, the conic is an ellipse, while if $e = 1$, the conic is a parabola.

Example 1.   Draw the graph of

$$r = \frac{4}{2 - \cos \theta}.$$

Solution.   Writing the equation in the form (13.8),

$$r = \frac{(1/2)(4)}{1 - (1/2) \cos \theta},$$

we see that the curve is an ellipse with $e = 1/2$ and $p = 4$. After noting that the ellipse is symmetric with respect to the polar axis and plotting the points $(4, 0)$, $(2, \pi/2)$, and $(4/3, \pi)$, the graph is drawn in Fig. 13.13.

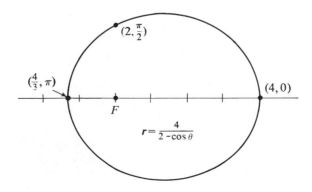

Figure 13.13

13.6   *Arc Length of a Polar Curve*

If the variable polar angle θ is chosen as the parameter t, equation (12.3) becomes

$$L = \int_{\theta_1}^{\theta_2} \sqrt{\left(\frac{dx}{d\theta}\right)^2 + \left(\frac{dy}{d\theta}\right)^2} \, d\theta. \tag{13.9}$$

Remembering that $r = f(\theta)$ defines a function of θ, assumed to be differentiable, and that $x = r \cos \theta$ and $y = r \sin \theta$, we compute

$$\frac{dx}{d\theta} = -r \sin \theta + \frac{dr}{d\theta} \cos \theta \tag{13.10}$$

and

$$\frac{dy}{d\theta} = r \cos \theta + \frac{dr}{d\theta} \sin \theta. \tag{13.11}$$

By substituting (13.10) and (13.11) into (13.9) and simplifying, we obtain

$$L = \int_{\theta_1}^{\theta_2} \sqrt{r^2 + \left(\frac{dr}{d\theta}\right)^2} \, d\theta. \tag{13.12}$$

The formula

$$ds^2 = r^2 \, d\theta^2 + dr^2 \qquad \text{or} \qquad ds = \sqrt{r^2 + \left(\frac{dr}{d\theta}\right)^2} \, d\theta, \tag{13.13}$$

readily obtained from the formula $ds^2 = dx^2 + dy^2$ and formulas (13.10) and (13.11), is called the formula for the differential of arc in polar coordinates.

Example 1.   Find the length of the cardioid $r = 1 + \cos \theta$, shown in Fig. 13.6.

Solution.   Using $dr/d\theta = -\sin \theta$, we find from formula (13.12) that

$$L = 2 \int_0^\pi \sqrt{(1 + \cos \theta)^2 + (-\sin \theta)^2} \, d\theta$$

$$= 2 \int_0^\pi \sqrt{2 + 2 \cos \theta} \, d\theta$$

$$= 2 \int_0^\pi \sqrt{4 \cos^2 \frac{\theta}{2}} \, d\theta = 4 \int_0^\pi \cos \frac{\theta}{2} \, d\theta = 8 \text{ units.}$$

Example 2.   Find the surface area generated by revolving about the polar axis the portion of the lemniscate $r^2 = a^2 \cos 2\theta$ of Fig. 13.7 corresponding to the interval $0 \leqslant \theta \leqslant \pi/4$.

Solution

$$S = 2\pi \int y \, ds = 2\pi \int_0^{\pi/4} r \sin \theta \sqrt{r^2 + \left(\frac{dr}{d\theta}\right)^2} \, d\theta$$

$$= 2\pi \int_0^{\pi/4} \sin \theta \sqrt{r^4 + \left(r\frac{dr}{d\theta}\right)^2} \, d\theta.$$

By differentiating $r^2 = a^2 \cos 2\theta$ implicitly, we obtain

$$r\frac{dr}{d\theta} = -a^2 \sin 2\theta.$$

Therefore

$$S = 2\pi \int_0^{\pi/4} \sin\theta \sqrt{a^4 \cos^2 2\theta + a^4 \sin^2 2\theta}\, d\theta$$

$$= 2\pi a^2 \int_0^{\pi/4} \sin\theta\, d\theta = \pi a^2 (2 - \sqrt{2})\ \text{square units.}$$

13.7 Intersections of Polar Curves

To find the intersections of the curves $r = f(\theta)$ and $r = g(\theta)$, we solve the equations of the curves simultaneously as we did with rectangular equations. However, all points of intersection may not be found by this method, since a point has an infinite number of representations in polar coordinates. For example, the line $\theta = \pi/3$ and the circle $r = \cos\theta$ intersect at $(1/2, \pi/3)$ and at the pole, but the pole has representation $(0, \pi/3)$ on the line and $(0, \pi/2 + n\pi)$ on the circle. Since $\pi/2 + n\pi \neq \pi/3$ for any integer n, the coordinates of the pole are not obtained by solving the equations simultaneously. This difficulty is easily overcome by investigating the pole separately.

Another possibility is that r_1 and θ_1, coordinates of (r_1, θ_1), may satisfy $r = f(\theta)$, and $-r_1$ and $\theta_1 + [2n + 1]\pi$, another set of coordinates of the same point, may satisfy $r = g(\theta)$. An intersection of this type may be found by solving simultaneously $r = f(\theta)$ and $-r = g(\theta + [2n + 1]\pi)$.

Example 1. Find the intersections of $r = 1$ and $r = \cos 2\theta$.

Solution. Eliminating r yields $\cos 2\theta = 1$, $2\theta = 2n\pi$, and $\theta = n\pi$.
Setting $n = 0$ and 1, we obtain the intersections $(1, 0)$ and $(1, \pi)$ shown in Fig. 13.14.

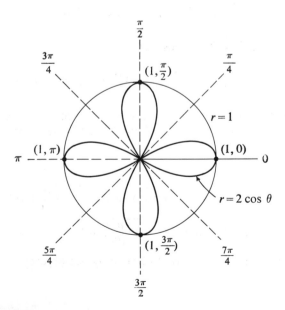

Figure 13.14

By solving $r = 1$ and $-r = \cos 2(\theta + [2n + 1]\pi) = \cos 2\theta$, we obtain

$$\cos 2\theta = -1,$$
$$2\theta = \pi + 2n\pi,$$
$$\theta = \frac{\pi}{2} + n\pi.$$

Then, setting $n = 0$ and 1, we obtain the intersections $(1, \pi/2)$ and $(1, 3\pi/2)$.

Example 2.   Find the intersections of $r = 3 \cos \theta$ and $r = 1 + \cos \theta$.

Solution.   From $3 \cos \theta = 1 + \cos \theta$ we obtain

$$\cos \theta = \frac{1}{2} \qquad \text{and} \qquad \theta = \pm \frac{\pi}{3} + 2n\pi.$$

Since it is easily determined that the pole is on both curves, the intersections are $(0, 0)$, $(3/2, \pi/3)$, and $(3/2, -\pi/3)$. See Fig. 13.15.

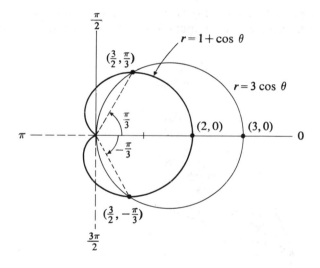

Figure 13.15

Another method of finding intersections of $r = f(\theta)$ and $r = g(\theta)$ is to solve $r = f(\theta)$ and $r = g(\theta + 2n\pi)$ simultaneously. In most simple cases, all intersections can be determined by solving $r = f(\theta)$ and $r = g(\theta)$ simultaneously and studying the graphs of the two equations.

13.8   *Area in Polar Coordinates*

Let $r = f(\theta)$ define a continuous function of θ for $\alpha \leqslant \theta \leqslant \beta$. We consider the problem of finding the area in Fig. 13.16 bounded by the curve $r = f(\theta)$ and the radial lines $\theta = \alpha$ and $\theta = \beta$. We divide $\beta - \alpha$ into n angles by employing the angles $\theta_0 = \alpha$, $\theta_1, \theta_2, \cdots, \theta_{n-1}, \theta_n = \beta$. Let the ith angle be denoted by $\Delta\theta_i = \theta_i - \theta_{i-1}$ and let θ_i^* be any value of θ satisfying

$$\theta_{i-1} \leqslant \theta_i^* \leqslant \theta_i.$$

The shaded sector of a circle shown in Fig. 13.16 has area

$$\frac{1}{2}[f(\theta_i^*)]^2 \Delta\theta_i$$

and it is reasonable to expect that

$$\sum_{i=1}^{n} \frac{1}{2}[f(\theta_i^*)]^2 \Delta\theta_i$$

will approximate the required area if n is large and max $(\Delta\theta_i)$ is small.

Since $(1/2)f^2(\theta)$ is continuous on $\alpha \leqslant \theta \leqslant \beta$, it follows from Theorem 4-X that

$$\lim_{\substack{n\to\infty \\ \max(\Delta\theta_i)\to 0}} \sum_{i=1}^{n} \frac{1}{2}[f(\theta_i^*)]^2 \Delta\theta_i$$

exists and is denoted by

$$\int_{\alpha}^{\beta} \frac{1}{2} f^2(\theta)\, d\theta. \tag{13.14}$$

It can be proved that (13.14) is equal to the required area. We will omit this proof, which involves the computation of the area by the methods of Sec. 8.1.

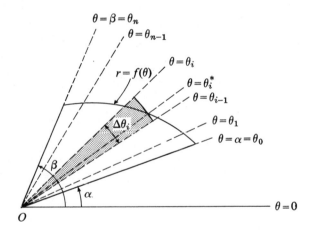

Figure 13.16

The area formula in polar coordinates is usually written in the form

$$A = \frac{1}{2}\int_{\alpha}^{\beta} r^2\, d\theta. \tag{13.15}$$

Example 1.   Find the area bounded by the lines $\theta = \pi/4$, $\theta = \pi/2$, and the arc of the spiral $r = \theta/\pi$ corresponding to $\pi/4 \leqslant \theta \leqslant \pi/2$.

Solution.   From (13.15),

$$A = \frac{1}{2}\int_{\pi/4}^{\pi/2} \frac{\theta^2}{\pi^2}\, d\theta = \frac{1}{6\pi^2}\theta^3\Big]_{\pi/4}^{\pi/2} = \frac{7\pi}{384} \quad \text{square unit.}$$

See Fig. 13.17.

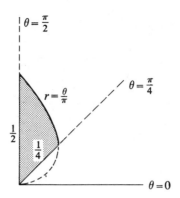

Figure 13.17

Example 2.   Find the total area inside both loops of the lemniscate $r^2 = a^2 \cos 2\theta$ of Fig. 13.7.

Solution.   Owing to symmetry, we compute the area swept out as θ increases from 0 to $\pi/4$ and multiply the answer by 4. Thus

$$A = (4)\left(\frac{1}{2}\right) \int_0^{\pi/4} a^2 \cos 2\theta \, d\theta$$

$$= a^2 \sin 2\theta \Big]_0^{\pi/4} = a^2 \quad \text{square units.}$$

Note that $1/2 \int_0^{2\pi} a^2 \cos 2\theta \, d\theta = 0$ does not yield the correct answer. The interval of integration must not include the intervals $\pi/4 < \theta < 3\pi/4$ and $5\pi/4 < \theta < 7\pi/4$ over which r^2 is negative and for which no points on the curve exist.

Example 3.   Find the area inside the circle $r = 2a \sin \theta$ and outside the circle $r = a$.

Solution.   Solving the equations simultaneously, we find that the circles intersect at $(a, \pi/6)$ and $(a, 5\pi/6)$. By symmetry, the shaded area in Fig. 13.18 is twice the shaded area between $\theta = \pi/6$ and $\theta = \pi/2$. Therefore

$$A = 2\left(\frac{1}{2}\right) \int_{\pi/6}^{\pi/2} (2a \sin \theta)^2 \, d\theta - 2\left(\frac{1}{2}\right) \int_{\pi/6}^{\pi/2} a^2 \, d\theta$$

$$= a^2 \int_{\pi/6}^{\pi/2} (4 \sin^2 \theta - 1) \, d\theta$$

$$= a^2 \int_{\pi/6}^{\pi/2} (2 - 2 \cos 2\theta - 1) \, d\theta$$

$$= a^2 \Big[\theta - \sin 2\theta\Big]_{\pi/6}^{\pi/2} = \frac{a^2}{6}(2\pi + 3\sqrt{3}) \quad \text{square units.}$$

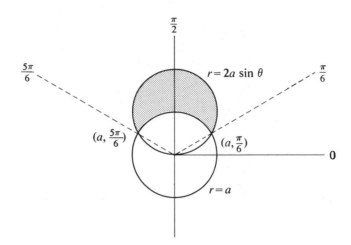

Figure 13.18

PROBLEM LIST 79

1. Draw the graphs of the following conics:

(a) $r = \dfrac{6}{1 - \cos\theta}$.

(f) $r = \dfrac{9}{1 - 2\sin\theta}$.

(b) $r = \dfrac{6}{2 - \cos\theta}$.

(g) $r = \dfrac{6}{3 + 2\sin\theta}$.

(c) $r = \dfrac{6}{1 - 2\cos\theta}$.

(h) $r = \dfrac{2}{1 + \sin\theta}$.

(d) $r = \dfrac{12}{4 - 5\cos\theta}$.

(i) $r = \dfrac{10}{5 + 3\sin\theta}$.

(e) $r = \dfrac{4}{1 - \sin\theta}$.

(j) $r = \dfrac{4}{1 + \sin\theta + \cos\theta}$.

2. Find a polar equation of the parabola having focus at the pole and directrix $r = -4\sec\theta$ ($x = -4$).

3. Find the lengths of the major and minor axes of the ellipse

$$r = \frac{ep}{1 - e\cos\theta} \qquad (0 < e < 1).$$

4. Draw the graph of $r = a\sec^2(\theta/2)$ and show that the curve is a parabola.

5. Given $r = 1/(1 - \cos\theta)$, investigate

$$\lim_{\theta \to 0} y = \lim_{\theta \to 0} (r\sin\theta).$$

6. A comet has a parabolic orbit with the sun as focus. How close to the sun does the comet come if $(50{,}000{,}000, \pi/3)$ is a point of its orbit?

7. Show that the polar normal equation of line l in Fig. 13.19 is $r = p\sec(\theta - \omega)$.

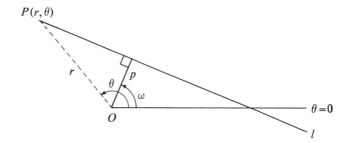

Figure 13.19

8. Show that the circle of radius a with center at (r_1, θ_1) has polar equation
$$r^2 + r_1^2 - 2rr_1 \cos(\theta - \theta_1) = a^2.$$

9. Find the length of the arc of the cardioid $r = a(1 + \cos \theta)$ corresponding to the interval $0 \leqslant \theta \leqslant \pi/2$.

10. Find the circumference of the circle $r = 2a \cos \theta$ by formula (13.12).

11. Find the length of the arc of the spiral $r = e^\theta$ corresponding to the interval $0 \leqslant \theta \leqslant \pi$.

12. Find the length of the spiral $r = 4\theta^2$ from $(0, 0)$ to $(4\pi^2, \pi)$.

13. Find the length of $r = \sin^2(\theta/2)$ from $(0, 0)$ to $(1, \pi)$.

14. Find the total length of $r = \sin^3(\theta/3)$.

15. Find the surface area generated by revolving the right loop of the lemniscate $r^2 = a^2 \cos 2\theta$ about the y-axis.

16. Find the surface area generated by revolving the upper half of the cardioid $r = a(1 - \cos \theta)$ about the x-axis.

17. Find the surface of a sphere by using the formula
$$S = 2\pi \int r \sin \theta \sqrt{r^2 + \left(\frac{dr}{d\theta}\right)^2} \, d\theta.$$

18. Find the intersections of the following curves. Illustrate graphically.
    (a) $\theta = \pi/2$, $r = \sin \theta$.
    (b) $r = 1$, $r = 2 \cos \theta$.
    (c) $r = 1$, $r = \theta^2$.
    (d) $r = 5$, $r = 3 \sec \theta$.
    (e) $r = \dfrac{4}{1 - \cos \theta}$, $\theta = \dfrac{\pi}{3}$.
    (f) $r = 2 \sin \theta$, $r = 2 \cos \theta$.
    (g) $r = 1 + \sin \theta$, $r = 3 \sin \theta$.
    (h) $r = \cos \theta$, $r = \sqrt{3} \sin \theta$.
    (i) $r = 6 \sin \theta$, $r = 2 + 2 \sin \theta$.
    (j) $r = \sin \theta$, $r = \sin 2\theta$.

(k) $r^2 = a^2 \cos 2\theta,\ r = a/\sqrt{2}$.

(l) $r = \tan \theta,\ r = 1$.

(m) $r = \dfrac{4}{1-\cos\theta},\ r = \dfrac{8}{3}$.

(n) $r = a(1 - \cos\theta),\ r = a\cos\theta$.

(o) $r = 2\cos 2\theta,\ r = 1$.

(p) $r = \cos 2\theta,\ r = \cos\theta - 1$.

19. Find the area

   (a) of the circle $r = a$;

   (b) of the circle $r = 2a\cos\theta$;

   (c) of one loop of the lemniscate $r^2 = a^2\cos 2\theta$;

   (d) inside $r = 4 + \cos\theta$;

   (e) of one loop of $r = 2\sin 2\theta$;

   (f) of one loop of $r = 4\cos^2\theta$;

   (g) inside the cardioid $r = a(1 + \cos\theta)$;

   (h) bounded by $r = e^\theta,\ \theta = \pi,\ \theta = 2\pi$;

   (i) bounded by $r = 2a\cos\theta$ and $r = 2a\sin\theta$;

   (j) bounded by $r = 1 + \cos\theta$ and $r = \sin\theta$;

   (k) inside $r = 2a\,(1 + \cos\theta)$ and outside $r = 3a$;

   (l) inside $r = 2a\sin\theta$ and outside $r = a\sqrt{2}$;

  (m) bounded by $r(1 - \cos\theta) = p$ and $\theta = \pi/2$;

   (n) of the loop of $r = a(4\cos\theta - \sec\theta)$;

   (o) of the inside loop of $r = 1 + 2\sin\theta$;

   (p) of the loop of the folium

$$r = \frac{3a\sin\theta\cos\theta}{\cos^3\theta + \sin^3\theta};$$

   (q) of the ellipse

$$r = \frac{6}{2 - \cos\theta}.$$

20. Find a polar equation corresponding to the rectangular equation $xy = c$. Rotate the polar axis through $\pi/4$ radian by letting $\theta = \theta' + (\pi/4)$. Show that $xy = c$ represents a hyperbola, by changing the new polar equation to rectangular coordinates.

Chapter 14

Hyperbolic functions

14.1 Definitions

The functions defined by $f(x) = (1/2)(e^x - e^{-x})$ and $g(x) = (1/2)(e^x + e^{-x})$ appear so frequently in mathematics that they have been given special names, studied as functions in their own right, and extensively tabulated. The former is called the hyperbolic sine of x and the latter the hyperbolic cosine of x. Their values are denoted by

$$\sinh x = \frac{e^x - e^{-x}}{2}, \qquad \cosh x = \frac{e^x + e^{-x}}{2}. \qquad (14.1)$$

By analogy with the trigonometric functions, four other hyperbolic functions are defined by

$$\tanh x = \frac{\sinh x}{\cosh x}, \qquad \coth x = \frac{1}{\tanh x},$$

$$\text{sech } x = \frac{1}{\cosh x}, \qquad \text{csch } x = \frac{1}{\sinh x}. \qquad (14.2)$$

The graphs of $\sinh x$, $\cosh x$, and $\tanh x$, which are easily drawn, are shown in Fig. 14.1.

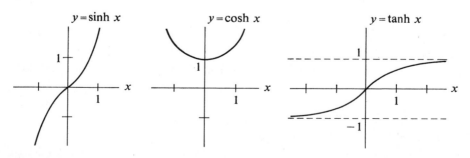

Figure 14.1

373

14.2   Identities

The hyperbolic functions satisfy the following identities, which resemble the basic trigonometric identities.

$$\cosh^2 x - \sinh^2 x = 1. \tag{14.3}$$

$$1 - \tanh^2 x = \operatorname{sech}^2 x. \tag{14.4}$$

$$\coth^2 x - 1 = \operatorname{csch}^2 x. \tag{14.5}$$

$$\sinh (x \pm y) = \sinh x \cosh y \pm \cosh x \sinh y. \tag{14.6}$$

$$\cosh (x \pm y) = \cosh x \cosh y \pm \sinh x \sinh y. \tag{14.7}$$

$$\sinh 2x = 2 \sinh x \cosh x. \tag{14.8}$$

$$\cosh 2x = \cosh^2 x + \sinh^2 x = 2 \cosh^2 x - 1$$
$$= 1 + 2 \sinh^2 x. \tag{14.9}$$

These identities are easily verified by applying definitions (14.1) and (14.2). For example, to verify (14.3) we note that

$$\cosh^2 x - \sinh^2 x = \left(\frac{e^x + e^{-x}}{2}\right)^2 - \left(\frac{e^x - e^{-x}}{2}\right)^2$$

$$= \frac{1}{4}(e^{2x} + 2 + e^{-2x} - e^{2x} + 2 - e^{-2x}) = 1.$$

14.3   Differentiation and Integration Formulas

If u denotes a differentiable function of x, the following formulas hold:

$$\frac{d(\sinh u)}{dx} = \cosh u \frac{du}{dx}. \tag{14.10}$$

$$\frac{d(\cosh u)}{dx} = \sinh u \frac{du}{dx}. \tag{14.11}$$

$$\frac{d(\tanh u)}{dx} = \operatorname{sech}^2 u \frac{du}{dx}. \tag{14.12}$$

$$\frac{d(\coth u)}{dx} = -\operatorname{csch}^2 u \frac{du}{dx}. \tag{14.13}$$

$$\frac{d(\operatorname{sech} u)}{dx} = -\operatorname{sech} u \tanh u \frac{du}{dx}. \tag{14.14}$$

$$\frac{d(\operatorname{csch} u)}{dx} = -\operatorname{csch} u \coth u \frac{du}{dx}. \tag{14.15}$$

To establish (14.10) we note that

$$\frac{d(\sinh u)}{dx} = \frac{d}{dx}\left(\frac{e^u - e^{-u}}{2}\right) = \frac{e^u + e^{-u}}{2}\frac{du}{dx}$$

$$= \cosh u \frac{du}{dx}.$$

The proofs of the remaining formulas are left to the problems.
The following integration formulas follow immediately from (14.10) to (14.15):

$$\int \sinh u \; du = \cosh u + C. \tag{14.16}$$

$$\int \cosh u \; du = \sinh u + C. \tag{14.17}$$

$$\int \text{sech}^2 u \; du = \tanh u + C. \tag{14.18}$$

$$\int \text{csch}^2 u \; du = -\coth u + C. \tag{14.19}$$

$$\int \text{sech}\, u \tanh u \; du = -\text{sech}\, u + C. \tag{14.20}$$

$$\int \text{csch}\, u \coth u \; du = -\text{csch}\, u + C. \tag{14.21}$$

14.4   Relation to the Equilateral Hyperbola

The hyperbolic functions are related to the equilateral hyperbola in much the same way that the trigonometric functions are related to the circle. This is the reason they are termed "hyperbolic" functions, just as the trigonometric functions are often termed "circular" functions.

Let the unit circle be represented parametrically by $x = \cos t$, $y = \sin t$. Then, in Fig. 14.2, t can be interpreted as angle AOP. But since the shaded sector $POBA$ has area $(1/2)(1)^2(2t) = t$, t can also be interpreted as the area of the shaded sector.

Formula (14.3) makes it clear that $x = \cosh t$, $y = \sinh t$ constitute a parametric representation of the right branch of the equilateral hyperbola $x^2 - y^2 = 1$, shown in Fig. 14.3. The area S of the shaded region $POBA$ is equal to the area of $\triangle POB$ minus the area bounded by the hyperbola and the line $x = \cosh t$, or

$$S = \sinh t \cosh t - 2 \int y \; dx$$

$$= \sinh t \cosh t - 2 \int_0^t \sinh u(\sinh u \; du)$$

$$= \sinh t \cosh t - \int_0^t (\cosh 2u - 1) \; du$$

$$= \sinh t \cosh t - \left[\frac{1}{2}\sinh 2u - u\right]_0^t$$

$$= \sinh t \cosh t - \frac{1}{2}\sinh 2t + t = t.$$

Thus t can be interpreted as the area of shaded region $POBA$.

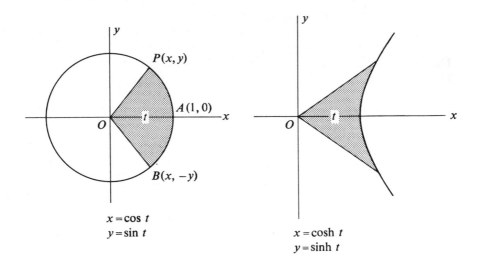

$$x = \cos t$$
$$y = \sin t$$

$$x = \cosh t$$
$$y = \sinh t$$

Figure 14.2   **Figure 14.3**

PROBLEM LIST 80

1. Prove that
   (a) $\sinh(-u) = -\sinh u$,
   (b) $\cosh(-u) = \cosh u$,
   (c) $\tanh(-u) = -\tanh u$.

2. Evaluate
   (a) $\sinh 0$,   (d) $\cosh(-1)$,
   (b) $\sinh 1$,   (e) $\tanh 1$.
   (c) $\cosh 0$,

3. Prove that $\lim\limits_{x \to \infty} \tanh x = 1$.

4. Prove that $\lim\limits_{x \to -\infty} \tanh x = -1$.

5. Prove that $\cosh x > \sinh x$ for all x.

6. Draw the graphs of $\coth x$, $\operatorname{sech} x$, and $\operatorname{csch} x$.

7. Prove the following formulas and identities:
   (a) (14.4).   (e) (14.8).
   (b) (14.5).   (f) (14.9).
   (c) (14.6).   (g) $e^x = \cosh x + \sinh x$.
   (d) (14.7).   (h) $e^{-x} = \cosh x - \sinh x$.
   (i) $(\cosh x + \sinh x)^n = \cosh nx + \sinh nx$.
   (j) $\tanh 2x = \dfrac{2 \tanh x}{1 + \tanh^2 x}$

8. Solve the equation $\sinh x = 1$.

9. Prove the formulas
   (a) (14.11),   (d) (14.14),
   (b) (14.12),   (e) (14.15).
   (c) (14.13),

10. Find dy/dx:
    (a) $y = \sinh 2x$.   (f) $y = \cosh^3 (x^2 - 1)$.
    (b) $y = \cosh 3x$.   (g) $y = \tanh 5x$.
    (c) $y = \sinh (1 - x^2)$.   (h) $y = \coth (ax + b)$.
    (d) $y = \cosh \sqrt{1 - x^2}$.   (i) $y = 2 \operatorname{sech} (x/2)$.
    (e) $y = \sinh^2 4x$.   (j) $y = \operatorname{csch} \sqrt{x}$.

11. Evaluate

    (a) $\displaystyle\int \sinh 2x \, dx$;

    (f) $\displaystyle\int \sinh 2x \cosh x \, dx$;

    (b) $\displaystyle\int x \cosh x^2 \, dx$;

    (g) $\displaystyle\int \cosh^2 3x \, dx$;

    (c) $\displaystyle\int \operatorname{sech}^2 3x \, dx$;

    (h) $\displaystyle\int \sinh^4 x \, dx$;

    (d) $\displaystyle\int \operatorname{csch}^2 (1 - x) \, dx$;

    (i) $\displaystyle\int_0^{\log 2} \sinh 2x \, dx$;

    (e) $\displaystyle\int \frac{\sinh 2x \, dx}{\cosh^3 2x \, dx}$;

    (j) $\displaystyle\int_0^1 e^x \cosh x \, dx$.

12. Find the area bounded by $y = \cosh x$, $y = 0$, $x = 0$, and $x = 1$.

13. Find the volume generated by revolving about the x-axis the area bounded by $y = \sinh x$, $y = 0$, and $x = 1$.

14. Find the length of $y = \cosh x$ from $(0, 1)$ to $(1, \cosh 1)$.

15. A purely flexible cable which is held fixed at two points hangs in a plane curve known as a catenary. An equation of a catenary is

$$y = c \cosh \left(\frac{x}{c}\right),$$

where the parameter c denotes the length of a piece of the cable having a given weight. Find the height of the cable $y = 200 \cosh (x/200)$ at its end points if it is fixed at $x = -100$ and at $x = 200$.

16. In Fig. 14.3 find the intersection of OP and the line $x = 1$.

14.5   The Inverse Hyperbolic Functions

The inverse hyperbolic functions are constructed by the methods of Secs. 2.4 and 3.9. The approach is the same as that employed in constructing the inverse trigonometric functions. We will restrict ourselves to the inverses of $y = \sinh x$, $y = \cosh x$, and $y = \tanh x$.

Since to each y there exists one and only one x such that $y = \sinh x$, the inverse function defined by $y = \sinh^{-1} x$ is assigned domain $-\infty < x < +\infty$ and has range $-\infty < y < +\infty$. The function is given by

$$y = \sinh^{-1} x \qquad \text{if } x = \sinh y. \tag{14.22}$$

The graph of $y = \sinh^{-1} x$, shown in Fig. 14.4, is obtained by reflecting the curve $y = \sinh x$ of Fig. 14.1 in the line $y = x$.

An alternate expression for $\sinh^{-1} x$ is obtained as follows:

Since $y = \sinh^{-1} x$ implies $x = \sinh y = (1/2)(e^y - e^{-y})$, then $2x = e^y - e^{-y}$ or $2xe^y = e^{2y} - 1$. Rewriting as a quadratic equation in e^y

$$(e^y)^2 - 2xe^y - 1 = 0, \tag{14.23}$$

we solve for e^y by the quadratic formula to obtain

$$e^y = x \pm \sqrt{x^2 + 1}.$$

The minus sign does not yield a solution of (14.23), since $e^y > 0$, and hence is discarded. Taking the logarithm of both sides, we obtain

$$y = \sinh^{-1} x = \log(x + \sqrt{x^2 + 1}). \tag{14.24}$$

Since the hyperbolic functions are defined in terms of exponential functions, and since the inverses of exponential functions involve logarithmic functions, it is not surprising that the inverse hyperbolic functions can be written as logarithms.

The construction of $y = \tanh^{-1} x$ is similar to that of $y = \sinh^{-1} x$. The function defined by $y = \tanh^{-1} x$ is given by

$$y = \tanh^{-1} x \qquad \text{if } x = \tanh y, \tag{14.25}$$

and has domain $-1 < x < +1$ and range $-\infty < y < +\infty$. Its graph, shown in Fig. 14.5, is obtained by reflecting the curve $y = \tanh x$ of Fig. 14.1 in the line $y = x$.

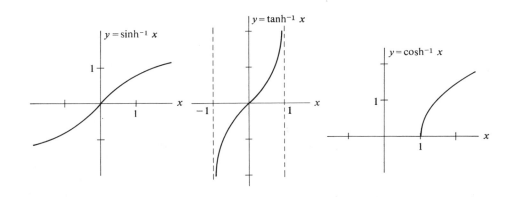

Figure 14.4   Figure 14.5   Figure 14.6

It is left as an exercise to show that

$$y = \tanh^{-1} x = \frac{1}{2} \log \frac{1 + x}{1 - x}. \tag{14.26}$$

Since there are two values of x for each $y > 1$ satisfying $y = \cosh x$, we con-struct the inverse function defined by $y = \cosh^{-1} x$ by employing only the portion of $y = \cosh x$ for which $x \geq 0$. The inverse function, given by

$$y = \cosh^{-1} x \qquad \text{if } x = \cosh y, \tag{14.27}$$

has domain $1 \leq x < \infty$ and range $0 \leq y < \infty$. Its graph, shown in Fig. 14.6, is obtained by reflecting in the line $y = x$ the portion of the curve $y = \cosh x$ of Fig. 14.1 for which $x \geq 0$.

It is left as an exercise to show that

$$y = \cosh^{-1} x = \log (x + \sqrt{x^2 - 1}). \tag{14.28}$$

14.6   Derivatives of the Inverse Hyperbolic Functions

To differentiate $y = \sinh^{-1} x$, we write $\sinh y = x$ and differentiate implicitly with respect to x. Thus

$$\cosh y \frac{dy}{dx} = 1$$

and

$$\frac{dy}{dx} = \frac{1}{\cosh y} = \frac{1}{\sqrt{1 + \sinh^2 y}} = \frac{1}{\sqrt{1 + x^2}}. \tag{14.29}$$

The denominator in (14.29) is positive, since $\cosh y > 0$.

The formulas

$$\frac{d}{dx} \cosh^{-1} x = \frac{1}{\sqrt{x^2 - 1}} \qquad \text{and} \qquad \frac{d}{dx} \tanh^{-1} x = \frac{1}{1 - x^2} \tag{14.30}$$

are obtained similarly, using (14.3) and (14.4).

If u denotes a differentiable function of x, the following formulas follow from the chain rule:

$$\frac{d}{dx} \sinh^{-1} u = \frac{1}{\sqrt{1 + u^2}} \frac{du}{dx}. \tag{14.31}$$

$$\frac{d}{dx} \cosh^{-1} u = \frac{1}{\sqrt{u^2 - 1}} \frac{du}{dx}. \tag{14.32}$$

$$\frac{d}{dx} \tanh^{-1} u = \frac{1}{1 - u^2} \frac{du}{dx}. \tag{14.33}$$

Example

$$\frac{d}{dx} \sinh^{-1} (3x - 1) = \frac{3}{\sqrt{1 + (3x - 1)^2}}$$

$$= \frac{3}{\sqrt{9x^2 - 6x + 2}}.$$

14.7   Integrals Involving Inverse Hyperbolic Functions

The following formulas are usually listed in a table of integrals. The letter a denotes a positive constant.

$$\int \frac{du}{\sqrt{a^2 + u^2}} = \sinh^{-1} \frac{u}{a} + C. \tag{14.34}$$

$$\int \frac{du}{\sqrt{u^2 - a^2}} = \cosh^{-1} \frac{u}{a} + C. \tag{14.35}$$

$$\int \frac{du}{a^2 - u^2} = \frac{1}{a} \tanh^{-1} \frac{u}{a} + C \qquad (u^2 < a^2). \tag{14.36}$$

$$\int \sqrt{a^2 + u^2} \, du = \frac{1}{2} \left(u\sqrt{a^2 + u^2} + a^2 \sinh^{-1} \frac{u}{a} \right) + C. \tag{14.37}$$

$$\int \sqrt{u^2 - a^2} \, du = \frac{1}{2} \left(u\sqrt{u^2 - a^2} - a^2 \cosh^{-1} \frac{u}{a} \right) + C. \tag{14.38}$$

Formula (14.34) follows from (14.31) when

$$\int \frac{du}{\sqrt{a^2 + u^2}}$$

is written in the form

$$\int \frac{(1/a) \, du}{\sqrt{1 + (u/a)^2}} .$$

Similarly, formulas (14.35) and (14.36) are obtained from (14.32) and (14.33). To obtain formula (14.37) we make the hyperbolic substitution

$$u = a \sinh t.$$

Then

$$du = a \cosh t \, dt$$

and

$$\int \sqrt{a^2 + u^2} \, du = \int \sqrt{a^2 + a^2 \sinh^2 t} \quad a \cosh t \, dt$$

$$= a^2 \int \cosh^2 t \, dt$$

$$= \frac{a^2}{2} \int (\cosh 2t + 1) \, dt$$

$$= \frac{a^2}{4} \sinh 2t + \frac{a^2 t}{2} + C$$

$$= \frac{a^2}{2} \sinh t \cosh t + \frac{a^2 t}{2} + C.$$

We now replace $\sinh t$ by u/a,

$$\cosh t = \sqrt{1 + \sinh^2 t}$$

by

$$\sqrt{1 + \frac{u^2}{a^2}} = \frac{\sqrt{a^2 + u^2}}{a},$$

and t by $\sinh^{-1}(u/a)$ to obtain (14.37).

Similarly, (14.38) is obtained by making a hyperbolic substitution $u = a \cosh t$.

Example 1

$$\int \frac{dx}{\sqrt{4 + 9x^2}} = \frac{1}{3} \int \frac{3dx}{\sqrt{(2)^2 + (3x)^2}}$$

$$= \frac{1}{3} \sinh^{-1}\left(\frac{3x}{2}\right) + C.$$

Example 2

$$\int \sqrt{x^2 + 6x + 5}\, dx = \int \sqrt{(x + 3)^2 - (2)^2}\, dx$$

$$= \frac{1}{2}\left[(x + 3)\sqrt{x^2 + 6x + 5} - 4 \cosh^{-1}\frac{x + 3}{2}\right] + C.$$

Example 3.   Evaluate $\int \sinh^{-1} x\, dx$.

Solution.   Let $u = \sinh^{-1} x$ and $dv = dx$. Then

$$du = \frac{dx}{\sqrt{1 + x^2}} \quad \text{and} \quad v = x.$$

Thus

$$\int \sinh^{-1} x\, dx = x \sinh^{-1} x - \int \frac{x\, dx}{\sqrt{1 + x^2}}$$

$$= x \sinh^{-1} x - \frac{1}{2} \int (1 + x^2)^{-1/2}(2x)\, dx$$

$$= x \sinh^{-1} x - \sqrt{1 + x^2} + C.$$

PROBLEM LIST 81

1. Derive (14.26).

2. Derive (14.28).

3. Derive (14.30).

4. Find dy/dx:
    (a) $y = \sinh^{-1} 2x$.   (d) $y = \cosh^{-1}(\sec x)$.
    (b) $y = \cosh^{-1}(3x - 1)$.   (e) $y = x \cosh^{-1} x$.
    (c) $y = \tanh^{-1}(x^2 - 1)$.   (f) $y = x^2 \sinh^{-1} x$.

5. Investigate $y = \sinh^{-1} x$, $y = \cosh^{-1} x$, and $y = \tanh^{-1} x$ for extrema and points of inflection.

6. Investigate $\lim_{x \to 1^-} \tanh^{-1} x$.

7. Draw the graphs of $y = \coth x$ and $y = \coth^{-1} x$.

8. Derive (14.35).

9. Derive (14.36).

10. Derive (14.38).

11. Evaluate

(a) $\int \dfrac{dx}{\sqrt{4 + x^2}}$;

(b) $\int \dfrac{dx}{\sqrt{4x^2 - 1}}$;

(c) $\int \dfrac{dx}{9 - 4x^2}$, $(4x^2 < 9)$;

(d) $\int \sqrt{9 + 4x^2}\, dx$;

(e) $\int \sqrt{25x^2 - 4}\, dx$;

(f) $\int \dfrac{dx}{\sqrt{x^2 - 4x + 1}}$;

(g) $\int \sqrt{9x^2 - 12x + 8}\, dx$;

(h) $\int \dfrac{dx}{x^2\sqrt{x^2 + 1}}$;

(i) $\int \dfrac{x^2\, dx}{(a^2 + x^2)^{3/2}}$;

(j) $\int \dfrac{x^2\, dx}{\sqrt{a^2 - x^2}}$;

(k) $\int \cosh^{-1} x\, dx$;

(l) $\int \tanh^{-1} x\, dx$;

(m) $\int x^2 \tanh^{-1} x\, dx$;

(n) $\int_{-1}^{1} \dfrac{dx}{4 - x^2}$

12. Find the length of the parabola $y = x^2/2$ from $(0, 0)$ to $(1, 1/2)$.

13. Find the area bounded by $4x^2 - 9y^2 = 36$ and $x = 5$.

14. Prove (14.28) by considering the derivatives of both members with respect to x.

Chapter

15

Vector treatment of three-dimensional analytic geometry

15.1 Three-dimensional Rectangular Coordinates

In Fig. 15.1 the x- and y-axes determine the xy-plane employed in plane analytic geometry. The line perpendicular to the x- and y-axes at the origin is called the z-axis. The points on the z-axis are associated with the real numbers in the same manner as are the points on the x- and y-axes. The positive z-axis is so chosen that if the xy-plane is viewed from a point on the positive z-axis, the right angle measured from the positive x-axis to the positive y-axis appears counterclockwise.

The xy-, xz-, and yz-planes, determined by the three mutually perpendicular axes, are also mutually perpendicular and are called the coordinate planes. A point $P(x, y, z)$ in three dimensions is determined by the ordered triple of numbers (x, y, z). The x-coordinate of P denotes the directed distance from the yz-plane to P, the y-coordinate the directed distance from the xz-plane to P, and the z-coordinate the directed distance from the xy-plane to P. A few points are plotted in Fig. 15.1.

The set of points having positive x-, y-, and z-coordinates constitutes the portion of three-space known as the first octant. The other seven octants determined by the coordinate planes are seldom numbered.

The system described for locating a point in three-space is known as a right-handed system of rectangular coordinates. The system establishes a one-to-one correspondence between the set of ordered triples of real numbers and the set of points in three-space.

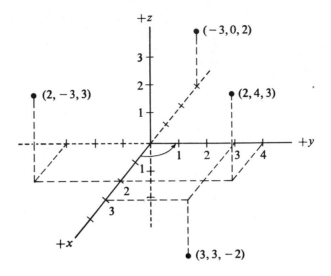

Figure 15.1

If the positive and negative z-axes are interchanged, a left-handed system of rectangular coordinates is determined. In a left-handed system, if the xy-plane is viewed from a point on the positive z-axis, the right angle measured from the positive x-axis to the positive y-axis appears clockwise. See Fig. 15.2. Although a left-handed system is sometimes useful, we will restrict ourselves to a right-handed system.

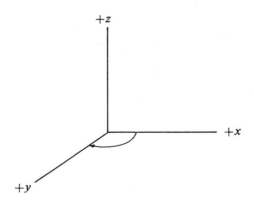

Figure 15.2

15.2 *Distance Between Two Points*

Let $P_1(x_1, y_1, z_1)$ and $P_2(x_2, y_2, z_2)$ be distinct points in three-space. If $y_1 = y_2$ and $z_1 = z_2$, the distance from P_1 to P_2 is $x_2 - x_1$. This distance is directed, since it can be positive or negative. Similarly, if $x_1 = x_2$ and $z_1 = z_2$, the directed distance from P_1 to P_2 is $y_2 - y_1$. Also, if $x_1 = x_2$ and $y_1 = y_2$, the directed distance from P_1 to P_2 is $z_2 - z_1$.

If P_1 and P_2 do not lie on a line parallel to one of the coordinate axes, the distance d from P_1 to P_2 is taken to be positive and is determined from Fig. 15.3. Six planes through P_1 and P_2 and parallel to the coordinate planes determine the rectangular box shown.

Applying the Pythagorean theorem to right triangle P_1AB, we obtain

$$(P_1B)^2 = (P_1A)^2 + (AB)^2$$
$$= (x_2 - x_1)^2 + (y_2 - y_1)^2.$$

Applying the Pythagorean theorem to right triangle P_1BP_2, we obtain

$$(P_1P_2)^2 = (P_1B)^2 + (BP_2)^2$$
$$= (x_2 - x_1)^2 + (y_2 - y_1)^2 + (z_2 - z_1)^2.$$

Thus the distance formula in three dimensions is

$$d = \sqrt{(x_2 - x_1)^2 + (y_2 - y_1)^2 + (z_2 - z_1)^2}. \tag{15.1}$$

If $z_1 = z_2$, formula (15.1) reduces to the distance formula of two dimensions.

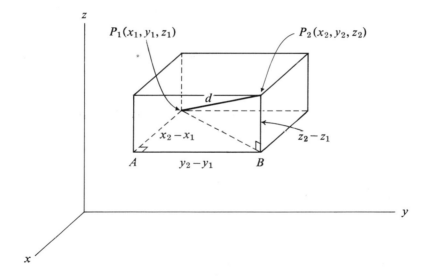

Figure 15.3

If P_1 coincides with P_2, the distance from P_1 to P_2 is defined to be 0. Formula (15.1) is also valid in this special case.

Example 1.   Find the distance from $(2, -4, 3)$ to $(2, -4, -6)$.

Solution.   Since the points lie on a line parallel to the z-axis, the distance is directed and is equal to $(-6) - (3) = -9$.

Example 2.   Find the distance from $(5, -1, 2)$ to $(3, 4, -6)$.

Solution.   By (15.1)

$$d = \sqrt{(3-5)^2 + (4+1)^2 + (-6-2)^2} = \sqrt{93}.$$

PROBLEM LIST 82

1. Plot the following points: $(0, 0, 0)$, $(5, 0, 0)$, $(0, 5, 0)$, $(0, 0, -5)$, $(2, 3, 6)$, $(-3, 4, -1)$, $(4, -2, 3)$, $(4, -1, -7)$.

2. Describe the location in three-space of the points $P(x, y, z)$ for which

    (a) $x > 0$,

    (b) $x = 0$ and $y = 0$,

    (c) $x = y$,

    (d) $x = 2$ and $y = -3$,

    (e) $y > x$,

    (f) $x^2 + y^2 = 1$ and $z = 2$,

    (g) $z > y > x > 0$,

    (h) $z = |x|$.

3. Find the distance from A to B:

    (a) $A(0, 0, 0)$, $B(2, 4, -3)$.

    (b) $A(0, 6, 5)$, $B(0, -1, 5)$.

    (c) $A(4, 1, -3)$, $B(-5, 1, -3)$.

    (d) $A(2, 0, 4)$, $B(0, -3, 6)$.

    (e) $A(4, -2, 5)$, $B(0, 1, 2)$.

    (f) $A(3, -1, 0)$, $B(-2, 3, -6)$.

    (g) $A(6, 0, -1)$, $B(7, -1, 2)$.

    (h) $A(5, 9, -2)$, $B(8, -3, 4)$.

4. Find the perimeter of the triangle having vertices $(3, -4, 2)$, $(1, -3, 4)$, and $(-6, -1, 0)$.

5. Find the distance from $(-2, 4, 5)$ to each of the coordinate axes.

6. Show that the points $(3, -2, 4)$, $(5, 1, 3)$, and $(-1, -8, 6)$ are collinear.

7. Show that $(3, -1, 3)$, $(2, 1, 0)$, and $(-5, -4, -1)$ are vertices of a right triangle.

8. Show that the points $(3, -1, 2)$, $(-1, -1, -2)$, and $(3, 3, -2)$ are vertices of an equilateral triangle.

15.3   Vectors

We interrupt our study of three-dimensional analytic geometry to introduce a new type of mathematical element called a vector. Vectors play an important role in mathematics and its applications and greatly simplify the study of geometry.

Definition.   A vector **A** is an ordered triple (a_1, a_2, a_3) of real numbers.

The numbers a_1, a_2, and a_3 are called the components of the vector. Vectors will be denoted by capital boldfaced letters.

A vector $\mathbf{A} = (a_1, a_2, a_3)$ can be interpreted as a directed-line segment from an arbitrary point $P(x, y, z)$ to the point $Q(x + a_1, y + a_2, z + a_3)$. See Fig. 15.4. We term P the initial point and Q the terminal point of **A**. Since P can be located anywhere in three-space, **A** is called a *free vector*. If, as sometimes happens, P is a specific point or a point on a specific line, **A** is called a *bound vector*.

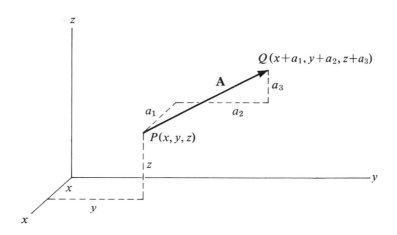

Figure 15.4

The distance PQ is called the length or magnitude of **A** and is denoted by $|\mathbf{A}|$. By the distance formula

$$|\mathbf{A}| = \sqrt{a_1^2 + a_2^2 + a_3^2}. \tag{15.2}$$

The vector $\mathbf{B} = (b_1, 0, 0)$ has length $|\mathbf{B}| = \sqrt{b_1^2} = |b_1|$. Thus the symbol for the length of a vector is a generalization of the absolute value symbol used in the algebra of real numbers.

The zero vector $\mathbf{Z} = (0, 0, 0)$ has length 0.

A nonzero vector also has direction. To specify direction of $\mathbf{A} = (a_1, a_2, a_3)$, we select P as the origin in Fig. 15.5; Q then becomes the point (a_1, a_2, a_3). The direction of **A** is specified by giving the angles α, β, and γ between PQ and the positive x-, y-, and z-axes. These are called the direction angles of **A**. It is usually easier to work with the cosines of the direction angles than with the angles themselves, since $\cos \alpha$, $\cos \beta$, and $\cos \gamma$, called the direction cosines of **A**, are readily determined from the components of **A**. We have

$$\cos \alpha = \frac{a_1}{|\mathbf{A}|}, \qquad \cos \beta = \frac{a_2}{|\mathbf{A}|}, \qquad \cos \gamma = \frac{a_3}{|\mathbf{A}|}. \tag{15.3}$$

By squaring both sides of the three equations (15.3) and adding, we find that the direction cosines of any nonzero vector satisfy

$$\cos^2 \alpha + \cos^2 \beta + \cos^2 \gamma \equiv 1. \tag{15.4}$$

The zero vector $\mathbf{Z} = (0, 0, 0)$ has neither direction angles nor direction cosines. Its direction is not specified.

In two dimensions a direction is specified by giving the slope or inclination of a line. An alternate method is to give a vector of the form $\mathbf{B} = (b_1, b_2, 0)$. This is similar to giving two numbers b_1 and b_2 whose ratio b_2/b_1 is a slope if $b_1 \neq 0$. In

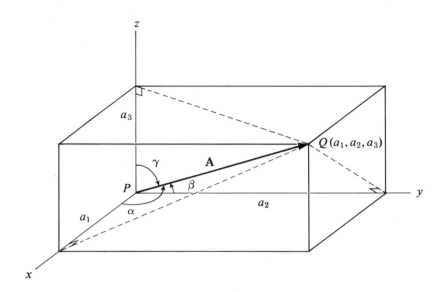

Figure 15.5

three dimensions a direction is specified by giving three numbers or by giving a vector whose components are the three numbers. When a direction is specified by a vector, a positive and a negative direction are determined.

If a_1, a_2, a_3 are not all 0, it is easy to determine from equations (15.3) that $\mathbf{A} = (a_1, a_2, a_3)$ and $\mathbf{B} = (ka_1, ka_2, ka_3)$ specify the same direction if $k > 0$ and opposite directions if $k < 0$.

Elements such as displacements, velocities, accelerations, and forces, all of which possess both magnitude and direction, are called vector quantities, since they are conveniently represented by vectors. In contrast, elements such as lengths, areas, volumes, temperatures, and pressures can be represented by real numbers and are termed scalar quantities.

15.4 Vector Algebra

Vectors as well as numbers can be added, subtracted, and multiplied, but the rules of operation are not identical in both systems. The branch of mathematics which deals with the algebra of vectors is known as vector analysis. We will consider some of the operations involving vectors. Let $\mathbf{A} = (a_1, a_2, a_3)$, $\mathbf{B} = (b_1\ b_2, b_3)$, and $\mathbf{C} = (c_1, c_2, c_3)$ be arbitrary vectors.

We now define the equality of two vectors.

Definition.   Two vectors are equal if and only if their respective components are equal.

Example 1. $\mathbf{A} = \mathbf{B}$ if and only if $a_1 = b_1$, $a_2 = b_2$, and $a_3 = b_3$.

The vector $(-a_1, -a_2, -a_3)$ is called the negative of $\mathbf{A}$ and is written $-\mathbf{A}$. By (15.3), $\mathbf{A}$ and $-\mathbf{A}$ specify opposite directions (assuming $\mathbf{A} \neq \mathbf{Z}$).
The sum of $\mathbf{A}$ and $\mathbf{B}$ is defined by

$$\mathbf{A} + \mathbf{B} = (a_1 + b_1, a_2 + b_2, a_3 + b_3). \tag{15.5}$$

That is, the sum of two vectors is a vector whose components are the sums of the corresponding components of the addends. Let us interpret (15.5) geometrically. In Fig. 15.6 we see that if $\mathbf{A}$ is drawn with the origin as initial point and $\mathbf{B}$ with the terminal point of $\mathbf{A}$ as initial point, the vector whose initial point is the initial point of $\mathbf{A}$ and whose terminal point is the terminal point of $\mathbf{B}$ has components $a_1 + b_1$, $a_2 + b_2$, and $a_3 + b_3$, and hence represents the vector $\mathbf{A} + \mathbf{B}$. If $\mathbf{A}$ represents a displacement from $(0, 0, 0)$ to (a_1, a_2, a_3) and $\mathbf{B}$ represents a displacement from (a_1, a_2, a_3) to $(a_1 + b_1, a_2 + b_2, a_3 + b_3)$, then $\mathbf{A} + \mathbf{B}$ represents a displacement from $(0, 0, 0)$ to $(a_1 + b_1, a_2 + b_2, a_3 + b_3)$, the latter being equivalent to the combined displacements represented by $\mathbf{A}$ and $\mathbf{B}$. In other words, the definition of addition of vectors is suggested by the manner in which vector quantities combine.

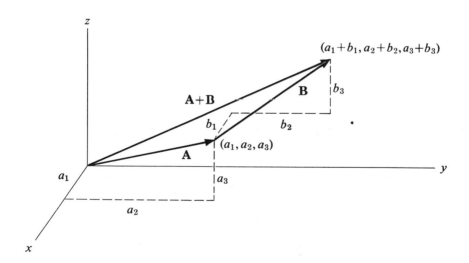

Figure 15.6

If $\mathbf{A}$ and $\mathbf{B}$ are both drawn with initial point at the origin, it can be shown that $\mathbf{A} + \mathbf{B}$ is represented by the diagonal of the parallelogram having adjacent sides representing $\mathbf{A}$ and $\mathbf{B}$. For this reason vectors are said to be added according to the parallelogram law.
The difference of $\mathbf{A}$ and $\mathbf{B}$, written $\mathbf{A} - \mathbf{B}$, is defined by

$$\mathbf{A} - \mathbf{B} = \mathbf{A} + (-\mathbf{B}) \tag{15.6}$$

or

$$\mathbf{A} - \mathbf{B} = (a_1 - b_1, a_2 - b_2, a_3 - b_3). \qquad (15.7)$$

In Fig. 15.7 the diagonals of the parallelogram represent $\mathbf{A} + \mathbf{B}$ and $\mathbf{A} - \mathbf{B}$. Note that

$$\mathbf{B} + (\mathbf{A} - \mathbf{B}) = \mathbf{A}.$$

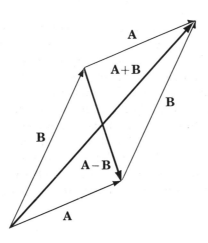

Figure 15.7

If k is an arbitrary real number, the product of the scalar k and the vector $\mathbf{A}$ is defined by

$$k\mathbf{A} = k(a_1, a_2, a_3) = (ka_1, ka_2, ka_3). \qquad (15.8)$$

If $k = 0$, then $k\mathbf{A} = \mathbf{Z} = (0, 0, 0)$. If $k \neq 0$, $k\mathbf{A}$ has length $|k| \, |\mathbf{A}|$. This result follows from (15.2). An important special case occurs when $k = 1/|\mathbf{A}|$, for then $k\mathbf{A}$ has length 1 and is called a unit vector.

The vectors $\mathbf{A}$ and $\mathbf{B}$ are said to be parallel if $\mathbf{B} = k\mathbf{A}$ for some $k \neq 0$; that is, if $\mathbf{B}$ is a scalar multiple of $\mathbf{A}$.

The following laws are easily established and their proofs are left to the problems:

$$\mathbf{A} + \mathbf{B} = \mathbf{B} + \mathbf{A} \quad \text{(commutative law).} \qquad (15.9\text{a})$$

$$\mathbf{A} + (\mathbf{B} + \mathbf{C}) = (\mathbf{A} + \mathbf{B}) + \mathbf{C} \quad \text{(associative law).} \qquad (15.9\text{b})$$

$$k(\mathbf{A} + \mathbf{B}) = k\mathbf{A} + k\mathbf{B}. \qquad (15.9\text{c})$$

$$(k_1 + k_2)\mathbf{A} = k_1\mathbf{A} + k_2\mathbf{A}. \qquad (15.9\text{d})$$

Example 2.   Find the length of $\mathbf{A} = (2, -2, 1)$.

Solution.   By (15.2),

$$|\mathbf{A}| = \sqrt{4 + 4 + 1} = 3.$$

Example 3.   Find the direction cosines of the vector $\mathbf{A} = (-3, 4, 12)$.

Solution.   By (15.2), $\mathbf{A}$ has length

$$|\mathbf{A}| = \sqrt{9 + 16 + 144} = 13$$

and by (15.3)

$$\cos\alpha = -\frac{3}{13}, \qquad \cos\beta = \frac{4}{13}, \qquad \cos\gamma = \frac{12}{13}.$$

Example 4.   Find the coordinates of the midpoint M of the line segment joining $P_1(x_1, y_1, z_1)$ and $P_2(x_2, y_2, z_2)$.

Solution.   In Fig. 15.8, $\mathbf{A} = (x_1, y_1, z_1)$ denotes the vector from the origin to P_1, $\mathbf{B} = (x_2 - x_1, y_2 - y_1, z_2 - z_1)$ denotes the vector from P_1 to P_2, and M denotes the vector from the origin to the midpoint M of P_1P_2. From

$$\mathbf{M} = \mathbf{A} + \frac{1}{2}\mathbf{B}$$

$$= (x_1, y_1, z_1) + \left(\frac{x_2 - x_1}{2}, \frac{y_2 - y_1}{2}, \frac{z_2 - z_1}{2}\right)$$

$$= \left(\frac{x_1 + x_2}{2}, \frac{y_1 + y_2}{2}, \frac{z_1 + z_2}{2}\right)$$

we see that M has coordinates

$$(1/2)(x_1 + x_2), \qquad (1/2)(y_1 + y_2), \qquad \text{and} \qquad (1/2)(z_1 + z_2).$$

To find the coordinates of the point 2/3 of the distance from P_1 to P_2, merely replace 1/2 by 2/3 in the solution.

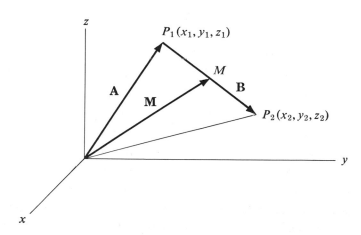

Figure 15.8

PROBLEM LIST 83

1.   Draw each vector:

  (a) $\mathbf{A} - (3, 1, 5)$ with initial point $(0, 0, 0)$.
  (b) $\mathbf{B} = (2, 5, -3)$ with initial point $(1, 2, 4)$.
  (c) $\mathbf{C} = (4, -2, 1)$ with initial point $(3, 0, 2)$.

    (d) D $= (3, 2, -1)$ with terminal point $(4, 6, 5)$.

2. Find the length and direction cosines of

    (a) A $= (2, 2, 1)$,   **(c) C** $= (1, -1, 0)$,

    (b) B $= (3, -4, 12)$,   **(d) D** $= (-2, 3, 6)$.

3. If **A** has $\cos \alpha = 1/3$ and $\cos \beta = 2/5$, find $\cos \gamma$.

4. If **A** $= (x, 3, 2) = $ **B** $= (-4, y, 2)$, find x and y.

5. Given **A** $= (2, -1, 4)$ and **B** $= (-3, 5, 2)$, find

    (a) A $+$ **B**,   **(e)** $-$**A**,

    (b) A $-$ **B**,   **(f)** -3**B**,

    (c) 2**A**,   **(g)** 2**A** $+ 3$**B**,

    (d) 3**B**,   **(h)** -3**A** $+ 4$**B**.

6. Add the vectors **A** $= (2, 1, 3)$ and **B** $= (3, -4, 5)$ and illustrate graphically.

7. Subtract **B** $= (4, 2, 1)$ from **A** $= (2, -3, 6)$ and illustrate graphically.

8. Show that **A** $+$ **B** is represented by a diagonal of a parallelogram whose adjacent sides represent **A** and **B**.

9. Write **A** $= (2, -6, 9)$ as the product of a scalar and a unit vector having the same direction as **A**.

10. Prove (15.9a).

11. Prove (15.9b).

12. Prove (15.9c).

13. Prove (15.9d).

14. Find the midpoint of the line segment joining $(2, -3, 6)$ and $(8, -5, 4)$.

15. Find the point which is $2/3$ of the distance from $(2, -1, 3)$ to $(8, -4, 12)$.

16. Prove, using vectors, that the diagonals of a parallelogram bisect each other.

17. Prove the following identities in which **Z** $= (0, 0, 0)$ is the zero vector:

    (a) A $+$ **Z** $=$ **A**.   **(e)** 1**A** $=$ **A**.

    (b) A $+ (-$**A**$) =$ **Z**.   **(f)** 0 **A** $=$ **Z**.

    (c) (mn) **A** $= m(n$**A**$)$.   **(g)** k**Z** $=$ **Z**.

    (d) $(-k)$ **A** $= -(k$**A**$)$.   **(h)** $|k$**A**$| = |k| \, |$**A**$|$.

18. The angle between **A** and the x-axis is $2\pi/3$ and the angle between **A** and the y-axis is $\pi/4$. Find the angle between **A** and the z-axis. Assume **A** has initial point at the origin.

19. Prove that the three line segments joining the midpoints of the opposite edges of a tetrahedron intersect in a point which bisects each of them.

20. Let **U**, **V**, and **W** be nonzero, noncoplanar vectors. Show that if $a + b + c = 1$, and the vectors **U**, **V**, **W**, and a**U** $+ b$**V** $+ c$**W** have the same initial point, then the terminal point of a**U** $+ b$**V** $+ c$**W** lies in the plane determined by the terminal points of **U**, **V**, and **W**.

21. Prove that the line segment joining the midpoints of the diagonals of a trapezoid is parallel to the bases and equal to one-half their difference.

15.5   The Three Unit Coordinate Vectors

The unit vectors

$$\mathbf{i} = (1, 0, 0), \qquad \mathbf{j} = (0, 1, 0), \qquad \mathbf{k} = (0, 0, 1) \qquad (15.10)$$

are particularly useful. They will be denoted by lower-case boldfaced letters. In Fig. 15.9, **i**, **j**, and **k** are drawn, each with initial point at the origin.

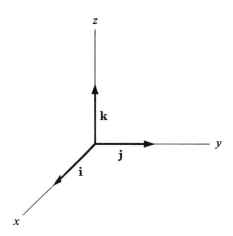

Figure 15.9

Every vector $\mathbf{A} = (a_1, a_2, a_3)$ can be written in the form

$$\mathbf{A} = a_1\mathbf{i} + a_2\mathbf{j} + a_3\mathbf{k}, \qquad (15.11)$$

and we will find it convenient to adopt this method of designating vectors. When form (15.11) is used, a_1, a_2, and a_3 are still called the *x*-, *y*-, and *z*-components of **A**. The vectors $a_1\mathbf{i}$, $a_2\mathbf{j}$, and $a_3\mathbf{k}$ are called vector components of **A**.

Vectors given in **i**, **j**, **k** form are added and subtracted by adding or subtracting the coefficients of **i**, **j**, and **k**.

Example 1

$$(2\mathbf{i} - 3\mathbf{j} + 4\mathbf{k}) + (5\mathbf{i} + 6\mathbf{j} - 8\mathbf{k}) = (2 + 5)\mathbf{i} + (-3 + 6)\mathbf{j} + (4 - 8)\mathbf{k}$$
$$= 7\mathbf{i} + 3\mathbf{j} - 4\mathbf{k}.$$

15.6   The Dot Product of Two Vectors

We will consider two kinds of products of vectors

$$\mathbf{A} = a_1\mathbf{i} + a_2\mathbf{j} + a_3\mathbf{k} \qquad \text{and} \qquad \mathbf{B} = b_1\mathbf{i} + b_2\mathbf{j} + b_3\mathbf{k}.$$

The first type called a dot product, since the product operation is denoted by a dot. It is defined by

$$\mathbf{A} \cdot \mathbf{B} = a_1 b_1 + a_2 b_2 + a_3 b_3. \qquad (15.12)$$

Equation (15.12) states that the dot product of two vectors is the sum of the products of the corresponding components of the two vectors. The dot product is also called the scalar product, since it is a number or scalar rather than a vector.

Example 1

$$(5\mathbf{i} - 2\mathbf{j} + 3\mathbf{k})\cdot(2\mathbf{i} - 4\mathbf{j} - 7\mathbf{k}) = (5)(2) + (-2)(-4) + (3)(-7)$$
$$= 10 + 8 - 21 = -3.$$

If $\mathbf{B} = \mathbf{A}$, (15.12) becomes

$$\mathbf{A}\cdot\mathbf{A} = a_1^2 + a_2^2 + a_3^2 = |\mathbf{A}|^2, \tag{15.13}$$

and if $\mathbf{A}$ is a unit vector, $\mathbf{A}\cdot\mathbf{A} = 1$. In particular

$$\mathbf{i}\cdot\mathbf{i} = \mathbf{j}\cdot\mathbf{j} = \mathbf{k}\cdot\mathbf{k} = 1. \tag{15.14}$$

The following laws involving dot products are easily established, and hence their proofs are left to the problems.

$$\mathbf{A}\cdot\mathbf{B} = \mathbf{B}\cdot\mathbf{A} \quad \text{(commutative law).} \tag{15.15}$$

$$(\mathbf{A} \pm \mathbf{B})\cdot\mathbf{C} = \mathbf{A}\cdot\mathbf{C} \pm \mathbf{B}\cdot\mathbf{C} \quad \text{(distributive law).} \tag{15.16}$$

$$(k\mathbf{A})\cdot\mathbf{B} = \mathbf{A}\cdot(k\mathbf{B}) = k(\mathbf{A}\cdot\mathbf{B}). \tag{15.17}$$

$$\mathbf{Z}\cdot\mathbf{A} = 0. \tag{15.18}$$

To obtain a geometric interpretation of the dot product of two nonzero vectors $\mathbf{A}$ and $\mathbf{B}$, we draw $\mathbf{A}$ and $\mathbf{B}$ with common initial point P as shown in Fig. 15.10. The angle θ, satisfying $0 \leqslant \theta \leqslant \pi$, between their positive directions is defined to be the angle between $\mathbf{A}$ and $\mathbf{B}$.

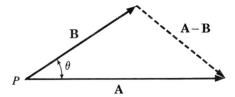

Figure 15.10

By the law of cosines

$$|\mathbf{A} - \mathbf{B}|^2 = |\mathbf{A}|^2 + |\mathbf{B}|^2 - 2|\mathbf{A}||\mathbf{B}|\cos\theta. \tag{15.19}$$

By (15.13) and (15.16),

$$|\mathbf{A} - \mathbf{B}|^2 = (\mathbf{A} - \mathbf{B})\cdot(\mathbf{A} - \mathbf{B})$$
$$= (\mathbf{A} - \mathbf{B})\cdot\mathbf{A} - (\mathbf{A} - \mathbf{B})\cdot\mathbf{B}$$
$$= \mathbf{A}\cdot\mathbf{A} - \mathbf{B}\cdot\mathbf{A} - \mathbf{A}\cdot\mathbf{B} + \mathbf{B}\cdot\mathbf{B}$$
$$= |\mathbf{A}|^2 - 2\mathbf{A}\cdot\mathbf{B} + |\mathbf{B}|^2. \tag{15.20}$$

By combining (15.19) and (15.20) we obtain

$$\mathbf{A}\cdot\mathbf{B} = |\mathbf{A}||\mathbf{B}|\cos\theta. \tag{15.21}$$

Equation (15.21) states that the dot product of two vectors is the product of their lengths and the cosine of the angle between them. It is easy to show that (15.21) holds for $\theta = 0$ and for $\theta = \pi$.

Since $|\mathbf{B}| \cos \theta$ is equal to the projection of $\mathbf{B}$ on $\mathbf{A}$, (15.21) also states that the dot product of two vectors is equal to the length of either vector times the projection of the other vector upon it.

An important special case arises when $\mathbf{B}$ is a unit vector. Equation (15.21) then states that the dot product of a vector $\mathbf{A}$ and a unit vector is equal to the projection of $\mathbf{A}$ in the direction of the unit vector. In physics and mechanics, if $\mathbf{A}$ represents a force and $\mathbf{B}$ is a unit vector, $\mathbf{A} \cdot \mathbf{B} = |\mathbf{A}| \cos \theta$ is called the component of the force in the direction of $\mathbf{B}$.

Example 2.   Find the component of $\mathbf{A} = 2\mathbf{i} - 3\mathbf{j} + 6\mathbf{k}$ in the direction of $\mathbf{B} = 2\mathbf{i} + 2\mathbf{j} - \mathbf{k}$.

Solution.   Before forming the dot product, $\mathbf{B}$ must be unitized by dividing by its length 3. Thus

$$\mathbf{A} \cdot \left(\frac{\mathbf{B}}{|\mathbf{B}|}\right) = (2)\left(\frac{2}{3}\right) + (-3)\left(\frac{2}{3}\right) + (6)\left(\frac{-1}{3}\right)$$

$$= \frac{-8}{3}.$$

Note that the x-component of $\mathbf{A}$ is given by $\mathbf{A} \cdot \mathbf{i} = 2$. Similarly, $\mathbf{A}$ has y-component $\mathbf{A} \cdot \mathbf{j} = -3$ and z-component $\mathbf{A} \cdot \mathbf{k} = 6$.

Example 3.   Find the angle θ between

$$\mathbf{A} = \mathbf{i} + 4\mathbf{j} + 8\mathbf{k} \qquad \text{and} \qquad \mathbf{B} = 5\mathbf{i} + 4\mathbf{j} + 3\mathbf{k}.$$

Solution.   By (15.21),

$$\cos \theta = \frac{\mathbf{A} \cdot \mathbf{B}}{|\mathbf{A}||\mathbf{B}|} = \frac{(1)(5) + (4)(4) + (8)(3)}{9\sqrt{50}}$$

$$= \frac{1}{\sqrt{2}},$$

and hence $\theta = \pi/4$.

We see from (15.21) that if $\theta = \pi/2$, then $\cos \theta = 0$ and $\mathbf{A} \cdot \mathbf{B} = 0$. Conversely, if $\mathbf{A} \cdot \mathbf{B} = 0$, and $|\mathbf{A}| < 0$, and $|\mathbf{B}| > 0$, then $\cos \theta = 0$ and $\theta = \pi/2$. If one of or both $\mathbf{A}$ and $\mathbf{B}$ are the zero vector, then $\mathbf{A} \cdot \mathbf{B} = 0$. Since the direction of the zero vector is undefined, it is convenient to agree that the zero vector is perpendicular to every vector. This enables us to state the following theorem.

Theorem 15-I.   Vectors $\mathbf{A} = a_1\mathbf{i} + a_2\mathbf{j} + a_3\mathbf{k}$ and $\mathbf{B} = b_1\mathbf{i} + b_2\mathbf{j} + b_3\mathbf{k}$ are perpendicular if and only if

$$\mathbf{A} \cdot \mathbf{B} = a_1b_1 + a_2b_2 + a_3b_3 = 0.$$

Example 4.   Determine c so that

$$\mathbf{A} = 3\mathbf{i} + 4\mathbf{j} - 2\mathbf{k} \qquad \text{and} \qquad \mathbf{B} = c\mathbf{i} + 5\mathbf{j} - 3\mathbf{k}$$

are perpendicular.

Solution.   We determine c so that $\mathbf{A} \cdot \mathbf{B} = 0$. It will then follow from Theorem 15–I that $\mathbf{A}$ and $\mathbf{B}$ are perpendicular. From

$$\mathbf{A} \cdot \mathbf{B} = 3c + (4)(5) + (-2)(-3) = 0$$

we obtain $c = -26/3$.

PROBLEM LIST 84

1.   Find $\mathbf{A} \cdot \mathbf{B}$:
    (a) $\mathbf{A} = 2\mathbf{i} + 4\mathbf{j} - 3\mathbf{k}$, $\mathbf{B} = 3\mathbf{i} + 4\mathbf{j} - 2\mathbf{k}$.
    (b) $\mathbf{A} = 4\mathbf{i} - 2\mathbf{j} + 5\mathbf{k}$, $\mathbf{B} = 5\mathbf{i} - 4\mathbf{j} - 4\mathbf{k}$.
    (c) $\mathbf{A} = 6\mathbf{i} - \mathbf{j} + 3\mathbf{k}$, $\mathbf{B} = 2\mathbf{i} + 2\mathbf{j} - 3\mathbf{k}$.
    (d) $\mathbf{A} = -4\mathbf{i} - 3\mathbf{j} + 2\mathbf{k}$, $\mathbf{B} = 5\mathbf{i} - 6\mathbf{j} + 7\mathbf{k}$.

2.   Given $\mathbf{A} = 3\mathbf{i} - 4\mathbf{j} + 5\mathbf{k}$, find:
    (a) $\mathbf{A} \cdot \mathbf{A}$.   (c) $\mathbf{A} \cdot \mathbf{j}$.
    (b) $\mathbf{A} \cdot \mathbf{i}$.   (d) $\mathbf{A} \cdot \mathbf{k}$.

3.   Verify (15.16) when $\mathbf{A} = 2\mathbf{i} - 3\mathbf{j} - 2\mathbf{k}$, $\mathbf{B} = 3\mathbf{i} - 4\mathbf{j} + 2\mathbf{k}$, and $\mathbf{C} = 2\mathbf{i} + 5\mathbf{j} - 6\mathbf{k}$.

4.   Prove (15.15).

5.   Prove (15.16).

6.   Prove (15.17).

7.   Prove (15.18).

8.   Find the component of $4\mathbf{i} - 6\mathbf{j} + 2\mathbf{k}$ in the direction of $\mathbf{i} + 4\mathbf{j} - 8\mathbf{k}$.

9.   Find the angle between $2\mathbf{i} + 2\mathbf{j} + \mathbf{k}$ and $\mathbf{i} + 4\mathbf{j} + 8\mathbf{k}$.

10.   Find the angle between $2\mathbf{i} - \mathbf{j} + 2\mathbf{k}$ and $3\mathbf{i} + 2\mathbf{j} - 6\mathbf{k}$.

11.   Find the cosines of the angles of the triangle having vertices $(0, 0, 0)$, $(2, 6, 9)$, and $(6, -3, 2)$.

12.   Determine c so that $\mathbf{A} = 3\mathbf{i} - 4\mathbf{j} + 6\mathbf{k}$ and $\mathbf{B} - 3\mathbf{i} - 5\mathbf{j} + c\mathbf{k}$ are perpendicular.

13.   Show that the points $(1, 3, -2)$, $(3, 0, 2)$, and $(-1, 6, -6)$ are collinear.

14.   Show that $(3, 2, -3)$, $(6, 0, 1)$, and $(5, 7, -2)$ are vertices of a right triangle.

15.   Show that $(-1, 1, 7)$, $(5, -2, 9)$, $(2, 7, 1)$, and $(8, 4, 3)$ are vertices of a parallelogram.

16.   Determine c and d so that
$$\mathbf{A} = 4\mathbf{i} + 3\mathbf{j} - 2\mathbf{k} \quad \text{and} \quad \mathbf{B} = 6\mathbf{i} + c\mathbf{j} + d\mathbf{k}$$
    are parallel.

17.   Given that $\mathbf{A}$ and $\mathbf{B}$ are arbitrary vectors, prove the triangle inequality
$$|\mathbf{A} + \mathbf{B}| \leqslant |\mathbf{A}| + |\mathbf{B}|.$$

15.7   *The Cross Product of Two Vectors*

[*Remark.* This section does not require a knowledge of determinants. However, students familiar with determinant language will recognize that the technique presented is that of evaluating a third-order determinant.]

A second type product of $\mathbf{A} = a_1\mathbf{i} + a_2\mathbf{j} + a_3\mathbf{k}$ and $\mathbf{B} = b_1\mathbf{i} + b_2\mathbf{j} + b_3\mathbf{k}$ is called a cross product because the product operation is denoted by a cross. It is defined by

$$\mathbf{A} \times \mathbf{B} = (a_2b_3 - a_3b_2)\mathbf{i} + (a_3b_1 - a_1b_3)\mathbf{j} + (a_1b_2 - a_2b_1)\mathbf{k}. \quad \textbf{(15.22)}$$

The cross product is also called the vector product, since it is a vector rather than a scalar or number. The motivation for definition (15.22) will be apparent when the geometric interpretation of the cross product is considered. We first consider the technique of forming the cross product. Instead of memorizing the components of $\mathbf{A} \times \mathbf{B}$, we form the following square array:

$$\begin{array}{ccc} \mathbf{i} & \mathbf{j} & \mathbf{k} \\ a_1 & a_2 & a_3 \\ b_1 & b_2 & b_3 \end{array} \quad \textbf{(15.23)}$$

To find the coefficient $a_2b_3 - a_3b_2$ of $\mathbf{j}$, we delete the row and column containing $\mathbf{i}$ and then cross-multiply and subtract, beginning with a_2 in the remaining array

$$\begin{array}{cc} a_2 & a_3 \\ b_2 & b_3 \end{array}$$

The coefficient $a_1b_2 - a_2b_1$ of $\mathbf{k}$ is found similarly from the array:

$$\begin{array}{cc} a_1 & a_2 \\ b_1 & b_2 \end{array}$$

The coefficient $a_3b_1 - a_1b_3$ of $\mathbf{j}$ is found similarly, except that we start with a_3 rather than a_1 in the array:

$$\begin{array}{cc} a_1 & a_3 \\ b_1 & b_3 \end{array}$$

Example 1.   Find $(2\mathbf{i} - 3\mathbf{j} + 4\mathbf{k}) \times (4\mathbf{i} + 2\mathbf{j} - 6\mathbf{k})$.

Solution.   From the array

$$\begin{array}{ccc} \mathbf{i} & \mathbf{j} & \mathbf{k} \\ 2 & -3 & 4 \\ 4 & 2 & -6 \end{array}$$

we obtain

$$\begin{aligned} (2\mathbf{i} - 3\mathbf{j} + 4\mathbf{k}) \times (4\mathbf{i} + 2\mathbf{j} - 6\mathbf{k}) &= [(-3)(-6) - (4)(2)]\mathbf{i} \\ &\quad + [(4)(4) - (2)(-6)]\mathbf{j} \\ &\quad + [(2)(2) - (-3)(4)]\mathbf{k} \\ &= 10\mathbf{i} + 28\mathbf{j} + 16\mathbf{k}. \end{aligned}$$

To form $\mathbf{B} \times \mathbf{A}$, the second and third rows of array (15.23) are interchanged. It is easy to see that this changes the signs of the coefficients of $\mathbf{i}$, $\mathbf{j}$, and $\mathbf{k}$. Hence

$$\mathbf{B} \times \mathbf{A} = -(\mathbf{A} \times \mathbf{B}). \quad \textbf{(15.24)}$$

Thus, the operation of forming a cross product is noncommutative. If the order of the factors is reversed, the sign of the vector product is changed.

Cross products involving the unit coordinate vectors are given by the following equations:

$$\mathbf{i} \times \mathbf{i} = \mathbf{Z}, \qquad \mathbf{j} \times \mathbf{j} = \mathbf{Z}, \qquad \mathbf{k} \times \mathbf{k} = \mathbf{Z},$$
$$\mathbf{i} \times \mathbf{j} = \mathbf{k}, \qquad \mathbf{j} \times \mathbf{k} = \mathbf{i}, \qquad \mathbf{k} \times \mathbf{i} = \mathbf{j}, \qquad (15.25)$$
$$\mathbf{j} \times \mathbf{i} = -\mathbf{k}, \qquad \mathbf{k} \times \mathbf{j} = -\mathbf{i}, \qquad \mathbf{i} \times \mathbf{k} = -\mathbf{j}.$$

Formulas (15.25) are easily remembered. The cross product of two consecutive unit coordinate vectors taken in the order indicated by the arrows in Fig. 15.11 is equal to the third unit coordinate vector. The cross product of two consecutive vectors taken in the reverse order is equal to the negative of the third vector.

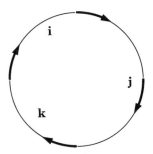

Figure 15.11

Formulas (15.25) are easily proved by applying the array scheme of (15.23) to the products in question. For example, to find $\mathbf{i} \times \mathbf{j}$, we write

$$\begin{array}{ccc} \mathbf{i} & \mathbf{j} & \mathbf{k} \\ 1 & 0 & 0 \\ 0 & 1 & 0 \end{array}$$

and obtain

$$\mathbf{i} \times \mathbf{j} = 0\mathbf{i} + 0\mathbf{j} + 1\mathbf{k} = \mathbf{k}.$$

The geometric interpretation of $\mathbf{A} \times \mathbf{B}$ is given in Fig. 15.12. $\mathbf{A} \times \mathbf{B}$ is a vector perpendicular to both $\mathbf{A}$ and $\mathbf{B}$. This fact is verified (see Problem 5) by showing that

$$\mathbf{A} \times \mathbf{B} \cdot \mathbf{A} = 0 \qquad \text{and} \qquad \mathbf{A} \times \mathbf{B} \cdot \mathbf{B} = 0.$$

If $\mathbf{A}$, $\mathbf{B}$, and $\mathbf{A} \times \mathbf{B}$ have the same initial point, the angle θ between $\mathbf{A}$ and $\mathbf{B}$ measured from $\mathbf{A}$ to $\mathbf{B}$ appears counterclockwise from the terminal point of $\mathbf{A} \times \mathbf{B}$. Although we will not prove this statement, it is easily verified when $\mathbf{A} = \mathbf{i}$, $\mathbf{B} = \mathbf{j}$, and $\mathbf{A} \times \mathbf{B} = \mathbf{k}$.

The length of $\mathbf{A} \times \mathbf{B}$ is given by

$$|\mathbf{A} \times \mathbf{B}| = |\mathbf{A}||\mathbf{B}| \sin \theta. \qquad (15.26)$$

Equation (15.26) states that the length of the cross product of two vectors is the product of their lengths and the sine of the angle between them. One sees from

Fig. 15.12 that $|\mathbf{A} \times \mathbf{B}|$ is also equal to the area of the parallelogram having adjacent sides $\mathbf{A}$ and $\mathbf{B}$. The proof of (15.26) is left to Problem 19.

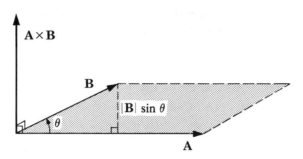

Figure 15.12

If one of or both $\mathbf{A}$ and $\mathbf{B}$ are the zero vector $\mathbf{Z}$, then $\mathbf{A} \times \mathbf{B} = \mathbf{Z}$.

Adopting the convention that $\mathbf{Z}$ is parallel to every vector, the following result is an immediate consequence of (15.26).

Theorem 15-II.   Two vectors $\mathbf{A}$ and $\mathbf{B}$ are parallel if and only if $\mathbf{A} \times \mathbf{B} = \mathbf{Z} = 0\mathbf{i} + 0\mathbf{j} + 0\mathbf{k}$.

PROBLEM LIST 85

1. Evaluate:
    (a) $(2\mathbf{i} + 4\mathbf{j} - 3\mathbf{k}) \times (2\mathbf{i} - 3\mathbf{j} + 4\mathbf{k})$.
    (b) $(5\mathbf{i} - 4\mathbf{j} - 2\mathbf{k}) \times (4\mathbf{i} - 6\mathbf{j} + \mathbf{k})$.
    (c) $(\mathbf{i} - \mathbf{j} + 3\mathbf{k}) \times (3\mathbf{i} + \mathbf{j} - \mathbf{k})$.
    (d) $(3\mathbf{i} + 6\mathbf{j} - 2\mathbf{k}) \times (5\mathbf{i} - 2\mathbf{j} + 7\mathbf{k})$.

2. Show that $\mathbf{i} \times \mathbf{i} = \mathbf{Z} = 0\mathbf{i} + 0\mathbf{j} + 0\mathbf{k}$.

3. Show that $\mathbf{k} \times \mathbf{i} = \mathbf{j}$.

4. Show that $\mathbf{k} \times \mathbf{j} = -\mathbf{i}$.

5. Show that $\mathbf{A} \times \mathbf{B} \cdot \mathbf{A} = 0$ and $\mathbf{A} \times \mathbf{B} \cdot \mathbf{B} = 0$.

6. Show that $2\mathbf{i} - 3\mathbf{j} + 4\mathbf{k}$ and $-4\mathbf{i} + 6\mathbf{j} - 8\mathbf{k}$ are parallel.

7. Show that $\mathbf{A} \times \mathbf{B} = \mathbf{Z}$ if either $\mathbf{A}$ or $\mathbf{B}$ is equal to the zero vector $\mathbf{Z}$.

8. Show that $\mathbf{A} \times \mathbf{A} = \mathbf{Z}$ for every $\mathbf{A}$.

9. Find a unit vector perpendicular to both $2\mathbf{i} - 3\mathbf{j} + \mathbf{k}$ and $3\mathbf{i} - \mathbf{j} + 2\mathbf{k}$.

10. Find the area of the parallelogram having vertices $(-1, 1, 7)$, $(5, -2, 9)$, $(2, 7, 1)$, and $(8, 4, 3)$.

11. Verify (15.26) when $\mathbf{A} = \mathbf{i}$ and $\mathbf{B} = \mathbf{i} + \mathbf{j}$.

12. Find the area of the triangle having vertices $(0, 0, 0)$, $(2, 2, -1)$, and $(3, -4, 12)$.

13. Prove the identity $(k\mathbf{A}) \times \mathbf{B} = \mathbf{A} \times (k\mathbf{B}) = k(\mathbf{A} \times \mathbf{B})$.

14. Prove the identity $(\mathbf{A} + \mathbf{B}) \times \mathbf{C} = (\mathbf{A} \times \mathbf{C}) + (\mathbf{B} \times \mathbf{C})$.

15. Prove the identity $C \times (A + B) = (C \times A) + (C \times B)$.

16. Show that $(i \times j) \times j \neq i \times (j \times j)$.

17. Prove that $A \times (B \times C) \neq (A \times B) \times C$. This establishes the fact that the operation of forming a cross product is nonassociative.

18. Prove the following identities:

    (a) $A \cdot (B \times C) = (A \times B) \cdot C$.

    (b) $A \times (B \times C) = (A \cdot C)B - (A \cdot B)C$.

    (c) $(A \times B) \cdot (C \times D) = (A \cdot C)(B \cdot D) - (A \cdot D)(B \cdot C)$.

19. Prove that $|A \times B|^2 = |A|^2|B|^2 - (A \cdot B)^2$. Then replace $A \cdot B$ by $|A||B| \cos \theta$ and simplify to obtain (15.26).

20. The expression $A \times B \cdot C$ is known as a scalar triple product. Show that $|A \times B \cdot C|$ is equal to the volume of the parallelepiped having A, B, and C as adjacent edges.

21. Line m passes through $(0, 0, 0)$ and $(2, 2, -1)$ while line n passes through $(0, -4, 0)$ and $(-4, 4, 1)$. Use a cross product and a dot product to find the distance between m and n.

15.8   Equation of a Plane

In Fig. 15.13, $P_0(x_0, y_0, z_0)$ is a fixed point and $N = Ai + Bj + Ck$ a nonzero vector. The plane π through P_0 perpendicular to the direction of N is defined as the set of points $P(x, y, z)$ such that the vector representing line segment P_0P is perpendicular to the direction of N. The point P_0 is on π, since we have agreed that

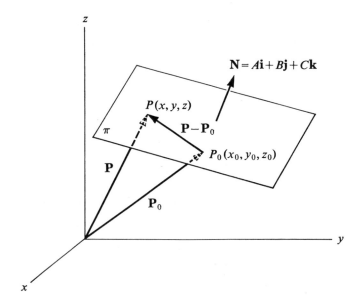

Figure 15.13

the zero vector is perpendicular to every vector. Since the vector from P_0 to P is equal to $\mathbf{P} - \mathbf{P}_0$, we have for all points P on π,

$$\mathbf{N} \cdot (\mathbf{P} - \mathbf{P}_0) = 0 \qquad\qquad (15.27)$$

or

$$A(x - x_0) + B(y - y_0) + C(z - z_0) = 0. \qquad\qquad (15.28)$$

Conversely, if the coordinates of $P_1(x_1, y_1, z_1)$ satisfy (15.28), they also satisfy (15.27) and hence line segment P_0P_1 is perpendicular to the direction of $\mathbf{N}$. Therefore, P_1 is on π. This completes the proof that (15.27) or (15.28) is an equation of π.

Equation (15.28) can also be written in the form

$$Ax + By + Cz = D \qquad\qquad (15.29)$$

where $D = Ax_0 + By_0 + Cz_0$. An equation of the form (15.29) in which A, B, and C are not all zero is called a linear equation in three variables.

Now let us assume that a linear equation of the form (15.29) is given and that $C \neq 0$. (If $C = 0$, we assume $B \neq 0$ or $A \neq 0$ and proceed in similar fashion.)

Then the coordinates of $(0, 0, D/C)$ clearly satisfy (15.29), which we write in the form

$$A(x - 0) + B(y - 0) + C\left(z - \frac{D}{C}\right) = 0.$$

By comparison with (15.28) we see that this is an equation of the plane through $(0, 0, D/C)$ perpendicular to the direction of $\mathbf{N} = A\mathbf{i} + B\mathbf{j} + C\mathbf{k}$. Our results are summarized in the following theorem.

Theorem 15-III.   Every plane can be represented by a linear equation. Conversely, every linear equation in three variables represents a plane.

Two planes

$$A_1x + B_1y + C_1z = D_1 \qquad \text{and} \qquad A_2x + B_2y + C_2z = D_2$$

are parallel if and only if they have parallel normal vectors. This will be true when

$$\mathbf{N}_1 = A_1\mathbf{i} + B_1\mathbf{j} + C_1\mathbf{k} \qquad \text{and} \qquad \mathbf{N}_2 = A_2\mathbf{i} + B_2\mathbf{j} + C_2\mathbf{k}$$

are parallel. It is important to remember that the coefficients in an equation of a plane are components of a vector perpendicular to the plane.

Two planes are perpendicular if and only if their normals $\mathbf{N}_1$ and $\mathbf{N}_2$ are perpendicular. This holds whenever $\mathbf{N}_1 \cdot \mathbf{N}_2 = 0$.

The angle between two planes is defined as the angle between their normals $\mathbf{N}_1$ and $\mathbf{N}_2$. The normals can be so chosen that the angle between them is $\leqslant \pi/2$.

Example 1.   Find an equation of the plane through $P(2, -3, 4)$ perpendicular to the line through $Q(5, 3, -2)$ and $R(8, 1, 7)$.

Solution.   A normal to the plane is the vector $\mathbf{N} = 3\mathbf{i} - 2\mathbf{j} + 9\mathbf{k}$ from Q to R. By (15.28), the plane has equation

$$3(x - 2) - 2(y + 3) + 9(z - 4) = 0$$

or

$$3x - 2y + 9z = 48.$$

Example 2.   Sketch the plane $2x + 3y + 4z = 12$.

Solution.   Setting $y = 0$ and $z = 0$, we find that the plane has x-intercept 6. Similarly, we find that the plane has y-intercept 4 and z-intercept 3. The graph is drawn in Fig. 15.14.

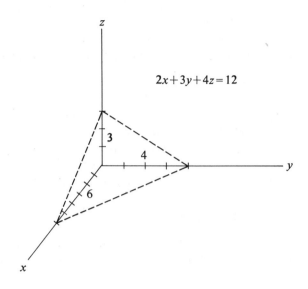

$$2x + 3y + 4z = 12$$

Figure 15.14

Example 3.   Find the distance from $P(2, 3, 1)$ to the plane $2x - 2y + z = 5$.

Solution.   Setting $x = 0$ and $y = 0$, we find that $Q(0, 0, 5)$ is a point on the plane. The vector $\mathbf{A}$ from P to Q is $\mathbf{A} = -2\mathbf{i} - 3\mathbf{j} + 4\mathbf{k}$. A unit vector normal to the plane is $\mathbf{N} = (2/3)\mathbf{i} - (2/3)\mathbf{j} + (1/3)\mathbf{k}$. The required distance d is the absolute value of the component or projection of $\mathbf{A}$ in the direction of $\mathbf{N}$, or

$$d = |\mathbf{A} \cdot \mathbf{N}| = \left|(-2)\left(\frac{2}{3}\right) + (-3)\left(-\frac{2}{3}\right) + (4)\left(\frac{1}{3}\right)\right| = 2.$$

The method is clarified by Fig. 15.15.

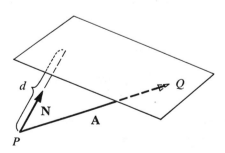

Figure 15.15

Example 4.   Find an equation of the plane through $P(2, 1, -3)$, $Q(4, 3, 5)$, and $R(6, -4, 0)$.

Solution.   The vector $\mathbf{A} = 2\mathbf{i} + 2\mathbf{j} + 8\mathbf{k}$ is the vector from P to Q and the vector $\mathbf{B} = 4\mathbf{i} - 5\mathbf{j} + 3\mathbf{k}$ is the vector from P to R. The vector $\mathbf{A} \times \mathbf{B} = 46\mathbf{i} + 26\mathbf{j} - 18\mathbf{k}$ is perpendicular to the plane, which therefore has equation

$$46(x - 2) + 26(y - 1) - 18(z + 3) = 0$$

or

$$23x + 13y - 9z = 86.$$

It is easily verified that the coordinates of P, Q, and R satisfy this equation of the plane.

PROBLEM LIST 86

1. Sketch the plane
    (a) $3x + 2y + 6z = 18$,   (d) $4x - 3z = 12$,
    (b) $4x - 6y + 3z = 24$,   (e) $5z = 4$,
    (c) $3x + 4y = 12$,   (f) $x + 3 = 0$.

2. Find an equation of the plane
    (a) through $(4, 2, -3)$ perpendicular to the line through $(2, -4, 1)$ and $(6, 2, -5)$;
    (b) through $(2, -3, 1)$ parallel to the plane $2x - 5y + 4z = 5$;
    (c) which is the perpendicular bisector of the line segment joining $(3, -2, 4)$ and $(5, 6, -8)$;
    (d) through $P(2, -1, 2)$ and perpendicular to the line through the origin and P;
    (e) through $(4, 2, -3)$ and $(2, -6, 5)$ and parallel to the z-axis;
    (f) through $(4, 1, -3)$ and $(2, -1, -3)$ and perpendicular to the plane $2x + 3y -4 = 5$;
    (g) through $(-1, 2, 3)$ and perpendicular to the planes $2x - 3y + 4z = 1$ and $3x - 5y + 2z = 3$;
    (h) through $(0, 0, 0)$, $(1, 2, 3)$, and $(2, 5, 4)$;
    (i) through $(1, 1, 2)$, $(3, 4, -6)$, and $(5, 0, 3)$;
    (j) through $(8, -1, 2)$, $(4, 3, -2)$, and $(6, 4, 0)$;
    (k) through $(2, -4, 2)$, $(3, 2, -1)$, and $(2, 4, -3)$.

3. Show that the plane through $(a, 0, 0)$, $(0, b, 0)$, and $(0, 0, c)$ has equation $(x/a) + (y/b) + (z/c) = 1$. This is known as the intercept form of an equation of a plane.

4. Find the distance from
    (a) $(0, 0, 0)$ to $3x - 6y + 2z = 12$;
    (b) $(1, 2, -1)$ to $4x - y + 8z = 16$;
    (c) $(4, 6, -3)$ to $12x + 3y + 4z = 12$;
    (d) $(3, 4, -2)$ to $x - y = 5$.

5. Find the point on $3x + 12y - 4z = 12$ which is closest to the origin.

6. Determine k so that the planes $2x + 3y - 4z = 5$ and $3x - 2y + kz = 2$ will be perpendicular.

7. Find the distance between the planes $2x + 2y - z = 6$ and $2x + 2y - z = -4$.

8. Find the intersection of the planes $4x - y + 2z = 3$, $3x + 2y - 4z = 16$, and $x - 3y + 5z = -12$.

9. Find the acute angle between the planes $3x - 6y + 6z = 2$ and $x + 2y - 2z = 5$.

10. A plane that is p units from the origin has intercepts a, b, and c. Show that $(1/a^2) + (1/b^2) + (1/c^2) = (1/p^2)$.

11. A plane has x-intercept 1, y-intercept 2, and z-intercept 3. Find direction cosines of a vector normal to the plane.

15.9 Straight Lines

A fixed point and a fixed direction characterize a line in three dimensions as well as one in two dimensions. In Fig. 15.16, $P_0(x_0, y_0, z_0)$ is a point on line l which has the direction of vector $\mathbf{A} = a\mathbf{i} + b\mathbf{j} + c\mathbf{k}$. If $P(x, y, z)$ is any point on l, there exists a scalar t such that

$$\mathbf{P} = \mathbf{P}_0 + t\mathbf{A}. \tag{15.30}$$

Conversely, if a vector $\mathbf{P} = \mathbf{P}_1 = x_1\mathbf{i} + y_1\mathbf{j} + z_1\mathbf{k}$ satisfies vector equation (15.30), then point $P_1(x_1, y_1, z_1)$ coincides with P_0 or is in the direction of $\mathbf{A}$ (or $-\mathbf{A}$) from P_0, and hence P_1 is on l. Thus (15.30) is a vector equation of line l.

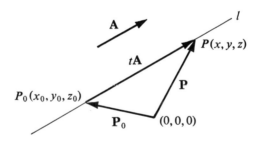

Figure 15.16

When $t = 0$, P coincides with P_0; when $t > 0$, P is in the direction of $\mathbf{A}$ from P_0; and when $t < 0$, P is in the direction of $-\mathbf{A}$ from P_0.

Every vector equation is equivalent to three scalar equations, obtained by equating the components of both sides of the equation. Vector equation (15.30) is equivalent to the three scalar equations

$$x = x_0 + at, \tag{15.31}$$

$$y = y_0 + bt, \tag{15.32}$$

$$z = z_0 + ct. \tag{15.33}$$

These three equations are parametric equations of l with t serving as parameter. By eliminating t, the three equations can be written in the forms

$$b(x - x_0) - a(y - y_0) = 0, \tag{15.34}$$

$$c(x - x_0) - a(z - z_0) = 0, \tag{15.35}$$

$$c(y - y_0) - b(z - z_0) = 0. \tag{15.36}$$

If the coordinates of a point P satisfy (15.31) to (15.33), they also satisfy (15.34). But (15.34) is an equation of a plane which is perpendicular to the vector $b\mathbf{i} - a\mathbf{j} + 0\mathbf{k}$ and which is therefore parallel to the z-axis. Thus (15.34) represents a plane through l parallel to the z-axis. Similarly, equations (15.35) and (15.36) represent planes through l parallel to the y- and x-axes. These three planes are called the projecting planes of l.

If a, b, and c are all different from 0, equations (15.31) to (15.33) can be written in the form

$$\frac{x - x_0}{a} = \frac{y - y_0}{b} = \frac{z - z_0}{c}. \tag{15.37}$$

Equations (15.37) are called symmetric equations of l.

Example 1. Find parametric equations of the line through $(2, -3, 4)$ parallel to the direction of $3\mathbf{i} + 5\mathbf{j} - 6\mathbf{k}$.

Solution. From equations (15.31) to (15.33) we obtain

$$x = 2 + 3t, \qquad y = -3 + 5t, \qquad z = 4 - 6t.$$

Example 2. Find the intersection of the line of Example 1 and the plane $2x - 3y - 3z = 4$.

Solution. Solving $2(2 + 3t) - 3(-3 + 5t) - 3(4 - 6t) = 4$ for t, we obtain $t = 1/3$. This value of t yields the intersection $(3, -4/3, 2)$.

Example 3. Find symmetric equations of the line l which is the intersection of the planes

$$3x - 2y + 4z = 2, \qquad 2x + y - 3z = 13.$$

Solution. Setting $z = 0$ and solving for x and y, we find that $(4, 5, 0)$ is a point on l. Since l is perpendicular to the normals to the given planes, l is parallel to

$$(3\mathbf{i} - 2\mathbf{j} + 4\mathbf{k}) \times (2\mathbf{i} + \mathbf{j} - 3\mathbf{k}) = 2\mathbf{i} + 17\mathbf{j} + 7\mathbf{k}.$$

By (15.37), l has symmetric equations

$$\frac{x - 4}{2} = \frac{y - 5}{17} = \frac{z - 0}{7}.$$

PROBLEM LIST 87

1. Find parametric equations of the line
   (a) through $(4, 3, -6)$ parallel to $5\mathbf{i} - 3\mathbf{j} + 2\mathbf{k}$;
   (b) through $(3, -4, 2)$ perpendicular to $3x + 5y - 4z = 2$;
   (c) through $(4, -6, 1)$ parallel to the y-axis;
   (d) through $(-3, 2, 1)$ parallel to the line $x = 5 - 2t, y = -4 + 3t, z = 7 + 8t$;
   (e) through $(-6, 4, 2)$ and $(8, -3, 0)$;
   (f) through $(5, 4, -2)$ parallel to the line determined by $3x - 2y + 5 = 4$ and $2x - 4y + z = 6$.

2. Find the point where the line $x = 3 + 2t$, $y = -4 - 3t$, $z = 2 + t$ pierces (a) the xy-plane, (b) the yz-plane, (c) the plane $2x - 3y + z = 10$.

3. Find symmetric equations of the line determined by
   (a) $8x - y + z = 2$ and $3x + 4y - 2z = 1$,
   (b) $5x + 2y - 3z = 6$ and $4x + 6y - 2z = 5$.

4. Line l makes equal angles with the x-, y-, and z-axes. Find this angle.

5. Find the distance from from $(2, 4, -1)$ to the line
   $$\frac{x-3}{2} = \frac{y+4}{3} = \frac{z-1}{5}.$$

6. Find the distance between the lines
   $$\frac{x+2}{3} = \frac{y+4}{4} = \frac{z-2}{-3} \quad \text{and} \quad \frac{x+1}{4} = \frac{y-3}{5} = \frac{z-2}{1}.$$

7. Show that the line $x = -3 + 9t$, $y = 2 - 2t$, $z = 2 - 2t$ lies in the plane $2x + 3y + 6z = 12$.

8. Show that the line
   $$\frac{x-3}{4} = \frac{y+2}{3} = \frac{z+1}{2}$$
   is parallel to the plane $2x + 4y - 10z = 5$. Find the distance from the plane to the line.

9. Line l passes through $(-2, 4, 1)$ and is perpendicular to the plane $3x + 2y - 6z = 4$. Find the intersection of the line and the plane.

10. Find an equation of the plane passing through $(-1, 2, 4)$ and containing the line of intersection of the planes $5x - y + z = 1$ and $x - 6y + z = 2$.

11. Show that the following lines intersect:
    $$x = 5 + 3t, \qquad y = -1 - 4t, \qquad z = -3 + t,$$
    and
    $$x = -8 + 5u, \qquad y = 1 + u, \qquad z = -2u;$$
    find their point of intersection.

15.10   Surfaces

The set of points whose coordinates satisfy an equation of the form $f(x, y, z) = 0$ is called a surface. A plane is a simple example of a surface. The problems of finding an equation of a surface and graphing a surface having a given equation are analogous to the two major problems of plane analytic geometry involving curves and equations.

Example 1.   A sphere is the set of points equally distant from a fixed point called the center. Find an equation of the sphere of radius r having center at $P_0(x_0, y_0, z_0)$.

Solution.   Let $P(x, y, z)$ denote an arbitrary point on the sphere. By the distance formula we obtain

$$(x - x_0)^2 + (y - y_0)^2 + (z - z_0)^2 = r^2. \tag{15.38}$$

Conversely, if the coordinates of $P_1(x_1, y_1, z_1)$ satisfy (15.38), P_1 is r units from P_0 and lies on the sphere. Hence (15.38) is an equation of the sphere. This equation can also be written in the form

$$x^2 + y^2 + z^2 + ax + by + cz + d = 0. \tag{15.39}$$

It is easily shown by completing the square that an equation of the form (15.39) represents a sphere, a point sphere, or an imaginary sphere. The development is analogous to that employed in the study of the circle.

Example 2.   Find the center and radius of the sphere

$$x^2 + y^2 + z^2 - 4x + 8y - 6z + 25 = 0.$$

Solution.   Completing the square, we obtain

$$(x^2 - 4x + 4) + (y^2 + 8y + 16) + (z^2 - 6z + 9) = +4 + 16 + 9 - 25$$

or

$$(x - 2)^2 + (y + 4)^2 + (z - 3)^2 = (2)^2.$$

By (15.38) the sphere has center $(2, -4, 3)$ and radius 2.

Example 3.   Find an equation of the surface, known as a paraboloid of revolution, obtained by revolving the first-quadrant portion of the parabola $y = x^2$ about the y-axis.

Solution.   In Fig. 15.17, $P(x, y, z)$ denotes an arbitrary point on the paraboloid. Since $P_0 P_1 = x_1 = r$, $y = x_1^2 = r^2$. But $r^2 = (P_0 P)^2 = x^2 + z^2$, and hence

$$y = x^2 + z^2. \tag{15.40}$$

Conversely, if the coordinates of a point satisfy (15.40), it is easily shown

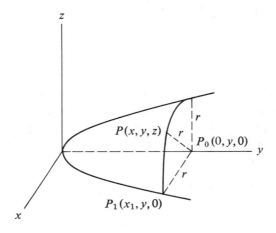

Figure 15.17

that the point lies on the paraboloid. Thus (15.40) is an equation of the paraboloid.

The techniques for graphing an equation in two dimensions are also employed in graphing an equation in three dimensions. However, the plotting of points has little value, partly because the graph is depicted in a two-dimensional drawing. A very useful technique for visualizing a surface is to determine the curves in which planes parallel to the coordinate planes intersect the surface. These curves are called traces of the surface.

Example 1.   Draw the graph of the surface $x^2 + y^2 = 1$.

Solution.   In Fig. 15.18 we first draw the circle $x^2 + y^2 = 1$ in the xy-plane. If $P_0(x, y, 0)$ is any point on this circle, it is clear that P_0 is a point of the required surface, since its coordinates satisfy $x^2 + y^2 = 1$. But this is also true for all points on line l through P_0 parallel to the z-axis, and for no other points. Thus the surface is a right-circular cylinder whose trace in the xy-plane is the circle $x^2 + y^2 = 1$. It is convenient to think of the surface as being generated by moving the generator l around the circle, with l remaining parallel to the z-axis.

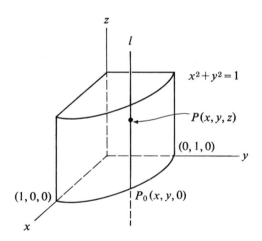

Figure 15.18

A surface whose equation contains only two variables is known as a cylindrical surface. For example, a surface having an equation of the form $g(y, z) = 0$ is a cylindrical surface whose trace in the yz-plane is the curve $g(y, z) = 0$ and whose generator is a line through this curve parallel to the x-axis. The plane $2y + 3z = 6$ is a special cylindrical surface of this type.

Example 2.   Draw the graph of the surface

$$\frac{x^2}{a^2} + \frac{y^2}{b^2} + \frac{z^2}{c^2} = 1.$$

Solution.   The surface has intercepts $(\pm a, 0, 0)$, $(0, \pm b, 0)$, and $(0, 0, \pm c)$

and is symmetric with respect to each of the coordinate planes. Setting $z = 0$, we find that the surface intersects the xy-plane in the ellipse $(x^2/a^2) + (y^2/b^2) = 1$. The traces in the xz- and yz-planes are also ellipses which are easily drawn. The trace of the surface in the plane $z = k$ is an ellipse (or a point) for $-c \leqslant k \leqslant c$. This is seen by writing the equation of the surface in the form

$$\frac{x^2}{a^2} + \frac{y^2}{b^2} = 1 - \frac{z^2}{c^2},$$

substituting $z = k$ and dividing both sides by $1 - (k^2/c^2)$. Traces in planes parallel to the xz- and yz-planes are also ellipses. The first-octant portion of the surface is shown in Fig. 15.19. The surface is called an ellipsoid.

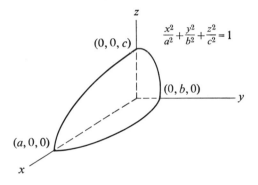

Figure 15.19

Example 3. Draw the graph of the surface

$$\frac{x^2}{a^2} + \frac{y^2}{b^2} - \frac{z^2}{c^2} = 1.$$

Solution. The surface has intercepts $(\pm a, 0, 0)$ and $(0, \pm b, 0)$ and is symmetric with respect to each of the coordinate planes. Traces in planes parallel to the xy-plane are ellipses, the smallest of these being the ellipse $(x^2/a^2) + (y^2/b^2) = 1$ in the xy-plane. Traces in planes parallel to the yz- and xz-planes are hyperbolas. The surface, known as an elliptic hyperboloid of one sheet, is shown in Fig. 15.20.

Example 4. Draw the graph of the surface

$$\frac{x^2}{a^2} - \frac{y^2}{b^2} - \frac{z^2}{c^2} = 1.$$

Solution. The surface has intercepts $(\pm a, 0, 0)$ and is symmetric with respect to each of the coordinate planes. Traces in planes $x = k$ are ellipses for $|k| > a$, while traces in planes $y = k$ and $z = k$ are hyperbolas. The surface, known as an elliptic hyperboloid of two sheets, is shown in Fig. 15.21.

Example 5. Draw the graph of the surface

$$cz = \frac{x^2}{a^2} + \frac{y^2}{b^2}.$$

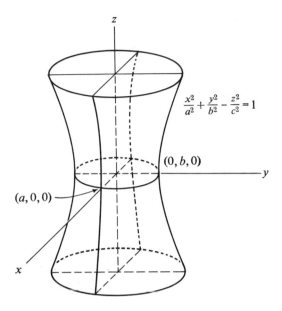

$$\frac{x^2}{a^2} + \frac{y^2}{b^2} - \frac{z^2}{c^2} = 1$$

Figure 15.20

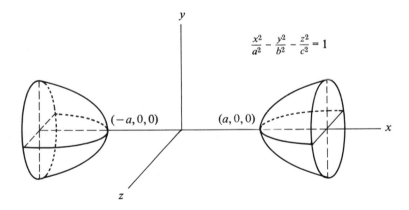

$$\frac{x^2}{a^2} - \frac{y^2}{b^2} - \frac{z^2}{c^2} = 1$$

Figure 15.21

Solution.   The surface has intercept $(0, 0, 0)$ and is symmetric with respect to the xz- and yz-planes. Traces in planes $z = k$ are ellipses for $k > 0$, while traces in planes $x = k$ and $y = k$ are parabolas. The surface, known as an elliptic paraboloid when $a \neq b$ and a paraboloid of revolution when $a = b$, is shown in Fig. 15.22.

Example 6.   Draw the graph of the surface

$$\frac{x^2}{a^2} + \frac{y^2}{b^2} - \frac{z^2}{c^2} = 0.$$

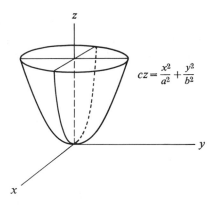

Figure 15.22

Solution.   The surface has intercept $(0, 0, 0)$ and is symmetric with respect to each of the coordinate planes. The trace in the xy-plane is the origin, while the traces in the xz- and yz-planes are straight lines. For example, setting $y = 0$, we obtain $(x^2/a^2) - (z^2/c^2) = 0$ or $z = \pm(cx/a)$. Traces in planes $z = k \neq 0$ are ellipses, while traces in planes $x = k \neq 0$ and $y = k \neq 0$ are hyperbolas. The surface, known as an elliptic cone when $a \neq b$ and a right-circular cone when $a = b$, is shown in Fig. 15.23.

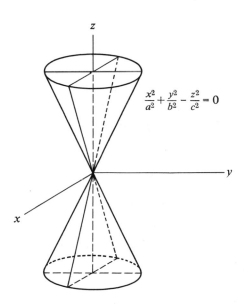

Figure 15.23

Example 7.   Draw the graph of the surface

$$cz = \frac{x^2}{a^2} - \frac{y^2}{b^2}.$$

Solution.   The surface has intercept $(0, 0, 0)$ and is symmetric with respect to the xz- and yz-planes. Traces in planes $x = k$ and $y = k$ are parabolas, while traces in planes $z = k \neq 0$ are hyperbolas. The traces in the xy-plane (or plane $z = 0$) are the straight lines $y = \pm(bx/a)$. The saddle-shaped surface, known as a hyperbolic paraboloid, is shown in Fig. 15.24.

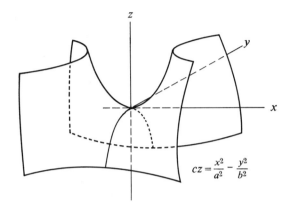

$$cz = \frac{x^2}{a^2} - \frac{y^2}{b^2}$$

Figure 15.24

PROBLEM LIST 88

1. Write an equation of the sphere
   (a) with center $(0, 0, 0)$ and radius 5;
   (b) with center $(2, -3, 6)$ and radius 2;
   (c) with center $(-3, 2, 1)$ and passing through $(4, 8, -5)$;
   (d) with $(4, 3, -6)$ and $(7, 8, -2)$ as ends of a diameter;
   (e) with radius 5 and tangent to the xy-plane at $(6, 4, 0)$;
   (f) with center $(4, 3, 6)$ and tangent to the z-axis.

2. Find the center and radius of the sphere
   (a) $x^2 + y^2 + z^2 - 2x + 4y - 6z + 13 = 0$;
   (b) $x^2 + y^2 + z^2 - 4x + 6y - 8z + 4 = 0$;
   (c) $x^2 + y^2 + z^2 - 10x + 4y - 20 = 0$;
   (d) $2x^2 + 2y^2 + 2z^2 - 5y + 8z = 0$.

3. Find an equation of the surface of revolution obtained by revolving the given plane curve about the indicated axis:
   (a) $y = x^2/4$ about the x-axis.
   (b) $y = \sqrt{4 - x^2}$ about the x-axis.
   (c) $y = (b/a)\sqrt{a^2 - x^2}$ about the x-axis.
   (d) $y = 5x$ about the y-axis.
   (e) $z = 4 - x^2$ about the z-axis.
   (f) $(x^2/a^2) - (y^2/b^2) = 1$ about the x-axis.

4. Draw the graphs of the following cylindrical surfaces:

$$\text{(a) } x^2 + 4y^2 = 4.$$

$$\text{(b) } 2x + 3y = 12.$$

$$\text{(c) } y = |x|.$$

$$\text{(d) } z = x^2.$$

$$\text{(e) } z = 9 - x^2.$$

$$\text{(f) } y^2 + z^2 = 4.$$

$$\text{(g) } z = y^3.$$

$$\text{(h) } y = \sin x.$$

5. Draw the graphs of the following surfaces:

$$\text{(a) } x^2 + 4y^2 + 9z^2 = 36.$$

$$\text{(b) } x^2 + 4y^2 + 4z^2 = 4.$$

$$\text{(c) } 4x^2 + y^2 + 4z^2 = 4.$$

$$\text{(d) } 4x^2 + 4y^2 + z^2 = 4.$$

$$\text{(e) } z = \frac{x^2}{9} + \frac{y^2}{4}.$$

$$\text{(f) } z = \frac{x^2}{9} - \frac{y^2}{4}.$$

$$\text{(g) } z = \frac{y^2}{4} - \frac{x^2}{9}.$$

$$\text{(h) } \frac{x^2}{16} + \frac{y^2}{9} - \frac{z^2}{4} = 1.$$

$$\text{(i) } \frac{x^2}{16} - \frac{y^2}{4} + \frac{z^2}{9} = 1.$$

$$\text{(j) } \frac{x^2}{16} - \frac{y^2}{9} - \frac{z^2}{4} = 1.$$

$$\text{(k) } \frac{z^2}{25} - \frac{x^2}{9} - \frac{y^2}{4} = 1.$$

$$\text{(l) } x^2 + y^2 + z^2 - 8z + 15 = 0.$$

$$\text{(m) } x^2 + 4y^2 - z^2 = 0.$$

$$\text{(n) } 9x^2 - 4y^2 + z^2 = 0.$$

6. Show that the cylindrical surface $x^2 + y^2 = 4$ contains the intersection of $z = x^2 + y^2$ and $z = 8 - x^2 - y^2$.

7. Sketch the solid bounded by $z = x^2 + y^2$ and $4x + 2y + z = 9$.

8. Find an equation of the surface whose points are equidistant from the point $(0, 0, p)$ and the plane $z = -p$. Identify the surface and draw its graph.

9. Find an equation of the set of points $P(x, y, z)$ having the property that the line through the origin and P makes an angle of $\pi/4$ (or $3\pi/4$) with the z-axis.

10. Find an equation of the sphere with center at $(2, 1, 3)$ and tangent to the plane $3x - 4y + 2z = 12$.

11. Find an equation of the surface whose points are equidistant from $(3, 2, -7)$ and $(5, 6, -3)$.

12. Find symmetric equations of the line whose points are equidistant from $(0, 0, 0)$, $(4, -3, 6)$, and $(5, 1, -2)$.

13. Find the volume of an ellipsoid.

14. Find an equation of the sphere through $(0, 0, 0)$, $(4, 0, 0)$, $(0, 4, 0)$, and $(0, 0, 4)$.

15. Find an equation of the surface whose points are three times as far from $(0, 0, 0)$ as from $(8, 0, 0)$. Identify the surface.

16. Find the points where the line through $(-1, 0, 19)$ and $(11, 4, -5)$ intersects the surface $z = x^2 + 9y^2$.

15.11   *Vector Functions*

A vector function of a real variable is a correspondence between a set of real numbers and a set of vectors. To each real number t in the domain of the function there corresponds one and only one vector $\mathbf{V} = x\mathbf{i} + y\mathbf{j} + z\mathbf{k}$ in the range of the function. Since the length and direction of **V** define functions of t, the components x, y, and z of **V** also define functions of t.

Example.   Let the vector function defined by $\mathbf{V} = \cos t\mathbf{i} + \sin t\mathbf{j} + 0\mathbf{k}$ have domain $0 \leqslant t \leqslant 1$. The range of the function consists of all unit vectors perpendicular to the z-axis.

15.12   Derivative of a Vector Function

The derivative of a vector function given by $\mathbf{V} = \mathbf{V}(t)$ is defined by

$$\frac{d\mathbf{V}(t)}{dt} = \lim_{\Delta t \to 0} \frac{\mathbf{V}(t + \Delta t) - \mathbf{V}(t)}{\Delta t} = \lim_{\Delta t \to 0} \frac{\Delta \mathbf{V}}{\Delta t}. \tag{15.41}$$

The vector $\Delta \mathbf{V}$ is equal to

$$\begin{aligned}
[x(t + \Delta t)\mathbf{i} &+ y(t + \Delta t)\mathbf{j} + z(t + \Delta t)\mathbf{k}] \\
- [x(t)\mathbf{i} &+ y(t)\mathbf{j} + z(t)\mathbf{k}] \\
= [x(t + \Delta t) &- x(t)]\mathbf{i} \\
&+ [y(t + \Delta t) - y(t)]\mathbf{j} \\
&+ [z(t + \Delta t) - z(t)]\mathbf{k}.
\end{aligned}$$

By $\lim_{\Delta t \to 0} (\Delta \mathbf{V}/\Delta t)$, we mean

$$\left[\lim_{\Delta t \to 0} \frac{x(t + \Delta t) - x(t)}{\Delta t} \right]\mathbf{i} + \left[\lim_{\Delta t \to 0} \frac{y(t + \Delta t) - y(t)}{\Delta t} \right]\mathbf{j}$$
$$+ \left[\lim_{\Delta t \to 0} \frac{z(t + \Delta t) - z(t)}{\Delta t} \right]\mathbf{k}$$

and hence **V** defines a differentiable function of t if its components are differentiable. Furthermore,

$$\frac{d\mathbf{V}(t)}{dt} = \left(\frac{dx}{dt}\right)\mathbf{i} + \left(\frac{dy}{dt}\right)\mathbf{j} + \left(\frac{dz}{dt}\right)\mathbf{k}. \tag{15.42}$$

Higher derivatives of **V** are defined similarly. For example

$$\frac{d^2\mathbf{V}(t)}{dt^2} = \left(\frac{d^2x}{dt^2}\right)\mathbf{i} + \left(\frac{d^2y}{dt^2}\right)\mathbf{j} + \left(\frac{d^2z}{dt^2}\right)\mathbf{k}. \tag{15.43}$$

The branch of mathematics which deals with the differentiation of vector functions is known as the vector differential calculus. We will derive the following formula from this subject.

Theorem 15-IV.   Let $y = y(t)$ define a differentiable function of t and let $\mathbf{V} = \mathbf{V}(t)$ define a differentiable vector function of t. Then

$$\frac{d}{dt}(y\mathbf{V}) = y\frac{d\mathbf{V}}{dt} + \frac{dy}{dt}\mathbf{V}. \tag{15.44}$$

Proof

$$\frac{d}{dt}(y\mathbf{V}) = \lim_{\Delta t \to 0} \left[\frac{y(t + \Delta t)\mathbf{V}(t + \Delta t) - y(t)\mathbf{V}(t)}{\Delta t} \right]$$

$$= \lim_{\Delta t \to 0} \left[\frac{(y + \Delta y)(\mathbf{V} + \Delta \mathbf{V}) - y\mathbf{V}}{\Delta t} \right]$$

$$= \lim_{\Delta t \to 0} \left[y \frac{\Delta \mathbf{V}}{\Delta t} + \frac{\Delta y}{\Delta t} \mathbf{V} + \Delta y \frac{\Delta \mathbf{V}}{\Delta t} \right]$$

$$= y \frac{d\mathbf{V}}{dt} + \frac{dy}{dt} \mathbf{V}.$$

Example 1.   If $\mathbf{V} = (t^3 + t)\mathbf{i} + t^2\mathbf{j} + (t^3 - t^2)\mathbf{k}$, then

$$\frac{d\mathbf{V}}{dt} = (3t^2 + 1)\mathbf{i} + 2t\mathbf{j} + (3t^2 - 2t)\mathbf{k}$$

and

$$\frac{d^2\mathbf{V}}{dt^2} = 6t\mathbf{i} + 2\mathbf{j} + (6t - 2)\mathbf{k}.$$

At $t = 1$,

$$\frac{d\mathbf{V}}{dt} = 4\mathbf{i} + 2\mathbf{j} + \mathbf{k} \qquad \text{and} \qquad \frac{d^2\mathbf{V}}{dt^2} = 6\mathbf{i} + 2\mathbf{j} + 4\mathbf{k}.$$

Example 2.   If $\mathbf{V} = (\cos \theta)\mathbf{i} + (\sin \theta)\mathbf{j} + (0)\mathbf{k}$, then $\mathbf{V}$ makes an angle θ with the positive x-axis and

$$\frac{d\mathbf{V}}{d\theta} = (-\sin \theta)\mathbf{i} + (\cos \theta)\mathbf{j} + (0)\mathbf{k}$$

$$= \cos\left(\theta + \frac{\pi}{2}\right)\mathbf{i} + \sin\left(\theta + \frac{\pi}{2}\right)\mathbf{j} + 0\mathbf{k}.$$

This example shows that differentiating a unit vector which lies in the xy-plane merely rotates the vector through an angle of $\pi/2$, the sense of rotation being counterclockwise when viewed from a point on the positive z-axis. The differentiation must be with respect to θ.

Example 3.   Given $y = t^3$ and $\mathbf{V} = t^2\mathbf{i} + 5t\mathbf{j} - t^4\mathbf{k}$, find $d/dt\,(y\mathbf{V})$.

Solution A.   Since $y\mathbf{V} = t^5\mathbf{i} + 5t^4\mathbf{j} - t^7\mathbf{k}$,

$$\frac{d}{dt}(y\mathbf{V}) = 5t^4\mathbf{i} + 20t^3\mathbf{j} - 7t^6\mathbf{k}.$$

Solution B.   By (15.44),

$$\frac{d}{dt}(y\mathbf{V}) = t^3(2t\mathbf{i} + 5\mathbf{j} - 4t^3\mathbf{k}) + 3t^2(t^2\mathbf{i} + 5t\mathbf{j} - t^4\mathbf{k})$$

$$= 5t^4\mathbf{i} + 20t^3\mathbf{j} - 7t^6\mathbf{k}.$$

PROBLEM LIST 89

1. Describe the range of the vector functions given by the following expressions and defined on $0 \leqslant t \leqslant 1$:

(a) $\mathbf{V} = 0\mathbf{i} + \cos t\mathbf{j} + \sin t\mathbf{k}$.

   (b) $\mathbf{V} = t\mathbf{i} + t\mathbf{j} + \mathbf{k}$.

   (c) $\mathbf{V} = \cos t\mathbf{i} + \sin t\mathbf{j} + t\mathbf{k}$.

   (d) $\mathbf{V} = t\mathbf{i} + t\mathbf{j} + t\mathbf{k}$.

2. Find $d\mathbf{V}/dt$ and $d^2\mathbf{V}/dt^2$:

   (a) $\mathbf{V} = t^3\mathbf{i} + t^2\mathbf{j} - t^4\mathbf{k}$.

   (b) $\mathbf{V} = t^2\mathbf{i} + (t^2 - t)\mathbf{j} + 5\mathbf{k}$.

   (c) $\mathbf{V} = t^4\mathbf{i} + (t - t^3)\mathbf{j} + \sqrt{t}\ \mathbf{k}$.

   (d) $\mathbf{V} = t\mathbf{i} + \sin t\mathbf{j} - \cos t\mathbf{k}$.

3. Given $\mathbf{V} = 3t^2\mathbf{i} - 5t^3\mathbf{j} + (1 - 6t)\mathbf{k}$, find $d\mathbf{V}/dt$ and $d^2\mathbf{V}/dt^2$ when $t = 3$.

4. Show that $\cos t\mathbf{i} + \sin t\mathbf{j}$ and $-\sin t\mathbf{i} + \cos t\mathbf{j}$ are perpendicular.

5. If $\mathbf{V} = \cos \theta\mathbf{i} + \sin \theta\mathbf{j}$ has initial point $(0, 0, 0)$ and terminal point $(-3/5, 4/5, 0)$ when $\theta = \theta_0$, find the terminal point of $d\mathbf{V}/d\theta$ when $\theta = \theta_0$ if its initial point is $(0, 0, 0)$.

6. Find $d/dt\ (y\mathbf{V})$ by two methods:

   (a) $y = t^2$, $\mathbf{V} = t\mathbf{i} + t^2\mathbf{j} - t^3\mathbf{k}$.

   (b) $y = 1 + t^3$, $\mathbf{V} = 2t\mathbf{i} - t^2\mathbf{j} + 3t\mathbf{k}$.

   (c) $y = 3t^2 - t$, $\mathbf{V} = 3\mathbf{i} + t^3\mathbf{j} - 7t\mathbf{k}$.

   (d) $y = \cos t$, $\mathbf{V} = \cos t\mathbf{i} + \sin t\mathbf{j} + t^2\mathbf{k}$.

7. Derive the following formulas:

   (a) $\dfrac{d}{dt}(\mathbf{U} \pm \mathbf{V}) = \dfrac{d\mathbf{U}}{dt} \pm \dfrac{d\mathbf{V}}{dt}$.

   (b) $\dfrac{d}{dt}(\mathbf{U} \cdot \mathbf{V}) = \mathbf{U} \cdot \dfrac{d\mathbf{V}}{dt} + \dfrac{d\mathbf{U}}{dt} \cdot \mathbf{V}$.

   (c) $\dfrac{d}{dt}(\mathbf{U} \times \mathbf{V}) = \mathbf{U} \times \dfrac{d\mathbf{V}}{dt} + \dfrac{d\mathbf{U}}{dt} \times \mathbf{V}$.

15.13   *Plane Curvilinear Motion*

    In Chapter 7 we discussed the motion of particles and noted that particles may be idealized as points. We now find it convenient to refer to "moving points," even though this is a contradiction in terms. A point is an ordered pair of numbers and, of course, does not move around.

    Vectors are particularly useful when studying the motion of a point. We did not employ vectors in the study of rectilinear motion, since the two possible directions of motion on a line can be distinguished by using positive and negative numbers. We now consider the motion of a point moving along a curve in the xy-plane. The vectors we employ will all be parallel to the xy-plane and it will be convenient to assume that they are actually contained in the xy-plane. Thus any vector can be written in the simplified form $a_1\mathbf{i} + a_2\mathbf{j}$ instead of in the form $a_1\mathbf{i} + a_2\mathbf{j} + 0\mathbf{k}$.

    We assume that the point $P(x, y)$ moves along the curve (see Fig. 15.25) having parametric representation

$$x = x(t), \qquad y = y(t), \tag{15.45}$$

where the parameter t denotes time. That is, the moving point P is at $(x(t), y(t))$ at time t.

The vector $\mathbf{R}$ from the origin to P is called the position or displacement vector of P. Its direction indicates the direction of P from the origin and its length indicates the distance from the origin to P.

The vector $\mathbf{V} = d\mathbf{R}/dt$ is called the velocity vector of P. Since $\mathbf{R} = x\mathbf{i} + y\mathbf{j}$, $\mathbf{V} = (dx/dt)\mathbf{i} + (dy/dt)\mathbf{j}$.

The length of $\mathbf{V}$ is given by

$$v = |\mathbf{V}| = \sqrt{\left(\frac{dx}{dt}\right)^2 + \left(\frac{dy}{dt}\right)^2} = \left|\frac{ds}{dt}\right|.$$

Thus the length of $\mathbf{V}$ indicates the absolute value of the rate at which the curve is being traversed. This is called the speed of P. The arc length s along the curve is usually measured so that s increases with t; that is, so that $ds/dt > 0$. [Unless $ds/dt = 0$.] We will make this assumption.

From Fig. 15.26 it is seen that

$$\tan \theta = \frac{dy}{dt} \div \frac{dx}{dt} = \frac{dy}{dx} \qquad \text{when } \frac{dx}{dt} \neq 0.$$

The velocity vector $\mathbf{V}$ has the direction of the tangent to the curve at P and indicates the direction in which P is moving.

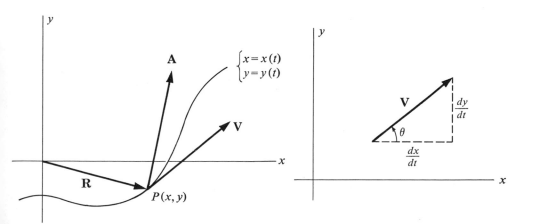

Figure 15.25   Figure 15.26

It is also instructive to examine Fig. 15.27. The vector

$$\Delta\mathbf{R} = \mathbf{R}(t + \Delta t) - \mathbf{R}(t) = (\mathbf{R} + \Delta\mathbf{R}) - \mathbf{R}$$

has the same direction as the vector $\Delta\mathbf{R}/\Delta t$. As $\Delta t \to 0$, $\Delta\mathbf{R}/\Delta t \to \mathbf{V}$ and the direction of $\Delta\mathbf{R}/\Delta t$ approaches the direction of the tangent to the curve at P.

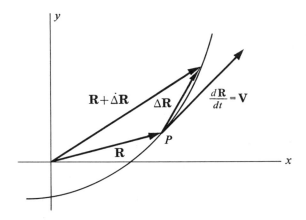

Figure 15.27

The vector

$$\mathbf{A} = \frac{d\mathbf{V}}{dt} = \left(\frac{d^2 x}{dt^2}\right)\mathbf{i} + \left(\frac{d^2 y}{dt^2}\right)\mathbf{j}$$

is called the acceleration vector of P. In general, $\mathbf{A}$ and $\mathbf{V}$ do not have the same direction. The importance of the acceleration vector is due to Newton's second law of motion:

$$\mathbf{F} = m\mathbf{A} = m\frac{d^2\mathbf{R}}{dt^2}, \qquad (15.46)$$

which states that the resultant force, represented by the vector $\mathbf{F}$, of all the forces acting upon a moving particle is proportional to the acceleration $\mathbf{A}$ of the particle. When the units involved are appropriately chosen, the constant of proportionality m denotes the mass of the moving particle. Equation (15.46), known as a second-order vector differential equation, plays a vital role in the subject of mechanics.

Example 1.   A point $P(x, y)$ moves along the curve $x = 4t$, $y = 2t^2$, the parameter t denoting time. Find $\mathbf{R}$, $\mathbf{V}$, and $\mathbf{A}$ when $t = 1$ and illustrate graphically.

Solution.   From

$$\mathbf{R} = 4t\mathbf{i} + 2t^2\mathbf{j}, \qquad \mathbf{V} = 4\mathbf{i} + 4t\mathbf{j}, \qquad \mathbf{A} = 4\mathbf{j},$$

we find that at $t = 1$,

$$\mathbf{R} = 4\mathbf{i} + 2\mathbf{j}, \qquad \mathbf{V} = 4\mathbf{i} + 4\mathbf{j}, \qquad \mathbf{A} = 4\mathbf{j}.$$

Eliminating t, we find that the curve has cartesian equation $y = x^2/8$ and that P is at $(4, 2)$ when $t = 1$. It is customary to draw $\mathbf{V}$ and $\mathbf{A}$ with initial point P as shown in Fig. 15.28.

Example 2.   A point $P(x, y)$ moves counterclockwise around the circle $x^2 + y^2 = a^2$ at constant speed, starting from $(a, 0)$ at time $t = 0$. Find $\mathbf{R}$, $\mathbf{V}$, and $\mathbf{A}$ at time t.

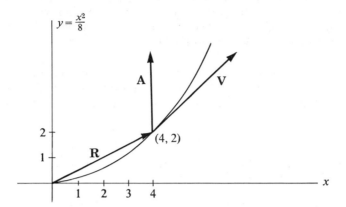

Figure 15.28

Solution.   Angle θ in Fig. 15.29 is given by $\theta = s/a$ and hence $d\theta/dt = v/a$. Since v is constant, $d\theta/dt = v/a = \omega$, called the angular velocity of line *OP*, is also constant. Since $\theta = 0$ when $t = 0$, $\theta = \omega t$ and

$$\mathbf{R} = (a \cos \omega t)\mathbf{i} + (a \sin \omega t)\mathbf{j},$$
$$\mathbf{V} = (-a\omega \sin \omega t)\mathbf{i} + (a\omega \cos \omega t)\mathbf{j},$$

and

$$\mathbf{A} = (-a\omega^2 \cos \omega t)\mathbf{i} + (-a\omega^2 \sin \omega t)\mathbf{j}.$$

Since $\mathbf{A} = -\omega^2 \mathbf{R}$, $\mathbf{A}$ has direction opposite to that of $\mathbf{R}$ and magnitude

$$\omega^2 |\mathbf{R}| = \omega^2 a = \left(\frac{v}{a}\right)^2 a = \frac{v^2}{a}.$$

Thus $\mathbf{A}$ has constant magnitude and is always directed toward the center of the circle. The motion of *P* is called uniform circular motion.

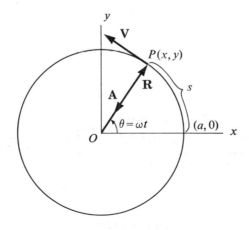

Figure 15.29

Example 3. A projectile, assumed to be acted upon only by gravity, has, at time $t = 0$, position vector $\mathbf{R}_0 = 0\mathbf{i} + 0\mathbf{j}$ and velocity vector $\mathbf{V}_0 = (v_0 \cos \alpha)\mathbf{i} + (v_0 \sin \alpha)\mathbf{j}$. The angle α is called the angle of elevation and v_0 is the initial speed. Find $\mathbf{R}$, $\mathbf{V}$, and $\mathbf{A}$ at arbitrary time t.

Solution. At time t the only force acting on the projectile is the downward pull of the earth, and hence $\mathbf{A} = 0\mathbf{i} - g\mathbf{j}$ at arbitrary time t. The components of $\mathbf{V}$ are obtained by integrating the components of $\mathbf{A}$ with respect to t. This yields

$$\mathbf{V} = c_1\mathbf{i} + (-gt + c_2)\mathbf{j}.$$

When $t = 0$, $\mathbf{V} = (v_0 \cos \alpha)\mathbf{i} + (v_0 \sin \alpha)\mathbf{j}$, and hence $c_1 = v_0 \cos \alpha$ and $c_2 = v_0 \sin \alpha$. Therefore, at time t,

$$\mathbf{V} = (v_0 \cos \alpha)\mathbf{i} + (-gt + v_0 \sin \alpha)\mathbf{j}.$$

Again integrating with respect to t, we obtain

$$\mathbf{R} = [(v_0 \cos \alpha)t + c_3]\mathbf{i}$$
$$+ \left[-\frac{gt^2}{2} + (v_0 \sin \alpha)t + c_4\right]\mathbf{j}.$$

Since $\mathbf{R}_0$ is the zero vector, $c_3 = c_4 = 0$ and, at time t,

$$\mathbf{R} = [(v_0 \cos \alpha)t]\mathbf{i} + \left[-\frac{gt^2}{2} + (v_0 \sin \alpha)t\right]\mathbf{j}.$$

The path of the projectile has parametric equations

$$x = (v_0 \cos \alpha)t, \qquad y = -\frac{gt^2}{2} + (v_0 \sin \alpha)t.$$

By eliminating t, it is easily shown that the path is the parabola having cartesian equation

$$y = x \tan \alpha - \frac{gx^2}{2v_0^2} \sec^2 \alpha.$$

See Fig. 15.30.

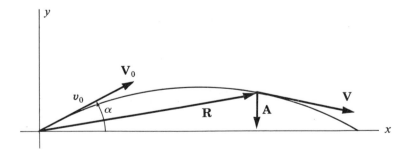

Figure 15.30

15.14   *Tangential and Normal Components of Acceleration*

It is often useful to know the components of **A** tangent and normal to a curve. Let **T** be a unit vector having the same direction as **V** and let θ be the angle between the positive direction of **T** and the positive direction of the *x*-axis. See Fig. 15.31.

We next differentiate **T**, called the unit tangent vector, with respect to the time *t* by the chain rule. It is easily proved that the chain rule applies to the differentiation of vectors as well as scalars. Thus

$$\frac{d\mathbf{T}}{dt} = \frac{d\mathbf{T}}{d\theta} \cdot \frac{d\theta}{ds} \cdot \frac{ds}{dt}. \tag{15.47}$$

By Example 2 of Sec. 15.12, $d\mathbf{T}/d\theta$ is a unit vector perpendicular to **T** and making an angle $\theta + \pi/2$ with the positive direction of the *x*-axis. The second factor $d\theta/ds$ in the right member of (15.47) denotes the rate at which the angle θ is changing with respect to the arc length *s*. Its value is positive if the curve is concave upward and negative if the curve is concave downward. The absolute value of $d\theta/ds$ is denoted by the small Greek letter κ (kappa) and is called the curvature. Letting **N**, called the unit normal vector, be a unit vector having the direction of $d\mathbf{T}/dt$, (15.47) becomes

$$\frac{d\mathbf{T}}{dt} = \kappa v \mathbf{N}. \tag{15.48}$$

Since $\mathbf{N} = d\mathbf{T}/d\theta$ when $d\theta/ds > 0$ and $\mathbf{N} = -(d\mathbf{T}/d\theta)$ when $(d\theta/ds) < 0$, it follows that **N** is directed toward the concave side of the curve. (We assume that $v = ds/dt > 0$.)

We now obtain the acceleration vector **A** by applying Theorem 15-IV to

$$\mathbf{V} = v\mathbf{T}.$$

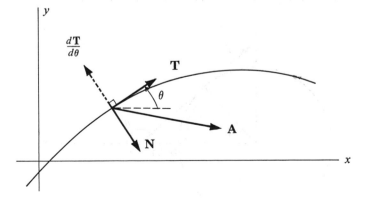

Figure 15.31

This yields

$$\mathbf{A} = \frac{d\mathbf{V}}{dt} = v\frac{d\mathbf{T}}{dt} + \frac{dv}{dt}\mathbf{T}.$$

Replacing $d\mathbf{T}/dt$ by its value in (15.48), we obtain

$$\mathbf{A} = \frac{dv}{dt}\mathbf{T} + v^2\kappa\mathbf{N}. \tag{15.49}$$

Thus $\mathbf{A}$ is directed toward the concave side of the path, has tangential component $dv/dt = d^2s/dt^2$, and normal component $v^2\kappa$.

It is often convenient to employ

$$dv/dt = \mathbf{A}\cdot\mathbf{T} \text{ and } v^2\kappa = \mathbf{A}\cdot\mathbf{N} = |\mathbf{A} - (\mathbf{A}\cdot\mathbf{T})\mathbf{T}|.$$

15.15   Curvature Formula

To obtain a formula for the curvature κ, we differentiate

$$\tan\theta = \frac{dy}{dx}$$

implicitly with respect to s. This yields

$$(\sec^2\theta)\frac{d\theta}{ds} = \frac{d^2y}{dx^2}\frac{dx}{ds}.$$

Therefore

$$\kappa = \left|\frac{d\theta}{ds}\right| = \frac{|d^2y/dx^2|}{(1 + \tan^2\theta)(ds/dx)}$$

or, by (8.11) of Sec. 8.3,

$$\kappa = \frac{|d^2y/dx^2|}{[1 + (dy/dx)^2]^{3/2}}. \tag{15.50}$$

If the curve in question is a straight line, θ does not change with s and hence $d\theta/ds = 0$. Thus, a straight line has curvature 0 at every point.

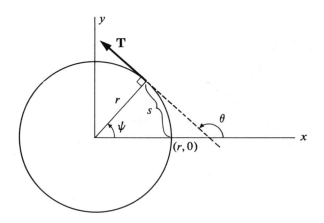

Figure 15.32

To find the curvature of a circle, let the circle have equation $x^2 + y^2 = r^2$. See Fig. 15.32.

From $s = r\psi$, we obtain $\psi = s/r$ and $d\psi/ds = 1/r$. But $d\theta/ds = d\psi/ds = 1/r = \kappa$, since θ and ψ differ by the constant $\pi/2$. Therefore, the curvature of a circle is constant and is equal to the reciprocal of the radius.

If P is a point on an arbitrary curve and κ is the curvature at P, then $\rho = 1/\kappa$ is called the radius of curvature at P. The circle of radius ρ, tangent to the curve at P and with center on the concave side of the curve, is called the circle of curvature at P. The circle of curvature and the curve have the same curvature κ at P. The circle is called the osculating circle and its center is called the center of curvature.

Example 1. Find the curvature of the parabola $y = x^2$ at $(0, 0)$.

Solution. Substituting $dy/dx = 2x$ and $d^2y/dx^2 = 2$ into (15.50), we obtain

$$\kappa = \frac{2}{[1 + 4x^2]^{3/2}}.$$

At $x = 0$, $\kappa = 2$ radians per unit of arc. It is seen by inspection that the curvature of the parabola is maximum at its vertex $(0, 0)$.

15.16   *Space Curves*

By a space curve or a curve in three dimensions we mean a set of points whose coordinates may be represented parametrically by three equations of the form

$$x = x(t), \qquad y = y(t), \qquad z = z(t). \tag{15.51}$$

The parameter t varies over an interval $t_1 \leqslant t \leqslant t_2$ and the functions defined by (15.51) are assumed to be continuous functions of t over this interval. Equations (15.51) are called parametric equations of the curve. The two equations $x = x(t)$ and $y = y(t)$ are parametric equations of the projection of the space curve in the xy-plane. The equation $z = z(t)$ gives the height of the space curve above or below its projection in the xy-plane.

A straight line is a special case of a space curve, since equations (15.31) to (15.33) are of the form (15.51).

A space curve may also be represented by two equations, the curve being the intersection of the two surfaces represented by the equations.

Example 1. Find parametric equations for the space curve which is the first-octant intersection of the sphere $x^2 + y^2 + z^2 = 1$ and the parabolic cylinder $z = y^2$.

Solution. Replacing y^2 by z in the equation of the sphere and solving for x we obtain $x = \sqrt{1 - z - z^2}$. This equation, together with the equations $y = \sqrt{z}$ and $z = z$, yields a parametric representation of the space curve, with z serving as the parameter. The curve extends from

$$(1, 0, 0) \text{ to } \left(0, \sqrt{\frac{\sqrt{5} - 1}{2}}, \frac{\sqrt{5} - 1}{2}\right)$$

and the parametric interval consists of all values of z satisfying $0 \leqslant z \leqslant$ $(1/2)(\sqrt{5} - 1)$. The value $z = (1/2)(\sqrt{5} - 1)$ is obtained by finding the intersection of the circle $y^2 + z^2 = 1$ and the parabola $z = y^2$ in the yz-plane. See Fig. 15.33.

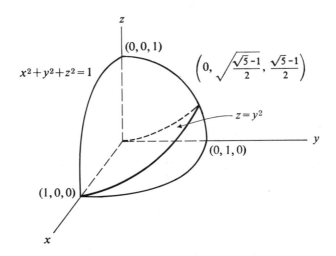

Figure 15.33

Formula (12.3) is easily extended to obtain the following formula defining the length of a space curve defined on the interval $t_1 \leqslant t \leqslant t_2$.

$$L = \int_{t_1}^{t_2} \sqrt{\left(\frac{dx}{dt}\right)^2 + \left(\frac{dy}{dt}\right)^2 + \left(\frac{dz}{dt}\right)^2}\, dt. \tag{15.52}$$

Example 2.   Find the length of the space curve $x = 3t$, $y = 3t^2$, $z = 2t^3$ from $(0, 0, 0)$ to $(3, 3, 2)$.

Solution.   The arc in question corresponds to the parametric interval $0 \leqslant t \leqslant 1$. By (15.52)

$$L = \int_0^1 \sqrt{(3)^2 + (6t)^2 + (6t^2)^2}\, dt$$

$$= 3 \int_0^1 (1 + 2t^2)\, dt = 5 \text{ units.}$$

• 15.17   Curvilinear Motion in Three Dimensions

In this section we assume that the parameter t in (15.51) denotes time and that the functions defined by (15.51) possess continuous first and second derivatives.

The vector $\mathbf{R} = x(t)\mathbf{i} + y(t)\mathbf{j} + z(t)\mathbf{k}$ is called the position vector of a point $P(x, y, z)$ on the space curve. The vectors $\mathbf{V} = (dx/dt)\,\mathbf{i} + (dy/dt)\,\mathbf{j} + (dz/dt)\,\mathbf{k}$, and $\mathbf{A} = (d^2x/dt^2)\mathbf{i} + (d^2y/dt^2)\mathbf{j} + (d^2z/dt^2)\mathbf{k}$ are called the velocity and acceleration vectors of P.

The length of **V** is given by

$$|\mathbf{V}| = v = \sqrt{(dx/dt)^2 + (dy/dt)^2 + (dz/dt)^2} = ds/dt, \qquad \textbf{(15.53)}$$

where, as in our treatment in two dimensions, we assume that $ds/dt > 0$.

Since $\mathbf{V} = d\mathbf{R}/dt$, the direction of **V** at P is the limiting direction of the vector

$$\frac{\Delta \mathbf{R}}{\Delta t} = \left(\frac{\Delta x}{\Delta t}\right)\mathbf{i} + \left(\frac{\Delta y}{\Delta t}\right)\mathbf{j} + \left(\frac{\Delta z}{\Delta t}\right)\mathbf{k} \qquad \text{as } \Delta t \to 0,$$

providing dx/dt, dy/dt, and dz/dt are not all zero at P, in which case **V** is the zero vector. The direction of the tangent at P is defined to be the direction of **V**, provided **V** is not the zero vector.

If **V** is written in the form $\mathbf{V} = v\mathbf{T}$, where **T** is the unit tangent vector, it is easy to show that **A** lies in the plane determined by **T** and $d\mathbf{T}/dt$, which is perpendicular to **T**. This plane is known as the osculating plane at P.

Example 1.   The point P, initially at $(a, 0, 0)$ on the right-circular cylinder $x^2 + y^2 = a^2$, moves upward on the cylinder at $b = dz/dt$ units per second. Find **R**, **V**, and **A** for P if the cylinder rotates on the z-axis at $\omega = d\theta/dt$ radians per second.

Solution.   The point P, which moves on the circular helix shown in Fig. 15.34, has

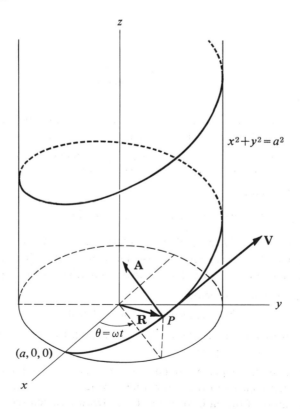

$x^2 + y^2 = a^2$

$\theta = \omega t$

$(a, 0, 0)$

Figure 15.34

$$\mathbf{R} = (a \cos \omega t)\mathbf{i} + (a \sin \omega t)\mathbf{j} + (bt)\mathbf{k},$$
$$\mathbf{V} = (-a\omega \sin \omega t)\mathbf{i} + (a\omega \cos \omega t)\mathbf{j} + b\mathbf{k},$$

and

$$\mathbf{A} = (-a\omega^2 \cos \omega t)\mathbf{i} + (-a\omega^2 \sin \omega t)\mathbf{j}.$$

As t increases, P moves upward along the helix. By writing $\mathbf{A}$ in the form $\mathbf{A} = -\omega^2[(a \cos \omega t)\mathbf{i} + (a \sin \omega t)\mathbf{j}]$ and comparing its components with the x- and y-components of $\mathbf{R}$, it is easy to see that $\mathbf{A}$ is always directed toward the z-axis.

PROBLEM LIST 90

1. In each of the following, a point P moves along the given plane curve. Sketch the curve and draw the vectors $\mathbf{R}$, $\mathbf{V}$, and $\mathbf{A}$ associated with P at the given time t.

    (a) $x = 4t,\ y = 2t^2;\ t = 2$.

    (b) $x = 2t,\ y = 4t^2;\ t = 1$.

    (c) $x = 2t,\ y = 4(1 - t^2);\ t = 1$.

    (d) $x = t/2,\ y = t^3/8;\ t = 2$.

    (e) $x = t^2,\ y = t^3;\ t = 3$.

    (f) $x = \cos t,\ y = \sin t;\ t = \pi/6$.

    (g) $x = \sin t,\ y = \cos t;\ t = 0$.

    (h) $x = a \cos t,\ y = b \sin t;\ t = \pi/4$.

    (i) $x = t,\ y = \sin t;\ t = \pi/2$.

2. Point P, moving on a plane curve, has position vector $\mathbf{R} = (t^2 - t)\mathbf{i} + 3t\mathbf{j}$. Find the speed and direction of P when $t = 2$. Also find the position vector of P when the speed is a minimum.

3. Point P moves along the curve $xy = 9$ with $dx/dt \equiv 3$ units per second. If P is at $(3, 3)$ when $t = 0$, draw a sketch showing $\mathbf{R}$, $\mathbf{V}$, and $\mathbf{A}$ at $t = 2$ sec.

4. A point P moves around a circle at constant speed. Show that $\mathbf{V}$ is always perpendicular to $\mathbf{R}$ and that $\mathbf{A}$ is always perpendicular to $\mathbf{V}$.

5. A projectile has position vector

    $$\mathbf{R} = [(v_0 \cos \alpha)t]\mathbf{i} + \left[-\frac{gt^2}{2} + (v_0 \sin \alpha)t\right]\mathbf{j}.$$

    Determine the value of t (other than $t = 0$), called the time of flight, at which the y-component of $\mathbf{R}$ is zero. Find the x-component of $\mathbf{R}$, called the range, corresponding to this value of t. Also find the maximum height assumed by the projectile.

6. A projectile has position vector

    $$\mathbf{R} = (240t)\mathbf{i} + (-16t^2 + 320t)\mathbf{j}.$$

    Find the velocity and acceleration of the projectile (a) at $t = 2$ sec, (b) when the projectile is at its highest point.

7. Point P moves in the xy-plane with position vector $\mathbf{R} = t\mathbf{i} + t^2\mathbf{j}$. Find the tangential and normal components of the acceleration $\mathbf{A}$ when $t = 1$. What is the speed of P and the curvature of the path when $t = 1$ sec? Draw a sketch showing $\mathbf{R}$, $\mathbf{V}$, and $\mathbf{A}$ at $t = 1$.

8. Point P has position vector

$$\mathbf{R} = (4\cos t)\mathbf{i} + (4\sin t)\mathbf{j}.$$

Find the speed and the tangential and normal components of the acceleration $\mathbf{A}$ when $t = \pi/6$ seconds.

9. Point P has position vector

$$\mathbf{R} = (3\cos t)\mathbf{i} + (2\sin t)\mathbf{j}.$$

Find the tangential and normal components of the acceleration $\mathbf{A}$ when $t = \pi/2$ seconds. Illustrate graphically.

10. What is the curvature of the circle $x^2 + y^2 = 9$?

11. Find the curvature of the parabola $y = x^2$ at the point $(1, 1)$.

12. Find the points on the ellipse $(x^2/a^2) + (y^2/b^2) = 1$ where the curvature is **(a)** a minimum, **(b)** a maximum.

13. Find the maximum curvature of $y = e^x$ and determine the point on the curve where this maximum occurs.

14. Find the curvature of the curve $x = 3t$, $y = t^2$ at the point where $t = 1$.

15. In each of the following, a point P moves along the given space curve. Sketch the curve for $0 \leqslant t \leqslant 2$ and draw the vectors $\mathbf{R}$, $\mathbf{V}$, and $\mathbf{A}$ associated with P at the given time t.

    (a) $x = t$, $y = 2t$, $z = 3t$; $t = 1$.

    (b) $x = t$, $y = t^2$, $z = t^3$; $t = 1$.

    (c) $x = t$, $y = 1 - t$, $z = t^3/3$; $t = 2$.

    (d) $x = \cos t$, $y = \sin t$, $z = t/\pi$; $t = \pi/4$.

16. Find parametric equations of the first-octant intersection of the sphere $x^2 + y^2 + z^2 = 1$ and the right-circular cylinder $(x - 1)^2 + y^2 = 1$. Illustrate graphically.

17. Find parametric equations of the intersection of the plane $z = y$ and the paraboloid $z = x^2 + y^2$. Illustrate graphically.

18. Find equations of the line tangent to the space curve $x = 2t$, $y = 4t^2$, $z = t^3 - t$ at $(2, 4, 0)$.

19. Find an equation of the plane perpendicular to the space curve $x = t^2$, $y = 3t^2$, $z = t^3 + t^2$ at $(1, 3, 2)$.

20. Point P moves along the curve $x = 4\cos t$, $y = 6\sin t$, $z = 2t$. Find the speed and velocity of P at $t = \pi/4$ seconds.

21. Find the length of the circular helix $x = a\cos \omega t$, $y = a\sin \omega t$, $z = bt$ between $(a, 0, 0)$ and $(-a, 0, b\pi/\omega)$.

22. Find the length of the curve $x = t^2$, $y = t$, $z = 2t^3/3$ between $(0, 0, 0)$ and $(1, 1, 2/3)$.

23. Show that if a point P moves along a space curve at constant speed, the velocity and acceleration vectors of P are perpendicular.

24. Let $\mathbf{R} = r\mathbf{L}$ be the position vector of a point P moving along a plane curve, r denoting the length of $\mathbf{R}$ and $\mathbf{L}$ being a unit vector. Show that

$$\mathbf{V} = \frac{dr}{dt}\mathbf{L} + r\frac{d\theta}{dt}\mathbf{M} \qquad \text{where} \qquad \mathbf{M} = \frac{d\mathbf{L}}{d\theta}.$$

See Fig. 15.35. The components dr/dt and $r\,d\theta/dt$ are known as the radial and transverse components of the velocity of P. Show also that

$$\mathbf{A} = \left[\frac{d^2r}{dt^2} - r\left(\frac{d\theta}{dt}\right)^2\right]\mathbf{L} + \left[r\frac{d^2\theta}{dt^2} + 2\frac{dr}{dt}\frac{d\theta}{dt}\right]\mathbf{M}.$$

These expressions for $\mathbf{V}$ and $\mathbf{A}$ are particularly useful when the path of P is an equation in polar coordinates of the form $r = f(\theta)$.

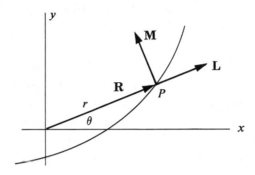

Figure 15.35

REFERENCES

15.1 L. BRAND, *Vectorial Mechanics*, John Wiley, New York, 1930.

15.2 H. LASS, *Vector and Tensor Analysis*, McGraw-Hill, New York, 1950.

Chapter

16

Functions of two

or more variables

16.1 Definitions

A real-valued function of two real variables, defined by the expression $z = f(x, y)$, is a correspondence between a set D of ordered pairs (x, y) of real numbers and a set R of real numbers, having the property that to each number pair (x, y) in D there corresponds one and only one element in R. The set D is called the domain of the function and the set R the range of the function. If the domain D of f is not stated or implied, it is understood that D consists of all pairs (x, y) for which $f(x, y)$ is a real number.

Example 1. The domain D of the function defined by $z = f(x, y)$ $= \sqrt{1 - x^2 - y^2}$ consists of all pairs (x, y) satisfying $x^2 + y^2 \leqslant 1$, and the range R of f consists of the interval $0 \leqslant z \leqslant 1$.

Example 2. The domain of the function defined by $V = \pi r^2 h$ consists of all possible pairs (r, h) of real numbers, and the range consists of all possible real numbers. However, if it is understood that V denotes the volume of a right-circular cylinder of height h and base radius r, then r, h, and V are restricted to positive values.

Geometrically, it is convenient to interpret the domain D of a function defined by $z = f(x, y)$ as a set of points in the xy-plane, the number pair (x_0, y_0) corresponding to the point having rectangular coordinates x_0 and y_0. The set of points (x, y, z) whose coordinates satisfy $z = f(x, y)$, where (x, y) is a pair in D, is called the graph of the function. •

The graph of the function defined by $z = \sqrt{1 - x^2 - y^2}$ consists of all points on the hemisphere (and its boundary) shown in Fig. 16.1. The domain D consists of all points on and inside the circle $x^2 + y^2 = 1$.

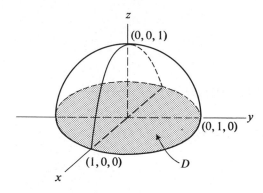

Figure 16.1

The definition of a real-valued function of three real variables, defined by the expression $u = f(x, y, z)$, is the same as that of a function of two variables except that the domain D consists of ordered triples (x, y, z) rather than ordered pairs. The domain D can be interpreted as a set of points in three-space, but no simple geometric interpretation of the value of the function is available.

Example 3.   The volume $V = lwh$ of a rectangular box is a function of its dimensions l, w, and h.

The extension to more than three independent variables follows readily. The domain D of a function of n variables, which is defined by the expression $u = f(x_1, x_2, \cdots, x_n)$, consists of a set of ordered n-tuples $(x_1, x_2, \cdots, x_n)$ of real numbers.

16.2   Limit of a Function of Two Variables

Let $P_0(x_0, y_0)$ be a fixed number pair, conveniently referred to as a point, and let $P(x, y)$ be any point other than P_0 in the domain D of the function defined by $z = f(x, y)$. Although the point P_0 may or may not be in D, it is assumed that every circle in the xy-plane, having center at P_0, contains at least one point of D other than P_0. The function f is said to approach the limit L as P approaches P_0, provided $|f(x, y) - L|$ can be made arbitrarily small by keeping P sufficiently close to P_0. More specifically, let ϵ be an arbitrary positive number. If there exists a positive number δ such that

$$|f(x, y) - L| < \epsilon$$

whenever

$$0 < \sqrt{(x - x_0)^2 + (y - y_0)^2} < \delta,$$

then

$$\lim_{(x,y)\to(x_0,y_0)} f(x, y) = L. \qquad (16.1)$$

Geometrically, the definition states that it is possible to draw a circle with radius δ and center P_0 such that, for all points P in D and inside the circle (excepting P_0), the height of the graph of $z = f(x, y)$ differs from L in absolute value by less than ϵ. It is important to note in (16.1) that (x, y) is permitted to approach (x_0, y_0) in any manner whatsoever, except that (x, y) must not coincide with (x_0, y_0).

The function defined by $z = f(x, y)$ is said to be continuous at $P_0(x_0, y_0)$, provided

$$\lim_{(x,y)\to(x_0,y_0)} f(x, y) = f(x_0, y_0).$$

[Exception: If $P_0(x_0, y_0)$ is an isolated point of f, then f is continuous at P_0.]

Exsample 1.   The graph of

$$z = f(x, y) = \left(\frac{x^2 + y^2}{x^2 + y^2}\right)(x^2 + y^2 + 1)$$

consists of the points of the paraboloid $z = x^2 + x^2 + 1$ except for the point $(0, 0, 1)$. It is easy to see that

$$\lim_{(x, y)\to(0, 0)} f(x, y) = 1.$$

The function f is not defined at $(0, 0)$, and it is technically incorrect to say that a function is continuous or discontinuous at a point not belonging to its domain of definition. If we define $f(0, 0) = 1$, then f is continuous at $(0, 0)$; if we define $f(0, 0) = k \neq 1$, then f is discontinuous at $(0, 0)$.

———————

The definitions of limit and continuity are easily extended to functions of three or more variables. The distance d from $(x_1, x_2, \cdots, x_n)$ to $(a_1, a_2, \cdots, a_n)$ is defined by

$$d = \sqrt{(x_1 - a_1)^2 + (x_2 - a_2)^2 + \cdots + (x_n - a_n)^2}.$$

PROBLEM LIST 91

1.   Give the domain D and the range R of the functions defined by

(a) $z = x^2 + y^2$,

(b) $z = \sqrt{4 - x^2}$,

(c) $z = 4 - x^2 - y^2$,

(d) $z = \sqrt{xy}$,

(e) $z = \log(x + y)$,

(f) $z = \sin(x + 2y)$,

(g) $u = \sqrt{1 - x^2 - y^2 - z^2}$,

(h) $u = x\sqrt{4 - z^2 - y^2}$.

2.   Evaluate

(a) $\displaystyle\lim_{(x,y)\to(1, 2)} (x^2 + 2y^2)$;

(b) $\displaystyle\lim_{(x,y)\to(0, \pi/2)} (\sin x + \sin y)$;

(c) $\displaystyle\lim_{(x,y)\to(0,0)} \left[\frac{x(x^2 + y^2 + 3)}{x}\right]$.

3. Show that $z = \sqrt{1 - x^2 - y^2}$ defines a function which is continuous at $(0, 0)$.

4. Show that

$$\lim_{(x, y) \to (0, 0)} \frac{x^2 - y^2}{x^2 + y^2}$$

does not exist. *Hint.* Employ polar coordinates.

16.3   Partial Derivatives

Let $u = f(x_1, x_2, \cdots, x_n)$ define a function of n variables. If all the n variables except x_1 are fixed, u becomes a function of the one variable x_1. The derivative of u with respect to x_1, regarding $x_2, x_3, \cdots, x_n$ as fixed, is called the partial derivative of u with respect to x_1 and is denoted by $\partial u / \partial x_1$ or $\partial f / \partial x_1$. The symbol ∂ is a special form of the Greek delta and is employed to denote the process of partial differentiation.

If $z = f(x, y)$, then

$$\frac{\partial z}{\partial x} = \frac{\partial f}{\partial x} = \lim_{\Delta x \to 0} \frac{f(x + \Delta x, y) - f(x, y)}{\Delta x}$$

and

$$\frac{\partial z}{\partial y} = \frac{\partial f}{\partial y} = \lim_{\Delta y \to 0} \frac{f(x, y + \Delta y) - f(x, y)}{\Delta y}.$$

Example 1.   If $z = x^3 y^2 - 2xy + 4y^3$, then

$$\frac{\partial z}{\partial x} = 3x^2 y^2 - 2y$$

and

$$\frac{\partial z}{\partial y} = 2x^3 y - 2x + 12y^2.$$

Example 2.   If $u = xy^2 e^{xz}$, then

$$\frac{\partial u}{\partial x} = (xy^2)(ze^{xz}) + (e^{xz})(y^2) = y^2 e^{xz}(xz + 1),$$

$$\frac{\partial u}{\partial y} = 2xye^{xz},$$

and

$$\frac{\partial u}{\partial z} = x^2 y^2 e^{xz}.$$

Example 3.   The symbol $(\partial z / \partial x)_{(x_0, y_0)}$ denotes the value of $\partial z / \partial x$ when $x = x_0$ and $y = y_0$.

For example, if $z = x^2 y^2 + 3x^4$, then

$$\frac{\partial z}{\partial x} = 2xy^2 + 12x^3$$

and

$$\left(\frac{\partial z}{\partial x}\right)_{(1, 2)} - 8 \mid 12 - 20.$$

Example 4.   Find $\partial z/\partial x$ and $\partial z/\partial y$ for any function z of x and y defined implicitly by the equation

$$9x^2 + 4y^2 + 36z^2 - 36 = 0.$$

Solution.   With y fixed, any function denoted by $z = f(x, y)$ and defined by the equation becomes a function of x alone. Differentiating implicitly with respect to x, we obtain

$$18x + 72z\frac{\partial z}{\partial x} = 0$$

or

$$\frac{\partial z}{\partial x} = \frac{-x}{4z}.$$

Similarly, differentiation with respect to y yields

$$8y + 72z\frac{\partial z}{\partial y} = 0$$

or

$$\frac{\partial z}{\partial y} = \frac{-y}{9z}.$$

For a function of two variables, denoted by $z = f(x, y)$, the partial derivatives have a simple geometric interpretation. The equation $z = f(x, y_0)$ represents the

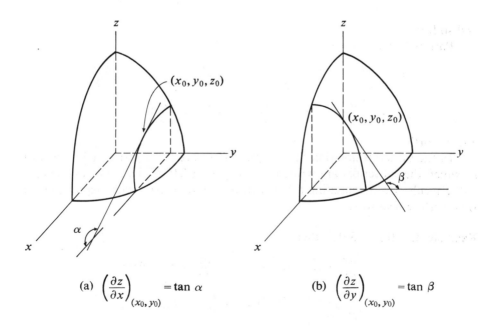

$$\text{(a)} \left(\frac{\partial z}{\partial x}\right)_{(x_0, y_0)} = \tan \alpha \qquad\qquad \text{(b)} \left(\frac{\partial z}{\partial y}\right)_{(x_0, y_0)} = \tan \beta$$

Figure 16.2

curve which is the intersection of the surface $z = f(x, y)$ and the plane $y = y_0$. Thus $\partial z/\partial x$ represents the slope of this curve at an arbitrary point (x, y_0, z) and $(\partial z/\partial x)_{(x_0, y_0)}$ represents the slope of the curve at (x_0, y_0, z_0). Similarly, $(\partial z/\partial y)_{(x_0, y_0)}$ represents the slope of the intersection of $z = f(x, y)$ and the plane $x = x_0$ at (x_0, y_0, z_0). See Fig. 16.2.

16.4 Partial Derivatives of Higher Order

If the function f defined by $z = f(x, y)$ possesses partial derivatives with respect to x and y, these partial derivatives define functions of x and y. Continued partial differentiation gives rise to partial derivatives of higher order. The following notations are employed:

$$\frac{\partial}{\partial x}\left(\frac{\partial f}{\partial x}\right) = \frac{\partial^2 f}{\partial x^2}, \qquad \frac{\partial}{\partial y}\left(\frac{\partial f}{\partial y}\right) = \frac{\partial^2 f}{\partial y^2},$$

$$\frac{\partial}{\partial y}\left(\frac{\partial f}{\partial x}\right) = \frac{\partial^2 f}{\partial y\,\partial x}, \qquad \frac{\partial}{\partial x}\left(\frac{\partial f}{\partial y}\right) = \frac{\partial^2 f}{\partial x\,\partial y}.$$

Similarly,

$$\frac{\partial}{\partial x}\left(\frac{\partial^2 f}{\partial x^2}\right) = \frac{\partial^3 f}{\partial x^3}, \qquad \frac{\partial}{\partial y}\left(\frac{\partial^2 f}{\partial x^2}\right) = \frac{\partial^3 f}{\partial y\,\partial x^2},$$

$$\frac{\partial}{\partial y}\left(\frac{\partial^2 f}{\partial y\,\partial x}\right) = \frac{\partial^3 f}{\partial y^2\,\partial x}, \qquad \frac{\partial}{\partial x}\left(\frac{\partial^2 f}{\partial y\,\partial x}\right) = \frac{\partial^3 f}{\partial x\,\partial y\,\partial x},$$

and so forth.

Partial derivatives are sometimes denoted by subscripts. Thus

$$f_x = \frac{\partial f}{\partial x}, \qquad f_y = \frac{\partial f}{\partial y}, \qquad f_{xx} = \frac{\partial^2 f}{\partial x^2}, \qquad f_{xy} = \frac{\partial^2 f}{\partial y\,\partial x},$$

$$f_{yx} = \frac{\partial^2 f}{\partial x\,\partial y}, \qquad f_{xxx} = \frac{\partial^3 f}{\partial x^3}, \qquad f_{xxy} = \frac{\partial^3 f}{\partial y\,\partial x^2},$$

and so forth.

In the subscript notation the differentiations are to be performed in the order in which the subscripts are written, reading from left to right. For example, f_{xxy} is the result of differentiating f first with respect to x, next with respect to x, and then with respect to y.

Example 1.   If $z = 3x^4 y^2$, then

$$\frac{\partial z}{\partial x} = z_x = 12x^3 y^2, \qquad \frac{\partial z}{\partial y} = z_y = 6x^4 y,$$

$$\frac{\partial^2 z}{\partial x^2} = z_{xx} = 36x^2 y^2, \qquad \frac{\partial^2 z}{\partial y^2} = z_{yy} = 6x^4,$$

$$\frac{\partial^2 z}{\partial y\,\partial x} = z_{xy} = 24x^3 y, \qquad \frac{\partial^2 z}{\partial x\,\partial y} = z_{yx} = 24x^3 y.$$

It is no accident that $z_{xy} = z_{yx}$. In Ref. 16.2 it is proved that if $z = f(x, y)$ together with f_x, f_y, f_{xy}, and f_{yx} are defined in some circle with center at (x_0, y_0), and if f_{xy} and f_{yx} are continuous at (x_0, y_0), then $f_{xy} = f_{yx}$ at (x_0, y_0).

Example 2. An equation involving partial derivatives is known as a *partial differential equation*. Show that the function defined by $z = x^3 - 3xy^2$ is a solution of the partial differential equation $z_{xx} + z_{yy} = 0$.

Solution. From $z_x = 3x^2 - 3y^2$, $z_y = -6xy$, $z_{xx} = 6x$, and $z_{yy} = -6x$, we obtain

$$z_{xx} + z_{yy} = (6x) + (-6x) = 0.$$

PROBLEM LIST 92

1. Find $\partial z/\partial x$ and $\partial z/\partial y$:

   (a) $z = x^2 - 2x^3 y^4$.   (d) $z = x^2 \sin xy$.

   (b) $z = 3xy^2 + 4xy^3 + 1$.   (e) $z = \cos x \cos y - \sin x \sin y$.

   (c) $z = x^2 y^2 e^{xy}$.   (f) $z = (x^2 + 2y^3)^4$.

2. Given $z = x^2 + 4y^2$, find

   $$\left(\frac{\partial z}{\partial x}\right)_{(1,2)} \quad \text{and} \quad \left(\frac{\partial z}{\partial y}\right)_{(1,2)}.$$

3. Find $\partial u/\partial x$, $\partial u/\partial y$, and $\partial u/\partial z$:

   (a) $u = 2x^2 y + 3xz^2$.

   (b) $u = \sqrt{xy} + yz^3$.

   (c) $u = xy^2 \sin x^2 z$.

   (d) $u = e^{xy} \sin 2y^2 z$.

4. Given $u = x^2 y + 3x^3 z^2 - 4y^2 z^3$, find

   $$\left(\frac{\partial u}{\partial x}\right)_{(1,2,3)}, \quad \left(\frac{\partial u}{\partial y}\right)_{(1,2,3)}, \quad \left(\frac{\partial u}{\partial z}\right)_{(1,2,3)}.$$

5. Given $z = 3x^3 y^2 - 4x^2 y^4$, evaluate

   (a) $\dfrac{\partial^2 z}{\partial x^2}$;   (c) $\dfrac{\partial^2 z}{\partial y \, \partial x}$;

   (b) $\dfrac{\partial^2 z}{\partial y^2}$;   (d) $\dfrac{\partial^3 z}{\partial x^3}$.

6. For the function defined by $z = 4x^3 y^2 - 5x^2 y^5$, verify that $z_{xy} = z_{yx}$.

7. Find x_r, y_r, x_θ, and y_θ, given $x = r \cos \theta$ and $y = r \sin \theta$.

8. Find the slope of the parabola $z = x^2 + 3y^2$, $y = 1$ at the point $(2, 1, 7)$. Also find equations of the line tangent to the parabola at the same point.

9. Verify that the function defined by $z = \text{Tan}^{-1}(y/x)$ is a solution of the partial differential equation $z_{xx} + z_{yy} = 0$.

10. Verify that the function defined by $u = r^n \cos n\theta$ satisfies the partial differential equation $u_{rr} - r^{-2} u_{\theta\theta} - r^{-1} u_r = 0$ for all values of n.

11. Verify that the function defined by $u = e^{x+at}$ satisfies the wave equation $a^2 u_{xx} = u_t$.

12. Show that for the function defined by $z = \sqrt{x} + x^2 y^3$, $(z_{xy})_{(0,0)} \neq (z_{yx})_{(0,0)}$.

13. Find z_x and z_y by implicit differentiation:

(a) $x^2 + y^2 + z^2 - 4 = 0$.　　　　　　(d) $z - x^2 - 4y^2 = 0$.

(b) $4x^2 + 9y^2 + 4z^2 - 36 = 0$.　　　　(e) $x^3 + y^3 + z^3 - 3xyz = 12$.

(c) $9x^2 + 4y^2 - 36z^2 = 0$.　　　　　　(f) $(x^2 + y^2 + z^2)^3 - 27z^2 = 0$.

14. The manufacture of p pounds of a certain product requires x pounds of one ingredient and y pounds of a second ingredient. The function f given by $p = f(x, y)$ is known as the production function for the product. The partial derivatives $\partial f/\partial x$ and $\partial f/\partial y$ are termed the marginal products of the ingredients x and y, respectively. If f is given by $p = 36x^{1/3}y^{2/3}$, find the marginal product of x and the marginal product of y when $x = 8000$ and $y = 27,000$. (*Remark.* These concepts are readily extended to functions of more than two variables.)

16.5　A Differentiable Function of Two Variables

Let $z = f(x, y)$ define a continuous function f for which f_x and f_y are also continuous. If the variables x and y are given increments Δx and Δy, the corresponding change, Δz, in the value of the function is given by

$$\Delta z = f(x + \Delta x, y + \Delta y) - f(x, y).$$

This expression for Δz can also be written in the form

$$\Delta z = [f(x + \Delta x, y + \Delta y) - f(x, y + \Delta y)]$$
$$+ [f(x, y + \Delta y) - f(x, y)].$$

Since the quantity in the first brackets involves a change in x only, we apply the form of the mean-value theorem given in Problem 9 of Sec. 4.5 to obtain

$$f_x(x + \theta_1 \Delta x, y + \Delta y) \Delta x,$$

where $0 < \theta_1 < 1$.

Similarly, the quantity in the second brackets involves a change in y only and can be written in the form

$$f_y(x, y + \theta_2 \Delta y) \Delta y,$$

where $0 < \theta_2 < 1$.

Since f_x is continuous,

$$f_x(x + \theta_1 \Delta x, y + \Delta y) = f_x(x, y) + \epsilon_1,$$

where $\epsilon_1 \to 0$ as Δx and $\Delta y \to 0$.

Similarly, due to the continuity of f_y,

$$f_y(x, y + \theta_2 \Delta y) = f_y(x, y) + \epsilon_2,$$

where $\epsilon_2 \to 0$ as Δx and $\Delta y \to 0$.

The expression for Δz now becomes

$$\Delta z = [f_x(x, y) + \epsilon_1] \Delta x + [f_y(x, y) + \epsilon_2] \Delta y$$

or

$$\Delta z = f_x \, \Delta x + f_y \, \Delta y + \epsilon_1 \, \Delta x + \epsilon_2 \, \Delta y \tag{16.2}$$

where ϵ_1 and ϵ_2 approach zero as Δx and Δy approach zero.

If Δz for $z = f(x, y)$ can be written in the form (16.2), where ϵ_1 and $\epsilon_2 \to 0$ as Δx and $\Delta y \to 0$, the function f is said to be differentiable at (x, y). Since (16.2) implies the existence of $f_x(x, y)$ and $f_y(x, y)$, a function f must possess partial derivatives f_x and f_y at a point in order to be differentiable at that point. This condition is necessary but not sufficient to insure differentiability. We have shown that the continuity of f, f_x, and f_y at (x, y) are sufficient to insure differentiability at (x, y). In the case of a function f of a single variable x, the function is differentiable at x if $f'(x)$ exists; no further condition is required.

16.6   The Differential of a Function of Two Variables

Let $z = f(x, y)$ define a differentiable function of x and y. The differential of the function is defined by

$$dz = f_x \, dx + f_y \, dy, \tag{16.3}$$

where dx and dy are arbitrary real numbers. Thus dz defines a function of the four variables x, y, dx, and dy.

If we interpret Δx as dx and Δy as dy in (16.2), the first two terms on the right become dz, and Δz becomes

$$\Delta z = dz + \epsilon_1 \, dx + \epsilon_2 \, dy.$$

It can now be shown (see Ref. 16.2) that

$$\lim_{|dx|+|dy| \to 0} \frac{\Delta z - dz}{|dx| + |dy|} = 0. \tag{16.4}$$

This means that $\Delta z - dz$ is small compared with dx and dy, even when the latter are themselves small. Consequently, dz yields an approximation to Δz, provided both dx and dy are small numerically. In the case of a differentiable function of one variable, defined by $y = f(x)$, dy was an approximation to Δy, provided $dx = \Delta x$ was small numerically.

Example 1.   Given $z = 3x^2 + y^3$, find dz when $x = 2$, $y = 3$, $dx = 0.2$, and $dy = -0.3$.

   Solution. $dz = 6x \, dx + 3y^2 \, dy$ and

$$dz \Big|_{\substack{x=2 \\ y=3 \\ dx=0.2 \\ dy=-0.3}} = 6(2)(0.2) + 3(3)^2(-0.3) = -5.7.$$

Example 2.   A right-circular cylinder has base radius $r = 2$ in. and height $h = 5$ in. Find the approximate change in the volume of the cylinder if r is increased by 0.3 in. and h decreased by 0.4 in.

Solution.   From $V = \pi r^2 h$, we obtain

$$\Delta V \cong dV = 2\pi r h \, dr + \pi r^2 \, dh.$$

Hence

$$dV \Big|_{\substack{r=2 \\ h=5 \\ dr=0.3 \\ dh=-0.4}} = 2\pi(2)(5)(0.3) + \pi(2)^2(-0.4) = 4.4\pi.$$

The volume will increase by approximately 4.4π cubic inches.

Example 3.   Find the approximate maximum relative error in the value of the fraction $z = x/y$ if the maximum relative error in measuring x is 2% and the maximum relative error in measuring y is 3%.

Solution.   From $z = x/y$ we obtain

$$\Delta z \cong dz = \frac{1}{y} \, dx - \frac{x}{y^2} \, dy.$$

Thus

$$\frac{dz}{z} = \frac{dx}{x} - \frac{dy}{y}$$

and

$$\left| \frac{dz}{z} \right| \leqslant \left| \frac{dx}{x} \right| + \left| \frac{dy}{y} \right|.$$

Thus the value of the fraction may be in error by as much as 5%. This situation would prevail when

$$\left| \frac{dx}{x} \right| = 0.02, \qquad \left| \frac{dy}{y} \right| = 0.03,$$

and dx/x and dy/y had opposite signs.

The results of this section can be extended to functions of more than two variables. For example, if $u = F(x, y, z)$, then

$$du = F_x \, dx + F_y \, dy + F_z \, dz \tag{16.5}$$

and F is said to be differentiable at (x, y, z) if $\Delta u = F(x + \Delta x, y + \Delta y, z + \Delta z) - F(x, y, z)$ can be written in the form

$$\Delta u = F_x \, \Delta x + F_y \, \Delta y + F_z \, \Delta z + \epsilon_1 \, \Delta x + \epsilon_2 \, \Delta y + \epsilon_3 \, \Delta z, \tag{16.6}$$

where ϵ_1, ϵ_2, and ϵ_3 approach zero as Δx, Δy, and Δz approach zero.

Formulas such as (16.5) hold even if the variables x, y, and z define functions of other variables. A proof of this result, which is a generalization of Theorem 3-IX, is given in Ref. 16.2.

PROBLEM LIST 93

1. Find dz:

   (a) $z = 3x^2 + x^3$.

   (b) $z = x^3 - 3xy + y^3$.

   (c) $z = 2x^4 + xy^2 - 4$.

   (d) $z = 3 \sin x - 4 \cos y$.

   (e) $z = x \cos y - y^2 \cos 2x$.

   (f) $z = e^{xy} \cos x$.

(g) $z = \cos^2 xy - \sin^2 xy$.   (i) $z = y^2 - \log xy$.

(h) $z = \cos^2 x + x^2 y$.   (j) $z = x \operatorname{Tan}^{-1}(x^2 y^2)$..

2. Given $z = x^2 + 2y^3$, find dz when $x = 1$, $y = 2$, $dx = -0.3$, and $dy = 0.2$.

3. Given $z = x^2 + xy + y^2$, find dz when $x = -2$, $y = 1$, $dx = 0.3$, and $dy = 0.2$.

4. Given $z = e^x \cos y$, find dz when $x = 0$, $y = \pi/6$, $dx = 0.04$, and $dy = -0.03$.

5. Given $z = x^2 + y^3$, find Δz, dz, and $\Delta z - dz$ when $x = 2$, $y = 1$, $dx = \Delta x = 0.03$, and $dy = \Delta y = 0.05$.

6. A right-circular cylinder has base radius $r = 3$ in. and height $h = 10$ in. Find the approximate change in the volume of the cylinder if r is increased by 0.2 in. and h is increased by 0.3 in.

7. Find the approximate amount of metal required to make a rectangular box (including the top) if the inside dimensions are 5 in. by 7 in. by 4 in., and the sides are 1/16 in. thick.

8. Find the approximate maximum relative error in the value of the product $P = xy$ if the maximum relative error in measuring x is 3% and the maximum relative error in measuring y is 2%.

9. Approximate $(3.002)^4(4.999)^3$ by employing the function defined by $z = x^4 y^3$.

10. A rectangular box has inside dimensions of 4.03 in., 6.02 in., and 4.97 in. Find the approximate length of the inside diagonal of the box.

11. A triangle has sides $x = 8.02$ and $y = 4.99$ and included angle 61 deg. Find (a) the approximate area of the triangle, (b) the approximate length of the third side.

12. Let $f(x, y) = xy/(x^2 + y^2)$ when x and y are not both zero and let $f(0, 0) = 0$. Show that f is discontinuous at $(0, 0)$.

16.7   Plane Tangent to a Surface

In Fig. 16.3, P_0 is a fixed point of a surface, P an arbitrary point of the surface distinct from P_0, π a fixed plane through P_0, and θ the angle between plane π and line segment P_0P. Plane π is defined as the tangent plane to the surface at P_0 if and only if θ approaches zero as P approaches P_0. The manner of approach is irrelevant except that P must not coincide with P_0.

Now let $z = f(x, y)$ be an equation of a surface and let $P_0(x_0, y_0, z_0)$ be a fixed point of the surface $[z_0 = f(x_0, y_0)]$. Assume that the partial derivatives $f_x(x_0, y_0)$ and $f_y(x_0, y_0)$ of $f(x, y)$ exist. Since the planes $x = x_0$ and $y = y_0$ cut the surface in curves having slopes $f_y(x_0, y_0)$ and $f_x(x_0, y_0)$ at P_0, it follows that $\theta_1 \to 0$ as $P \to P_0$ in the plane $x = x_0$ shown in Fig. 16.4 and that $\theta_2 \to 0$ as $P \to P_0$ in the plane $y = y_0$ shown in Fig. 16.5. Hence, if the surface has a tangent plane at P_0, it must be the plane determined by vectors $\mathbf{A}$ and $\mathbf{B}$ of Fig. 16.4 and Fig. 16.5.

The existence of $f_x(x_0, y_0)$ and $f_y(x_0, y_0)$ is not sufficient to guarantee that the surface $z = f(x, y)$ has a tangent plane at P_0. It is not to be expected that the behavior of $f(x, y)$ in the planes $x = x_0$ and $y = y_0$ will determine the behavior of $f(x, y)$ in another plane such as $y - y_0 = x - x_0$. However, if f is differentiable

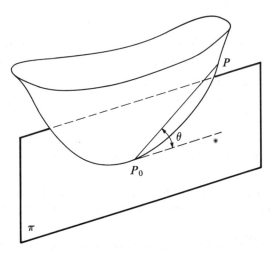

Figure 16.3

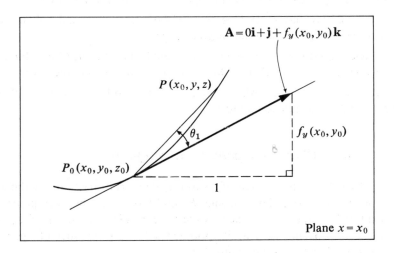

Figure 16.4

at a point where the partial derivatives exist, then the surface has a tangent plane at the point. This fact is proved in Ref. 16.2. We assume that f is differentiable at P_0.

A vector $\mathbf{N}$ perpendicular to both $\mathbf{A}$ and $\mathbf{B}$ is given (in determinant notation) by

$$\mathbf{N} = \mathbf{A} \times \mathbf{B} = \begin{vmatrix} \mathbf{i} & \mathbf{j} & \mathbf{k} \\ 0 & 1 & f_y(x_0, y_0) \\ 1 & 0 & f_x(x_0, y_0) \end{vmatrix}$$
$$= f_x(x_0, y_0)\mathbf{i} + f_y(x_0, y_0)\mathbf{j} - \mathbf{k}.$$

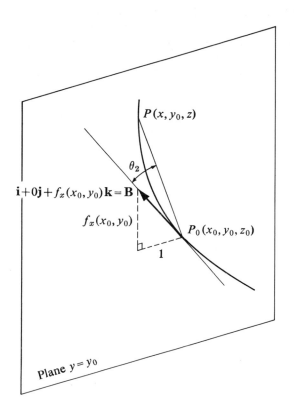

Figure 16.5

The vector $\mathbf{N}$ is also said to be normal to the surface $z = f(x, y)$ at P_0. By equations (15.27) and (15.28) the tangent plane at P_0 has equation

$$\mathbf{N} \cdot (\mathbf{P} - \mathbf{P}_0) = 0 \qquad (16.7)$$

or

$$f_x(x_0, y_0)(x - x_0) + f_y(x_0, y_0)(y - y_0) - (z - z_0) = 0. \qquad (16.8)$$

By equations (15.30) and (15.37) the line through P_0 perpendicular to the tangent plane has equation

$$\mathbf{P} = \mathbf{P}_0 + t\mathbf{N} \qquad (16.9)$$

or [when neither $f_x(x_0, y_0)$ nor $f_y(x_0, y_0)$ is zero]

$$\frac{x - x_0}{f_x(x_0, y_0)} = \frac{y - y_0}{f_y(x_0, y_0)} = \frac{z - z_0}{-1}. \qquad (16.10)$$

This line is also said to be perpendicular to the surface $z = f(x, y)$ at P_0 and is termed the normal line.

If we replace x by $x_0 + dx$ and y by $y_0 + dy$ in (16.8), we see that the height of the tangent plane at $(x_0 + dx, y_0 + dy)$ is given by $z_0 + dz$. Since the surface

$z = f(x, y)$ has height $f(x_0 + dx, \ y_0 + dy) = z_0 + \Delta z$ at $(x_0 + dx, \ y_0 + dy)$, the height of the tangent plane will be close to the height of the surface for small values of dx and dy. We say that the height of the tangent plane is a linear approximation of the height of the surface in the neighborhood of (x_0, y_0).

Example.   Find equations of the tangent plane and normal line for the surface $z = x^2 + 4y^2$ at $(3, 2, 25)$.

Solution.   From $z_x = 2x$ and $z_y = 8y$ we obtain $z_x(3, 2) = 6$ and $z_y(3, 2) = 16$. By (16.8) the tangent plane has equation

$$6(x - 3) + 16(y - 2) - (z - 25) = 0.$$

By (16.10) the normal line has equation

$$\frac{x - 3}{6} = \frac{y - 2}{16} = \frac{z - 25}{-1}.$$

PROBLEM LIST 94

1.   Find equations of the tangent plane and normal line for each surface at the specified point.

   (a) $z = x^2 + y^2$, at $(1, 2, 5)$.

   (b) $z = 4x^2 + 9y^2$, at $(2, -1, 25)$.

   (c) $z = x^2 - 4y^2$, at $(3, 0, 9)$.

   (d) $z = 4 - x^2 - y^2$, at $(1, 1, 2)$.

   (e) $z = xy$, at $(3, 4, 12)$.

   (f) $z = \sin xy$, at $(1, \pi/6, 1/2)$.

   (g) $xz + yz - xy = 1$, at $(1, 1, 1)$.

   (h) $z = ye^x$, at $(1, 2, 2e)$.

2.   Prove that every normal line to a sphere passes through the center of the sphere.

3.   Prove that all tetrahedrons formed by the coordinate planes and the planes tangent to $xyz = 1$ have the same volume.

4.   Find the z-intercept of the plane tangent to $x^2 + y^2 + z^2 = 9$ at $(1, 2, 2)$.

5.   Find the distance from $(3, -2, 1)$ to the plane tangent to $z = 4x^2 + y^2$ at $(1, 3, 13)$.

6.   Find the angle between the planes which are tangent to $z = x^3 + y^2$ at $(1, 2, 5)$ and $(1, 3, 10)$.

7.   Plane π is tangent to surface $z = x^2 + 3y^2$ at $(2, 1, 7)$. Find the height of the plane and the surface when $x = 2.01$ and $y = 1.02$.

8.   Find the angle between the normals to $z = xy$ and $z = x^2 + 5y^2 - 7$ at $(2, 1, 2)$.

9.   Show that the sum of the intercepts of the plane tangent to $\sqrt{x} + \sqrt{y} + \sqrt{z} = \sqrt{a}$ at any point is a.

10.   Two surfaces are said to intersect orthogonally if their normals are perpendicular at every point common to the two surfaces. Show that the surfaces $z = 16 - x^2 - y^2$ and $63z = x^2 + y^2$ intersect orthogonally.

11. Find an equation of the common tangent plane to $x^2 + y^2 + (z - 2)^2 = 1$ and $(x - 1)^2 + (y - 2)^2 + z^2 = 4$.

16.8   The Chain Rule for Functions of More Than One Variable

Let $u = f(x, y, z)$ define a differentiable function of x, y, and z and let $x = g(s, t)$, $y = h(s, t)$, and $z = k(s, t)$ define differentiable functions of s and t. Then u is a function of s and t through x, y, and z. We call x, y, and z the first-class variables and s and t the second-class variables.

If we fix s, then u becomes a function of t through x, y, and z. We now give t an increment (or decrement) $\Delta t \neq 0$, and the corresponding changes in x, y, and z are given by

$$\Delta x = g(s, t + \Delta t) - g(s, t);$$

$$\Delta y = h(s, t + \Delta t) - h(s, t);$$

$$\Delta z = k(s, t + \Delta t) - k(s, t).$$

We next write $\Delta u = f(x + \Delta x, y + \Delta y, z + \Delta z) - f(x, y, z)$ in the form (16.6) and divide by Δt to obtain

$$\frac{\Delta u}{\Delta t} = \frac{\partial f}{\partial x}\frac{\Delta x}{\Delta t} + \frac{\partial f}{\partial y}\frac{\Delta y}{\Delta t} + \frac{\partial f}{\partial z}\frac{\Delta z}{\Delta t} + \epsilon_1\frac{\Delta x}{\Delta t} + \epsilon_2\frac{\Delta y}{\Delta t} + \epsilon_3\frac{\Delta z}{\Delta t}.$$

As $\Delta t \to 0$, Δx, Δy, and $\Delta z \to 0$, and ϵ_1, ϵ_2, and $\epsilon_3 \to 0$, and we obtain

$$\frac{\partial u}{\partial t} = \frac{\partial f}{\partial x}\frac{\partial x}{\partial t} + \frac{\partial f}{\partial y}\frac{\partial y}{\partial t} + \frac{\partial f}{\partial z}\frac{\partial z}{\partial t}. \tag{16.11}$$

This equation can also be written as

$$\frac{\partial u}{\partial t} = \frac{\partial u}{\partial x}\frac{\partial x}{\partial t} + \frac{\partial u}{\partial y}\frac{\partial y}{\partial t} + \frac{\partial u}{\partial z}\frac{\partial z}{\partial t}, \tag{16.12}$$

but it must be remembered that in $\partial u/\partial t$, $u = f[g(s, t), h(s, t), k(s, t)]$ denotes a function of s and t, while in $\partial u/\partial x$, $\partial u/\partial y$, and $\partial u/\partial z$, $u = f(x, y, z)$ denotes a function of x, y, and z.

If t is fixed and s allowed to vary, the same procedure which led to (16.12) yields

$$\frac{\partial u}{\partial s} = \frac{\partial u}{\partial x}\frac{\partial x}{\partial s} + \frac{\partial u}{\partial y}\frac{\partial y}{\partial s} + \frac{\partial u}{\partial z}\frac{\partial z}{\partial s}. \tag{16.13}$$

Thus, with two second-class variables and three first-class variables, the chain rule yields two equations of three terms each. In similar fashion, if u is a function of n second-class variables through m first-class variables, the chain rule yields n equations, each of which contains m terms.

Example 1.   Find $\partial u/\partial t$ and $\partial u/\partial s$ if $u = 3x^2 + y^2 - z^2$ and $x = 2s + 5t$, $y = s^2 - t^2$, and $z = st$.

    Solution.   By (16.12) and (16.13),

$$\frac{\partial u}{\partial t} = (6x)(5) + (2y)(-2t) + (-2z)(s),$$

$$\frac{\partial u}{\partial s} = (6x)(2) + (2y)(2s) + (-2z)(t).$$

Example 2. Find $\partial^2 u/\partial t^2$ if $u = x^2 + y^3$ and $x = 4s - 3t$ and $y = st^2$.

Solution. By the chain rule,

$$\frac{\partial u}{\partial t} = \frac{\partial u}{\partial x}\frac{\partial x}{\partial t} + \frac{\partial u}{\partial y}\frac{\partial y}{\partial t}$$
$$= 2x(-3) + 3y^2(2st)$$
$$= -6x + 6st\, y^2.$$

Continuing to keep s fixed, we differentiate $\partial u/\partial t$ partially with respect to t to obtain

$$\frac{\partial^2 u}{\partial t^2} = -6(-3) + 6s[t2y(2st) + y^2(1)]$$
$$= 18 + 24ys^2 t^2 + 6y^2 s = 18 + 30s^3 t^4.$$

The same result is obtained if $\partial u/\partial t$ is written in terms of s and t before differentiating partially with respect to t.

Example 3. Show that the partial differential equation $\partial^2 y/(\partial u\, \partial v) = 0$ becomes $\partial^2 y/\partial t^2 = a^2(\partial^2 y/\partial x^2)$ if the variables u and v are related to the variables x and t by the equations

$$x = \frac{v + u}{2}; \qquad t = \frac{v - u}{2a}.$$

Solution

$$\frac{\partial y}{\partial v} = \frac{\partial y}{\partial x}\left(\frac{1}{2}\right) + \frac{\partial y}{\partial t}\left(\frac{1}{2a}\right)$$

$$\frac{\partial^2 y}{\partial u\, \partial v} = \frac{1}{2}\left[\frac{\partial^2 y}{\partial x^2}\frac{1}{2} + \frac{\partial^2 y}{\partial t\, \partial x}\left(\frac{-1}{2a}\right)\right]$$

$$+ \frac{1}{2a}\left[\frac{\partial^2 y}{\partial x\, \partial t}\frac{1}{2} + \frac{\partial^2 y}{\partial t^2}\left(\frac{-1}{2a}\right)\right]$$

$$= \frac{1}{4}\frac{\partial^2 y}{\partial x^2} - \frac{1}{4a^2}\frac{\partial^2 y}{\partial t^2} = 0.$$

Multiplying both sides by $4a^2$ yields the desired result.

16.9   Directional Derivative and Gradient Vector

Let $u = f(x, y, z)$ and let curve C have parametric equations

$$x = x(s); \qquad y = y(s); \qquad z = z(s),$$

where s denotes arc length along C.

If u is defined at every point of C, then u on C is a function of the second-class variable s through the first-class variables x, y, and z. The rate of change of u with respect to s on C at a point (x, y, z) of C is given by the chain rule. This rate of change is an ordinary derivative and is denoted by du/ds, since there is but one second-class variable s. Similarly, the rates of change of x, y, and z with respect to s are ordinary derivatives. Thus

$$\frac{du}{ds} = \frac{\partial f}{\partial x}\frac{dx}{ds} + \frac{\partial f}{\partial y}\frac{dy}{ds} + \frac{\partial f}{\partial z}\frac{dz}{ds}. \tag{6.14}$$

The value of du/ds, given by (16.14), is called the directional derivative of f at (x, y, z) in the direction of C in which s increases.

The form of (16.14) suggests a dot product of two vectors. The vector having components $\partial f/\partial x$, $\partial f/\partial y$, and $\partial f/\partial z$ is called the gradient of f and is written

$$\textbf{grad}\ \textbf{f} = \frac{\partial f}{\partial x}\textbf{i} + \frac{\partial f}{\partial y}\textbf{j} + \frac{\partial f}{\partial z}\textbf{k}. \tag{16.15}$$

[An alternate notation for **grad f** is ∇**f**, read as "del f."]

The derivatives dx/ds, dy/ds, and dz/ds are components of the unit vector **T** tangent to C at (x, y, z). This is easily seen by dividing $\textbf{V} = (dx/dt)\textbf{i} + (dy/dt)\textbf{j} + (dz/dt)\textbf{k}$ by $v = |\textbf{V}| = ds/dt$. We are now able to write (16.14) as

$$\frac{du}{ds} = (\textbf{grad}\ \textbf{f}) \cdot \textbf{T}. \tag{16.16}$$

Equation (16.16) makes it clear that du/ds does not depend upon a particular curve C having **T** as its unit tangent vector at P. The directional derivative at P is the same for any curve having **T** as its unit tangent vector. The curve might be a straight line through P in the direction of **T**.

Since $(\textbf{grad}\ \textbf{f}) \cdot \textbf{T} = |\textbf{grad}\ \textbf{f}|\cos\theta$, where θ is the angle between the vectors **grad f** and **T**, it follows that du/ds assumes its maximum value $= |\textbf{grad}\ \textbf{f}|$ when $\cos\theta = 1$. Since this occurs when $\theta = 0$, du/ds is a maximum in the direction of **grad f**. Similarly, du/ds assumes its minimum value $= -|\textbf{grad}\ \textbf{f}|$ in the direction opposite to that of **grad f**, since $\cos\theta$ then has the value -1.

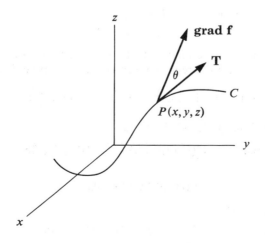

Figure 16.6

If $u = f(x, y, z)$ denotes the temperature at the point $P(x, y, z)$, the direction of **grad f** is the hottest direction from P, while the opposite direction is the coldest direction. The curve C and the vectors **grad f** and **T** are shown in Fig. 16.6.

* **Example 1.**   Find the directional derivative of $u = x^2 + 2y^2 + 3z^2$ at $(2, 4, 8)$ in the direction of the curve C having parametric equations

$$x = t, \qquad y = t^2, \qquad z = t^3.$$

Solution.   At (x, y, z), **grad u** $= 2x\mathbf{i} + 4y\mathbf{j} + 6z\mathbf{k}$, and hence at $(2, 4, 8)$, **grad u** $= 4\mathbf{i} + 16\mathbf{j} + 48\mathbf{k}$. At (x, y, z), a vector tangent to C is given by $(dx/dt)\mathbf{i} + (dy/dt)\mathbf{j} + (dz/dt)\mathbf{k} = \mathbf{i} + 2t\mathbf{j} + 3t^2\mathbf{k}$. Since $t = 2$ corresponds to the point $(2, 4, 8)$ on C, the vector $\mathbf{i} + 4\mathbf{j} + 12\mathbf{k}$ is tangent to C at $(2, 4, 8)$ and the unit tangent vector is

$$\mathbf{T} = \frac{\mathbf{i} + 4\mathbf{j} + 12\mathbf{k}}{\sqrt{161}}.$$

The required directional derivative du/ds is given by

$$(\text{grad } u) \cdot \mathbf{T} = (4\mathbf{i} + 16\mathbf{j} + 48\mathbf{k}) \cdot \left(\frac{\mathbf{i} + 4\mathbf{j} + 12\mathbf{k}}{\sqrt{161}}\right)$$

$$= \frac{(4 \cdot 1) + (16 \cdot 4) + (48 \cdot 12)}{\sqrt{161}}$$

$$= \frac{644}{\sqrt{161}}.$$

If u denoted the temperature in degrees at (x, y, z) and s were measured in inches, du/ds would be measured in degrees per inch.

Example 2.   Find the directional derivative of $u = x^2 y + z^3$ at $(3, -2, 1)$ in the direction of the point $(5, 0, 2)$. What is the maximum value of du/ds at $(3, -2, 1)$?

Solution.   At $(3, -2, 1)$,

$$\text{grad } \mathbf{f} = 2xy\mathbf{i} + x^2\mathbf{j} + 3z^2\mathbf{k}]_{(3, -2, 1)}$$

$$= -12\mathbf{i} + 9\mathbf{j} + 3\mathbf{k}.$$

A unit vector **T** in the direction from $(3, -2, 1)$ to $(5, 0, 2)$ is $(2/3)\mathbf{i} + (2/3)\mathbf{j} + (1/3)\mathbf{k}$. Hence the required directional derivative du/ds is given by

$$(\text{grad } \mathbf{f}) \cdot \mathbf{T} = (-12)\left(\frac{2}{3}\right) + (9)\left(\frac{2}{3}\right) + (3)\left(\frac{1}{3}\right) = -1.$$

The maximum du/ds at $(3, -2, 1)$ is equal to

$$|\text{grad } \mathbf{f}| = \sqrt{(-12)^2 + (9)^2 + (3)^2} = 3\sqrt{26}.$$

PROBLEM LIST 95

1.   Find $\partial u/\partial t$ and $\partial u/\partial s$ if:

(a) $u = x^2 - y^0 + z^2$, $x - 3s + 2t$, $y - 2s - 5t$, $z - st$.

(b) $u = x^2 y^3 - z^2$; $x = s + 2t$, $y = st^2$, $z = s^2 t$.

(c) $u = xy \cos z$; $x = s + t$, $y = 2s - t$, $z = st^2$.

(d) $u = x^2 + y^2$; $x = s \cos t$, $y = s \sin t$.

2. Given $u = x^2 + 2y^2 - z^2$ and $x = 2s + t$, $y = 3s - 2t$, $z = s - 3t$, find $\partial u/\partial t$ and $\partial u/\partial s$ when $s = 2$ and $t = 1$.

3. Given $u = x^2 - y^2$ and $x = 3s + t$, $y = 2s - t$, find

(a) $\dfrac{\partial^2 u}{\partial t^2}$,

(b) $\dfrac{\partial^2 u}{\partial s^2}$,

(c) $\dfrac{\partial^2 u}{\partial s \, \partial t}$.

4. Show that the partial differential equation $\partial^2 y/(\partial u \, \partial v) = 0$ becomes

$$\frac{\partial^2 y}{\partial t^2} = 4 \frac{\partial^2 y}{\partial x^2}$$

if $x = (1/2)(v + u)$ and $t = (1/4)(v - u)$.

5. Given $u = y^4 - 2x^2 y^2 + x^4$, show that

$$y \frac{\partial u}{\partial x} + x \frac{\partial u}{\partial y} = 0.$$

6. Given $u = e^{x/y}$, show that

$$x \frac{\partial u}{\partial x} + y \frac{\partial u}{\partial y} = 0.$$

7. Show that Laplace's equation,

$$\frac{\partial^2 u}{\partial r^2} + \frac{1}{r} \frac{\partial u}{\partial r} + \frac{1}{r^2} \frac{\partial^2 u}{\partial \theta^2} + \frac{\partial^2 u}{\partial z^2} = 0,$$

transforms into

$$\frac{\partial^2 u}{\partial x^2} + \frac{\partial^2 u}{\partial y^2} + \frac{\partial^2 u}{\partial z^2} = 0$$

if $x = r \cos \theta$, $y = x \sin \theta$, and $z = z$.

8. Find **grad u** if

(a) $u = 3x^2 + y^2 + 2z^2$,　　　　　　(d) $u = ze^{x/y}$,

(b) $u = x^2 - y^2 - xyz$,　　　　　　(e) $u = x^2 y^3 z^4$,

(c) $u = xy + yz + xz$,　　　　　　(f) $u = x \sin yz$.

9. Find $|\,\text{grad } u\,|$ if

(a) $u = x^2 + y^2 + z^2$, (b) $u = xy + 3z^4$.

10. Find **grad u** and $|\,\text{grad } u\,|$ at $(1, 2, 4)$ if $u = x^3 + 2y^2 + z$.

11. Find **grad u** and $|\,\text{grad } u\,|$ at $(-3, -1, 2)$ if $u = x^2 y + z^3$.

12. Find the directional derivative of $u = x^2 - y^2 - z^2$ at $(4, 4, 8)$ in the direction of the curve C having parametric equations $x = 2t$, $y = t^2$, $z = t^3$.

13. Find the directional derivative of $u = x + 2y + z^2$ at $(3, -1, 2)$ in the direction of the point $(-2, 6, 3)$. Find also the maximum and minimum values of du/ds at $(3, -1, 2)$.

14. Find the rate of change of $u = \log(x^2 + y^2 + z^2)$ at $(1, 0, 0)$ in the direction of the vector $3\mathbf{i} + 4\mathbf{j}$.

15. Let the temperature τ at (x, y, z) be given by $\tau = x^2 + 4y^2 + 9z^2$. Find the hottest and coldest directions from the point $(4, 2, 1)$.

16. Explain the difference between $\partial u/\partial x$ and the directional derivative of u in the direction of the positive x-axis. [Consider $(\textbf{grad } u) \cdot (\textbf{i})$ and $(\textbf{grad } u) \cdot (-\textbf{i})$].

16.10 *Level Surfaces*

Let $u = f(x, y, z)$ define a function of the three space coordinates x, y, and z. The set of points at which u has the constant value k lies on the surface whose equation is $f(x, y, z) = k$. This surface is called a level surface of the function f. If u is a temperature function, a level surface of this function is a surface having the same temperature at every point. Level surfaces for temperature, pressure, density, and similar functions play an important role in applied mathematics.

Example 1.   The level surfaces of the function defined by $u = f(x, y, z) = x^2 + y^2 + z^2$ are the members of the one-parameter family of spheres

$$x^2 + y^2 + z^2 = k.$$

The function f has the value 1 everywhere on the sphere $x^2 + y^2 + z^2 = 1$. On the sphere $x^2 + y^2 + z^2 = 4$ the function f has the value 4. If we set $k = 0$, the corresponding level surface of f consists of the single point $(0, 0, 0)$.

In Fig. 16.7, $P(x, y, z)$ is an arbitrary point of the level surface S of the function defined by $u = f(x, y, z)$. Let $f(x, y, z) = k$ be an equation of S and let C be any curve which passes through P, lies entirely in S, and has the unit tangent vector $\textbf{T}$ at P. We assume that $|\textbf{grad } u| \neq 0$ at P. In the direction of C at P the directional derivative

$$\frac{du}{ds} = \lim_{\Delta s \to 0} \frac{\Delta u}{\Delta s} = 0$$

since $\Delta u \equiv 0$ on C because u does not change on S or on C. Therefore, at P,

$$\frac{du}{ds} = (\textbf{grad } u) \cdot \textbf{T} = 0.$$

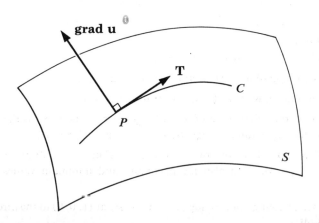

Figure 16.7

Since C is any curve which is contained in S and which possesses a tangent at P, **grad u** is perpendicular to every such curve C. It follows from the definition of the tangent plane to a surface (given in Sec. 16.7) that the tangents **T** to the set of curves C at P determine the tangent plane at P. Hence we have established the important fact that at any point P of S **grad u** is perpendicular to the level surface of f which passes through P.

16.11 *Directional Derivative and Gradient of a Function of Two Variables*

If $u = f(x, y)$ defines a scalar field in the xy-plane,

$$x = x(t) \qquad \text{and} \qquad y = y(t)$$

are parametric equations of a curve C in the xy-plane having unit tangent vector **T** at $P(x, y)$, and s denotes arc length along C, then

$$\frac{du}{ds} = \lim_{\Delta s \to 0} \frac{\Delta u}{\Delta s}$$
$$= (\textbf{grad u}) \cdot \textbf{T}$$
$$= \frac{\partial f}{\partial x}\frac{dx}{ds} + \frac{\partial f}{\partial y}\frac{dy}{ds}.$$

The quantity du/ds is the directional derivative of the function f in the direction of C at P. See Fig. 16.8.

A curve $f(x, y) = k$ in the xy-plane along which $u = f(x, y)$ has the value k at each point is called a level curve of the function f. On a weather map the curves called isotherms are level curves of the temperature function, while the curves called isobars are level curves of the pressure function.

At any point P of a level curve $f(x, y) = k$ of f, the vector **grad u** is perpendicular to the unit tangent vector **T** to the level curve at P. See Fig. 16.9.

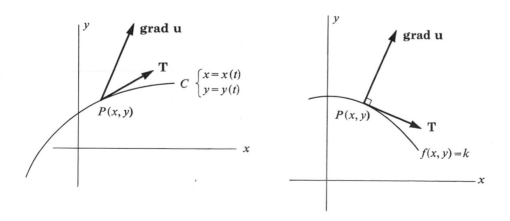

Figure 16.8   Figure 16.9

Note in Fig. 16.8 that **grad u** is not perpendicular to **T**. This is due to the fact that C is an arbitrary curve in the xy-plane rather than a level curve of $u = f(x, y)$.

The directional derivative du/ds of a function of two variables, defined by $u = f(x, y)$, has a geometric interpretation. In Fig. 16.10, S is the surface having equation $u = f(x, y)$, $P(x, y, 0)$ is a point in the plane π perpendicular to the xy-plane and containing the unit vector **T** which lies in the xy-plane, and $Q(x, y, u)$ is the point of S above P. As $\Delta s \rightarrow 0$, $\Delta u/\Delta s$ approaches $du/ds = \tan \psi$, where ψ is the angle between the line determined by **T** in the xy-plane and the tangent L to Γ, where Γ is the intersection of the plane π and the surface S. But du/ds is the directional derivative of u at P in the direction θ of any curve C in the xy-plane for which **T** is a unit tangent vector to C at P. Thus du/ds can be interpreted geometrically as the slope $m = \tan \psi$ of L.

If $\theta = 0$,

$$\frac{du}{ds} = (\textbf{grad u}) \cdot \textbf{i} = \frac{\partial u}{\partial x}$$

while if $\theta = \pi/2$,

$$\frac{du}{ds} = (\textbf{grad u}) \cdot \textbf{j} = \frac{\partial u}{\partial y}.$$

See Fig. 16.2.

It may seem strange that $\tan \psi$ for arbitrary θ can be computed, knowing only $\tan \psi$ for $\theta = 0$ and $\theta = \pi/2$, but it must be remembered that we are dealing with a special class of functions, namely, differentiable functions of two variables x and y.

Since $du/ds = (\textbf{grad u}) \cdot \textbf{T}$ is the directional derivative of u in the direction of the unit vector **T** in the xy-plane, du/ds will assume its maximum numerical value

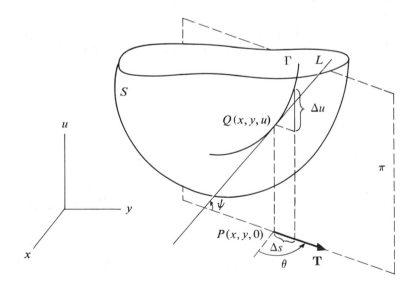

Figure 16.10

in the direction of **grad u.** The surface $u = f(x, y)$ will be steepest, that is, $\tan \psi$ will be a maximum when θ is in the direction of **grad u.**

When $u = f(x, y)$ is regarded as an equation of a surface S, the level curves $u = k$ of the function are called contour lines on maps. The surface S has the same height above every point of a particular contour line $f(x, y) = k$. These curves help one to visualize the three-dimensional surface S when looking at a two-dimensional map.

PROBLEM LIST 96

1. Sketch three level surfaces of the function defined by
   (a) $u = x + y + z$,   (d) $u = z$,
   (b) $u = x^2 + y^2 + z^2$,   (e) $u = x^2 + y^2 + z$.
   (c) $u = x + 2y$,

2. Sketch the level surface $u = 0$ of the function defined by $u = x^2 + y^2 - z$. Find **grad u** at $(1, 2, 5)$ and show that it is perpendicular to the level surface $u = 0$ at $(1, 2, 5)$.

3. Show that the curve $x = \cos t$, $y = \sin t$, $z = \sqrt{3}$ lies in a level surface of the function given by $u = x^2 + y^2 + z^2$. Show that **grad u** is perpendicular to this curve at $(1/2, \sqrt{3}/2, \sqrt{3})$.

4. Find **grad u** if
   (a) $u = f(x, y) = x^2 - 8y^3$,
   (b) $u = f(x, y) = x^3 + xy + y^2$.

5. Find **grad u** at $(2, 3)$ for each of the functions of Problem 4.

6. Draw three level curves of the function defined by
   (a) $u = x^2 + y^2$,   (c) $u = x + 2y$,
   (b) $u = x^2 + 4y^2$,   (d) $u = x$.

7. Sketch the level curve $u = 4$ of the surface $u = x^2 + 4y^2$. Show that **grad u** at $(1, \sqrt{3}/2)$ is perpendicular to $u = 4$ at $(1, \sqrt{3}/2)$.

8. Find the directional derivative of $u = f(x, y) = x^3 - xy^2$ at $(2, 4)$ in the direction away from the origin along the parabola $y = x^2$.

9. Find the slope of the line tangent to the intersection of the surface $u = x^2 + 4y^2$ and the plane $y = 2x$ at $(2, 1, 8)$.

10. Find the maximum value of $|du/ds|$ at $(1, 2)$ if $u = f(x, y) = 2x^2 + y^2$. Interpret geometrically.

11. Find the directional derivative of $u = x^2 + 3xy + 2y^2$ at $(1, 2)$ in the direction making an angle of $\pi/6$ with the positive direction of the x-axis. What is the maximum value of du/ds at $(1, 2)$? In what direction is it assumed?

12. The temperature τ of a thin plate in the xy-plane is given by $\tau = x \cos 2y$. Find the rate of change of τ at $(10, \pi/6)$ in the direction of $(13, \pi/6 + 4)$. What is the hottest direction from $(10, \pi/6)$?

16.12   *Implicit Functions*

Let us assume that the equation $F(x, y) = 0$ defines one or more differentiable functions denoted by $y = f(x)$. If we write $u = F(x, y)$ we can regard u as a function of the first-class variables x and y, and also regard $x = x$ and $y = f(x)$ as functions of the single second-class variable x. Since u defines a function of the second-class variable x through the first-class variables x and y, we can compute du/dx by the chain rule. But since u has the constant value zero, du/dx must be identically zero; that is,

$$\frac{du}{dx} = \frac{\partial F}{\partial x}\frac{dx}{dx} + \frac{\partial F}{\partial y}\frac{dy}{dx} = 0. \tag{16.17}$$

Since $dx/dx = 1$, we can solve (16.17) for dy/dx, providing $\partial F/\partial y \neq 0$. This yields

$$\frac{dy}{dx} = -\frac{\partial F/\partial x}{\partial F/\partial y} \quad (\partial F/\partial y \neq 0). \tag{16.18}$$

Example 1.   Find dy/dx, given $x^2 + 4y^2 - 4 = 0$.

    Solution.   By (16.18) we obtain

$$\frac{dy}{dx} = \frac{-2x}{8y} = \frac{-x}{4y}.$$

This result yields the slope of the ellipse $x^2 + 4y^2 - 4 = 0$ except at $(\pm 2, 0)$.

The method described leads to the same result as the method of implicit differentiation given in Sec. 3.8.

_____

We next consider the somewhat more complicated situation in which the equation $F(x, y, z) = 0$ defines one or more differentiable functions denoted by $z = f(x, y)$. We regard $u = F(x, y, z)$ as a function of the three first-class variables $x, y,$ and z and also regard $x = x$, $y = y$, and $z = f(x, y)$ as functions of the two second-class variables x and y. Since u has the constant value zero, its partial derivatives with respect to the second-class variables x and y must be identically zero. By the chain rule we obtain

$$\frac{\partial u}{\partial x} = \frac{\partial F}{\partial x}\frac{\partial x}{\partial x} + \frac{\partial F}{\partial y}\frac{\partial y}{\partial x} + \frac{\partial F}{\partial z}\frac{\partial z}{\partial x}$$

$$= 0,$$

$$\frac{\partial u}{\partial y} = \frac{\partial F}{\partial x}\frac{\partial x}{\partial y} + \frac{\partial F}{\partial y}\frac{\partial y}{\partial y} + \frac{\partial F}{\partial z}\frac{\partial z}{\partial y}$$

$$= 0. \tag{16.19}$$

Since

$$\frac{\partial x}{\partial x} = \frac{\partial y}{\partial y} = 1 \quad \text{and} \quad \frac{\partial y}{\partial x} = \frac{\partial x}{\partial y} = 0,$$

we can solve (16.19) for $\partial z/\partial x$ and $\partial z/\partial y$ providing $\partial F/\partial z \neq 0$. We thus obtain

$$\frac{\partial z}{\partial x} = -\frac{\partial F/\partial x}{\partial F/\partial z}; \quad \frac{\partial z}{\partial y} = -\frac{\partial F/\partial y}{\partial F/\partial z} \quad (\partial F/\partial z \neq 0). \qquad \textbf{(16.20)}$$

Example 2.   Find $\partial z/\partial x$ and $\partial z/\partial y$, given

$$9x^2 + 4y^2 + 36z^2 - 36 = 0.$$

Solution.   By (16.20) we obtain

$$\frac{\partial z}{\partial x} = -\frac{18x}{72z} = \frac{-x}{4z}; \quad \frac{\partial z}{\partial y} = -\frac{8y}{72z} = \frac{-y}{9z}.$$

If π is the plane tangent to $F(x, y, z) = 0$ at (x_0, y_0, z_0), where $z = f(x, y)$, then by (16.8) π has equation

$$\frac{\partial z}{\partial x}\bigg|_{(x_0, y_0)} (x - x_0) + \frac{\partial z}{\partial y}\bigg|_{(x_0, y_0)} (y - y_0) - (z - z_0) = 0.$$

Replacing the coefficients of $(x - x_0)$ and $(y - y_0)$ by their expressions from (16.20), and then multiplying by $-(\partial F/\partial z)$, the equation of π becomes

$$F_x(x_0, y_0, z_0)(x - x_0) + F_y(x_0, y_0, z_0)(y - y_0)$$
$$+ F_z(x_0, y_0, z_0)(z - z_0) = 0. \qquad \textbf{(16.21)}$$

Similarly, the equation (16.10) of the normal line at (x_0, y_0, z_0) can be written

$$\frac{x - x_0}{F_x(x_0, y_0, z_0)} = \frac{y - y_0}{F_y(x_0, y_0, z_0)} = \frac{z - z_0}{F_z(x_0, y_0, z_0)}. \qquad \textbf{(16.22)}$$

Observe that the coefficients in (16.21) are the components of **grad F**. This is a verification of the fact that **grad F** is perpendicular to the level surface $F(x, y, z) = 0$ of the function F.

Example 3.   Find an equation of the plane tangent to the ellipsoid $3x^2 + y^2 + z^2 - 16 = 0$ at $(1, 2, -3)$.

Solution.   From $F_x = 6x$, $F_y = 2y$, and $F_z = 2z$, we obtain $F_x(1, 2, -3) = 6$, $F_y(1, 2, -3) = 4$, and $F_z(1, 2, -3) = -6$. We then employ (16.21) to obtain the following equation of the tangent plane:

$$6(x - 1) + 4(y - 2) - 6(z + 3) = 0,$$

or

$$3x + 2y - 3z - 16 = 0.$$

If two equations $F(x, y, u, v) = 0$ and $G(x, y, u, v) = 0$ define u and v as functions of x and y, the chain rule can be applied to compute u_x, v_x, u_y, and v_y.

Instead of deriving formulas for these partial derivatives, we will present a specific example.

Example 4.   Given that the equations

$$xy + u^2 - 2v^2 = 0 \qquad \text{and} \qquad 3x - y - uv = 0$$

define u and v as functions of x and y, find u_x, v_x, u_y, and v_y.

    Solution.   We first hold y fixed and differentiate both equations with respect to x to obtain

$$y + 2uu_x - 4vv_x = 0, \qquad 3 - uv_x - vu_x = 0.$$

Solving simultaneously for u_x and v_x yields

$$u_x = \frac{12v - uy}{2(u^2 + 2v^2)}; \qquad v_x = \frac{6u + vy}{2(u^2 + 2v^2)}.$$

    Similarly, by holding x fixed and differentiating both equations with respect to y, we obtain

$$x + 2uu_y - 4vv_y = 0, \qquad -1 - uv_y - vu_y = 0.$$

Solving simultaneously for u_y and v_y yields

$$u_y = \frac{-ux - 4v}{2(u^2 + 2v^2)}; \qquad v_y = \frac{vx - 2u}{2(u^2 + 2v^2)}.$$

PROBLEM LIST 97

1.   Find dy/dx where y denotes any differentiable function of x defined by
   - (a) $x^2 + 2y^2 - 9 = 0$,
   - (b) $4x^2 - 9y^2 + 1 = 0$,
   - (c) $x^4 + 2x - 3y^2 - 5 = 0$,
   - (d) $1 - e^x \sin y - e^y \sin x = 0$.

2.   Find $\partial z/\partial x$ and $\partial z/\partial y$ where z denotes any differentiable function of x and y defined by
   - (a) $x^2 + y^2 + z^2 - 4 = 0$,   (d) $xy^2 + xyz + z^3 - 2 = 0$,
   - (b) $4x^2 + 9y^2 + z^2 - 36 = 0$,   (e) $yz^2 - xz^2 + xy^2z - 4 = 0$,
   - (c) $x^2 + 5y^2 - z^2 - 9 = 0$,   (f) $e^z - \log y + x^2y = 0$.

3.   Find z_x and z_y at the point $(-1, 2, 1)$ on the ellipsoid $x^2 + 2y^2 + 4z^2 - 13 = 0$.

4.   Find z_{xx} and z_{yy} if z is defined by $x^2 + 2y^2 + z^2 - 1 = 0$.

5.   Given that y is defined by $F(x, y) = 0$, show that

$$\frac{d^2y}{dx^2} = -\frac{F_{xx}F_y{}^2 - 2F_{xy}F_xF_y + F_{yy}F_x{}^2}{F_y{}^3}.$$

6.   Show that the function defined by $z = e^x \cos y$ satisfies Laplace's equation $z_{xx} + z_{yy} = 0$.

7.   Find an equation of the plane tangent to

(a) $x^2 + y^2 + z^2 = 14$, at $(1, -3, 2)$;

(b) $2x^2 + 3y^2 + z^2 = 12$, at $(2, 1, 1)$.

8. Find the direction of the normal to the surface $xy^3 + yz^3 + zx^3 = 1$ at $(1, 0, 1)$.

9. Find u_x, v_x, u_y, and v_y, given that the following equations define u and v as differentiable functions of x and y:

(a) $u^2 - v^2 + x^2 = 0$;

$u + v + xy = 0$.

(b) $x + y + uv = 0$;

$xy + u^2 - v^2 = 0$.

(c) $x - u \cos v = 0$;

$y - u \sin v = 0$.

(d) $x - e^u \sin v = 0$;

$y - e^u \cos v = 0$.

10. Given that u and v are defined as differentiable functions of x and y by the equations $F(x, y, u, v) = 0$ and $G(x, y, u, v) = 0$, show that

$$u_x = -\frac{F_x G_v - F_v G_x}{F_u G_v - F_v G_u}; \qquad v_x = -\frac{F_u G_x - F_x G_u}{F_u G_v - F_v G_u}.$$

11. Find equations of the line tangent to the intersection of the surfaces $2x^2 + 3y^2 + z^2 - 9 = 0$ and $3x^2 + y^2 - z^2 = 0$ at $(1, -1, 2)$.

16.13   Maxima and Minima

A point $P(x, y)$ of a set D of points in the xy-plane is said to be an interior point of D if and only if there exists some circle in the xy-plane with center at P which lies entirely in D. The set D is called open if all its points are interior points.

The entire xy-plane is an open set. The set of points whose coordinates satisfy $x^2 + y^2 < 1$ is an open set. The set S of points whose coordinates satisfy $x^2 + y^2 \leqslant 1$ is not open, since there is no circle with center at $(1, 0)$ which lies entirely in S.

Let $f(x, y)$ define a differentiable function of x and y whose domain is an open set D. The function f is said to attain a relative maximum at $P(a, b)$ if and only if there exists a circle C with center P such that $f(a, b) \geqslant f(x, y)$ for all points (x, y) which are inside C and also in D. The function f is said to attain an absolute maximum at $P(a, b)$ if and only if $f(a, b) \geqslant f(x, y)$ for all points (x, y) in D. Corresponding definitions are readily formulated for a relative minimum and an absolute minimum of f on D. A relative maximum or minimum of f is called an extremum of f. An absolute maximum or minimum of f is automatically an extremum of f.

The following theorem is a generalization of the basic result of Sec. 5.3.

Theorem 16-I.   If f having value $f(x, y)$ is differentiable on an open set D and if $f(a, b)$ is an extremum of f, then

$$f_x(a, b) = 0 \qquad \text{and} \qquad f_y(a, b) = 0.$$

Proof.   The function denoted by $z = f(x, b)$ of the single variable x attains its absolute maximum or minimum $f(a, b)$ in some open interval $x_1 < x < x_2$ where $x_1 < a < x_2$, and furthermore, this open interval lies entirely in D.

This open interval is guaranteed by the existence of a circle C contained in D and having center (a, b). See Fig. 16.11 and also refer to Fig. 16.2.

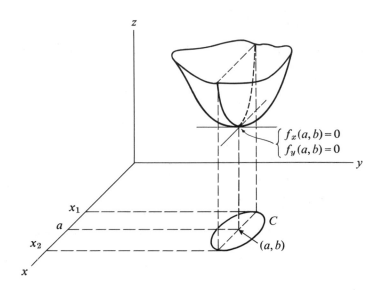

Figure 16.11

Then, by Theorem 4–II,

$$\frac{d}{dx} f(x, b)\bigg|_{x=a} = f_x(x, y)\bigg|_{(a, b)} = f_x(a, b) = 0.$$

By considering the function denoted by $z = f(a, y)$ of the single variable y, it is shown similarly that $f_y(a, b) = 0$.

If $f_x(a, b) = 0$ and $f_y(a, b) = 0$, the point (a, b) is called a critical point of f. Interior points of D where f_x and f_y do not both exist are also called critical points, but we will omit consideration of such points.

The contrapositive of Theorem 16–I states that if $P(a, b)$ is not a critical point of f, then $f(a, b)$ is not an extremum of f. Thus, to locate the extrema of f we need examine only the values of $f(x, y)$ at its critical points.

Example 1. Find the minimum distance from the origin to the plane $2x + 2y + z = 6$.

Solution. We assume from the nature of the problem that the required minimum s exists. To minimize s, we minimize

$$s^2 = x^2 + y^2 + z^2 = x^2 + y^2 + (6 - 2x - 2y)^2.$$

From

$$\frac{\partial}{\partial x}(s^2) = 2x - 4(6 - 2x - 2y) = 0$$

and

$$\frac{\partial}{\partial y}(s^2) = 2y - 4(6 - 2x - 2y) = 0$$

we obtain the critical point $(4/3, 4/3)$.

When $x = 4/3$ and $y = 4/3$, $z = 2/3$ and $s = \sqrt{(16/9) + (16/9) + (4/9)}$ $= 2$. This is the required minimum distance.

Example 2.   A rectangular box has one vertex at the origin and three adjacent edges along the coordinate axes. Find the maximum volume of the box if the vertex opposite the origin lies in the plane $3x + 2y + 6z = 18$. See Fig. 16.12.

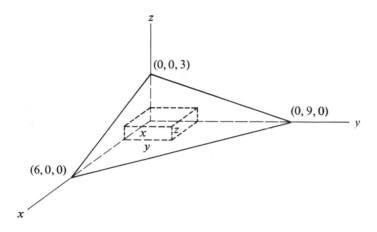

Figure 16.12

Solution.   From

$$V = xyz = xy\left(\frac{18 - 3x - 2y}{6}\right)$$

$$= \frac{1}{6}(18xy - 3x^2y - 2xy^2)$$

we obtain

$$\frac{\partial V}{\partial x} = \frac{1}{6}(18y - 6xy - 2y^2)$$

$$= \frac{y}{3}(9 - 3x - y) = 0$$

and

$$\frac{\partial V}{\partial y} = \frac{1}{6}(18x - 3x^2 - 4xy)$$

$$= \frac{x}{6}(18 - 3x - 4y) = 0.$$

These equations have solutions $x = 0$, $y = 0$, and $x = 2$, $y = 3$. Since the function given by

$$V = xy\left[\frac{18 - 3x - 2y}{6}\right]$$

is defined only for points in the open triangle having vertices $(0, 0, 0)$, $(6, 0, 0)$ and $(0, 9, 0)$, V can assume an extreme value only at $(2, 3)$. We assume from the nature of the problem that V assumes an absolute maximum which is therefore equal to

$$xyz\Big|_{\substack{x=2\\y=3\\z=1}} = \frac{xy}{6}\Big[18 - 3x - 2y\Big]_{\substack{x=2\\y=3}} = 6.$$

Let S be a set of points in the xy-plane. A point P is said to be a boundary point of S if and only if every circle with center P contains points which are in S and also points which are not in S. For example, the point $(1, 0)$ is a boundary point of the set of points whose coordinates satisfy $x^2 + y^2 < 1$. A set which contains all of its boundary points is called a closed set. For example, the set of points whose coordinates satisfy $x^2 + y^2 \leqslant 1$ is a closed set.

A set S of points in the xy-plane is said to be bounded if and only if every point of S is contained in some circle having center at the origin. For example, the set of points whose coordinates satisfy $x^2 + y^2 < 1$ is bounded, whereas the set of points whose coordinates satisfy $x^2 + y^2 > 1$ is not bounded.

These definitions enable us to state the following generalization of Theorem 4–I.

Theorem 16-II.   A function f of x and y which is continuous on a closed and bounded set D assumes an absolute maximum M and an absolute minimum m in D.

A proof of Theorem 16–II is given in Ref. 16.1. The theorem is illustrated in the following example.

Example 3.   Find the absolute maximum M and the absolute minimum m of the function defined by $z = f(x, y) = x^2 + y^2 - 2x - 4y + 8$ whose domain D is the set of points whose coordinates satisfy $x^2 + y^2 \leqslant 16$.

Solution.   Since D is a closed and bounded set of points, the existence of M and m is guaranteed by Theorem 16–II. From $\partial z/\partial x = 2x - 2 = 0$ and $\partial z/\partial y = 2y - 4 = 0$ we find that a possible extremum exists at $(1, 2)$. We find that $f(1, 2) = 3$.

We next express the boundary of D in the parametric form $x = 4 \cos \theta$ and $y = 4 \sin \theta$.

We then express z on the boundary of D as the function of θ given by

$$z = 16 \cos^2 \theta + 16 \sin^2 \theta - 8 \cos \theta - 16 \sin \theta + 8$$
$$= 8[3 - \cos \theta - 2 \sin \theta].$$

From

$$\frac{dz}{d\theta} = 8[\sin \theta - 2 \cos \theta] = 0,$$

we obtain $\tan \theta = 2$, $\cos \theta = \pm 1/\sqrt{5}$, and $\sin \theta = \pm 2/\sqrt{5}$.
Thus, on the circular boundary of D, z has minimum value

$$z - 8\Big[3 - \frac{1}{\sqrt{5}} - \frac{4}{\sqrt{5}}\Big] - 24 \qquad 8\sqrt{5}$$

and maximum value

$$z = 8\left[3 + \frac{1}{\sqrt{5}} + \frac{4}{\sqrt{5}}\right] = 24 + 8\sqrt{5}.$$

We conclude that $z = f(x, y)$ assumes its absolute maximum $M = 24 + 8\sqrt{5}$ at the boundary point $(-4/\sqrt{5}, -8/\sqrt{5})$, and its absolute minimum $m = 3$ at the interior point $(1, 2)$.

If $f(a, b)$ is an extremum of f and f is differentiable on an open set D, then $f_x(a, b) = 0$ and $f_y(a, b) = 0$. That is, the vanishing of the partial derivatives is a necessary condition for the existence of an extremum at the point. The condition is not sufficient, however, and one cannot conclude that $f(a, b)$ is an extremum if $f_x(a, b) = f_y(a, b) = 0$.

For example, $f(x, y) = y^3$ does not assume an extremum at $(0, 0)$ and yet $f_x(0, 0) = f_y(0, 0) = 0$. Similarly, the function defined by $z = x^2 - y^2$ does not assume an extremum at the origin, although $f_x(0, 0) = f_y(0, 0) = 0$. See Fig. 15.24.

PROBLEM LIST 98

In Problems 1–11 assume that the required maximum or minimum exists.

1. Find the minimum distance from the given point to the given plane:

    (a) $(0, 0, 0)$, $x - 2y + 2z = 9$.

    (b) $(1, 2, 4)$, $2x - 3y + z = 4$.

    (c) $(-1, 2, 3)$, $x - y + z = 4$.

    (d) $(4, 1, 2)$, $x + y - z = 0$.

2. Solve illustrative Example 2 with the plane $3x + 2y + 6z = 18$ replaced by the plane $4x + 3y + z = 24$.

3. The four sides and the bottom of a rectangular box have a total area of 48 sq in. Find the maximum possible volume of the box.

4. Find the minimum value of the function defined by $f(x, y) = 4x^2 + 3y^2 + 3x + 8y + 4$.

5. Show that the largest rectangular parallelepiped which can be inscribed in a sphere is a cube.

6. Find the volume of the largest rectangular parallelepiped which can be inscribed in the ellipsoid

    $$\frac{x^2}{a^2} + \frac{y^2}{b^2} + \frac{z^2}{c^2} = 1.$$

7. A rectangular box without a top is to have a volume of 768 cu ft. Find the dimensions for which the cost will be minimum if the material for the bottom is three times as expensive as the material for the sides.

8. A strip of metal 2 ft wide is to be bent into a trough whose cross section is an

isosceles trapezoid. In Fig. 16.13, find the values of x and θ which will make the area of the trapezoid a maximum.

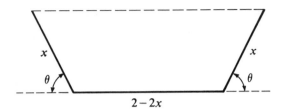

Figure 16.13

9. Find an equation of the plane which passes through $(2, 1, 4)$ and cuts off the least volume from the first octant.

10. Find the minimum distance between the line $x = t, y = 2t, z = 3t$ and the line $x = 3\tau, y = 2 - \tau, z = -4 + 5\tau$.

11. Determine a and b so that the sum of the squares of the vertical distances from the line $y = ax + b$ to the points $(0, 0), (1, 1), (3, 2)$, and $(4, 5)$ is a minimum. The solution is the basis of the method of least squares, a method of importance in statistics. The line that is determined is said to "best fit" the given points in the sense of least squares.

12. Solve illustrative Example 1 by the method of illustrative Example 3 of Sec. 15.8.

13. Find the absolute maximum M and the absolute minimum m of the function defined by $z = f(x, y) = x^2 + y^2 - 2y + 3$:
    (a) on and inside the circle $x^2 + y^2 = 4$;
    (b) on and inside the square having vertices $(\pm 1, 0)$ and $(\pm 1, 2)$.

14. Find the absolute maximum M and the absolute minimum m of the function defined by $z = f(x, y) = x^2 + y^2 - 6x - 4y + 20$:
    (a) on and inside the circle $x^2 + y^2 = 1$;
    (b) on and inside the circle $x^2 + y^2 = 16$;
    (c) on and inside the square having vertices $(0, 0), (4, 0), (0, 4)$, and $(4, 4)$;
    (d) on and inside the triangle having vertices $(0, 0), (4, 0)$, and $(0, 4)$.

15. Find the absolute maximum M and the absolute minimum m of the function defined by $z = f(x, y) = e^{-(x^2+y^2)}$:
    (a) on and inside the circle $x^2 + y^2 = 1$;
    (b) on and inside the triangle having vertices $(0, 0), (2, 0)$, and $(0, 1)$.

16. If the differentiable function defined by $z = f(x, y)$ assumes an extremum $f(a, b)$ at an interior point (a, b), what can be said about **grad f** at (a, b)? What can be said about the plane tangent to the surface $z = f(x, y)$ at (a, b)?

17. Show that the function defined by $z = xy$ does not assume an extremum at the origin although $z_x(0, 0) = z_y(0, 0) = 0$. Show that the function defined by $z = x^2 + 4xy + y^2$ has the same property.

REFERENCES

16.1 J. M. H. Olmsted, *Advanced Calculus*, Appleton-Century-Crofts, New York, 1961.

16.2 A. E. Taylor, *Advanced Calculus*, Ginn, Boston, 1955.

Chapter

17____

Multiple integrals

17.1   *Volume Under a Surface*

Let $z = f(x, y)$ define a function which is continuous and nonnegative at every point on and inside the closed rectangle R having vertices (a, c), (b, c), (b, d), and (a, d). We wish to determine the volume of the solid which is bounded above by the surface $z = f(x, y)$ and below by the rectangle R. See Fig. 17.1. This problem is a generalization of the problem considered in Chapter 4, that of finding the area under a curve $y = f(x)$ between the lines $x = a$ and $x = b$.

We subdivide the line segment from (a, c) to (b, c) into p subintervals (not necessarily equal in length) and the line segment from (a, c) to (a, d) into q subintervals (not necessarily equal in length). Using the points of subdivision obtained in this manner, we draw lines parallel to the x- and y-axes and obtain $pq = n$ closed rectangles $\Delta A_1, \Delta A_2, \cdots, \Delta A_i, \cdots, \Delta A_n$ as shown in Fig. 17.1. Since $z = f(x, y)$ is continuous on each closed rectangle ΔA_i, z assumes an absolute maximum M_i at some point (ξ_i, η_i) of ΔA_i by Theorem 16–II.

We now multiply the area ΔA_i by $M_i = f(\xi_i, \eta_i)$ to obtain the volume of a parallelepiped having base ΔA_i and height $f(\xi_i, \eta_i)$. The sum

$$\sum_{i=1}^{n} f(\xi_i, \eta_i)\, \Delta A_i \tag{17.1}$$

of the volumes of the n parallelepipeds based upon the n closed rectangles is greater than or equal to the real number V that we intuitively feel represents the required volume.

Similarly, $z = f(x, y)$ assumes an absolute minimum m_i at some point (α_i, β_i) of ΔA_i (also by Theorem 16–II). The sum

$$\sum_{i=1}^{n} f(\alpha_i, \beta_i)\, \Delta A_i \tag{17.2}$$

is less than or equal to V.

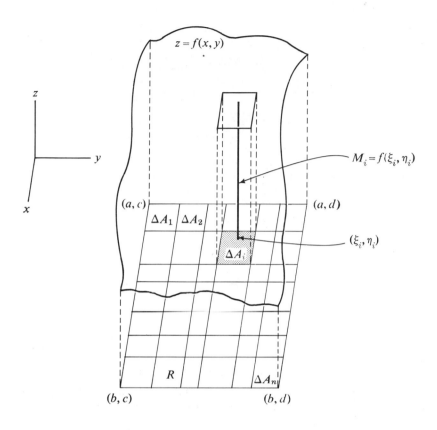

Figure 17.1

Let d represent the longest diagonal of the n rectangles ΔA_i. It is proved in Ref. 17.1 that if the number of rectangles n increases without limit in such a manner that d approaches zero in length, then the sums in (17.1) and (17.2) both approach the same limit. It is natural to define the volume V as this common limit. That is,

$$V = \lim_{\substack{n \to \infty \\ d \to 0}} \sum_{i=1}^{n} f(\xi_i, \eta_i)\, \Delta A_i. \tag{17.3}$$

It is not obvious that this definition of volume is consistent with the definition given in Sec. 4.13. We state without proof that the two definitions are consistent, meaning that both definitions yield the same answer when applied to compute a particular volume.

We next consider a more general region R. Let R consist of all points (x, y) in the xy-plane such that $a \leqslant x \leqslant b$ and $y_1(x) \leqslant y \leqslant y_2(x)$, where $y = y_1(x)$ and $y = y_2(x)$ define continuous functions of x on $a \leqslant x \leqslant b$. A closed rectangle Q, which has one side on $x = a$, one side on $x = b$, and which contains all points of R, is drawn as shown in Fig. 17.2. This rectangle is subdivided into closed subrectangles, as was the rectangle of Fig. 17.1.

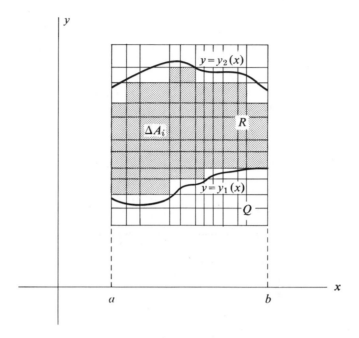

Figure 17.2

It is proved in Ref. 17.1 that V is still given by (17.3) if we employ only the shaded subrectangles which are contained entirely in R. As $d \rightarrow 0$, the portion of R not covered by the shaded rectangles approaches zero in area, and the volume above it approaches zero.

17.2 Definition of a Double Integral

A region S in the xy-plane is an open set of infinitely many points, any two of which can be joined by an arc consisting entirely of points of S. The points of a region S together with the points of the boundary of S form a set known as a closed region. Let $f(x, y)$ define a function continuous on a closed and bounded region R. We divide R into n closed subregions $\Delta A_1, \Delta A_2, \cdots, \Delta A_i, \cdots, \Delta A_n$ in arbitrary fashion, as shown in Fig. 17.3.

Let d_i denote the maximum distance between two points chosen arbitrarily from ΔA_i. It can be shown that this distance, called the diameter of the set, exists whenever the set is closed. It is seen by inspection that the diameter d_1 of ΔA_1 in Fig. 17.3 is PT. Let d denote the maximum of the diameters $d_1, d_2, \cdots, d_i, \cdots, d_n$.

Now let (ξ_i, η_i) be an arbitrary point of ΔA_i and form the sum

$$\sum_{i=1}^{n} f(\xi_i, \eta_i) \, \Delta A_i.$$

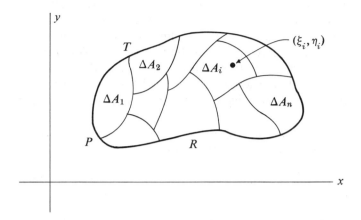

Figure 17.3

The limit of this sum as $n \longrightarrow \infty$ and $d \longrightarrow 0$, if it always exists and always has the same value, is called the double integral of the function f over the region R. This integral is denoted by

$$\iint_R f(x, y) \, dA = \lim_{\substack{n \to \infty \\ d \to 0}} \sum_{i=1}^{n} f(\xi_i, \eta_i) \, \Delta A_i. \tag{17.4}$$

If the limit in (17.4) exists, we say that the function f is integrable over R. More precisely, the integral exists if for every $\epsilon > 0$, there exists a $\delta > 0$ such that

$$\left| \iint_R f(x, y) \, dA - \sum_{i=1}^{n} f(\xi_i, \eta_i) \, \Delta A_i \right| < \epsilon \tag{17.5}$$

whenever $d < \delta$. Equation (17.5) must hold for all subdivisions of R for which $d < \delta$, irrespective of the manner in which (ξ_i, η_i) is chosen in ΔA_i. The quantity d is known as the norm of the subdivision.

The following important theorem, proved in Ref. 17.4, states sufficient conditions for the existence of a double integral.

Theorem 17-I. Let $f(x, y)$ define a function f continuous in a closed and bounded region R. Then f is integrable over R.

If $f(x, y)$ is nonnegative in R, then the double integral of f over R gives the volume under the surface $z = f(x, y)$ and above R. If $f(x, y)$ is negative in R, it is easy to see that the double integral of f over R gives the negative of the volume above $z = f(x, y)$ and under R. Finally, if $f(x, y)$ is positive in R_1 and negative in R_2, where R_1 and R_2 constitute a subdivision of R into two closed subregions, then the double integral of f over R gives the algebraic sum of the positive volume over R_1 and the negative of the volume under R_2. The argument is analogous to that used in connection with the area under a curve.

Although the double integral defined by (17.4) is independent of the concept of volume under a surface, it is always possible and often convenient to interpret the double integral as representing a volume. The integral in (17.4) is termed a double integral because it involves a function of two variables, x and y. In contrast, an integral of the form $\int f(x)\,dx$ is called a single integral, since it involves a function of a single variable x. The symbol dA in (17.4) does not denote the differential of a function, but was introduced historically to suggest the limiting process involving ΔA_i.

The following theorems express properties of double integrals which are analogous to the corresponding properties of single integrals.

Theorem 17-II.   If $f(x, y)$ and $g(x, y)$ are continuous on a closed and bounded region R, then

$$\iint_R [f(x, y) + g(x, y)]\,dA = \iint_R f(x, y)\,dA + \iint_R g(x, y)\,dA.$$

Theorem 17-III.   If $f(x, y)$ is continuous on a closed and bounded region R, and if R is divided into two closed subregions R_1 and R_2, then

$$\iint_R f(x, y)\,dA = \iint_{R_1} f(x, y)\,dA + \iint_{R_2} f(x, y)\,dA.$$

Theorem 17-IV.   If $f(x, y)$ is integrable over the region R, and if c is a constant, then

$$\iint_R cf(x, y)\,dA = c \iint_R f(x, y)\,dA.$$

PROBLEM LIST 99

1. Give five examples of closed and bounded regions in the xy-plane.

2. Give an example of a set of points in the xy-plane which is
    (a) closed, but not bounded;
    (b) bounded, but not closed;
    (c) open, and bounded;
    (d) open and bounded, but not a region.

3. Find the diameter of the set of points (x, y)
    (a) satisfying $x^2 + y^2 \leqslant 4$;
    (b) satisfying $x^2/9 + y^2/4 = 1$;
    (c) on and inside the closed rectangle having vertices $(0, 0)$, $(5, 0)$, $(5, 3)$, and $(0, 3)$.

4. Express the area S of a closed and bounded region R as a double integral.

5. Find the double integral of the function defined by $f(x, y) \equiv 7$ over the closed triangle having vertices $(0, 0)$, $(8, 0)$, and $(7, 3)$.

6. State the theorems involving single integrals which correspond to Theorems 17-II, 17-III, and 17-IV.

7. Prove

> (a) Theorem 17-II,
>
> (b) Theorem 17-III,
>
> (c) Theorem 17-IV.

17.3   Iterated Integrals

Single integrals are seldom evaluated by applying the definition of a single integral. Instead, the second fundamental theorem of calculus is usually applied. Similarly, it is quite difficult to evaluate the double integral $(\int\int)_R f(x, y) \, dA$ by applying definition (17.4). The purpose of this section is to develop a procedure for evaluating double integrals.

Let us assume that R is a region of the type illustrated in Fig. 17.2 and that $f(x, y)$ defines a function continuous and nonnegative in R. We will develop a method for computing the volume of the solid under the surface $z = f(x, y)$ and above R. Since the double integral can be interpreted as representing this volume, the method for computing the volume will also be a method of evaluating the double integral.

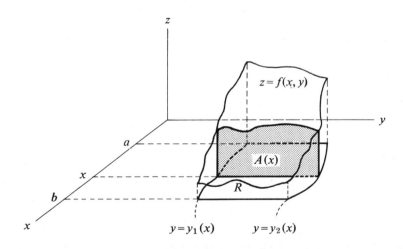

Figure 17.4

In Fig. 17.4, x represents any number satisfying $a \leqslant x \leqslant b$ and area $A(x)$ is the intersection of the plane perpendicular to the x-axis at $x = x$ and the solid whose volume we seek. If we temporarily regard x as fixed, the height $f(x, y)$ of $A(x)$ becomes a function of y alone, where y varies from $y_1(x)$ to $y_2(x)$. Hence $A(x)$ can be determined by the single integration

$$A(x) = \int_{y_1(x)}^{y_2(x)} f(x, y) \, dy. \tag{17.6}$$

We know that the integral in (17.6) exists because $f(x, y)$ defines a continuous function of y in $y_1(x) \leqslant y \leqslant y_2(x)$. This follows readily from the definition of continuity of a function of two variables x and y. Furthermore, it can be shown that $A(x)$ defines a continuous function of x in $a \leqslant x \leqslant b$ if we now regard x as variable. This fact is proved in Ref. 17.1. Thus the required volume can be computed by the moving cross-section method of Sec. 8.2. Substituting from (17.6) into (8.4),

$$V = \int_a^b A(x)\, dx,$$

we obtain

$$V = \int_a^b \left[\int_{y_1(x)}^{y_2(x)} f(x, y)\, dy \right] dx. \tag{17.7}$$

The right member of (17.7) is called an iterated integral, since its evaluation requires an integration followed by another integration. The value of the iterated integral is the value of the double integral of f over R.

To avoid the use of brackets we will write (17.7) as

$$V = \int_a^b dx \int_{y_1(x)}^{y_2(x)} f(x, y)\, dy. \tag{17.8}$$

We have thus arrived at the important formula

$$\iint_R f(x, y)\, dA = \int_a^b dx \int_{y_1(x)}^{y_2(x)} f(x, y)\, dy. \tag{17.9}$$

Although we assumed $f(x, y)$ to be nonnegative in R, it can be shown that (17.9) is valid if $f(x, y)$ is merely continuous in R. A proof of this fact is given in Ref. 17.6.

Example 1.   Evaluate the iterated integral

$$\int_1^2 dx \int_x^{x^2} 2xy\, dy.$$

Solution

$$\int_1^2 \left[xy^2 \right]_{y=x}^{y=x^2} dx = \int_1^2 (x^5 - x^3)\, dx$$

$$= \frac{x^6}{6} - \frac{x^4}{4} \Big]_1^2 = \frac{27}{4}.$$

Example 2.   Find the volume under the paraboloid $z = x^2 + y^2$ and above the region R in the xy-plane bounded by the lines $y = 0$, $x = 1$, and $y = x$. See Fig. 17.5.

Solution.   By (17.8),

$$V = \int_0^1 dx \int_0^x (x^2 + y^2)\, dy$$

$$= \int_0^1 \left[x^2 y + \frac{y^3}{3} \right]_{y=0}^{y=x} dx$$

$$= \int_0^1 \frac{4x^3}{3}\, dx = \frac{x^4}{3} \Big]_0^1 = \frac{1}{3} \text{ cubic unit.}$$

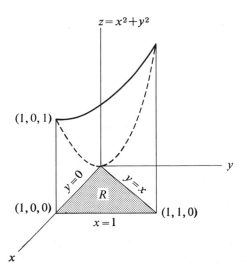

Figure 17.5

Example 3.   Express as a double integral the area in the xy-plane bounded by $x = -1$, $x = 1$, $y = 3x^2$, and $y = 2x - 1$. Evaluate the double integral by means of an iterated integral. See Fig. 17.6.

Solution.   Setting $f(x, y) \equiv 1$ in (17.4) we see that the resulting double integral gives the required area A, since

$$\sum_{i=1}^{n} \Delta A_i = A.$$

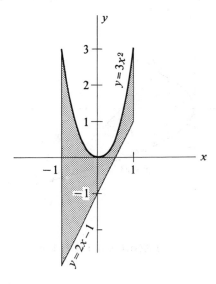

Figure 17.6

Hence

$$A = \iint_A dA = \int_{-1}^{1} dx \int_{2x-1}^{3x^2} dy$$

$$= \int_{-1}^{1} \left[y \right]_{y=2x-1}^{y=3x^2} dx$$

$$= \int_{-1}^{1} (3x^2 - 2x + 1) \, dx = x^3 - x^2 + x \Big]_{-1}^{1}$$

$$= (1) - (-3) = 4 \text{ square units.}$$

By interchanging the roles played by x and y, we can evaluate double integrals over a region bounded by the lines $y = c$ and $y = d$ and the curves $x = x_1(y)$ and $x = x_2(y)$. Equation (17.9) becomes

$$\iint_R f(x, y) \, dA = \int_c^d dy \int_{x_1(y)}^{x_2(y)} f(x, y) \, dx. \tag{17.10}$$

If a region R is more complicated, it is sometimes possible to subdivide it into subregions and then to apply Theorem 17–III.

Example 4.   Find the area A of the region R in the xy-plane bounded by the parabola $x = y^2$ and the line $x + y = 2$. See Fig. 17.7.

Solution.   We first find that the curves intersect at $(1, 1)$ and $(4, -2)$. We then apply (17.10) with $f(x, y) \equiv 1$ to obtain

$$A = \iint_R dA = \int_{-2}^{1} dy \int_{y^2}^{2-y} dx$$

$$= \int_{-2}^{1} (2 - y - y^2) \, dy$$

$$= 2y - \frac{y^2}{2} - \frac{y^3}{3} \Big]_{-2}^{1} = 4.5 \text{ square units.}$$

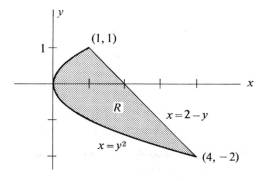

Figure 17.7

PROBLEM LIST 100

1. Evaluate

(a) $\int_1^2 dx \int_0^x xy \, dy$;

(b) $\int_0^3 dx \int_x^{x^2} (x + y) \, dy$;

(c) $\displaystyle\int_1^2 dx \int_{1-x^2}^{x+1} x\, dy;$

(g) $\displaystyle\int_0^{\pi/2} d\theta \int_0^{\cos\theta} r\, dr;$

(d) $\displaystyle\int_3^5 dx \int_2^4 x^2 y\, dy;$

(h) $\displaystyle\int_0^1 dy \int_y^{\sqrt{y}} 2xy^2\, dx;$

(e) $\displaystyle\int_3^4 dx \int_{\sin x}^{x^2} dy;$

(i) $\displaystyle\int_0^1 dy \int_{y^2-1}^y (x-y)\, dx.$

(f) $\displaystyle\int_1^2 dx \int_1^x x^2 e^{xy}\, dy;$

2. Find the volume under the surface $z = 1 - y^2$ and above the region bounded by $x = 0$, $y = 1$, and $y = x$.

3. Find the volume under the paraboloid $z = x^2 + y^2$ and above the triangle having vertices $(0, 0)$, $(2, 0)$, and $(2, 4)$.

4. Find the volume under the plane $z = x$ and above the region bounded by $x = y^2$ and $x = y + 2$.

5. Find the volume under the surface $z = 2y$ and above the rectangle having vertices $(0, 0)$, $(3, 0)$, $(0, 2)$, and $(3, 2)$.

6. Find the volume under the plane $z = x + y$ and above the first-quadrant region bounded by $x = 0$, $y = 1$, and $y = x^2$.

7. Find the volume bounded by the cylinder $x^2 + y^2 = 1$ and the planes $z = 2y + 3$ and $z = 0$.

8. Find the volume under the plane $z = x + 5$ and above the region bounded by $y = |x|$ and $y = 1$.

9. Find the volume of the tetrahedron bounded by the coordinate axes and the plane $(x/a) + (y/b) + (z/c) = 1$. Assume that a, b, and c are positive.

10. Each of the following iterated integrals gives the area of a region R in the xy-plane. Sketch the region in each case.

(a) $\displaystyle\int_0^1 dx \int_2^5 dy.$

(d) $\displaystyle\int_1^2 dx \int_{-3}^{4-2x} dy.$

(b) $\displaystyle\int_0^1 dy \int_2^5 dx.$

(e) $\displaystyle\int_0^1 dy \int_0^{e^y} dx.$

(c) $\displaystyle\int_1^3 dx \int_{-x}^{x^2} dy.$

(f) $\displaystyle\int_{-1}^2 dy \int_{y^2-4}^{4-y^2} dx.$

11. Employ an iterated integral to find the area bounded by
(a) $y = x^2$, $y = 0$, and $x = 2$;
(b) $y = x^3$ and $y = x$;
(c) $y = \sin x$, $y = 0$, $x = 0$, and $x = \pi/6$;
(d) $y = x$, $xy = 4$, and $y = 1$;
(e) $x = 0$, $y = 0$, and $(x/a) + (y/b) = 1$ (a and b positive);
(f) $y = x^2 - 1$ and $y = x + 1$;
(g) $x = y^2 - 2y$ and $x = 2y$;
(h) $x = y^2 + y$ and $x = 2y + 2$.

12. Without evaluating either integral explain the equality

$$\int_0^1 dx \int_0^{2x} (x^4 + y^4)\, dy = \int_0^2 dy \int_{y/2}^1 (x^4 + y^4)\, dx.$$

13. Find the volume of a sphere by means of an iterated integral.

17.4   Double Integrals Using Polar Coordinates

Let $f(x, y)$ define a function continuous in the region R consisting of all points (x, y) in the xy — plane whose polar coordinates satisfy $\alpha \leqslant \theta \leqslant \beta$ and $c \leqslant r \leqslant d$. We subdivide the interval $\alpha \leqslant \theta \leqslant \beta$ into p subintervals (not necessarily equal) and the interval $c \leqslant r \leqslant d$ into q subintervals (not necessarily equal). Using these subintervals, we draw radial lines and circular arcs to produce the subdivision of R into $pq = n$ closed subregions $\Delta A_1, \Delta A_2, \cdots, \Delta A_i, \cdots, \Delta A_n$ shown in Fig. 17.8.

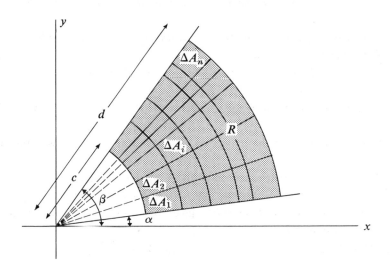

Figure 17.8

In Fig. 17.9 the polar coordinates of the vertices of ΔA_i are shown. The index j runs from 0 to p and the index k runs from 0 to q. The area of ΔA_i, found by Formula 3 of Appendix A, is given by

$$\frac{1}{2} r_k^2 \, \Delta\theta_j - \frac{1}{2} r_{k-1}^2 \, \Delta\theta_j = \frac{r_k + r_{k-1}}{2}(r_k - r_{k-1}) \, \Delta\theta_j$$

$$= r_i \, \Delta r_k \, \Delta\theta_j,$$

where $r_i = (1/2)(r_k + r_{k-1})$ is the average of r_k and r_{k-1}, $\Delta r_k = r_k - r_{k-1}$, and $\Delta\theta_j = \theta_j - \theta_{j-1}$.

We now let (r_i, θ_i) be an arbitrary point of ΔA_i subject to the restriction that $r_i = (1/2)(r_k + r_{k-1})$. Then, by (17.4), the double integral of f over R is given by

$$\iint_R f(x, y) \, dA = \lim_{\substack{n \to \infty \\ d \to 0}} \sum_{i=1}^{n} f(r_i \cos \theta_i, r_i \sin \theta_i) \, \Delta A_i, \qquad (17.11)$$

where d is the maximum of the diameters of the ΔA_i. Letting $f(r \cos \theta, r \sin \theta)$

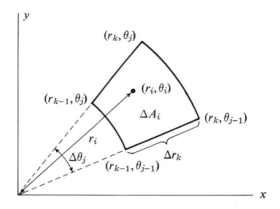

Figure 17.9

$= F(r, \theta)$ and $\Delta T_i = \Delta r_k \Delta \theta_j$, we have

$$f(r_i \cos \theta_i, r_i \sin \theta_i) \Delta A_i = F(r_i, \theta_i)[r_i \Delta T_i]$$
$$= [r_i F(r_i, \theta_i)] \Delta T_i.$$

It can be shown that, due to the continuity of f, the function defined by $rF(r, \theta)$ is continuous in the rectangular region T of the $r\theta$-plane defined by $\alpha \leqslant \theta \leqslant \beta$ and $c \leqslant r \leqslant d$. See Ref. 17.3 and Fig. 17.10. Thus

$$\lim_{\substack{n \to \infty \\ d \to 0}} \sum_{i=1}^{n} f(r_i, \cos \theta_i, r_i \sin \theta_i) \Delta A_i = \lim_{\substack{n \to \infty \\ \delta \to 0}} \sum_{i=1}^{n} r_i F(r_i, \theta_i) \Delta T_i, \qquad \textbf{(17.12)}$$

where δ is the maximum diameter of the ΔT_i.

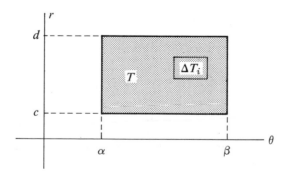

Figure 17.10

Since the right member of (17.12) gives the double integral of the function defined by $rF(r, \theta)$ over the region T, we have

$$\iint_R f(x, y) \, dA = \iint_T rF(r, \theta) \, dT. \qquad \textbf{(17.13)}$$

The integral on the right side of (17.13) can be evaluated by means of an iterated integral, and hence we obtain

$$\iint_R f(x, y)\, dA = \int_\alpha^\beta d\theta \int_c^d r F(r, \theta)\, dr$$

$$= \int_c^d r\, dr \int_\alpha^\beta F(r, \theta)\, d\theta. \qquad (17.14)$$

We state without proof that the method can be extended to include regions of the types shown in Fig. 17.11 and Fig. 17.12. This topic is considered in courses in advanced calculus as a change in the variables in a double integral.

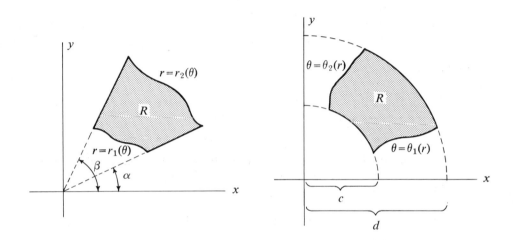

Figure 17.11   Figure 17.12

For a region of the type shown in Fig. 17.11, formula (17.14) becomes

$$\iint_R f(x, y)\, dA = \int_\alpha^\beta d\theta \int_{r_1(\theta)}^{r_2(\theta)} r F(r, \theta)\, dr, \qquad (17.15)$$

and for the type shown in Fig. 17.12,

$$\iint_R f(x, y)\, dA = \int_c^d r\, dr \int_{\theta_1(r)}^{\theta_2(r)} F(r, \theta)\, d\theta. \qquad (17.16)$$

The iterated integrals in (17.15) and (17.16) are often simpler to evaluate than those in (17.9) and (17.10). The student must remember to include the factor r in the integrand.

Example 1.   Find the volume under the surface $z = (x^2 + y^2)^{-1/2}$ and above the shaded region R in Fig. 17.13 bounded by the circles $x^2 + y^2 - 2y = 0$ and $x^2 + y^2 = 1$ and the lines $x = 0$ and $y = x$.

Solution.   In polar coordinates, $z = r^{-1}$ and the boundaries of R have equations $r = 2 \sin \theta, r = 1, \theta = \pi/2$, and $\theta = \pi/4$. Hence, by (17.15),

$$V = \iint_R (x^2 + y^2)^{-1/2} \, dA$$

$$= \int_{\pi/4}^{\pi/2} d\theta \int_1^{2\sin\theta} r^{-1} r \, dr$$

$$= \int_{\pi/4}^{\pi/2} (2\sin\theta - 1) \, d\theta$$

$$= -2\cos\theta - \theta \Big]_{\pi/4}^{\pi/2}$$

$$= \sqrt{2} - \frac{\pi}{4} \text{ cubic unit.}$$

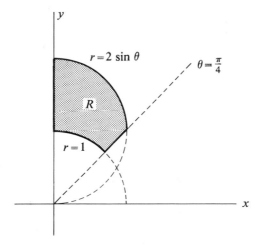

Figure 17.13

Example 2.   Derive the formula for the volume of a sphere.

Solution.   Let the sphere have equation $x^2 + y^2 + z^2 = a^2$. By symmetry, the volume is equal to eight times the first-octant volume which is above the first-quadrant portion of the circle $x^2 + y^2 = a^2$. Hence

$$V = 8 \int_0^a dx \int_0^{\sqrt{a^2 - x^2}} \sqrt{a^2 - (x^2 + y^2)} \, dy$$

$$= 8 \int_0^{\pi/2} d\theta \int_0^a r(a^2 - r^2)^{1/2} \, dr$$

$$= -4 \int_0^{\pi/2} d\theta \int_0^a (a^2 - r^2)^{1/2}(-2r \, dr)$$

$$= -4 \int_0^{\pi/2} \left[\frac{2}{3}(a^2 - r^2)^{3/2} \right]_0^a d\theta$$

$$= \frac{8a^3}{3} \int_0^{\pi/2} d\theta = \frac{4\pi a^3}{3} \text{ cubic units.}$$

Example 3.   Find the shaded area in Fig. 17.14 bounded by the circles $r = 1$ and $r = 3$, the line $\theta = 0$, and the spiral $\theta = 1/r$.

Solution. Equations (17.15) and (17.16) represent areas if $F(r, \theta) \equiv 1$. By (17.16) we obtain

$$A = \int_1^3 r \, dr \int_0^{1/r} d\theta$$

$$= \int_1^3 \left(\frac{r \, dr}{r} \right) = 2 \text{ square units.}$$

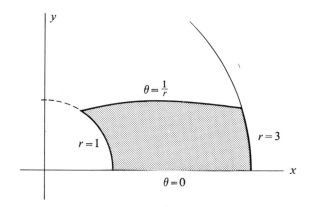

Figure 17.14

PROBLEM LIST 101

1. Find the volume under the paraboloid $z = x^2 + y^2$ and above the first-quadrant region between the circles $x^2 + y^2 = 1$ and $x^2 + y^2 = 4$.

2. Find the volume under the surface $z = (x^2 + y^2)^{-1}$ and above the region between the circles $x^2 + y^2 = 1$ and $x^2 + y^2 = 9$.

3. Find the volume under the paraboloid $z = x^2 + y^2$ and above the circle $x^2 + y^2 = 2x$.

4. Find the volume under the plane $z = x$ and above the first-quadrant segment of the circle $x^2 + y^2 = 2y$ cut off by the line $y = x$.

5. Find the volume bounded by the half-cone $z = \sqrt{x^2 + y^2}$ and the plane $z = 2$.

6. Solve illustrative Example 3 by subdividing the given region into two closed subregions and employing (17.15).

7. Find the volume under the surface $z = x^3 + xy^2$ and above the first-quadrant portion of the circle $x^2 + y^2 = 4$.

8. Find the volume under the sphere $x^2 + y^2 + z^2 = 4$ and above the first-quadrant region bounded by the y-axis, the circles $x^2 + y^2 = 1$ and $x^2 + y^2 = 4$, and the spiral having polar equation $\theta = r/2$.

9. Employ an iterated integral to find the area
   (a) inside the circle $r = 5$;
   (b) inside the circle $r = 5$ and to the right of the line $r = 2 \sec \theta$;
   (c) inside the first-quadrant loop of the curve $r = \sin 2\theta$;

(d) inside the cardioid $r = 1 + \cos \theta$ and outside the circle $r = 1$;

(e) in the first quadrant inside the lemniscate $r^2 = 2 \cos 2\theta$ and outside the circle $r = 1$;

(f) inside the cardioid $r = 1 - \cos \theta$;

(g) inside the circles $r = 1/2$ and $r = \sin \theta$, and outside the circle $r = 1/4$.

10. Find by two methods the area bounded by the line $\theta = \pi/2$ and the portion of the spiral $r = \sqrt{\theta}$ corresponding to the interval $0 \leqslant \theta \leqslant \pi/2$.

11. Derive a formula for the area of a segment of a circle. See Fig. 17.15.

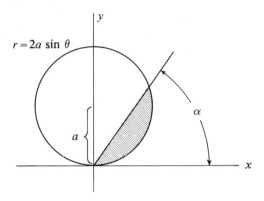

Figure 17.15

12. Find the volume common to the sphere $x^2 + y^2 + z^2 = a^2$ and the cylinder $x^2 + y^2 = b^2 (b < a)$.

13. Find the volume common to the sphere $x^2 + y^2 + z^2 = a^2$ and the cylinder $x^2 + y^2 = ax$.

14. Evaluate the integral

$$I = \int_0^\infty e^{-x^2} \, dx.$$

Hint.

$$I^2 = \left(\int_0^\infty e^{-x^2} \, dx \right) \left(\int_0^\infty e^{-x^2} \, dx \right)$$
$$= \left(\int_0^\infty e^{-x^2} \, dx \right) \left(\int_0^\infty e^{-y^2} \, dy \right)$$
$$= \int_0^\infty dx \int_0^\infty e^{-(x^2+y^2)} \, dy.$$

This integral plays an important role in the theory of probability and statistics.

15. Let $z = f(x)$ define a nonnegative function on $a \leqslant x \leqslant b$. Consider the area in the xz-plane bounded by the x-axis, the lines $x = a$ and $x = b$, and the curve $z = f(x)$. The volume generated when this area is revolved about the z-axis is given by

$$\iint_R f(\sqrt{x^2 + y^2}) \, dA$$

where R is the region in the xy-plane between the circles $x^2 + y^2 = b^2$ and $x^2 + y^2$

$= a^2$. Express the volume as an iterated integral in polar coordinates. Compare the result with formula (8.5) and thereby show that the double-integral definition of volume and the definition employed in the cylindrical-shell method are consistent.

17.5 Mass of a Plane Lamina

We assume that a thin plate, called a plane lamina, covers a closed bounded region R of the xy-plane. A subdivision of R into closed subregions ΔA_i yields a corresponding subdivision of the lamina. Let Δm be the mass of the portion of the lamina covering a closed subregion ΔA and let (x, y) be an arbitrary point in ΔA. We now allow ΔA to approach zero in such a manner that the diameter of ΔA approaches zero and ΔA always contains the point (x, y). If $\Delta m/\Delta A$ approaches a limit, this limit is called the areal density of the lamina at (x, y) and is denoted by $\rho(x, y)$. If the density function given by $\rho(x, y)$ is constant throughout R, the lamina is said to be homogeneous. We restrict ourselves to cases in which $\rho(x, y)$ is continuous and nonnegative in R.

If the diameter of ΔA_i is small and (x_i, y_i) is an arbitrary point of ΔA_i, the product $\rho(x_i, y_i) \Delta A_i$ would appear to be an approximation to the mass covering ΔA_i. Similarly, the sum

$$\sum_{i=1}^{n} \rho(x_i, y_i) \Delta A_i$$

would appear to be an approximation to the mass covering R. This prompts us to define the mass m covering R by

$$m = \lim_{\substack{n \to \infty \\ d \to 0}} \sum_{i=1}^{n} \rho(x_i, y_i) \, \Delta A_i = \iint_R \rho(x, y) \, dA, \tag{17.17}$$

where d denotes the maximum of the diameters of the subregions ΔA_i.

Example 1. Find the mass of the lamina covering the region R bounded by $y = x^2$, $y = 0$, and $x = 1$ if the density of the lamina is given by $\rho = kx^2y$, k being constant.

Solution. By (17.17),

$$m = \iint_R kx^2 y \, dA = \int_0^1 kx^2 \, dx \int_0^{x^2} y \, dy$$

$$= \int_0^1 kx^2 \left[\frac{y^2}{2} \right]_0^{x^2} dx$$

$$= k \int_0^1 \frac{x^6}{2} \, dx = \frac{k}{14}.$$

Example 2. Find the mass of the lamina covering the circle $r = \sin \theta$ if the density at any point of the lamina is proportional to the distance of the point from the pole.

Solution.   Using $\rho(r, \theta) = kr$, we obtain

$$m = \iint\limits_{R} kr \, dA = \int_0^\pi k \, d\theta \int_0^{\sin\theta} r^2 \, dr$$

$$= \frac{k}{3} \int_0^\pi \sin^3\theta \, d\theta$$

$$= \frac{k}{3}(2)\left(\frac{2}{3}\right) = \frac{4k}{9}.$$

17.6   First Moment and Center of Mass

In Fig. 17.16, (x_i, y_i) is an arbitrary point of the closed subregion ΔA_i of the closed bounded region R. We assume that R is covered by a plane lamina of density $\rho(x, y)$. If the mass Δm_i covering ΔA_i were concentrated at (x_i, y_i), the product of this mass Δm_i and the distance $x_i - x_0$ from (x_i, y_i) to the line $x = x_0$ would be a measure of the tendency of the mass Δm_i to rotate about the line $x = x_0$. A positive product would indicate a tendency to rotate in one direction, while a negative product would indicate a tendency to rotate in the opposite direction. The product $(x_i - x_0) \Delta m_i$ is called the first moment of Δm_i about the line $x = x_0$. If ΔA_i has a small diameter, the product $(x_i - x_0) \Delta m_i$ approximates the tendency of Δm_i to rotate about $x = x_0$. Similarly, the sum

$$\sum_{i=1}^{n} (x_i - x_0)\rho(x_i, y_i) \, \Delta A_i \qquad (17.18)$$

approximates the tendency of the entire lamina to rotate about $x = x_0$. The actual tendency of the lamina to rotate about $x = x_0$ is obtained by evaluating the limit of the sum in (17.18) as $n \to \infty$ and the maximum of the diameters of the ΔA_i's approaches zero. This limit, denoted by $M_{x=x_0}$, is called the first moment of the mass of the lamina about $x = x_0$ and is given by

$$M_{x=x_0} = \iint\limits_{R} (x - x_0)\rho(x, y) \, dA. \qquad (17.19)$$

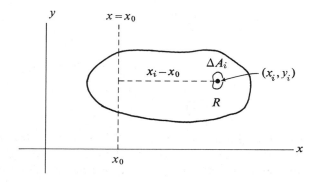

Figure 17.16

The value of x_0 for which $M_{x=x_0} = 0$ is called the x-coordinate of the center of mass of the lamina and is denoted by $\bar{x}$. The lamina would have no tendency to rotate about the line $x = \bar{x}$ and would balance on the axis $x = \bar{x}$. From (17.19) we obtain

$$\iint_R (x - \bar{x})\rho(x, y)\, dA = 0,$$

or

$$\iint_R x\rho(x, y)\, dA = \bar{x} \iint_R \rho(x, y)\, dA.$$

Solving for the constant $\bar{x}$ yields

$$\bar{x} = \frac{\displaystyle\iint_R x\rho(x, y)\, dA}{\displaystyle\iint_R \rho(x, y)\, dA} = \frac{M_{x=0}}{m}. \tag{17.20}$$

Similarly, the y-coordinate $\bar{y}$ of the center of mass is given by

$$\bar{y} = \frac{\displaystyle\iint_R y\rho(x, y)\, dA}{\displaystyle\iint_R \rho(x, y)\, dA} = \frac{M_{y=0}}{m}, \tag{17.21}$$

where

$$M_{y=y_0} = \iint_R (y - y_0)\rho(x, y)\, dA \tag{17.22}$$

is the first moment of the lamina about the line $y = y_0$. The lamina would balance on a pinpoint located at the center of mass $(\bar{x}, \bar{y})$.

If $\rho(x, y)$ is constant, the center of mass is called the centroid of the lamina and (17.20) and (17.21) become

$$\bar{x} = \frac{\displaystyle\iint_R x\, dA}{\displaystyle\iint_R dA} = \frac{\displaystyle\iint_R x\, dA}{A} \tag{17.23}$$

and

$$\bar{y} = \frac{\displaystyle\iint_R y\, dA}{\displaystyle\iint_R dA} = \frac{\displaystyle\iint_R y\, dA}{A}. \tag{17.24}$$

In many important applications formulas (17.23) and (17.24) are applied to plane areas. The integral $(\iint)_R x\, dA$ is called the first moment of the area with respect to the y-axis; the integral $(\iint)_R y\, dA$ is called the first moment of the area with respect to the x-axis; and the point $(\bar{x}, \bar{y})$ is called the centroid of the area.

The average or mean value f_m of $f(x, y)$ over a region R is defined by

$$f_m = \frac{\iint\limits_R f(x, y)\, dA}{A} . \qquad (17.25)$$

Thus the volume under the surface $z = f(x, y)$ and above R is equal to the volume under the plane of constant height $z = f_m$ and above (or below) R.

Equations (17.23) and (17.24) state that $\bar{x}$ is the average value of x over R and $\bar{y}$ is the average value of y over R.

Example 1.   A plane lamina covers the area bounded by the lines $y = x$, $y = 0$, and $x = 1$. Find the coordinates of the center of mass if the density at any point is proportional to the abscissa of the point.

Solution.   Employing $\rho(x, y) = kx$, we obtain

$$M_{x=0} = \int_0^1 dx \int_0^x xkx\, dy$$

$$= k \int_0^1 x^3\, dx = \frac{k}{4},$$

$$M_{y=0} = \int_0^1 dx \int_0^x ykx\, dy$$

$$= \frac{k}{2} \int_0^1 x^3\, dx = \frac{k}{8},$$

and

$$m = \int_0^1 dx \int_0^x kx\, dy$$

$$= k \int_0^1 x^2\, dx = \frac{k}{3}.$$

Equations (17.20) and (17.21) now yield

$$\bar{x} = \frac{k/4}{k/3} = \frac{3}{4}; \qquad \bar{y} = \frac{k/8}{k/3} = \frac{3}{8}.$$

Example 2.   Find the coordinates of the centroid of the area R bounded by a line and a semicircle.

Solution.   Since in Fig. 17.17,

$$\iint\limits_R x\, dA = \iint\limits_{R_1} x\, dA + \iint\limits_{R_2} x\, dA,$$

and since

$$\iint\limits_{R_1} x\, dA = -\iint\limits_{R_2} x\, dA,$$

it follows that $M_{x=0} = 0$ and hence $\bar{x} = 0$.

(Similarly, the centroid of any area lies on a line of symmetry of the area.)

From

$$M_{y=0} = \int_{-a}^{a} dx \int_{0}^{\sqrt{a^2 - x^2}} y \, dy$$

$$= \frac{1}{2} \int_{-a}^{a} (a^2 - x^2) \, dx$$

$$= \frac{a^2 x}{2} - \frac{x^3}{6} \Big]_{-a}^{a} = \frac{2a^3}{3},$$

we obtain

$$\bar{y} = \frac{M_{y=0}}{A} = \frac{2a^3/3}{\pi a^2/2} = \frac{4a}{3\pi}.$$

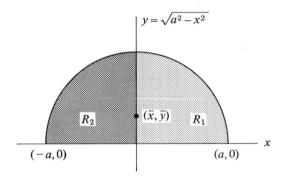

Figure 17.17

Example 3.   Find the coordinates of the centroid of the area bounded by the first-quadrant loop of the curve $r = \sin 2\theta$. See Fig. 17.18.

Solution.   From

$$M_{x=0} = \iint_{R} x \, dA = \int_{0}^{\pi/2} d\theta \int_{0}^{\sin 2\theta} (r \cos \theta) r \, dr$$

$$= \frac{1}{3} \int_{0}^{\pi/2} \sin^3 2\theta \cos \theta \, d\theta$$

$$= \frac{8}{3} \int_{0}^{\pi/2} \sin^3 \theta \cos^4 \theta \, d\theta$$

$$= \frac{8}{3} \frac{2 \cdot 3}{7 \cdot 5 \cdot 3} = \frac{16}{105},$$

and

$$A = \int_{0}^{\pi/2} d\theta \int_{0}^{\sin 2\theta} r \, dr$$

$$= \frac{1}{2} \int_{0}^{\pi/2} \sin^2 2\theta \, d\theta$$

$$= 2 \int_{0}^{\pi/2} \sin^2 \theta \cos^2 \theta \, d\theta$$

$$= 2 \cdot \frac{1}{4 \cdot 2} \cdot \frac{\pi}{2} = \frac{\pi}{8},$$

we obtain

$$\bar{x} = \frac{M_{x=0}}{A} = \frac{16/105}{\pi/8} = \frac{128}{105\pi}.$$

By symmetry, $\bar{y} = \bar{x}$.

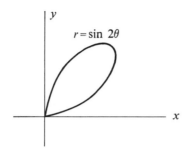

r = sin 2θ

Figure 17.18

PROBLEM LIST 102

1. Find the mass of the plane lamina
   (a) bounded by $y = 2x$, $y = 0$, and $x = 1$, with density proportional to the distance from the x-axis;
   (b) bounded by $y = \sqrt{x}$, $y = 0$, and $x = 4$, with density proportional to the distance from the y-axis;
   (c) bounded by $y = e^x$, $y = 0$, $x = 0$, and $x = 1$, with density proportional to the distance from the x-axis;
   (d) covering the rectangle having vertices $(0, 0)$, $(0, 1)$, $(1, 5)$, and $(0, 5)$, with density proportional to the square of the distance from the origin;
   (e) covering the circle $x^2 + y^2 = 2x$, with density proportional to the distance from the origin.

2. Find the coordinates of the center of mass of the plane lamina
   (a) covering the rectangle having vertices $(0, 0)$, $(0, 4)$, $(2, 4)$, and $(2, 0)$, with density proportional to the distance from the x-axis;
   (b) bounded by $y = x^2$, $y = 0$, and $x = 2$, with density proportional to the distance from the x-axis;
   (c) covering the triangle having vertices $(0, 0)$, $(1, 0)$, and $(2, 2)$, with density proportional to the distance from the y-axis;
   (d) bounded by $y = \log x$, $y = 0$, and $x = 2$, with density proportional to the distance from the y-axis;
   (e) covering the circle $r = 4 \sin \theta$, with density proportional to the square of the distance from the pole.

3. Find the average value of the function defined by $z = x^2 + 3xy$ over the square having vertices $(1, 1)$, $(1, 2)$, $(3, 2)$, and $(3, 1)$.

4. Find the average value of the function defined by $z = (x^2 + y^2)^5$ over the circle $x^2 + y^2 = 1$.

5. Find the centroid of the area bounded by

   (a) $y = x^3$, $y = 0$, and $x = 2$;

   (b) $y = \sqrt{x}$, $y = 1$, and $x = 4$;

   (c) $y = x^2$ and $y = x + 2$;

   (d) $y = 0$ and $y = \sin x$ from $x = 0$ to $x = \pi$;

   (e) $y = x^2$ and $y = \sqrt{x}$;

   (f) the cardioid $r = a(1 + \cos \theta)$;

   (g) the first-quadrant portion of the cardioid $r = 1 - \cos \theta$;

   (h) the limaçon $r = 2 + \cos \theta$;

   (i) the loop of the lemniscate $r^2 = \cos 2\theta$ in quadrants I and IV. (*Hint.* Let $\sin^2 \phi = \cos 2\theta$.)

6. Show that the centroid of a triangle coincides with the intersection of the medians.

7. Find the centroid of a sector of a circle having radius a and central angle 2α.

8. Find the centroid of the first-quadrant area bounded by the hypocycloid $x^{2/3} + y^{2/3} = a^{2/3}$.

9. Find the centroid of the first-quadrant area bounded by the ellipse $b^2 x^2 + a^2 y^2 = a^2 b^2$.

10. Find the centroid of the area bounded by $y = 1 + \sqrt{1 - x^2}$, $y = 0$, $x = -1$, and $x = 1$.

11. Find the centroid of the area bounded by $y = 6 - x^2$ and $y = |x|$.

12. A plane region is revolved about an axis (in its plane) which does not intersect the region. Prove that the volume of the solid generated is equal to the product of the area of the region and the circumference of the circle through which the centroid of the region revolves. This is known as the second theorem of Pappus, after a third-century Greek mathematician.

13. A circle of radius a is revolved about a line in its plane b units away from the center of the circle, where $b > a$. Find the volume of the solid, known as a torus, which is generated.

17.7   *Moment of Inertia*

If the quantity $x_i - x_0$ in equation (17.18) of Sec. 17.6 is replaced by $(x_i - x_0)^2$, the resulting product is an approximate measure of the distribution of the mass of the lamina of Fig. 17.16 relative to the line $x = x_0$. The limit

$$\lim_{\substack{n \to \infty \\ d \to 0}} \sum_{i=1}^{n} (x_i - x_0)^2 \rho(x_i, y_i) \, \Delta A_i$$

is called the second moment of the mass of the lamina, or moment of inertia, about the line $x = x_0$, and is given by

$$I_{x=x_0} = \iint_R (x - x_0)^2 \rho(x, y) \, dA. \tag{17.26}$$

The moment of inertia of the mass of the lamina about the line $y = y_0$ is a measure of the distribution of the mass relative to $y = y_0$, and is given by

$$I_{y=y_0} = \iint_R (y - y_0)^2 \rho(x, y) \, dA. \qquad (17.27)$$

Adding (17.26) and (17.27), we obtain the quantity

$$I_{\substack{x=x_0 \\ y=y_0}} = I_{x=x_0} + I_{y=y_0} = \iint_R [(x - x_0)^2 + (y - y_0)^2] \rho(x, y) \, dA. \qquad (17.28)$$

Since $(x - x_0)^2 + (y - y_0)^2$ is the square of the distance from (x_0, y_0) to (x, y), $I_{\substack{x=x_0 \\ y=y_0}}$ is a measure of the distribution of the mass of the lamina relative to the line l through (x_0, y_0) perpendicular to the xy-plane. The quantity $I_{\substack{x=x_0 \\ y=y_0}}$ is called the polar moment of inertia of the lamina with respect to the line l.

Moments of inertia of plane areas about $x = x_0, y = y_0$, and l are given by

$$I_{x=x_0} = \iint_R (x - x_0)^2 \, dA; \qquad I_{y=y_0} = \iint_R (y - y_0)^2 \, dA; \qquad (17.29)$$

and

$$I_{\substack{x=x_0 \\ y=y_0}} = \iint_R [(x - x_0)^2 + (y - y_0)^2] \, dA. \qquad (17.30)$$

Second moments or moments of inertia play an important role in such subjects as physics, mechanics, and statistics. It should be noted that second moments are nonnegative, whereas first moments may be positive, negative, or zero.

Example 1. A plane lamina covers the area R bounded by $y = \sqrt{x}, y = 0$, and $x = 4$. Find $I_{x=0}, I_{y=0}$, and $I_{\substack{x=0 \\ y=0}}$ if the density of the lamina is proportional to the distance from the y-axis. See Fig. 17.19.

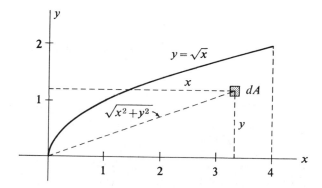

Figure 17.19

Solution

$$I_{x=0} = \iint_R x^2 kx \, dA = k \int_0^4 x^3 \, dx \int_0^{x^{1/2}} dy$$

$$= k \int_0^4 x^{7/2} \, dx = \frac{1024k}{9},$$

$$I_{y=0} = \iint_R y^2 kx \, dA = k \int_0^4 x \, dx \int_0^{x^{1/2}} y^2 \, dy$$

$$= \frac{k}{3} \int_0^4 x^{5/2} \, dx = \frac{256k}{21},$$

and

$$I_{\substack{x=0 \\ y=0}} = I_{x=0} + I_{y=0} = \frac{7936k}{63}.$$

Example 2. Find the polar moment of inertia $I_{\substack{x=0 \\ y=0}}$ for a circular lamina of constant density δ. See Fig. 17.20.

Solution

$$I_{\substack{x=0 \\ y=0}} = \iint_R \delta r^2 \, dA = \delta \int_0^{2\pi} d\theta \int_0^a r^3 \, dr = \frac{\delta \pi a^4}{2}.$$

The quantity $I_{\substack{x=0 \\ y=0}}$ is often written in the form $(\delta \pi a^2)(a^2/2) = m(a^2/2)$ where m is the mass of the lamina. The quantity $k_{\substack{x=0 \\ y=0}} = \sqrt{a^2/2} = a/\sqrt{2}$ is called the radius of gyration of the lamina with respect to the z-axis. If the mass of the lamina were concentrated at $k_{\substack{x=0 \\ y=0}}$ units from the origin, the new mass distribution would have the same polar moment of inertia about the z-axis as does the given mass distribution. Corresponding definitions hold for the radii of gyration $k_{x=0}$ and $k_{y=0}$ with respect to the x- and y-axes.

In Fig. 17.20 the vector $\mathbf{F}$ represents a force of f pounds acting tangent to the circular lamina. This force produces a torque fa tending to cause the lamina to rotate or turn through an angle θ about the z-axis. It is shown in books on mechanics (see Ref. 17.2) that

$$fa = I_{\substack{x=0 \\ y=0}} \times \alpha,$$

where $\alpha = d^2\theta/dt^2$ is the angular acceleration of the circular lamina. If the torque

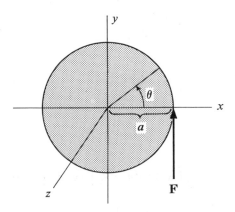

Figure 17.20

fa is constant, the resulting angular acceleration α is inversely proportional to $I_{\substack{x=0 \\ y=0}}$. That is, the quantity $I_{\substack{x=0 \\ y=0}}$ is a measure of the resistance of the lamina to being given angular acceleration. It is due to this application to dynamics that a second moment is called a moment of inertia.

Example 3.   Find $I_{y=0}$ for the area of the rectangle shown in Fig. 17.21(a). Assume $h > w$.

Solution

$$I_{y=0} = \iint_R y^2 \, dA = \int_{-h/2}^{h/2} y^2 \, dy \int_{-w/2}^{w/2} dx = \frac{wh^3}{12}.$$

For the area of the rectangle in Fig. 17.21(b),

$$I_{y=0} = \frac{hw^3}{12} < \frac{wh^3}{12}.$$

The moment of inertia is greater in Fig. 17.21(a) because the area is distributed farther from the *x*-axis.

It is shown in books on the strength of materials (see Ref. 17.5) that the greater the moment of inertia of the cross section of a beam about an axis through the centroid of the cross section, the greater is the resistance of the beam to bending. In Fig. 17.21(c) a cross section of an I-beam is shown. This beam would offer stronger resistance to bending than those having cross sections shown in Figs. 17.21(a) and (b), provided the cross-sectional area was still *wh*.

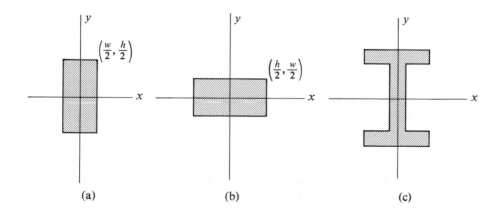

Figure 17.21

In Fig. 17.22, line $x = \bar{x}$ passes through the center of mass of the lamina, $x = x_0$ is any line in the *xy*-plane parallel to $x = \bar{x}$, and $d = |x_0 - \bar{x}|$ is the numerical distance between the two lines. From (17.26) and (17.19) we have

$$I_{x=x_0} = \iint_R (x - x_0)^2 \rho(x, y) \, dA$$

$$= \iint_R [(x - \bar{x}) + (\bar{x} - x_0)]^2 \rho(x, y) \, dA$$

$$= \iint_R (x - \bar{x})^2 \rho(x, y) \, dA$$

$$+ 2(\bar{x} - x_0) \iint_R (x - \bar{x}) \rho(x, y) \, dA$$

$$+ (\bar{x} - x_0)^2 \iint_R \rho(x, y) \, dA$$

$$= I_{x=\bar{x}} \pm 2dM_{x=\bar{x}} + md^2.$$

Denoting $I_{x=\bar{x}}$ by $\bar{I}$ and $M_{x=\bar{x}}$ by $\bar{M}$, and making use of the fact that $\bar{M} = 0$, we obtain the important result

$$I_{x=x_0} = \bar{I} + md^2. \qquad \qquad \textbf{(17.31)}$$

This result is called the parallel axis theorem, or the transfer theorem. To obtain $I_{x=x_0}$, one can look up $\bar{I}$ in a table or manual and "transfer" to $x = x_0$ by (17.31). Note that $\bar{I} \leqslant I_{x=x_0}$ for all values of x_0.

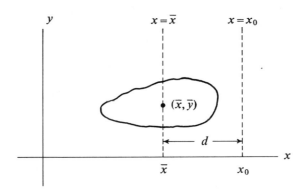

Figure 17.22

The transfer theorem for polar moments of inertia, proved in similar fashion, is given by

$$I_{\substack{x=x_0 \\ y=y_0}} = I_{\substack{x=\bar{x} \\ y=\bar{y}}} + mh^2, \qquad \qquad \textbf{(17.32)}$$

where h is the numerical distance from $(\bar{x}, \bar{y})$ to (x_0, y_0). Equations (17.31) and (17.32) hold for areas when m is replaced by A.

Example 4.   Find the moment of inertia of the area of a circle of radius a about a line l tangent to the circle if the moment of inertia about a diameter is $\pi a^4/4$.

Solution

$$I_l = \bar{I} + Aa^2 = \frac{\pi a^4}{4} + \pi a^4 = \frac{5\pi a^4}{4}.$$

PROBLEM LIST 103

1. Find the moment of inertia about the y-axis of the plane lamina
   (a) bounded by $y = x^2$, $y = 0$, and $x = 3$, with density proportional to the distance from the x-axis;
   (b) bounded by $y = \sqrt{x}$, $y = 0$, and $x = 4$, with density proportional to the square of the distance from the x-axis;
   (c) bounded by the square having vertices $(0, 0)$, $(0, 4)$, $(4, 4)$, and $(4, 0)$, with density proportional to the distance from the y-axis;
   (d) covering the circle $x^2 + y^2 = a^2$, with density proportional to the distance from the origin.

2. Find the moment of inertia about the x-axis of the plane lamina
   (a) bounded by $y = 3x$, $y = 0$, and $x = 2$, with density proportional to the distance from the y-axis;
   (b) bounded by $y = x^2$ and $y = 3x$, with density proportional to the distance from the x-axis;
   (c) covering the triangle having vertices $(0, 0)$, $(0, 4)$, and $(6, 0)$, with density proportional to the square of the distance from the x-axis;
   (d) covering the circle $x^2 + y^2 - 8x = 0$, with density proportional to the cube of the distance from the origin.

3. For the area bounded by $y = x^2$ and $y = x$, find (a) $I_{x=0}$, (b) $I_{y=0}$, (c) $I_{x=1}$, (d) $I_{y=2}$, (e) $I_{x=\bar{x}}$.

4. Find the polar moment of inertia of a circle about a line through the center perpendicular to the plane of the circle.

5. Find the moment of inertia of a rectangle of height h about its base b. What is the radius of gyration about the base?

6. Find $I_{x=0}$ and $I_{y=0}$ for the area bounded by $y = \sin x$ and $y = 0$ for $0 \leqslant x \leqslant \pi$.

7. Find $I_{y=0}$ for the area inside the cardioid $r = a(1 + \cos \theta)$.

8. Find $I_{\substack{x=0 \\ y=0}}$ for the area inside the cardioid $r = 4(1 + \sin \theta)$.

9. A region of area 12 sq in. has its centroid at $(4, 3)$. Given that $I = 16$, find $I_{x=7}$ and $I_{x=-5}$.

10. Find the moment of inertia of the area of an ellipse about the major axis.

11. Find the moment of inertia of the area of a square about a diagonal.

12. Find the moment of inertia about the y-axis for the area bounded by
    (a) $y = 5 + \sqrt{4 - x^2}$, $y = 0$, $x = 2$, and $x = -2$;
    (b) $y = |x|$, $y = 6$, $x = 1$, and $x = -1$.

17.8 Surface Area

Let $z = f(x, y)$ define a function f having continuous partial derivatives f_x and f_y in a closed, bounded region R. We wish to find the area of the surface $z = f(x, y)$ which is above R. We first subdivide R into n closed rectangles ΔA_i

as in Fig. 17.2. Let (ξ_i, η_i) be any point in ΔA_i and let T_i denote the plane tangent to $z = f(x, y)$ at $P_i(\xi_i, \eta_i, f(\xi_i, \eta_i))$. The area ΔT_i of T_i above ΔA_i is an approximation to the area ΔS_i of $z = f(x, y)$ above ΔA_i. The required surface area S is defined as the limit of the sum of the ΔT_i as $n \longrightarrow \infty$ and the maximum diameter d of the $\Delta A_i \longrightarrow 0$. See Fig. 17.23.

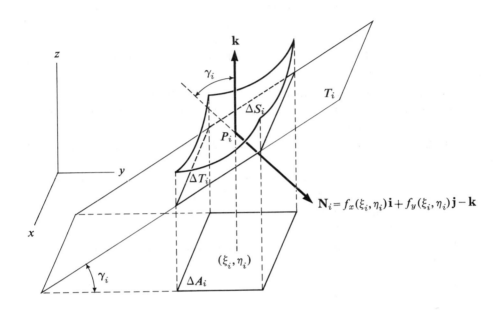

Figure 17.23

It is easy to show that $\Delta T_i = \Delta A_i |\sec \gamma_i|$, where γ_i is the angle between the xy-plane and the plane T_i. But γ_i is also the angle between the normals $\mathbf{k}$ and $\mathbf{N}_i$ to these two planes. (The vector $\mathbf{N}_i$ was discussed in Sec. 16.7.)

From

$$\cos \gamma_i = \frac{\mathbf{N}_i \cdot \mathbf{k}}{|\mathbf{N}_i|} = \frac{-1}{\sqrt{f_x^2(\xi_i, \eta_i) + f_y^2(\xi_i, \eta_i) + 1}},$$

we obtain

$$S = \lim_{\substack{n \to \infty \\ d \to 0}} \sum_{i=1}^{n} |\sec \gamma_i| \, \Delta A_i$$

$$= \lim_{\substack{n \to \infty \\ d \to 0}} \sum_{i=1}^{n} \sqrt{f_x^2(\xi_i, \eta_i) + f_y^2(\xi_i, \eta_i) + 1} \, \Delta A_i.$$

The continuity of $\sqrt{f_x^2 + f_y^2 + 1}$ in R follows from the continuity of f_x and f_y, as does the existence of the tangent plane at P_i.

Hence

$$S = \iint_R \sqrt{f_x^2 + f_y^2 + 1} \, dA. \qquad \textbf{(17.33)}$$

If the surface is represented in the form $F(x, y, z) = 0$, where F_x, F_y, and F_z are continuous and $F_z \neq 0$, (17.33) is replaced by

$$S = \iint_R \frac{\sqrt{F_x^2 + F_y^2 + F_z^2}}{|F_z|} \, dA. \tag{17.34}$$

The value of sec γ_i is obtained by replacing $\mathbf{N}_i$ at P_i by $\mathbf{grad\,F} = F_x\mathbf{i} + F_y\mathbf{j} + F_z\mathbf{k}$.

For a discussion of the definition of surface area the reader is referred to Refs. 17.4 and 17.6.

Example 1.   Find the area of the surface $z = 1 + x^2$ above the region R in the xy-plane bounded by $y = x$, $y = 0$, and $x = 1$. See Fig. 17.24.

Solution.   By (17.33),

$$S = \iint_R \sqrt{(2x)^2 + 1} \, dA$$

$$= \int_0^1 \sqrt{4x^2 + 1} \, dx \int_0^x dy$$

$$= \int_0^1 (4x^2 + 1)^{1/2} x \, dx$$

$$= \frac{1}{8} \cdot \frac{2}{3} (4x^2 + 1)^{3/2} \Big]_0^1$$

$$= \frac{5\sqrt{5} - 1}{12} \text{ square unit.}$$

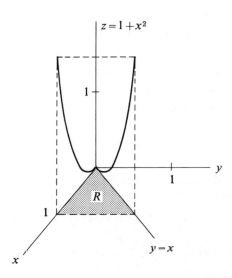

Figure 17.24

Example 2.   Find the surface area S of the sphere $x^2 + y^2 + z^2 - a^2 = 0$.

Solution.   We will employ (17.34) to find the area $S/2$ of the hemisphere above the circle $x^2 + y^2 = a^2$. Since $F_z \equiv 0$ on this circle, we compute the area above the circle $x^2 + y^2 = b^2 (b < a)$, and let $b \to a^-$ in the result. Thus

$$\frac{S}{2} = \lim_{b \to a^-} \iint_{x^2+y^2=b^2} \frac{\sqrt{(2x)^2 + (2y)^2 + (2z)^2}}{|2z|} \, dA$$

$$= \lim_{b \to a^-} \iint_{x^2+y^2=b^2} \frac{a}{\sqrt{a^2 - x^2 - y^2}} \, dA.$$

By changing to polar coordinates we obtain

$$\frac{S}{2} = \lim_{b \to a^-} \int_0^{2\pi} a \, d\theta \int_0^b (a^2 - r^2)^{-1/2} r \, dr$$

$$= \lim_{b \to a^-} \frac{-a}{2} \int_0^{2\pi} \left[2\sqrt{a^2 - r^2} \right]_0^b d\theta$$

$$= \lim_{b \to a^-} [-2\pi a(\sqrt{a^2 - b^2} - a)] = 2\pi a^2,$$

and hence $S = 4\pi a^2$ square units.

PROBLEM LIST 104

1. Find the area of the surface
   (a) $z = x^2$ above the region bounded by $x = 0$, $x = 2$, $y = 0$, and $y = 3$;
   (b) $z = 1 - x^2$ above the region bounded by $y = x$, $y = 0$, and $x = 1$;
   (c) $z = 2x + 3y$ above the region bounded by $y = x$ and $y = x^2$;
   (d) $z = \sqrt{a^2 - x^2 - y^2}$ above the region bounded by $4x^2 + 4y^2 = a^2$;
   (e) $z = y^2$ above the region bounded by $y = 2x$, $x = 0$, and $y = 1$;
   (f) $x^2 + z^2 = 9$ above the rectangle having vertices $(1, 0)$, $(2, 0)$, $(1, 4)$, and $(2, 4)$.

2. Find the area of the triangle cut off from the plane $(x/a) + (y/b) + (z/c) = 1$ by the three coordinate planes. Assume a, b, and c to be positive.

3. Find the surface area of the paraboloid $z = x^2 + y^2$ above the region bounded by $x^2 + y^2 = a^2$.

4. Find the surface area of the cylinder $z^2 + y^2 = a^2$ above the region bounded by $x^2 + y^2 = a^2$.

5. Show that the lateral surface S of a right-circular cone of base radius r and slant height l is given by $S = \pi r l$.

6. Find the area of the surface $z = xy$ above the first-quadrant region inside the circle $x^2 + y^2 = a^2$.

7. Find the surface area of the sphere $x^2 + y^2 + z^2 = 4a^2$ above the region bounded by the circle $x^2 + y^2 = 2ax$.

8. Find the area of the portion of the surface of the sphere $x^2 + y^2 + z^2 = 2a^2$ which is within the paraboloid $x^2 + y^2 = az$.

9. In Problem 8 find the surface area of the portion of the paraboloid which lies within the sphere.

10. Find the area of the portion of the surface $z^2 = y$ whose projection in the xz-plane is the triangle having vertices $(0, 0, 0)$, $(0, 0, 2)$, and $(2, 0, 2)$.

11. Find the area of the portion of the surface $x = y^2 + 1$ whose projection in the yz-plane is the rectangle having vertices $(0, 0, 0)$, $(0, 3, 0)$, $(0, 3, 4)$, and $(0, 0, 4)$.

12. Show that formula (8.19),

$$S = 2\pi \int_a^b f(x)\sqrt{1 + [f'(x)]^2}\, dx,$$

is a special case of formula (17.33).

17.9 *Definition of a Triple Integral*

The definition of a triple integral is analogous to that of a double integral. We consider a region Q in three-space consisting of infinitely many points, any two of which can be joined by an arc consisting entirely of points of Q. The set Q is assumed to be open, meaning that for every point P of Q there exists a sphere centered at P and contained entirely in Q. By a boundary point of Q we mean a point B having the property that every sphere centered at B contains points in Q and also points not in Q. The set T consisting of Q together with the boundary points of Q is called a closed region. We say that T is bounded if every point of T lies inside a sphere centered at the origin.

Let $f(x, y, z)$ define a function continuous on a closed and bounded region T. This means that if $P_0(x_0, y_0, z_0)$ is any point of T, then $f(x, y, z) \rightarrow f(x_0, y_0, z_0)$ as $P(x, y, z) \rightarrow P_0(x_0, y_0, z_0)$. In approaching P_0, point P must always be a point of T.

The region T is divided into n closed subregions $\Delta V_1, \Delta V_2, \cdots, \Delta V_i, \cdots, \Delta V_n$ in any manner whatever. Let (ξ_i, η_i, ζ_i) be an arbitrary point of ΔV_i and form the sum

$$\sum_{i=1}^{n} f(\xi_i, \eta_i, \zeta_i)\, \Delta V_i.$$

The limit of this sum as $n \rightarrow \infty$ and the maximum diameter d of the $\Delta V_i \rightarrow 0$, if it always exists and always has the same value, is called the triple integral of the function f over the region T. It is denoted by

$$\iiint_T f(x, y, z)\, dV = \lim_{\substack{n \to \infty \\ d \to 0}} \sum_{i=1}^{n} f(\xi_i, \eta_i, \zeta_i)\, \Delta V_i. \tag{17.35}$$

The following theorem is analogous to Theorem 17–I for the double integral.

Theorem 17-V. Let $f(x, y, z)$ define a function continuous on a closed and bounded region T. Then f is integrable over T.

———

Let us assume that the points (x, y, z) of T satisfy $a \leqslant x \leqslant b$; $y_1(x) \leqslant y \leqslant y_2(x)$; $z_1(x, y) \leqslant z \leqslant z_2(x, y)$, where y_1 and y_2 are continuous functions of x and z_1 and z_2 are continuous functions of x and y. As illustrated in Fig. 17.25, the inequalities $a \leqslant x \leqslant b$ and $y_1(x) \leqslant y \leqslant y_2(x)$ determine the projection R

of T on the xy-plane, while the equations $z = z_1(x, y)$ and $z = z_2(x, y)$ describe the lower and upper surfaces bounding T.

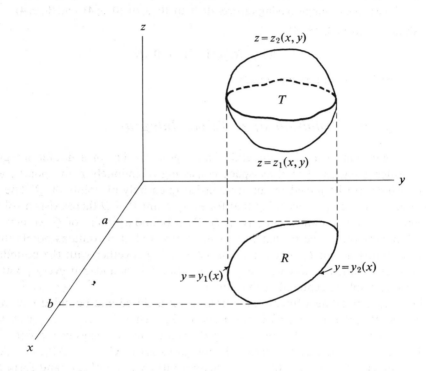

Figure 17.25

If T is subdivided into n closed rectangular parallelepipeds $\Delta V_i = \Delta x_j \, \Delta y_k \, \Delta z_l$ by planes parallel to the three coordinate planes, equation (17.35) still holds even though the ΔV_i do not completely fill the region T. The diameter d_i of ΔV_i is the diagonal of the rectangular parallelepiped.

The triple integral can be evaluated by an iterated integral. This is expressed in the formula

$$\iiint_T f(x, y, z) \, dV = \int_a^b dx \int_{y_1(x)}^{y_2(x)} dy \int_{z_1(x,y)}^{z_2(x,y)} f(x, y, z) \, dz. \tag{17.36}$$

For a discussion of the validity of (17.36) the reader is referred to Ref. 17.6. We can observe that if $f(x, y, z) \equiv 1$, the triple integral in (17.35) gives the volume of T, and that (17.36) reduces to

$$\int_a^b dx \int_{y_1(x)}^{y_2(x)} [z_2(x, y) - z_1(x, y)] \, dy = \int_a^b dx \int_{y_1(x)}^{y_2(x)} z_2(x, y) \, dy$$
$$- \int_a^b dx \int_{y_1(x)}^{y_2(x)} z_1(x, y) \, dy$$

which also gives the volume of T.

It should be observed that the limits on x and y in (17.36) are the limits which would be employed in evaluating a double integral over R. If R consists of points (x, y) satisfying $c \leqslant y \leqslant d$, $x_1(y) \leqslant x \leqslant x_2(y)$, where x_1 and x_2 are continuous functions of y, the triple integral is given by

$$\iiint_T f(x, y, z) \, dV = \int_c^d dy \int_{x_1(y)}^{x_2(y)} dx \int_{z_1(x, y)}^{z_2(x, y)} f(x, y, z) \, dz. \qquad (17.37)$$

If the roles of z and x are interchanged in (17.36) and (17.37), two additional iterated integrals are obtained for the triple integral. The region R becomes the projection of T on the yz-plane and the surface of T is divided into two surfaces, $x = x_1(y, z)$ and $x_2 = x_2(y, z)$. Two additional iterated integrals are obtained by interchanging the roles of z and y and letting R be the projection of T on the xz-plane. Thus, six orders of integration are possible. This will be illustrated in Example 2.

Example 1.   Evaluate the iterated integral

$$\int_0^1 dx \int_0^{x^2} dy \int_{xy}^1 2x^2 z \, dz.$$

Solution.   After integrating with respect to z, we have

$$\int_0^1 x^2 \, dx \int_0^{x^2} z^2 \Big]_{z=xy}^{z=1} dy = \int_0^1 x^2 \, dx \int_0^{x^2} (1 - x^2 y^2) \, dy$$

$$= \int_0^1 x^2 \left[y - \frac{x^2 y^3}{3} \right]_{y=0}^{y=x^2} dx$$

$$= \int_0^1 \left(x^4 - \frac{x^{10}}{3} \right) dx = \frac{28}{165}.$$

Example 2.   Find the volume of the solid bounded by the cylinder $y = x^2$ and the planes $z = 3$, $z = 6$, $x = 0$, and $y = 4$.

Solution.   Setting $f(x, y, z) \equiv 1$ in (17.36), we obtain

$$V = \int_0^2 dx \int_{x^2}^4 dy \int_3^6 dz$$

$$= \int_0^2 \left[3y \right]_{y=x^2}^{y=4} dx$$

$$= \int_0^2 (12 - 3x^2) \, dx$$

$$= 12x - x^3 \Big]_0^2 = 16 \text{ cubic units.}$$

If (17.37) is employed, the limits on x and y are still obtained from the region R_1 of Fig. 17.26. The volume is given by

$$V = \int_0^4 dy \int_0^{\sqrt{y}} dx \int_3^6 dz.$$

If the first integration is performed with respect to x, the limits on y and z are obtained from the projection R_2 of the solid on the yz-plane. We then obtain

$$V = \int_0^4 dy \int_3^6 dz \int_0^{\sqrt{y}} dx,$$

or

$$V = \int_3^6 dz \int_0^4 dy \int_0^{\sqrt{y}} dx.$$

If the first integration is performed with respect to y, region R_3 in the xz-plane determines the limits on x and z, and V is given by

$$V = \int_0^2 dx \int_3^6 dz \int_{x^2}^4 dy,$$

or

$$V = \int_3^6 dz \int_0^2 dx \int_{x^2}^4 dy.$$

The preferred order of integration is determined by the shape of the region T in three-space over which the integration takes place and the ease of carrying out the necessary integrations.

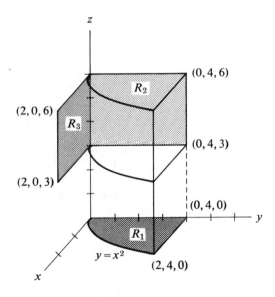

Figure 17.26

17.10 Cylindrical Coordinates

A point $P(x, y, z)$ can be located by giving the value of z and the polar coordinates r and θ of the projection $Q(x, y, 0)$ of P in the xy-plane. The numbers r, θ, and z are called cylindrical coordinates of P. To change from rectangular to cylindrical coordinates, replace x by $r \cos \theta$, y by $r \sin \theta$, and leave z unchanged. See Fig. 17.27.

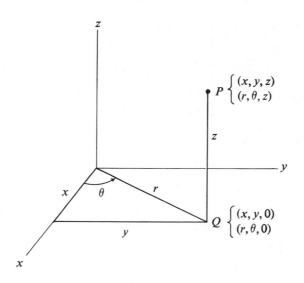

Figure 17.27

Example 1. The paraboloid $z = x^2 + y^2$ has equation $z = r^2$ in cylindrical coordinates.

Example 2. The sphere $x^2 + y^2 + z^2 = a^2$ has equation $r^2 + z^2 = a^2$ in cylindrical coordinates.

Example 3. The cylinder $x^2 + y^2 = a^2$ has equation $r = a$ (or $r = -a$) in cylindrical coordinates.

The use of cylindrical coordinates simplifies the solution of many problems, particularly problems involving solids which are symmetrical with respect to the z-axis.

If a region T is subdivided into n subregions by planes $\theta = $ constant, planes $z = $ constant, and cylinders $r = $ constant, a typical subregion ΔV_i will have the shape shown in Fig. 17.28.

The triple integral of $f(x, y, z)$ over T is denoted by

$$\iiint_T F(r, \theta, z) \, dV,$$

where $F(r, \theta, z) = f(r \cos \theta, r \sin \theta, z)$. This integral can be evaluated by an iterated integral, provided dV is replaced by $r \, d\theta \, dr \, dz$. The factor r occurs for the same reason it occurred in the double integral in polar coordinates. Thus

$$\iiint_T F(r, \theta, z) \, dV = \int_\alpha^\beta d\theta \int_{r_1(\theta)}^{r_2(\theta)} r \, dr \int_{z_1(r, \theta)}^{z_2(r, \theta)} F(r, \theta, z) \, dz. \qquad \textbf{(17.38)}$$

Six orders of integration are possible. The order indicated in (17.38) could also be obtained from (17.36) by first integrating with respect to z and then evaluating the resulting twofold iterated integral by means of polar coordinates.

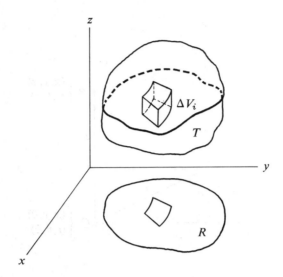

Figure 17.28

Example 4.   Find the volume of the region T bounded by the paraboloid $z = 4 - x^2 - y^2$ and the xy-plane. See Fig. 17.29.

Solution.   By (17.38), with $F(r, \theta, z) \equiv 1$,

$$V = \int_0^{2\pi} d\theta \int_0^2 r\, dr \int_0^{4-r^2} dz$$

$$= \int_0^{2\pi} d\theta \int_0^2 (4r - r^3)\, dr$$

$$= \int_0^{2\pi} \left[2r^2 - \frac{r^4}{4} \right]_0^2 d\theta$$

$$= \int_0^{2\pi} 4\, d\theta = 8\pi \text{ cubic units.}$$

$$z = 4 - x^2 - y^2 = 4 - r^2$$

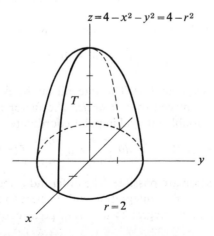

Figure 17.29

The limits on z are determined by the cylindrical coordinate equations of the lower and upper boundaries of T; the limits on θ and r are determined by the circle $r = 2$, which is the projection of T on the $r\theta$-plane.

17.11   Applications of Triple Integrals

In a single integral $\int_a^b f(x)\, dx$, the limits are determined by the interval over which the integration takes place. The integrand $f(x)$ has nothing to do with the interval $a \leqslant x \leqslant b$ except that it is defined over it. For different choices of $f(x)$ the integral represents different quantities. If $f(x) \equiv 1$ the integral represents the length $b - a$ of the interval; if $f(x) = A(x)$ the integral represents a volume; if $f(x) = \sqrt{1 + [g'(x)]^2}$ the integral represents an arc length; and so forth.

Similarly, in an iterated integral representing a double integral such as

$$\iint_R f(x, y)\, dA = \int_a^b dx \int_{y_1(x)}^{y_2(x)} f(x, y)\, dy,$$

the limits are determined by the region R in the xy-plane over which the integration takes place. For different choices of $f(x, y)$ the integral represents different quantities. If $f(x, y) \equiv 1$ the integral represents the area of R; if $f(x, y) = x^2$ the integral represents the moment of inertia of the area of R about the y-axis; if $f(x, y)$ defines a density function the integral represents the mass of a lamina covering R; and so forth.

An analogous situation prevails when an iterated integral represents a triple integral. For example, in

$$\iiint_T f(x, y, z)\, dV = \int_a^b dx \int_{y_1(x)}^{y_2(x)} dy \int_{z_1(x,y)}^{z_2(x,y)} f(x, y, z)\, dz, \qquad \textbf{(17.39)}$$

the limits are determined by the region T over which the integration takes place. The integral can represent many different quantities, depending on what we choose for the integrand $f(x, y, z)$. We have already seen that if $f(x, y, z) \equiv 1$ the integral represents the volume of T.

If $f(x, y, z)$ defines a density function $\rho(x, y, z)$ giving the density at (x, y, z), the integral represents the mass occupying T.

The coordinates of the center of mass $(\bar{x}, \bar{y}, \bar{z})$ are given by

$$\bar{x} = \frac{\displaystyle\iiint_T x\rho(x, y, z)\, dV}{m},$$

$$\bar{y} = \frac{\displaystyle\iiint_T y\rho(x, y, z)\, dV}{m}, \qquad \textbf{(17.40)}$$

$$\bar{z} = \frac{\displaystyle\iiint_T z\rho(x, y, z)\, dV}{m}.$$

The numerators in (17.40) represent the first moments of mass with respect to the yz-, xz-, and xy-planes, respectively. If ρ is constant, (17.40) yield the coordinates of the centroid.

Moments of inertia of mass with respect to the yz-, xz-, and xy-planes are given by

$$I_{x=0} = \iiint\limits_{T} x^2 \rho(x, y, z)\, dV,$$

$$I_{y=0} = \iiint\limits_{T} y^2 \rho(x, y, z)\, dV, \tag{17.41}$$

$$I_{z=0} = \iiint\limits_{T} z^2 \rho(x, y, z)\, dV.$$

The polar moment of inertia of mass with respect to the z-axis is given by

$$I_{\substack{x=0 \\ y=0}} = \iiint\limits_{T} (x^2 + y^2)\rho(x, y, z)\, dV = I_{x=0} + I_{y=0}, \tag{17.42}$$

with analogous formulas holding for $I_{\substack{x=0 \\ z=0}}$ and $I_{\substack{y=0 \\ z=0}}$.

Transfer theorems for moments of inertia are identical with equations (17.31) and (17.32) and are proved in similar fashion. The symbol $I_{x=x_0}$ denotes the moment of inertia with respect to the plane $x = x_0$ and the symbol $I_{\substack{x=x_0 \\ y=y_0}}$ denotes the polar moment of inertia with respect to the line which is the intersection of the planes $x = x_0$ and $y = y_0$.

Example 1.   Find the mass of the solid bounded by the planes $z = 0$, $z = y$, $x = 0$, $x = 1$, and $y = 2$, if the density is proportional to the distance from the xz-plane. See Fig. 17.30.

Solution.   Setting $f(x, y, z) = ky$ in (17.39), we obtain

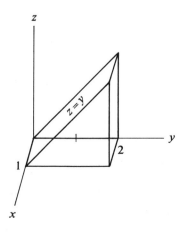

Figure 17.30

$$m = \int_0^1 dx \int_0^2 dy \int_0^y ky \, dz$$
$$= k \int_0^1 dx \int_0^2 y^2 \, dy = \frac{8k}{3}.$$

Example 2.   Find the center of mass of the solid bounded by the plane $z = 2$ and the cone $z = \sqrt{x^2 + y^2}$ if the density is given by $\rho = kz$. See Fig. 17.31.

Solution.   By symmetry, $\bar{x} = \bar{y} = 0$. From (17.40) we obtain

$$\bar{z} = \frac{\iiint_T kz^2 \, dV}{\iiint_T kz \, dV}.$$

Employing cylindrical coordinates,

$$\bar{z} = \frac{k \int_0^{2\pi} d\theta \int_0^2 r \, dr \int_r^2 z^2 \, dz}{k \int_0^{2\pi} d\theta \int_0^2 r \, dr \int_r^2 z \, dz}$$

$$= \frac{(k/3) \int_0^{2\pi} d\theta \int_0^2 (8r - r^4) \, dr}{(k/2) \int_0^{2\pi} d\theta \int_0^2 (4r - r^3) \, dr}$$

$$= \frac{32\pi k/5}{4\pi k} = \frac{8}{5}.$$

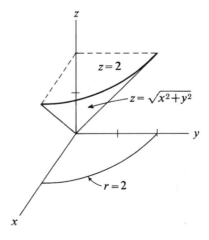

Figure 17.31

Example 3.   Find the moment of inertia of a sphere of constant density ρ about (a) a diameter, (b) a line tangent to the sphere.

Solution.   Representing the sphere by the equation $x^2 + y^2 + z^2 = a^2$ or

$z = \pm\sqrt{a^2 - r^2}$ in cylindrical coordinates, we first compute $I_{z=0}$, the moment of inertia with respect to the xy-plane. Thus

$$I_{z=0} = \iiint_V z^2 \rho \, dV = \rho \int_0^{2\pi} d\theta \int_0^a r \, dr \int_{-\sqrt{a^2-r^2}}^{\sqrt{a^2-r^2}} z^2 \, dz$$

$$= \frac{\rho}{3} \int_0^{2\pi} d\theta \int_0^a (a^2 - r^2)^{3/2} 2r \, dr$$

$$= \frac{-\rho}{3} \int_0^{2\pi} \frac{2}{5} \left[a^2 - r^2 \right]^{5/2} \Big]_0^a d\theta$$

$$= \frac{\rho}{3} \cdot \frac{2}{5} a^5 2\pi$$

$$= \frac{4\rho a^5 \pi}{15}.$$

Since $I_{y=0} = I_{z=0}$ by symmetry, and $I_{y=0 \atop z=0} = I_{y=0} + I_{z=0} = 2I_{z=0}$,

$$I_{y=0 \atop z=0} = \frac{8\rho a^5 \pi}{15} = \frac{2a^2}{5} \left(\rho \frac{4\pi a^3}{3} \right) = \frac{2}{5} ma^2,$$

where m denotes the mass of the sphere.

Since $I_{y=0 \atop z=0} = \bar{I}$, $I_{y=a \atop z=0}$ is obtained from the transfer theorem. Thus

$$I_{y=a \atop z=0} = \bar{I} + ma^2 = \frac{2}{5} ma^2 + ma^2 = \frac{7}{5} ma^2.$$

PROBLEM LIST 105

1. Evaluate the following iterated integrals:

(a) $\int_0^2 dx \int_0^x dy \int_0^{x+y} x \, dz.$

(b) $\int_0^3 dx \int_0^{x+1} dy \int_0^x 3yz^2 \, dz.$

(c) $\int_0^2 dx \int_{-x}^{x^2} dy \int_{-1}^{1+x} (x^2 + y^2) \, dz.$

(d) $\int_0^{\pi/2} d\theta \int_0^{2\cos\theta} dr \int_0^{r\sin\theta} 2rz \, dz.$

(e) $\int_0^3 dy \int_0^{2y} dz \int_0^{y-z} dx.$

(f) $\int_0^{2\pi} d\theta \int_0^a dr \int_0^{\sqrt{a^2-r^2}} rz \, dz.$

2. Find the volume of the solid bounded by the planes $y = 0$, $y = x$, $x = 2$, $z = x$, and $z = 0$.

3. Find the volume of the solid bounded by the paraboloid $z = x^2 + y^2$, the plane $z = 0$, and the cylinder $x^2 + y^2 = 16$.

4. Find the volume of the solid bounded by the paraboloid $z = x^2 + y^2$ and the plane $z = x$.

5. Find the volume bounded by the paraboloid $z = 6 - x^2 - y^2$ and the plane $z = 5$.

6. Find the volume of a sphere.

7. Find the volume of the ellipsoid

$$\frac{x^2}{a^2} + \frac{y^2}{b^2} + \frac{z^2}{c^2} = 1.$$

8. Find the volume of the tetrahedron having vertices $(0, 0, 0)$, $(a, 0, 0)$, $(0, b, 0)$, and $(0, 0, c)$. Assume a, b, and c to be positive.

9. A solid is bounded by the planes $z = x$, $z = 0$, $y = 0$, $y = 4$, and $x = 3$. Find the volume of the solid, using six different orders of integration.

10. A solid is bounded by the planes $z = y$, $z = 0$, $x = 0$, and $y = 4$ and the cylinder $y = x^2$. Find the volume of the solid (a) by first integrating with respect to z, (b) by first integrating with respect to x. Explain why it is inconvenient to integrate first with respect to y.

11. Find the volume bounded by the sphere $x^2 + y^2 + z^2 = 2$ and the paraboloid $z = x^2 + y^2$.

12. Find the volume of the region bounded by $z = e^{-x^2-y^2}$, $z = 0$, and $x^2 + y^2 = 1$.

13. The center of a sphere of radius 2 is on the surface of a right-circular cylinder of radius 1. Find the volume common to the sphere and the cylinder.

14. Find the mass of a cube of edge a, if the density is proportional to the distance from one of the faces.

15. A right-circular cylinder has height h and base radius a. Find the mass if the density is proportional to the square of the distance from the axis of the cylinder.

16. A solid is bounded by the planes $z = 0$, $z = 4$, $x = 0$, $x = 3$, $y = 0$, and $y = 6$. Find the center of mass of the solid if the density is proportional to the distance above the xy-plane.

17. Find the centroid of the volume of a hemisphere.

18. Find the centroid of the volume of a right-circular cone of height h and base radius a.

19. Find the centroid of the first-octant volume cut off by the plane $(x/a) + (y/b) + (z/c) = 1$. Assume a, b, and c to be positive.

20. Find the x-coordinate of the centroid of the first-octant volume cut off by the ellipsoid $(x^2/a^2) + (y^2/b^2) + (z^2/c^2) = 1$.

21. Find the center of mass of a right-circular cone of height h and base radius a if the density is proportional to the distance from the axis of the cone.

22. Sketch the region over which each of the following integrations takes place:

    (a) $\displaystyle\int_0^2 dx \int_x^{x^2+1} dy \int_0^y f(x, y, z)\, dz.$

    (b) $\displaystyle\int_0^1 dx \int_{-x}^{2x} dy \int_{x^2+y^2}^4 f(x, y, z)\, dz.$

23. Find the distance between $P_1(r_1, \theta_1, z_1)$ and $P_2(r_2, \theta_2, z_2)$ in terms of the cylindrical coordinates of the points.

24. Find the moment of inertia of a homogeneous cube of edge a with respect to (a) a face, (b) an edge, (c) a plane parallel to a face and passing through the centroid, (d) a diagonal plane.

25. A cube of edge a has density proportional to the square of the distance from an edge. Find the moment of inertia with respect to the same edge.

26. Find the moment of inertia of a homogeneous sphere with respect to a plane tangent to the sphere.

27. A homogeneous solid is bounded by the planes $z = 0$, $z = x + 2y + 1$, $y = 0$, $y = x$, and $x = 2$. Find its moment of inertia with respect to (a) the three coordinate planes, (b) the three coordinate axes.

28. A solid of density $\rho = kz$ is bounded by the plane $z = 4$ and the paraboloid $z = x^2 + y^2$. Find the moment of inertia of the solid with respect to the z-axis.

29. A homogeneous rectangular parallelepiped has dimensions a by b by c. Find the moment of inertia with respect to an edge of length c.

30. A homogeneous right-circular cylinder has height h and base radius a. Find the moment of inertia with respect to (a) the axis of the cylinder, (b) a diameter of the base, (c) a line through the centroid parallel to the base.

31. Find the moment of inertia of a homogeneous right-circular cone of height h and base radius a with respect to (a) the axis of the cone, (b) a diameter of the base.

32. A right-circular cylinder of height h and base radius a has density proportional to the square of the distance from the axis of the cylinder. Find the moment of inertia with respect to a line parallel to the axis and tangent to the cylinder.

17.12 Spherical Coordinates

Another method of locating a point $P(x, y, z)$ is to give its distance ρ from the origin, the polar coordinate θ of its projection $Q(x, y, 0)$ in the xy-plane, and the angle ϕ between the positive z-axis and the radial line OP. It is usual to take $\rho \geqslant 0, 0 \leqslant \theta \leqslant 2\pi$, and $0 \leqslant \phi \leqslant \pi$. See Fig. 17.32.

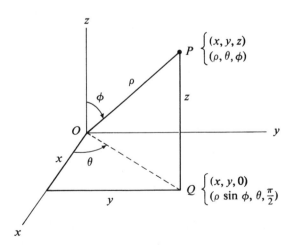

Figure 17.32

The coordinate ρ is called the radial distance of P, the angle θ the azimuth of P, and the angle ϕ the colatitude of P. These three quantities are called the spherical coordinates of P. Some authors denote the azimuth by ϕ and the colatitude by θ, but we prefer to have θ denote the same angle in both cylindrical and spherical coordinates. When employing spherical coordinates it is convenient to let $\sigma = \sigma(\rho, \theta, \phi)$ denote a density function, since ρ denotes one of the spherical coordinates of a point.

Noting in Fig. 17.32 that $OQ = \rho \sin \phi$, it is easy to see that the equations for transforming from spherical to rectangular coordinates are

$$x = \rho \sin \phi \cos \theta; \qquad y = \rho \sin \phi \sin \theta; \qquad z = \rho \cos \phi. \qquad \textbf{(17.43)}$$

In spherical coordinates the equations $\rho = $ constant represent spheres centered at the origin; the equations $\theta = $ constant represent planes through the z-axis; and the equations $\phi = $ constant represent cones with vertex at the origin and axes coincident with the z-axis. Spherical coordinates often simplify problems involving symmetry with respect to the origin.

To obtain a triple integral in spherical coordinates, a region T is subdivided into n closed subregions ΔV_i by spheres $\rho = \rho_j$, planes $\theta = \theta_k$, and cones $\phi = \phi_l$. The volume of subregion ΔV_i, shown in Fig. 17.33, is given by

$$\Delta V_i = \rho_i^2 \sin \phi_i \, \Delta \rho_j \, \Delta \theta_k \, \Delta \phi_l,$$

where $P_i(\rho_i, \theta_i, \phi_i)$ is some point of ΔV_i.

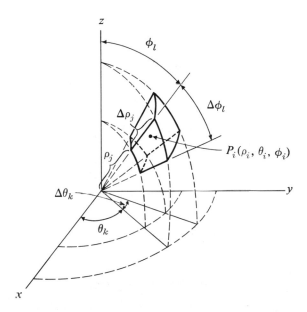

Figure 17.33

A triple integral $(\iiint)_T f(x, y, z) \, dV$ can be expressed in the form

$$\lim_{\substack{n \to \infty \\ d \to 0}} \sum_{i=1}^{n} F(\rho_i, \theta_i, \phi_i) \, \Delta V_i = \iiint_T F(\rho, \theta, \phi) \, dV,$$

where $F(\rho, \theta, \phi) = f(\rho \sin \phi \cos \theta, \rho \sin \phi \sin \theta, \rho \cos \phi)$ and d is the maximum diameter of the ΔV_i.

The triple integral is expressed in terms of an iterated integral by

$$\iiint_T F(\rho, \theta, \phi)\, dV = \int_\alpha^\beta d\theta \int_{\phi_1(\theta)}^{\phi_2(\theta)} d\phi \int_{\rho_1(\theta, \phi)}^{\rho_2(\theta, \phi)} F(\rho, \theta, \phi)\rho^2 \sin \phi \, d\rho. \qquad \textbf{(17.44)}$$

Six orders of integration are possible. For a more complete development of (17.44), see Ref. 17.6.

Example. A solid is bounded by the cone $z = \sqrt{x^2 + y^2}$ and the sphere $x^2 + y^2 + z^2 = 4$. Find the mass if the density σ is proportional to the square of the distance from the origin. See Fig. 17.34.

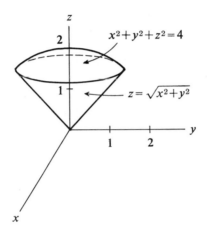

Figure 17.34

Solution.   Setting $F(\rho, \theta, \phi) = k\rho^2$ in (17.44), we obtain

$$m = \int_0^{2\pi} d\theta \int_0^{\pi/4} d\phi \int_0^2 k\rho^4 \sin \phi \, d\rho$$

$$= \frac{32k}{5} \int_0^{2\pi} d\theta \int_0^{\pi/4} \sin \phi \, d\phi$$

$$= \frac{64k\pi}{5} \Big[-\cos \phi \Big]_0^{\pi/4}$$

$$= \frac{32k\pi}{5}(2 - \sqrt{2}).$$

PROBLEM LIST 106

Employ spherical coordinates in the following problems.

1. Find the volume of a sphere.

2. A solid is bounded by the cone $z = \sqrt{x^2 + y^2}$ and the sphere $x^2 + y^2 + z^2 = 1$. Find the mass if the density is proportional to the distance above the xy-plane.

3. Find the moment of inertia about a diameter of a sphere of constant density.

4. Find the centroid of the volume bounded by a plane and a hemisphere.

5. Find the volume common to the sphere $x^2 + y^2 + z^2 = 4z$ and the cone $z = \sqrt{x^2 + y^2}$.

6. Find the volume of the oblate spheroid $(x^2/a^2) + (y^2/a^2) + (z^2/b^2) = 1$.

7. How are the latitude and longitude of a point on the earth's surface related to spherical coordinates?

8. Show that LaPlace's equation,

$$\frac{\partial^2 f}{\partial x^2} + \frac{\partial^2 f}{\partial y^2} + \frac{\partial^2 f}{\partial z^2} = 0$$

becomes

$$\rho^2 \sin \phi \frac{\partial^2 f}{\partial \rho^2} + 2\rho \sin \phi \frac{\partial f}{\partial \rho} + \sin \phi \frac{\partial^2 f}{\partial \phi^2} + \cos \phi \frac{\partial f}{\partial \phi} + \frac{1}{\sin \phi} \frac{\partial^2 f}{\partial \theta^2} = 0$$

in spherical coordinates.

REFERENCES

17.1 L. Brand, *Advanced Calculus*, John Wiley, New York, 1962.

17.2 D. E. Christie, *Vector Mechanics*, McGraw-Hill, New York, 1964.

17.3 W. Kaplan, *Advanced Calculus*, Addison-Wesley, Reading, Mass., 1959.

17.4 J. M. H. Olmsted, *Advanced Calculus*, Appleton-Century-Crofts, New York, 1961.

17.5 F. L. Singer, *Strength of Materials*, Harper, New York, 1951.

17.6 A. E. Taylor, *Advanced Calculus*, Ginn, Boston, 1955.

Chapter

18

Indeterminate forms

18.1 *The Limit of a Quotient*

Let f and g denote functions and let the function q be defined by the quotient $q(x) = f(x)/g(x)$. By Theorem 3–IV,

$$\lim_{x \to a} \left[\frac{f(x)}{g(x)} \right] = \frac{\lim_{x \to a} f(x)}{\lim_{x \to a} g(x)},$$

provided both limits on the right exist and $\lim_{x \to a} g(x) \neq 0$.

We now proceed to investigate the situation in which $\lim_{x \to a} g(x) = 0$. Under this assumption it can be shown that if $\lim_{x \to a} f(x) \neq 0$, then $\lim_{x \to a} [f(x)/g(x)]$ does not exist. (See Problem 56.) Therefore we consider only the situation in which both $f(x)$ and $g(x)$ approach zero as x approaches a. It is customary to say, assuming also that $f(a) = g(a) = 0$, that $f(x)/g(x)$ assumes the indeterminate form 0/0 when $x = a$. The quotient $q(x) = f(x)/g(x)$ may or may not approach a limit as $x \longrightarrow a$, and no information concerning the existence or nonexistence of the limit can be obtained by substitution of $x = a$ into $q(x)$. Situations in which we wish to know what is happening to a fraction whose numerator and denominator approach zero simultaneously occur frequently in mathematics. Let us consider some examples.

Example 1. $\lim_{x \to 0} (x/x) = 1$, since $x/x \equiv 1$ for $x \neq 0$.

Example 2. $\lim_{x \to 0} (x/x^3)$ does not exist, since $x/x^3 \equiv 1/x^2$ for $x \neq 0$, and $1/x^2$ becomes infinite as $x \longrightarrow 0$. It is customary to write

$$\lim_{x \to 0} \frac{x}{x^3} = \infty.$$

Clearly the denominator approaches zero more rapidly than the numerator.

Example 3. $\lim_{x\to 0}(x^2/x) = 0$, since $x^2/x \equiv x$ for $x \neq 0$. In this example the numerator approaches zero more rapidly than the denominator. These three examples illustrate various possible behaviors of a fraction whose numerator and denominator approach zero simultaneously.

Example 4. $\lim_{x\to 0}(\sin x/x) = 1$. This limit, developed in Sec. 9.2, is not obvious by inspection.

Example 5

$$\lim_{x\to a}\frac{f(x) - f(a)}{x - a} = f'(a),$$

provided f is differentiable at $x = a$. Thus a derivative is the limit of a quotient in which numerator and denominator approach zero simultaneously.

Example 6

$$\lim_{x\to 2}\frac{x^2 - 4}{x - 2} = \lim_{x\to 2}(x + 2) = 4.$$

This type of limit was discussed in Chapter 3.

Example 7

$$\lim_{x\to 4}\frac{\sqrt{x} - 2}{x - 4} = \lim_{x\to 4}\left[\frac{\sqrt{x} - 2}{x - 4} \cdot \frac{\sqrt{x} + 2}{\sqrt{x} + 2}\right]$$

$$= \lim_{x\to 4}\frac{1}{\sqrt{x} + 2} = \frac{1}{4}.$$

We next proceed to develop a general method which will render the special techniques of Examples 6 and 7 unnecessary. This method will be based upon a powerful theorem due to Cauchy.

18.2   *The Generalized Mean-Value Theorem (Theorem of Cauchy)*

Theorem 18-I.   Let the functions f and g be continuous on the closed interval $a \leqslant x \leqslant b$ and differentiable on the open interval $a < x < b$. Also assume that $g(a) \neq g(b)$ and that $g'(x) \neq 0$ in $a < x < b$. Then

$$\frac{f(b) - f(a)}{g(b) - g(a)} = \frac{f'(c)}{g'(c)} \tag{18.1}$$

for at least one c satisfying $a < c < b$.

Proof.   Consider the function h defined by

$$h(x) = f(x) - f(a) - \left[\frac{f(b) - f(a)}{g(b) - g(a)}\right][g(x) - g(a)].$$

It is seen by inspection that $h(a) = h(b) = 0$ and consequently h satisfies the hypotheses of Theorem 4–III (Rolle's theorem). Hence its derivative h', given by

$$h'(x) = f'(x) - \left[\frac{f(b) - f(a)}{g(b) - g(a)}\right] g'(x),$$

must equal zero for at least one c satisfying $a < c < b$. Therefore

$$h'(c) = f'(c) - \left[\frac{f(b) - f(a)}{g(b) - g(a)}\right] g'(c) = 0.$$

Equation (18.1) is obtained by transposing and dividing by the nonzero number $g'(c)$.

Theorem 18–I is called the generalized mean-value theorem because it reduces to Theorem 4–IV (mean-value theorem) when $g(x) = x$.

18.3 L'Hôpital's Rule

Theorem 18-II.   Let the functions f and g be continuous on the closed interval $a \leqslant x \leqslant b$ and differentiable on the open interval $a < x < b$. Also assume that $f(a) = g(a) = 0$, that $g'(x) \neq 0$ in $a < x < b$, and that

$$\lim_{x \to a^+} \frac{f'(x)}{g'(x)} = L.$$

Then

$$\lim_{x \to a^+} \frac{f(x)}{g(x)} = L.$$

Proof.   The value $g(x)$ of g is not equal to zero in $a < x \leqslant b$. For if $g(k) = 0$ for $a < k \leqslant b$, then by Rolle's theorem, $g'(x) = 0$ for at least one x in $a < x < k$, contradicting the assumption that $g'(x) \neq 0$ in $a < x < b$.

The functions f and g satisfy the hypotheses of Theorem 18–I, and hence by (18.1),

$$\frac{f(b) - f(a)}{g(b) - g(a)} = \frac{f(b)}{g(b)} = \frac{f'(c)}{g'(c)},$$

for at least one c in $a < x < b$.

We now replace b by x, since we wish to regard b as variable. Thus

$$\frac{f(x)}{g(x)} = \frac{f'(c)}{g'(c)}.$$

As $x \to a^+$, $c \to a^+$, and

$$\lim_{x \to a^+} \frac{f(x)}{g(x)} = \lim_{c \to a^+} \frac{f'(c)}{g'(c)} = \lim_{x \to a^+} \frac{f'(x)}{g'(x)} = L.$$

This completes the proof.

If the conditions of the theorem also hold for $d \leqslant x < a$, then

$$\lim_{x \to a^-} \frac{f(x)}{g(x)} = \lim_{x \to a^+} \frac{f(x)}{g(x)} = \lim_{x \to a} \frac{f(x)}{g(x)} = L.$$

Remark. It is sufficient but not necessary that $\lim_{x \to a} (f'(x)/g'(x))$ exist in order that $\lim_{x \to a} (f(x)/g(x))$ exist. For an example in which $\lim_{x \to a} (f'(x)/g'(x))$ does not exist but $\lim_{x \to a} (f(x)/g(x))$ does exist, see Ref. 18.1.

———————

Theorem 18–II is called L'Hôpital's rule after Guillaume François Antoine L' Hôpital (1661–1704). The rule was given in the first textbook on the differential calculus, published by L'Hôpital in Paris in 1696. L'Hôpital obtained the rule from the Swiss mathematician Johann Bernoulli (1667–1748).

Example 1

$$\lim_{x \to 2} \frac{x^2 - 4}{x - 2} = \lim_{x \to 2} \frac{d/dx \, (x^2 - 4)}{d/dx \, (x - 2)} = \lim_{x \to 2} \frac{2x}{1} = 4.$$

See Example 6 of Sec. 18.1.

Example 2

$$\lim_{x \to 0^+} \frac{\tan x}{\sqrt{x}} = \lim_{x \to 0^+} \frac{\sec^2 x}{1/(2\sqrt{x})}$$
$$= \lim_{x \to 0^+} (2\sqrt{x} \, \sec^2 x) = 0.$$

Example 3

$$\lim_{x \to 3} \frac{x^2 + 3}{x + 2} = \frac{12}{5}.$$

Note that

$$\lim_{x \to 3} \frac{x^2 + 3}{x + 2} \neq \lim_{x \to 3} \frac{2x}{1} = 6.$$

L'Hôpital's rule does not apply because $f(x) = x^2 + 3$ and $g(x) = x + 2$ do not approach zero as $x \to 3$.

Example 4. Evaluate

$$\lim_{x \to 0} \frac{e^x + e^{-x} - 2}{x^2}.$$

Solution. Applying L'Hôpital's rule, we obtain

$$\lim_{x \to 0} \frac{e^x + e^{-x} - 2}{x^2} = \lim_{x \to 0} \frac{e^x - e^{-x}}{2x}.$$

The limit on the right is evaluated by applying the rule a second time. Thus

$$\lim_{x \to 0} \frac{e^x - e^{-x}}{2x} = \lim_{x \to 0} \frac{e^x + e^{-x}}{2} = 1.$$

It may be necessary to apply the rule several times.

Example 5. Evaluate $\lim_{x \to \pi/2} (\sec x - \tan x)$.

Solution. For x near $\pi/2$, sec x and tan x have the same sign and have large numerical values. Thus the required limit is not obvious. The function defined by $f(x) = \sec x - \tan x$ is undefined at $\pi/2$, but it is customary to say that it assumes the indeterminate form $\infty - \infty$ at $x = \pi/2$. To apply L'Hôpital's rule, we write

$$\sec x - \tan x = \frac{1}{\cos x} - \frac{\sin x}{\cos x} = \frac{1 - \sin x}{\cos x}.$$

The rule is now applicable and we have

$$\lim_{x \to (\pi/2)} (\sec x - \tan x) = \lim_{x \to (\pi/2)} \frac{1 - \sin x}{\cos x}$$

$$= \lim_{x \to (\pi/2)} \frac{-\cos x}{-\sin x} = 0.$$

There are several variations of L'Hôpital's rule, proofs of which are given in Ref. 18.2. For example, the number L in Theorem 18–II may be replaced by $+\infty$ or $-\infty$.

Example 6

$$\lim_{x \to (\pi/2)^-} \frac{1 - \sin^3 x}{\cos^3 x} = \lim_{x \to (\pi/2)^-} \left[\frac{-3 \sin^2 x \cos x}{-3 \cos^2 x \sin x}\right]$$

$$= \lim_{x \to (\pi/2)^-} \tan x = +\infty.$$

Since

$$\lim_{x \to (\pi/2)^-} \frac{f'(x)}{g'(x)} = +\infty,$$

it follows that

$$\lim_{x \to (\pi/2)^-} \frac{f(x)}{g(x)} = +\infty.$$

In another variation, the assumption in Theorem 18–II that $f(a) = g(a) = 0$ is replaced by the assumption that

$$\lim_{x \to a^+} |g(x)| = \infty.$$

This is illustrated in the following example.

Example 7. Evaluate $\lim_{x \to 0^+} (x \log x)$.

Solution. Although $x \log x$ is undefined at $x = 0$, it is customary to say that $x \log x$ assumes the indeterminate form $0 \cdot \infty$ at $x = 0$. We write $x \log x = (\log x)/x^{-1}$ and note that $\lim_{x \to 0^+} |x^{-1}| = \infty$. Hence

$$\lim_{x \to 0^+} \frac{\log x}{x^{-1}} = \lim_{x \to 0^+} \frac{x^{-1}}{-x^{-2}}$$

$$= \lim_{x \to 0^+} (-x) = 0.$$

The variations we have considered are also true if the number a in Theorem 18–II is replaced by $+\infty$ or $-\infty$.

Example 8.   Evaluate

$$\lim_{x \to \infty} \frac{3x^2 + 4x - 1}{5x^2 - 2x + 7}.$$

Solution

$$\lim_{x \to \infty} \frac{3x^2 + 4x - 1}{5x^2 - 2x + 7} = \lim_{x \to \infty} \frac{6x + 4}{10x - 2}$$

$$= \lim_{x \to \infty} \frac{6}{10} = \frac{3}{5}.$$

Example 9.   Evaluate $\lim_{x \to \infty} (e^x/x^3)$.

Solution

$$\lim_{x \to \infty} \left(\frac{e^x}{x^3}\right) = \lim_{x \to \infty} \left(\frac{e^x}{3x^2}\right) = \lim_{x \to \infty} \left(\frac{e^x}{6x}\right)$$

$$= \lim_{x \to \infty} \left(\frac{e^x}{6}\right) = +\infty.$$

Example 10.   Evaluate

$$\lim_{x \to \infty} \frac{x - \sin x}{x}.$$

Solution.   Letting $f(x) = x - \sin x$ and $g(x) = x$, we find that

$$\lim_{x \to \infty} \frac{f'(x)}{g'(x)} = \lim_{x \to \infty} \frac{1 - \cos x}{1}$$

does not exist, since $\cos x$ oscillates between $+1$ and -1 as $x \to \infty$. It does not follow that $\lim_{x \to \infty} (f(x)/g(x))$ does not exist. In order for L'Hôpital's rule to apply, $\lim_{x \to \infty} (f'(x)/g'(x))$ must exist, or $f'(x)/g'(x)$ must approach $+\infty$ or $-\infty$. Actually,

$$\lim_{x \to \infty} \frac{x - \sin x}{x} = 1 - \lim_{x \to \infty} \frac{\sin x}{x} = 1,$$

since $(\sin x)/x$ approaches zero as $x \to \infty$.

PROBLEM LIST 107

Evaluate the following limits:

1. $\lim\limits_{x \to 3} \dfrac{x^2 - 9}{x - 3}.$

2. $\lim\limits_{x \to 2} \dfrac{x^3 - 2x^2 + x - 2}{x^3 - x^2 - 2x}.$

3. $\lim\limits_{x \to 1} \dfrac{3x^2 - 2x + 1}{x^2 + 1}.$

4. $\lim\limits_{x \to 0} \dfrac{\sqrt{1 + x} - 1}{x}.$

5. $\lim\limits_{x \to 9} \dfrac{\sqrt{x} - 3}{x - 9}.$

6. $\lim\limits_{x \to 0^+} \dfrac{\sin 2x}{\sqrt{x}}.$

7. $\lim\limits_{x\to\pi/2}\dfrac{1+\sin x}{1+\cos x}.$

8. $\lim\limits_{x\to0}\dfrac{\sin x - x}{x^3}.$

9. $\lim\limits_{x\to0}\dfrac{3x^2}{1-\cos x}.$

10. $\lim\limits_{x\to1}\dfrac{\log x}{x-1}.$

11. $\lim\limits_{x\to0}\dfrac{e^x-1-x}{x^2}.$

12. $\lim\limits_{x\to0^+}\dfrac{\sin\sqrt{x}}{\sqrt{x}}.$

13. $\lim\limits_{x\to1}\dfrac{x^3-1}{x^2-1}.$

14. $\lim\limits_{x\to\pi/2}\dfrac{\cos 5x}{\cos 3x}.$

15. $\lim\limits_{x\to0}\dfrac{x-\tan 3x}{x+\tan 3x}.$

16. $\lim\limits_{x\to0}\dfrac{e^x-e^{2x}+x}{x^2}.$

17. $\lim\limits_{x\to0}\dfrac{2^x-3^x}{x}.$

18. $\lim\limits_{x\to0}\dfrac{x-e^x+1}{\log(1+x)-x}.$

19. $\lim\limits_{x\to\pi/2}(\sec^2 x - \tan^2 x).$

20. $\lim\limits_{x\to(\pi/2)^+}(\sec^3 x - \tan^3 x).$

21. $\lim\limits_{r\to1}\dfrac{a-ar^n}{1-r}$, ($n$ a positive integer).

22. $\lim\limits_{x\to0^-}\left(\dfrac{1}{1-e^x}-\dfrac{1}{x}\right).$

23. $\lim\limits_{x\to\pi}\dfrac{1+\cos x}{\sin 2x}.$

24. $\lim\limits_{x\to0}\dfrac{x^3}{\mathrm{Tan}^{-1}x - x}.$

25. $\lim\limits_{x\to0}\dfrac{\mathrm{Tan}^{-1}x}{x}.$

26. $\lim\limits_{x\to1}\left(\dfrac{1}{\log x}-\dfrac{1}{x-1}\right).$

27. $\lim\limits_{x\to3}\dfrac{\sin\pi x}{x-3}.$

28. $\lim\limits_{x\to0}\dfrac{a^x-b^x}{x}$, ($a$ and b positive).

29. $\lim\limits_{x\to a}\dfrac{x^n-a^n}{x-a}.$

30. $\lim\limits_{x\to0}\dfrac{e^{-1/x^2}}{x}.$

31. $\lim\limits_{x\to0^+}(x^2\log x).$

32. $\lim\limits_{x\to0}\dfrac{\mathrm{Sin}^{-1}x}{x}.$

33. $\lim\limits_{x\to\infty}\dfrac{3x^2-2x}{4x^2+7}.$

34. $\lim\limits_{x\to\infty}\dfrac{2x^3-4x+1}{3+5x^2-7x^3}.$

35. $\lim\limits_{x\to\infty}\dfrac{e^x}{x^4}.$

36. $\lim\limits_{x\to\infty}\dfrac{\log x}{x}.$

37. $\lim\limits_{x\to\infty}\dfrac{\log x}{x^p}$, ($p>0$).

38. $\lim\limits_{x\to0^+}\dfrac{e^{-1/x}}{x}.$ (*Hint*. Let $t=1/x$.)

39. $\lim\limits_{x\to\infty}\dfrac{x^a}{e^{bx}}$, ($a$ and b positive).

40. $\lim\limits_{x\to\infty}\dfrac{2^{x^2}}{6^x}.$

41. $\lim\limits_{x\to\infty}\dfrac{x}{\sqrt{x^2+1}}.$

42. $\lim\limits_{x\to\infty}\dfrac{x+\cos x}{x}.$

Evaluate the following limits (i) by L'Hôpital's rule, (ii) without using L'Hôpital's rule.

43. $\lim\limits_{x\to4}\dfrac{x^2-16}{x-4}.$

44. $\lim\limits_{x\to0}\dfrac{x^2-\sin x}{x}.$

45. $\lim\limits_{x\to\infty}\dfrac{3x^2+4x-1}{4x^2-5x+3}.$

46. $\lim\limits_{x\to(\pi/2)^-} (\sec^3 x - \tan^3 x)$.

47. $\lim\limits_{x\to0} \dfrac{\sqrt{4+x}-2}{x}$.

48.   Criticize the following computations:

    (a) $\lim\limits_{x\to2} \dfrac{x^2-8}{x-2} = \lim\limits_{x\to2} \dfrac{2x}{1} = 4.$

    (b) $\lim\limits_{x\to0} \dfrac{\sin x}{e^x-1} = \lim\limits_{x\to0} \dfrac{\cos x}{e^x} = \lim\limits_{x\to0} \dfrac{-\sin x}{e^x} = 0.$

    (c) $\lim\limits_{x\to0} \dfrac{\tan x}{x-1} = \dfrac{\sec^2 x}{1} = 1.$

    (d) $\lim\limits_{x\to0} \dfrac{x}{\sqrt{x}} = \lim\limits_{x\to0} \sqrt{x} = 0.$

49.   Find $\lim_{x\to\infty} e^{-x}P(x)$ where $P(x)$ is a polynomial in x.

50.   Draw the graphs of the following curves:

    (a) $y = x \log x,\ (x > 0)$.

    (b) $y = x/e^x$.

    (c) $y = e^{-1/x^2}$. (See Problem 30.)

    (d) $y = \dfrac{\log x}{x},\ (x > 0)$.

    (e) $y = \dfrac{x}{1 - e^{1/x}}$.

    (f) $r = a/\theta,\ (a > 0)$. (This is a polar equation.)

51.   A regular polygon of n sides is inscribed in a circle of radius a. Show that as $n \longrightarrow \infty$, the perimeter of the polygon approaches the circumference of the circle and the area of the polygon approaches the area of the circle.

52.   Show that the line $y = (b/a)x$ is an asymptote for the hyperbola $(x^2/a^2) - (y^2/b^2) = 1$.

53.   Evaluate the following integrals:

    (a) $\displaystyle\int_0^1 \log x\, dx$.

    (b) $\displaystyle\int_0^1 x \log x\, dx$.

    (c) $\displaystyle\int_0^{\pi/2} \csc x\, dx$.

    (d) $\displaystyle\int_1^\infty \dfrac{dx}{x(x+1)}$.

54.   Find an equation of the family of curves through $(1, 0)$ for which $dy/dx = x^n$, $(n \neq -1)$. Show that as $n \longrightarrow -1$, the members of the family approach the curve $y = \log x$, the curve through $(1, 0)$ for which $dy/dx = x^{-1}$.

55.   In Theorem 18-I replace the assumption that $g'(x) \neq 0$ in $a < x < b$ by the assumption that $f'(x)$ and $g'(x)$ are not both zero at any x in $a < x < b$. Then prove the theorem.

56.   Show that if

$$\lim_{x \to a} g(x) = 0 \quad \text{and} \quad \lim_{x \to a} f(x) \neq 0,$$

then

$$\lim_{x \to a} \left[\frac{f(x)}{g(x)} \right]$$

does not exist. *Hint.* Show that if

$$\lim_{x \to a} \left[\frac{f(x)}{g(x)} \right] \quad \text{exists} \quad \left[\text{when } \lim_{x \to a} g(x) = 0 \right],$$

then $\lim_{x \to a} f(x) = 0$.

18.4   The Indeterminate Forms
$0^0, \infty^0, 0^\infty,$ and 1^∞

To evaluate the limit as x approaches a (or $+\infty$ or $-\infty$) of $[f(x)]^{g(x)}$, where $f(x) > 0$, we write

$$f(x) = \exp (\log f(x)).$$

Then, since the exponential function is continuous,

$$\lim_{x \to a} [f(x)]^{g(x)} = \lim_{x \to a} [\exp (\log f(x)]^{g(x)}$$

$$= \lim_{x \to a} \exp [g(x) \log f(x)] = \exp \left(\lim_{x \to a} [g(x) \log f(x)] \right).$$

Example 1.   Evaluate

$$\lim_{x \to 0^+} x^x.$$

Solution.   We first write x^x as $[\exp (\log x)]^x = \exp (x \log x)$. Since

$$\lim_{x \to 0^+} (x \log x) = 0$$

by Example 7 of Sec. 18.3,

$$\lim_{x \to 0^+} x^x = e^0 = 1.$$

This illustrates the form 0^0.

Example 2.   Evaluate

$$\lim_{x \to \infty} x^{1/x}.$$

Solution.   Since $x^{1/x} = \exp [(\log x)/x]$ and

$$\lim_{x \to \infty} \frac{\log x}{x} = \lim_{x \to \infty} \frac{x^{-1}}{1} = 0,$$

then

$$\lim_{x \to \infty} x^{1/x} = e^0 = 1.$$

This illustrates the form ∞^0.

Example 3.   Evaluate $\lim_{x \to 0^+} (x^{1/x})$.

Solution.   Since $x^{1/x} = \exp[(\log x)/x]$, and

$$\lim_{x \to 0^+} \frac{\log x}{x} = -\infty,$$

then

$$\lim_{x \to 0^+} x^{1/x} = 0.$$

This illustrates the form 0^∞.

Example 4.   Evaluate $\lim_{x \to 0} (1 + 3x)^{1/x}$.

Solution.   Since

$$(1 + 3x)^{1/x} = \exp\left(\frac{\log(1 + 3x)}{x}\right),$$

and

$$\lim_{x \to 0} \frac{\log(1 + 3x)}{x} = \lim_{x \to 0} \frac{3(1 + 3x)^{-1}}{1} = 3,$$

then

$$\lim_{x \to 0} (1 + 3x)^{1/x} = e^3.$$

This illustrates the form 1^∞.

Example 5.   Evaluate $\lim_{x \to \infty} (3^{x^2}/2^{x^3})$.

Solution.   Since

$$\frac{3^{x^2}}{2^{x^3}} = \exp(x^2 \log 3 - x^3 \log 2),$$

and since

$$\lim_{x \to \infty} [x^2(\log 3 - x \log 2)] = -\infty,$$

then

$$\lim_{x \to \infty} \left(\frac{3^{x^2}}{2^{x^3}}\right) = 0.$$

PROBLEM LIST 108

Evaluate the following limits:

1. $\lim_{x \to 0} (1 + x)^{1/x}$.

2. $\lim_{x \to 0^+} x^{\sqrt{x}}$.

3. $\lim_{x \to 0^+} (\sqrt{x})^x$.

4. $\lim_{x \to \infty} (x^2 - 1)^x$.

5. $\lim_{x \to 1} x^{1/(1-x)}$.

6. $\lim_{x \to 0} \left(\frac{1}{x^2}\right)^{\sin x}$.

7. $\lim_{x \to (\pi/2)^-} (\tan x)^{\sin 2x}$.

8. $\lim_{x \to 0} \left(\frac{1}{x^2}\right)^{x^2}$.

9. $\lim_{x \to \pi/2} (\sin x)^{\tan x}$.

10. $\lim_{x \to \infty} (2x)^{1/x}$.

11. $\lim_{x \to 0} (1 + \sin x)^{1/x}$.

12. $\lim_{x \to 0} (1 + \sqrt{2}\, x)^{1/x}$.

13. $\lim\limits_{x\to 0^+} \left(1 + \dfrac{1}{x}\right)^{4x}$.

20. $\lim\limits_{x\to 0} \left(\dfrac{\tan x}{x}\right)^{1/x^2}$.

14. $\lim\limits_{x\to 0^+} \left(1 + \dfrac{1}{x}\right)^{ax}$.

21. $\lim\limits_{x\to 1} x^{\cot \pi x}$.

15. $\lim\limits_{x\to 0^+} \left(1 + \dfrac{a}{x}\right)^{x}$.

22. $\lim\limits_{x\to\infty} \dfrac{3x}{e^{x^2}}$.

16. $\lim\limits_{x\to\infty} (e^x - x)$.

23. $\lim\limits_{x\to\infty} \dfrac{3^{x^2}}{2^x}$.

17. $\lim\limits_{x\to 0} \left(\dfrac{\sin x}{x}\right)^{1/x}$.

24. $\lim\limits_{x\to 1} \dfrac{x - x^x}{x - 1}$.

18. $\lim\limits_{x\to 0} (x + e^x)^{1/x}$.

25. $\lim\limits_{x\to 0} \dfrac{(1 + x)^{1/x} - e}{x}$.

19. $\lim\limits_{x\to 1} x^x$.

26. Draw the graphs of the functions defined by the following equations:

    (a) $y = x^x$, $(x > 0)$.

    (b) $y = x^{-x}$, $(x > 0)$.

    (c) $y = x^{1/x}$, $(x > 0)$.

27. For fixed k and t, show that

$$\lim_{n\to\infty} \left(1 - \frac{k}{n} + \frac{ke^t}{n}\right)^n = e^{k(e^t-1)}.$$

REFERENCES

18.1 L. Brand, *Advanced Calculus*, John Wiley, New York, 1962.

18.2 A. E. Taylor, *Advanced Calculus*, Ginn, Boston, 1955.

18.3 A. E. Taylor "L'Hôpital's Rule," *Am. Math. Monthly*, Vol. 59 (January 1952).

Chapter

19

Infinite series

19.1 *The Sum of an Infinite Series*

The expression

$$\sum_{i=1}^{n} ar^{i-1} = a + ar + ar^2 + \cdots + ar^{n-1}, \qquad (19.1)$$

where $a \neq 0$, $r \neq 0$, and n is a positive integer, is called a geometric progression. If $r = 1$, the sum s_n of the n terms of the progression is clearly na. If $r \neq 1$, then

$$s_n = a + ar + ar^2 + \cdots + ar^{n-1}$$
$$rs_n = \qquad ar + ar^2 + \cdots + ar^{n-1} + ar^n$$
$$s_n - rs_n = a - ar^n$$

and

$$s_n = \frac{a - ar^n}{1 - r} = \frac{a}{1 - r} - \left(\frac{a}{1 - r}\right)r^n. \qquad (19.2)$$

If $|r| < 1$, the sequence $\{s_n\}$ converges to $a/(1 - r)$ since $\lim_{n \to \infty} r^n = 0$. If $|r| \geqslant 1$, the sequence $\{s_n\}$ diverges since $\lim_{n \to \infty}(s_n)$ does not exist. (Sequences were discussed in Sec. 1.7.)

$$\sum_{i=1}^{\infty} ar^{i-1} = a + ar + ar^2 + \cdots + ar^{n-1} + \cdots \qquad (19.3)$$

is called a geometric series. When $|r| < 1$, the sum s_n of the first n terms of the series (19.3), given by (19.1) or (19.2), approaches $a/(1 - r)$ as $n \to \infty$, and hence it is natural in this case to define the sum of series (19.3) as $a/(1 - r)$. We say that the series converges to $a/(1 - r)$ or has sum $a/(1 - r)$. When $|r| \geqslant 1$, we say that the series diverges.

The preceding discussion prompts us to formulate the following definitions.

Given a sequence $\{a_n\}$, the infinite series

$$\sum_{i=1}^{\infty} a_i = a_1 + a_2 + \cdots + a_n + \cdots \tag{19.4}$$

is said to have the sum s if and only if the sequence $\{s_n\}$ of partial sums of the series converges to s. The elements of $\{s_n\}$ are

$$s_1 = a_1, \quad s_2 = a_1 + a_2, \quad \cdots, \quad s_n = a_1 + a_2 + \cdots + a_n.$$

The numbers $a_1, a_2, \cdots$ are called the terms of the series and the term a_n is called the general term or nth term of the series.

If the sequence $\{s_n\}$ converges to s, the series (19.4) is said to converge to s or to have sum s. If $\{s_n\}$ diverges, the series (19.4) is said to diverge. Although it is possible to assign a sum to a divergent series, we will not consider this possibility. A treatment of this extension is given in Refs. 19.1 and 19.2.

Let us interpret the convergence of (19.4) geometrically. Let the sequence $\{s_n\}$ converge to s and let ϵ be an arbitrarily small positive number. If the number s is plotted on the x-axis, then there exists an $n = N$ such that the points corresponding to $s_N, s_{N+1}, s_{N+2}, \cdots$ all lie in the interval $s - \epsilon < x < s + \epsilon$. See Fig. 19.1.

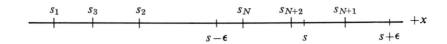

Figure 19.1

In defining the sum of an infinite series we have generalized the operation of addition so that, for convergent series, it now makes sense to talk about the sum of an infinite number of addends.

Example 1. The series

$$1 + \frac{1}{2} + \frac{1}{4} + \cdots + \frac{1}{2^{n-1}} + \cdots$$

converges, since it is a geometric series with $r = 1/2$. Since $a = 1$, we have

$$s_n = 1 + \frac{1}{2} + \frac{1}{4} + \cdots + \frac{1}{2^{n-1}}$$

$$= \frac{a - ar^n}{1 - r} = \frac{1 - (\frac{1}{2})^n}{1 - \frac{1}{2}}.$$

As $n \to \infty$, $s_n \to 2$, the sum of the series.

Example 2. The series $1 + 2 + 3 + \cdots + n + \cdots$ diverges, since $s_n = 1 + 2 + \cdots + n = n(1 + n)/2$ does not approach a limit as $n \to \infty$.

Example 3. The series $1 - 1 + 1 - 1 + \cdots + (-1)^{n-1} + \cdots$ diverges, since $s_n = 1$ for n odd but $s_n = 0$ for n even. Clearly $\{s_n\}$ diverges.

Example 4.   The series

$$\sum_{i=1}^{\infty} \frac{1}{i(i+1)} = \frac{1}{1\cdot2} + \frac{1}{2\cdot3} + \cdots + \frac{1}{n(n+1)} + \cdots$$

has sum $s = 1$. This is seen by noting that

$$\frac{1}{n(n+1)} = \frac{1}{n} - \frac{1}{n+1}$$

and that

$$s_n = \left(\frac{1}{1} - \frac{1}{2}\right) + \left(\frac{1}{2} - \frac{1}{3}\right) + \cdots + \left(\frac{1}{n} - \frac{1}{n+1}\right)$$

$$= \frac{1}{1} - \left(\frac{1}{2} - \frac{1}{2}\right) - \left(\frac{1}{3} - \frac{1}{3}\right) - \cdots - \left(\frac{1}{n} - \frac{1}{n}\right) - \frac{1}{n+1}$$

$$= 1 - \frac{1}{n+1}.$$

Hence $\lim_{n\to\infty} (s_n) = 1 = s$.

In the preceding examples convergence or divergence was decided by direct examination of s_n. Unfortunately it is not usually possible to obtain a simple expression for s_n. Theorem 4-IX is often useful in such cases.

Example 5.   The series

$$\sum_{i=1}^{\infty} \frac{1}{(i+1)^2} = \frac{1}{2^2} + \frac{1}{3^2} + \cdots + \frac{1}{(n+1)^2} + \cdots$$

converges by Theorem 4-IX, since $\{s_n\}$ is a bounded monotone sequence. This was established in Example 8 of Sec. 4.7. Although Theorem 4-IX implies that the series converges, it does not reveal the actual sum of the series. It is much simpler to decide whether or not a series converges than to determine the sum of the series.

The following theorem is often useful in determining that a series diverges.

Theorem 19-I.   If a series $\sum_{i=1}^{\infty} a_i$ conyerges, then $\lim_{n\to\infty} a_n = 0$.

Proof.   Let

$$s = \sum_{i=1}^{\infty} a_i.$$

Then $a_n = s_n - s_{n-1}$ and

$$\lim_{n\to\infty} a_n = \lim_{n\to\infty} (s_n - s_{n-1})$$

$$= \lim_{n\to\infty} s_n - \lim_{n\to\infty} s_{n-1}$$

$$= s - s = 0.$$

The contrapositive of Theorem 19-I states that if $\lim_{n \to \infty} (a_n) \neq 0$, then $\sum_{i=1}^{\infty} a_i$ does not converge; that is, the series diverges. The theorem is easier to apply in this form.

Example 6.   The series

$$\sum_{i=1}^{\infty} \frac{i}{i+1} = \frac{1}{2} + \frac{2}{3} + \frac{3}{4} + \cdots + \frac{n}{n+1} + \cdots$$

diverges since

$$\lim_{n \to \infty} \frac{n}{n+1} = \lim_{n \to \infty} \frac{1}{1 + (1/n)} = 1 \neq 0.$$

Example 7.   Show that

$$\sum_{i=2}^{\infty} \frac{\sqrt{i}}{\log i}$$

is divergent.

Solution.   By L'Hôpital's rule,

$$\lim_{n \to \infty} \frac{\sqrt{n}}{\log n} = \lim_{n \to \infty} \frac{1/(2\sqrt{n})}{1/n} = \lim_{n \to \infty} \frac{\sqrt{n}}{2} = \infty.$$

Since the nth term does not approach zero, the series diverges.

Theorem 19-I gives a necessary condition for the convergence of a series. However, the condition that the nth term approach zero is not sufficient to guarantee the convergence of a series. In other words, the converse of Theorem 19-I is false. To demonstrate this, we present a divergent series for which $\lim_{n \to \infty} a_n = 0$. We employ the harmonic series

$$\sum_{i=1}^{\infty} \frac{1}{i} = 1 + \frac{1}{2} + \frac{1}{3} + \cdots + \frac{1}{n} + \cdots.$$

Clearly

$$\lim_{n \to \infty} \frac{1}{n} = 0.$$

On the other hand,

$$s_{2n} = s_n + \frac{1}{n+1} + \frac{1}{n+2} + \cdots + \frac{1}{n+n}$$

$$\geqslant s_n + \frac{1}{n+n} + \frac{1}{n+n} + \cdots + \frac{1}{n+n}$$

$$= s_n + n \cdot \frac{1}{2n} = s_n + \frac{1}{2}.$$

Since s_2 exceeds s_1 by at least 1/2, and s_4 exceeds s_2 by at least 1/2, and s_6 exceeds s_3 by at least 1/2, and so forth, it follows that $s_{2n} \to \infty$ as $n \to \infty$. If the points corresponding to the sequence $\{s_{2n}\}$ were plotted on the x-axis, each point would be at least 1/2 unit to the right of the preceding point. Since $\{s_{2n}\}$ diverges, $\{s_n\}$ diverges and consequently the harmonic series diverges.

The following theorems are readily established by employing the definition of convergence of a series. Proofs are left to the problems.

Theorem 19-II.   The convergence or divergence of a series is not affected by the addition or subtraction of a finite number of terms. The sum, however, may be changed if the original series converges.

Theorem 19-III.   If

$$\sum_{i=1}^{\infty} a_i = s$$

and k is any constant, then

$$\sum_{i=1}^{\infty} ka_i = ks.$$

If $\sum_{i=1}^{\infty} a_i$ diverges, then $\sum_{i=1}^{\infty} ka_i$ diverges, provided $k \neq 0$.

Theorem 19-IV.   If

$$\sum_{i=1}^{\infty} a_i = s_1 \qquad \text{and} \qquad \sum_{i=1}^{\infty} b_i = s_2,$$

then

$$\sum_{i=1}^{\infty} (a_i \pm b_i) = s_1 \pm s_2.$$

This theorem states that two convergent series may be added or subtracted term by term. It also states that the sum or difference of two convergent series is a convergent series.

PROBLEM LIST 109

1. For the series $\sum_{i=1}^{\infty} (1/2^i)$, find **(a)** a_3, **(b)** s_5, **(c)** $\lim_{n \to \infty} (a_n)$, **(d)** s, the sum of the series.

2. For the series $\sum_{i=1}^{\infty} (-1/3)^{i-1}$, find **(a)** a_4, **(b)** s_6, **(c)** $\lim_{n \to \infty} (a_n)$, **(d)** s, the sum of the series.

3. Sum each of the following series:

    (a) $\sum_{i=1}^{\infty} \frac{1}{4^i}.$

    (b) $\sum_{i=2}^{\infty} \left(\frac{2}{3}\right)^i.$

    (c) $\sum_{i=4}^{\infty} \frac{1}{2^i}.$

    (d) $\sum_{i=1}^{\infty} 0^i.$

    (e) $\sum_{i=1}^{\infty} \left(\frac{-1}{2}\right)^{i-1}.$

    (f) $\sum_{i=1}^{\infty} \frac{(-1)^i}{5^{i-1}}.$

4. For the series $\sum_{i=1}^{\infty} (1/2^{i-1})$, plot on the x-axis the points corresponding to s_1, s_2, s_3, s_4, and s_5. Find the sum s of the series. Find the smallest value N of n such that $|s_n - s| < 0.001$ whenever $n \geq N$.

5. Show that each of the following series diverges:

    (a) $\sum_{i=1}^{\infty} i^2.$

    (b) $\sum_{i=1}^{\infty} \frac{2i}{3i + 1}.$

(c) $\displaystyle\sum_{i=1}^{\infty} \frac{\sqrt{i}}{\sqrt[3]{i}}.$

(f) $\displaystyle\sum_{i=1}^{\infty} \frac{e^i}{i^2}.$

(d) $\displaystyle\sum_{i=1}^{\infty} (-1)^i.$

(g) $\displaystyle\sum_{i=2}^{\infty} \frac{\sqrt[3]{i}}{\log i}.$

(e) $\displaystyle\sum_{i=1}^{\infty} \left(\frac{3}{2}\right)^i.$

(h) $\displaystyle\sum_{i=1}^{\infty} \left(1 + \frac{1}{i}\right)^i.$

6. Sum the following series:

(a) $\displaystyle\sum_{i=1}^{\infty} \frac{1}{(i+1)(i+2)}.$

(b) $\displaystyle\sum_{i=2}^{\infty} \left[\frac{1}{\log i} - \frac{1}{\log (i+1)}\right].$

7. Show that the series $\sum_{i=1}^{\infty} [\log i - \log (i+1)]$ diverges.

8. Evaluate the repeating decimal $0.333\cdots = (3/10) + (3/100) + (3/1000) + \cdots$.

9. Evaluate the repeating decimal $0.252525\cdots$.

10. Prove that every repeating decimal represents a rational number.

11. Prove that the sum of a convergent series is unique.

12. Prove that the series $\sum_{i=1}^{\infty} (1/i^i)$ converges.

13. Discuss the truth or falsity of the theorem "If a series does not converge, then its nth term does not approach zero as n becomes infinite."

14. Find a value N of n such that the nth partial sum $s_n = 1 + (1/2) + (1/3) + \cdots + (1/n)$ of the harmonic series is greater than 5 whenever $n \geqslant N$.

15. Given that $s_n = (n+1)/n$ for a series, find the general term a_n of the series.

16. Find the third term of the series for which $s_n = n^2/(n^2 + 3)$.

17. Prove Theorem 19-II.

18. Prove Theorem 19-III.

19. Prove Theorem 19-IV.

20. Show that the series

$$\sum_{i=1}^{\infty} \frac{1}{3i+3}$$

diverges.

21. Find the sum of the series

$$\sum_{i=1}^{\infty} \frac{3^i + 2^i}{2^i 3^i}.$$

22. Given that

$$\sum_{i=1}^{\infty} \frac{1}{i^2} = \frac{\pi^2}{6},$$

evaluate $\sum_{i=3}^{\infty} (1/i^2)$.

23. Prove that if parentheses are inserted in a convergent series, the new series formed converges to the same sum as the original series.

24. Give two examples showing that if parentheses are inserted in a divergent series, the new series formed may converge or diverge.

25. Show that

$$\sum_{i=2}^{\infty} \frac{i-1}{i!} = 1$$

where $i!$ (read factorial i) $= i(i-1)(i-2)\cdots(1)$.

26. Show that the series

$$\sum_{i=1}^{\infty} \log \frac{1}{i+1}$$

diverges.

19.2   Series of Nonnegative Terms

The following theorem is useful in demonstrating that a series converges.

Theorem 19-V (*comparison test*).   Let

$$\sum_{i=1}^{\infty} a_i \qquad \text{and} \qquad \sum_{i=1}^{\infty} b_i$$

be series of nonnegative terms and let $a_n \leqslant b_n$ for all positive integers n. If $\sum_{i=1}^{\infty} (b_i)$ converges, then $\sum_{i=1}^{\infty} (a_i)$ converges.

Proof.   Let

$$\sum_{i=1}^{\infty} b_i = B.$$

Then

$$\sum_{i=1}^{n} a_i \leqslant \sum_{i=1}^{n} b_i \leqslant B$$

for all positive integers n. Thus the sequence of partial sums of the series $\sum_{i=1}^{\infty} (a_i)$ is bounded above by B. Since the sequence is nondecreasing it converges to a number $\leqslant B$. This is a consequence of Theorem 4-IX. Hence the series $\sum_{i=1}^{\infty} (a_i)$ has sum $\leqslant B$.

The theorem can also be applied if the inequality $a_n \leqslant b_n$ holds for all n greater than some fixed positive integer N. We merely drop the first N terms of each series and apply Theorem 19-II. It is important to remember that in applying Theorem 19-V, the series to be tested must be compared with a series which is known to converge.

Example 1.   The series

$$\sum_{i=1}^{\infty} \frac{1}{i2^i}$$

converges, since

$$\frac{1}{n2^n} \leqslant \frac{1}{2^n}$$

for all positive integers n and the series $\sum_{i=1}^{\infty} (1/2^i)$ is a convergent geometric series of nonnegative terms.

Example 2.   The series $\sum_{i=1}^{\infty}(1/i\,!)$ converges, since $1/n! \leqslant 1/2^n$ for all positive integers $n > 3$.

Theorem 19-V can also be used to demonstrate that a series diverges. We write the contrapositive of the theorem and the second sentence becomes: "If $\sum_{i=1}^{\infty}(a_i)$ does not converge, then $\sum_{i=1}^{\infty}(b_i)$ does not converge." When the theorem is used in this form, the series to be tested must be compared with a series which is known to diverge.

Example 3.   The series

$$\sum_{i=1}^{\infty}\frac{i^2+i}{i^3}$$

diverges, since

$$\frac{n^2+n}{n^3}=\frac{1}{n}+\frac{1}{n^2}>\frac{1}{n}$$

for all positive integers n and the harmonic series $\sum_{i=1}^{\infty}(1/i)$ is known to diverge.

The following powerful test was devised by the Scottish mathematician Maclaurin (1698–1746) and developed by Cauchy.

Theorem 19-VI (*Cauchy integral test*).   Let the function f be positive, decreasing, and continuous for $x \geqslant 1$. If $\int_1^\infty f(x)\,dx$ converges, then $\sum_{i=1}^{\infty}f(i)$ converges.

Proof.   In Fig. 19.2 the shaded rectangles have areas $f(2), f(3), \cdots, f(n)$. Letting $\int_1^\infty f(x)\,dx = M$, and noting that from $x = 1$ to $x - n$ the total area of the shaded rectangles is less than the area under the curve $y = f(x)$, we have

$$f(2)+f(3)+\cdots+f(n) < \int_1^n f(x)\,dx < M$$

for all $n \geqslant 2$.

Since the partial sums of $\sum_{i=2}^{\infty}f(i)$ are increasing and bounded above by

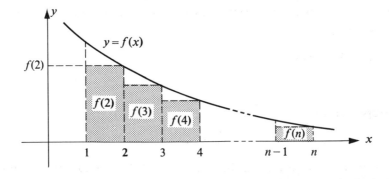

Figure 19.2

M, the series $\sum_{i=2}^{\infty} f(i)$ converges by Theorem 4-IX. By Theorem 19-II the series $\sum_{i=1}^{\infty} f(i)$ converges.

Example 4.   Show that $\sum_{i=1}^{\infty} (1/i^p)$ converges if $p > 1$.

   Solution.   Letting $f(x) = 1/x^p$, we obtain

$$\int_1^{\infty} \frac{dx}{x^p} = \lim_{t \to \infty} \int_1^t x^{-p} \, dx$$

$$= \lim_{t \to \infty} \left[\frac{x^{-p+1}}{-p+1} \right]_1^t$$

$$= \lim_{t \to \infty} \left[\frac{t^{-p+1} - 1}{-p+1} \right] = \frac{1}{p-1}.$$

Since f satisfies the conditions of Theorem 19-VI and $\int_1^{\infty} f(x) \, dx$ converges, the series $\sum_{i=1}^{\infty} (1/i^p)$ converges for $p > 1$.

We next prove the converse of Theorem 19-VI.

Theorem 19-VII.   Let the function f be positive, decreasing, and continuous for $x \geqslant 1$. If $\sum_{i=1}^{\infty} f(i)$ converges, then $\int_1^{\infty} f(x) \, dx$ converges.

   Proof.   In Fig. 19.3 the shaded rectangles have areas $f(1), f(2), \cdots,$ $f(n-1)$. From $x = 1$ to $x = n$ the total area of the shaded rectangles is greater than the area under the curve $y = f(x)$. Letting $\sum_{i=1}^{\infty} f(i) = K$, we have

$$\int_1^n f(x) \, dx < f(1) + f(2) + \cdots + f(n-1) < K$$

for all $n \geqslant 2$.

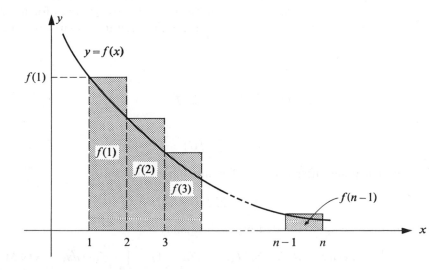

Figure 19.3

Since the sequence

$$\int_1^2 f(x)\,dx,\ \int_1^3 f(x)\,dx,\cdots,\ \int_1^n f(x)\,dx,\cdots$$

is increasing and bounded above by K, the sequence converges by Theorem 4-IX. Since $\int_1^t f(x)\,dx$ defines a bounded increasing function of t, it is easy to show that if $\lim_{n\to\infty}\int_1^n f(x)\,dx$ exists when n denotes a positive integer, then the limit also exists when n denotes a positive real number. The convergence of $\int_1^\infty f(x)\,dx$ follows from the existence of $\lim_{n\to\infty}\int_1^n f(x)\,dx$.

The contrapositive of Theorem 19-VII is useful in establishing the divergence of a series. The second sentence of the theorem becomes "If $\int_1^\infty f(x)\,dx$ does not converge, then $\sum_{i=1}^\infty f(i)$ does not converge." In other words, "If $\int_1^\infty f(x)\,dx$ diverges, then $\sum_{i=1}^\infty f(i)$ diverges."

Example 5.   Show that the harmonic series $\sum_{i=1}^\infty (1/i)$ diverges.

Solution.   Letting $f(x) = 1/x$, we obtain

$$\int_1^\infty \frac{dx}{x} = \lim_{t\to\infty} \int_1^t \frac{dx}{x} = \lim_{t\to\infty} (\log t).$$

Since $\log t \to \infty$ as $t \to \infty$, $\int_1^\infty (dx/x)$ diverges, and hence $\sum_{i=1}^\infty (1/i)$ diverges by the contrapositive of Theorem 19-VII.

In Sec. 19.1 the divergence of the harmonic series was established by a different method.

Since $1/n^p \geqslant 1/n$ for $p < 1$, it follows from the comparison test that $\sum_{i=1}^\infty (1/i^p)$ diverges for $p < 1$.

The series $\sum_{i=1}^\infty (1/i^p)$, which we have shown converges for $p > 1$ and diverges for $p \leqslant 1$, is known as the p-series and is useful as a comparison series for testing other series. The geometric series $\sum_{i=1}^\infty ar^{i-1}$ is another useful comparison series.

Let

$$\sum_{i=1}^\infty f(i) = \sum_{i=1}^n f(i) + \sum_{i=n+1}^\infty f(i) = s.$$

The quantity

$$R_n = \sum_{i=n+1}^\infty f(i)$$

is called the remainder after n terms. The amount by which

$$S_n = \sum_{i=1}^n f(i)$$

differs from s can be approximated by the inequality

$$\int_{n+1}^\infty f(x)\,dx < R_n - \sum_{i=n+1}^\infty f(i) < f(n+1) + \int_{n+1}^\infty f(x)\,dx, \qquad (19.5)$$

true for $n = 0, 1, 2, \cdots$.

Inequality (19.5) is readily obtained from a figure similar to Fig. 19.2. (See Problem 4.)

Example 6.   Approximate R_n for the series $\sum_{i=1}^{\infty} (1/i^2)$.

Solution.   By (19.5),

$$\int_{n+1}^{\infty} x^{-2}\, dx < R_n < \frac{1}{(n+1)^2} + \int_{n+1}^{\infty} x^{-2}\, dx.$$

Since

$$\int_{n+1}^{\infty} x^{-2}\, dx = \lim_{t \to \infty} \left[\frac{-1}{x} \right]_{n+1}^{t} = \lim_{t \to \infty} \left[\frac{-1}{t} + \frac{1}{n+1} \right] = \frac{1}{n+1},$$

R_n satisfies

$$\frac{1}{n+1} < R_n < \frac{1}{(n+1)^2} + \frac{1}{n+1} = \frac{n+2}{(n+1)^2}.$$

For example, if $n = 999$, then $0.001 < R_n < 0.001001$.

A digital computer can easily be programmed to compute s_n for values of n for which $R_n = s - s_n$ will be as small as required in applications.

PROBLEM LIST 110

1. Apply the comparison test to determine the convergence or divergence of the following series:

(a) $\sum_{i=1}^{\infty} \frac{1}{i^2 2^i}$.

(i) $\sum_{i=1}^{\infty} \frac{2}{2^i - 1}$.

(b) $\sum_{i=1}^{\infty} \frac{1}{i^i}$.

(j) $\sum_{i=2}^{\infty} \frac{1}{\log i}$.

(c) $\sum_{i=1}^{\infty} \frac{1}{\sqrt{i}}$.

(k) $\sum_{i=1}^{\infty} \frac{1}{\sqrt{9i^2 - 1}}$.

(d) $\sum_{i=1}^{\infty} \frac{i^3 + i}{i^4}$.

(l) $\sum_{i=1}^{\infty} \frac{i}{(i+1)2^i}$.

(e) $\sum_{i=1}^{\infty} \frac{1}{(2i+1)^2}$.

(m) $\sum_{i=1}^{\infty} \frac{i-2}{i^2}$.

(f) $\sum_{i=1}^{\infty} \frac{i}{(2i+1)^2}$.

(n) $\sum_{i=1}^{\infty} \frac{1}{\sqrt{i(i^2 + 3)}}$.

(g) $\sum_{i=1}^{\infty} \frac{\sin^2 i}{i^2}$.

(o) $\sum_{i=1}^{\infty} \frac{1}{i i^{1/i}}$.

(h) $\sum_{i=1}^{\infty} \frac{1}{3i^{3/2} + 1}$.

(p) $\sum_{i=1}^{\infty} \frac{i^{10}}{10^i}$.

2. Apply the integral test to determine the convergence or divergence of the following series.

(a) $\sum_{i=1}^{\infty} \frac{1}{3^i}$.

(d) $\sum_{i=1}^{\infty} \frac{i}{i^2 + 5}$.

(b) $\sum_{i=1}^{\infty} \frac{1}{i^2 + 9}$.

(e) $\sum_{i=1}^{\infty} \frac{1}{(i+2)^{3/2}}$.

(c) $\sum_{i=1}^{\infty} \frac{1}{(i+2)^3}$.

(f) $\sum_{i=1}^{\infty} \frac{1}{3i + 2}$.

(g) $\displaystyle\sum_{i=1}^{\infty} \frac{1}{e^i}$.

(l) $\displaystyle\sum_{i=2}^{\infty} \frac{\log i}{i}$.

(h) $\displaystyle\sum_{i=2}^{\infty} \frac{2}{\sqrt{2i-3}}$.

(m) $\displaystyle\sum_{i=2}^{\infty} \frac{1}{i \log i}$.

(i) $\displaystyle\sum_{i=1}^{\infty} \frac{1}{i(i+1)}$.

(n) $\displaystyle\sum_{i=2}^{\infty} \frac{1}{i \log^2 i}$.

(j) $\displaystyle\sum_{i=1}^{\infty} \frac{i}{e^i}$.

(o) $\displaystyle\sum_{i=2}^{\infty} \frac{\log^2 i}{i}$.

(k) $\displaystyle\sum_{i=2}^{\infty} \frac{1}{i^2 - 1}$.

3. Show that Theorems 19-VI and 19-VII are still true if the inequality $x \geqslant 1$ is replaced by $x \geqslant a$ and $\int_1^\infty f(x)\,dx$ is replaced by $\int_a^\infty f(x)\,dx$, where a is any positive integer greater than 1.

4. Prove inequality (19.5).

5. Approximate R_n for the series $\sum_{i=1}^\infty (1/i^2)$ when $n = 9999$.

6. Set $n = 0$ in (19.5) to show that

$$\frac{\pi}{4} < \sum_{i=1}^{\infty} \frac{1}{1+i^2} < \frac{1}{2} + \frac{\pi}{4} .$$

7. Prove the inequality

$$\log (n+1) < \sum_{i=1}^{n} \frac{1}{i} < 1 + \log (n+1).$$

Find the smallest value of n such that $\sum_{i=1}^n (1/i)$ is greater than (a) 2, (b) 3, (c) 4.

8. Let $\sum_{i=1}^\infty a_i$ and $\sum_{i=1}^\infty b_i$ be series of nonnegative terms and let $a_n \geqslant b_n$ for all positive integers n. If $\sum_{i=1}^\infty b_i$ converges, what conclusion can be drawn regarding the series $\sum_{i=1}^\infty a_i$?

9. Let $\sum_{i=1}^\infty a_i$ and $\sum_{i=1}^\infty b_i$ be series of nonnegative terms and let $a_n \leqslant b_n$ for all positive integers n. If $\sum_{i=1}^\infty b_i$ diverges, what conclusion can be drawn regarding the series $\sum_{i=1}^\infty a_i$?

10. Let $\sum_{i=1}^\infty a_i$ and $\sum_{i=1}^\infty b_i$ be series of positive terms and let $\lim_{n\to\infty} (a_n/b_n) = L > 0$. Prove that either both series converge or both series diverge. *Hint.* Show that there exists an $n = N$ such that

$$\frac{L}{2} < \frac{a_n}{b_n} < \frac{3L}{2}$$

for all $n \geqslant N$.

11. Use the result in Problem 10 to show that

(a) $\displaystyle\sum_{i=1}^{\infty} \frac{i+1}{i 3^i}$ converges;

(b) $\displaystyle\sum_{i=1}^{\infty} \frac{1}{\sqrt{9n^2 + 100}}$ diverges.

19.3   The Ratio Test

The following test is often useful when the ratio a_{n+1}/a_n is simple although the general term a_n is complicated.

Theorem 19-VIII (*ratio test*).   Let $\sum_{i=1}^{\infty} a_i$ be a series of positive terms.

(i) If

$$\lim_{n \to \infty} \frac{a_{n+1}}{a_n} = L < 1,$$

the series converges.

(ii) If

$$\lim_{n \to \infty} \frac{a_{n+1}}{a_n} = L > 1$$

or if

$$\lim_{n \to \infty} \frac{a_{n+1}}{a_n} = \infty,$$

the series diverges.

Proof of part (i).   Let r be any number satisfying $L < r < 1$. See Fig. 19.4. The number L is clearly nonnegative, since $a_{n+1}/a_n > 0$ for all n. Hence r is positive.

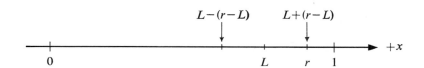

Figure 19.4

Since

$$\lim_{n \to \infty} \frac{a_{n+1}}{a_n} = L,$$

there exists a positive integer N such that

$$L - (r - L) < \frac{a_{n+1}}{a_n} < L + (r - L) = r$$

for all positive integers $n \geqslant N$.

Hence

$$a_{N+1} < a_N r$$

$$a_{N+2} < a_{N+1} r \quad < a_N r^2$$

$$a_{N+3} < a_{N+2} r \quad < a_N r^3$$

.
.
.

$$a_{N+m} < a_{N+m-1} r < a_N r^m$$

.
.
.

The series $\sum_{i=1}^{\infty} a_N r^i$ is geometric and converges, since $|r| = r < 1$. The series $\sum_{i=1}^{\infty} a_{N+i}$ converges by the comparison test, since each term is less than the corresponding term of the convergent geometric series $\sum_{i=1}^{\infty} a_N r^i$. Finally, the series $\sum_{i=1}^{\infty} a_i$ converges by Theorem 19-II.

Proof of part (ii).   It is necessary to show only that $\lim_{n \to \infty} (a_n) \neq 0$. (See Problem 2.)
If

$$\lim_{n \to \infty} \frac{a_{n+1}}{a_n} = 1,$$

the series may converge or diverge and hence the ratio test does not apply. (See Problem 3.)

Also, if $\lim_{n \to \infty} (a_{n+1}/a_n)$ does not exist and $\lim_{n \to \infty} (a_{n+1}/a_n) \neq \infty$, the series may converge or diverge, and again the ratio test does not apply. (See Problems 4 and 5.)

Example 1.   Apply the ratio test to the series

$$\sum_{i=1}^{\infty} \frac{i^2}{2^i}.$$

Solution.   Since

$$a_n = \frac{n^2}{2^n} \quad \text{and} \quad a_{n+1} = \frac{(n+1)^2}{2^{n+1}},$$

$$\lim_{n \to \infty} \frac{a_{n+1}}{a_n} = \lim_{n \to \infty} \left[\frac{(n+1)^2}{2^{n+1}} \cdot \frac{2^n}{n^2} \right]$$

$$= \lim_{n \to \infty} \frac{1}{2} \left(1 + \frac{1}{n} \right)^2 = \frac{1}{2}.$$

Since $1/2 < 1$, the series converges.

Example 2.   Apply the ratio test to the series

$$\sum_{i=1}^{\infty} \frac{i!}{2^i}.$$

Solution.   The ratio a_{n+1}/a_n is equal to

$$\frac{(n+1)!}{2^{n+1}} \div \frac{n!}{2^n} = \frac{(n+1)!}{2^{n+1}} \cdot \frac{2^n}{n!} = \frac{n+1}{2}.$$

Since

$$\lim_{n \to \infty} \frac{n+1}{2} = \infty,$$

the series diverges.

PROBLEM LIST 111

1. Apply the ratio test to the following series. If the test does not apply, use another method to determine convergence or divergence.

(a) $\sum_{i=1}^{\infty} \dfrac{i^2}{3^i}.$

(b) $\sum_{i=1}^{\infty} \dfrac{i^3}{2^i}.$

(c) $\sum_{i=1}^{\infty} \dfrac{1}{2i}.$

(d) $\sum_{i=1}^{\infty} \dfrac{2}{i^2}.$

(e) $\sum_{i=1}^{\infty} \dfrac{1}{i!}.$

(f) $\sum_{i=1}^{\infty} \dfrac{i!}{3^i}.$

(g) $\sum_{i=1}^{\infty} \dfrac{i}{2^i}.$

(h) $\sum_{i=1}^{\infty} \dfrac{i2^i}{e^i}.$

(i) $\sum_{i=1}^{\infty} i.$

(j) $\sum_{i=1}^{\infty} \dfrac{1}{(2i-1)!}.$

(k) $\sum_{i=1}^{\infty} \dfrac{i^4}{i!}.$

(l) $\sum_{i=2}^{\infty} \dfrac{1}{\log i}.$

(m) $\sum_{i=1}^{\infty} \dfrac{10^i}{i!}.$

(n) $\sum_{i=1}^{\infty} \dfrac{i+1}{i4^i}.$

(o) $\sum_{i=1}^{\infty} \dfrac{1+2^i}{1+3^i}.$

(p) $\sum_{i=1}^{\infty} \dfrac{1\cdot3\cdots(2i-1)}{2\cdot5\cdots(3i-1)}.$

(q) $\sum_{i=1}^{\infty} \dfrac{i^i}{i!}.$

(r) $\sum_{i=1}^{\infty} \dfrac{1}{i^i}.$

(s) $\sum_{i=1}^{\infty} \dfrac{i^{1000}}{2^i}.$

(t) $\sum_{i=1}^{\infty} \dfrac{i!}{(2i)!}.$

(u) $\sum_{i=1}^{\infty} \dfrac{i^i}{2^i}.$

2. Prove part (ii) of Theorem 19-VIII.

3. Show that

$$\lim_{n\to\infty} \frac{a_{n+1}}{a_n} = 1$$

for both the convergent series $\sum_{i=1}^{\infty} (1/i^2)$ and the divergent series $\sum_{i=1}^{\infty} (1/i)$.

4. Construct a convergent series $\sum_{i=1}^{\infty} a_i$ of positive terms such that $\lim_{n\to\infty} (a_{n+1}/a_n)$ does not exist.

5. Construct a divergent series $\sum_{i=1}^{\infty} a_i$ of positive terms such that $\lim_{n\to\infty} (a_{n+1}/a_n)$ does not exist.

6. Let $\sum_{i=1}^{\infty} a_i$ be a series of positive terms for which $a_{n+1}/a_n < 1$ for all positive integers n. Show by means of an example that the series does not necessarily converge.

7. Let $\sum_{i=1}^{\infty} a_i$ be a series of positive terms for which $a_{n+1}/a_n > 1$ for all positive integers n. Prove that the series diverges.

8. Let $\sum_{i=1}^{\infty} a_i$ be a series of positive terms which converges by the ratio test. Prove that the series $\sum_{i=1}^{\infty} ia_i$ converges. How could this result be applied to Problem 1(a)?

9. Let $\sum_{i=1}^{\infty} a_i$ be a series of positive terms. Prove that if

$$\lim_{n\to\infty} \frac{a_{n+1}}{a_n} = L < 1, \qquad \text{then} \qquad \lim_{n\to\infty} a_n = 0.$$

Use this result to prove that $\lim_{n\to\infty} (n!/n^n) = 0$.

10. Show that $\sum_{i=1}^{\infty} (x^i/i!)$ converges for all values of x.

11. Let $\sum_{i=1}^{\infty} a_i$ be a series of positive terms. Prove that if

$$\lim_{n\to\infty} \sqrt[n]{a_n} = L < 1$$

the series converges, while if

$$\lim_{n\to\infty} \sqrt[n]{a_n} > 1,$$

the series diverges. This is known as Cauchy's root test.

19.4 Series of Arbitrary Terms

We consider the series

$$\sum_{i=1}^{\infty} a_i = a_1 + a_2 + \cdots + a_n + \cdots \tag{19.6}$$

containing an infinite number of positive terms and an infinite number of negative terms. Series (19.6) is called a mixed series. (If only a finite number of terms had one sign, we could delete those terms and study the resulting series by the methods of the previous sections.)

Definition. The series $\sum_{i=1}^{\infty} a_i$ is absolutely convergent if and only if the series $\sum_{i=1}^{\infty} |a_i|$ is convergent.

In other words, if, when each term of a series is replaced by its absolute value, the new series converges, the original series is called absolutely convergent.

Example 1. The series

$$\sum_{i=1}^{\infty} \frac{(-1)^{i+1}}{i^2}$$

is absolutely convergent, since the series $\sum_{i=1}^{\infty} (1/i^2)$ is convergent. The question of whether or not the original series

$$\sum_{i=1}^{\infty} \frac{(-1)^{i+1}}{i^2}$$

is convergent is answered by the following theorem.

Theorem 19-IX. If the series $\sum_{i=1}^{\infty} |a_i|$ converges, then the series $\sum_{i=1}^{\infty} a_i$ converges. That is, if a series converges absolutely, then it converges.

Proof. Since $0 \leqslant |a_n| \pm a_n \leqslant 2|a_n|$ for all n, both the series

$$\sum_{i=1}^{\infty} (|a_i| + a_i) \quad \text{and} \quad \sum_{i=1}^{\infty} (|a_i| - a_i)$$

converge by comparison with the convergent series $\sum_{i=1}^{\infty} 2|a_i|$, the latter series being convergent by Theorem 19-III. By Theorem 19-IV, the difference

$$\sum_{i=1}^{\infty} [(|a_i| + a_i) - (|a_i| - a_i)] = \sum_{i=1}^{\infty} 2a_i$$

converges, and hence $\sum_{i=1}^{\infty} a_i$ converges by Theorem 19-III.

The convergence of

$$\sum_{i=1}^{\infty} \frac{(-1)^{i+1}}{i^2}$$

now follows from the convergence of

$$\sum_{i=1}^{\infty} \frac{1}{i^2} = \sum_{i=1}^{\infty} \left| \frac{(-1)^{i+1}}{i^2} \right|$$

and Theorem 19-IX.

An important special case of (19.6) occurs when the terms are alternately positive and negative. Such a series is called an alternating series and is conveniently represented by

$$\sum_{i=1}^{\infty} (-1)^{i+1} p_i = p_1 - p_2 + p_3 - p_4 + \cdots + (-1)^{n+1} p_n + \cdots \qquad \textbf{(19.7)}$$

where $p_n > 0$ for all n.

Example 2.   The series

$$\sum_{i=1}^{\infty} \frac{(-1)^{i+1}}{i} = \frac{1}{1} - \frac{1}{2} + \frac{1}{3} - \frac{1}{4} + \cdots + \frac{(-1)^{n+1}}{n} + \cdots$$

is an example of an alternating series and is called the alternating harmonic series.

If an alternating series converges absolutely, then it converges by Theorem 19-IX. However, all alternating series do not converge absolutely, as is easily seen by considering the alternating harmonic series of Example 2. This series does not converge absolutely, since the harmonic series diverges.

Definition.   A series is called conditionally convergent if and only if it is convergent but not absolutely convergent.

The following test gives sufficient conditions for the convergence of an alternating series.

Theorem 19-X (Leibniz's test).   If

$$\sum_{i=1}^{\infty} (-1)^{i+1} p_i$$

is an alternating series for which $p_n > p_{n+1}$ for all n, and if $\lim_{n \to \infty} (p_n) = 0$, then the series converges.

Proof.   Since

$$S_{2n} = p_1 - p_2 + p_3 - p_4 + \cdots - p_{2n-2} + p_{2n-1} - p_{2n}$$
$$= p_1 - (p_2 - p_3) - (p_4 - p_5) - \cdots - (p_{2n-2} - p_{2n-1}) - p_{2n} < p_1,$$

the sequence $\{S_{2n}\}$ is bounded above by p_1.

The sequence $\{S_{2n}\}$ is also increasing, since

$$S_{2n+2} = S_{2n} + (p_{2n+1} - p_{2n+2}) > S_{2n}.$$

Hence the sequence $\{S_{2n}\}$ converges by Theorem 4-IX. Since

$$S_{2n+1} = S_{2n} + p_{2n+1},$$

and $p_{2n+1} \to 0$ as $n \to \infty$, the sequence of odd partial sums $\{S_{2n+1}\}$ converges to the same limit as the sequence of even partial sums $\{S_{2n}\}$. This completes the proof.

Remark.   It is easily shown that $p_n > p_{n+1}$ need not be true for all n, but only for n greater than an arbitrary positive integer.

Example 3.   Show that the alternating harmonic series

$$\sum_{i=1}^{\infty} \frac{(-1)^{i+1}}{i}$$

converges.

Solution.   Since $1/n > 1/(n+1)$ for all n, and $\lim_{n\to\infty} (1/n) = 0$, the alternating harmonic series converges by Theorem 19-X.

Example 4.   The alternating series

$$\sum_{i=1}^{\infty} \frac{(-1)^{i+1}(i+1)}{i}$$

has $p_n > p_{n+1}$ for all n, but diverges since $\lim_{n\to\infty} (p_n) \neq 0$.

Example 5.   The series

$$\sum_{i=1}^{\infty} (-1)^{i+1} p_i = \frac{1}{1} - \frac{1}{1^2} + \frac{1}{2} - \frac{1}{2^2} + \frac{1}{3} - \frac{1}{3^2} + \cdots$$

where

$$p_n = \begin{cases} \dfrac{2}{n+1} & \text{for } n \text{ odd} \\[2mm] \left(\dfrac{2}{n}\right)^2 & \text{for } n \text{ even} \end{cases}$$

is an alternating series for which $\lim_{n\to\infty} p_n = 0$. Theorem 19-X does not apply, since p_n is not greater than p_{n+1} for all n. The establishment of the divergence of this series is left to Problem 8.

Example 6.   Show that the alternating series

$$\sum_{i=2}^{\infty} \frac{(-1)^i \log i}{i}$$

converges.

Solution.   By L'Hôpital's rule

$$\lim_{n\to\infty} \frac{\log n}{n} = \lim_{n\to\infty} \frac{1}{n} = 0.$$

To show that

$$\frac{\log n}{n} > \frac{\log (n+1)}{n+1}$$

we show that the function f defined by $f(x) = (\log x)/x$ decreases as x increases. Since

$$f'(x) = \frac{1 - \log x}{x^2} < 0 \qquad \text{for } x > e,$$

the function g defined by $g(n) = (\log n)/n$ decreases for $n \geqslant 3$. Thus the given series converges by Theorem 19-X.

It is instructive to plot the elements of the sequence $\{S_n\}$ of partial sums of a convergent alternating series $\sum_{i=1}^{\infty} (-1)^{i+1} p_i$. The sequence is bounded above by p_1 and below by $(p_1 - p_2)$. The sequence $\{S_{2n}\}$ of even partial sums is monotone-increasing, while the sequence $\{S_{2n-1}\}$ of odd partial sums is monotone-decreasing. See Fig. 19.5.

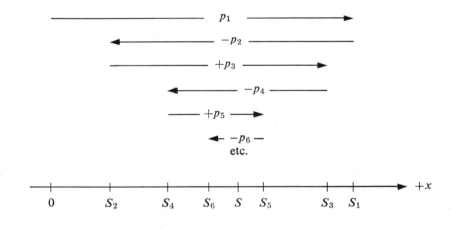

$$p_1$$
$$-p_2$$
$$+p_3$$
$$-p_4$$
$$+p_5$$
$$-p_6$$
etc.

$$0 \qquad S_2 \qquad S_4 \qquad S_6 \quad S \quad S_5 \qquad S_3 \quad S_1 \qquad +x$$

Figure 19.5

The sum S of a convergent alternating series is often approximated by the sum S_n of the first n terms. The following important theorem gives an indication of how close S_n is to S.

Theorem 19-XI.   Let

$$\sum_{i=1}^{\infty} (-1)^{i+1} p_i$$

be a convergent alternating series. Then the absolute value of the remainder after n terms is less than the absolute value of the $(n + 1)$st term. That is,

$$|R_n| = |S - S_n| < |(-1)^{n+2}p_{n+1}| = p_{n+1}.$$

Proof.   If n is even, the alternating series

$$p_{n+1} - p_{n+2} + p_{n+3} - \cdots,$$

which converges because it is obtained by deleting the first n terms of the given convergent series, has sum R_n satisfying $0 < R_n < p_{n+1}$. The argument is essentially that employed in the proof of Theorem 19-X.

If n is odd, the alternating series

$$-p_{n+1} + p_{n+2} - p_{n+3} + \cdots$$

also converges because it is obtained by deleting the first n terms of the given convergent series and also has sum R_n. Thus the series

$$p_{n+1} - p_{n+2} + p_{n+3} - \cdots$$

has sum $-R_n$ satisfying $0 < -R_n < p_{n+1}$, and R_n satisfies $-p_{n+1} < R_n < 0$. Whether n is odd or even,

$$-p_{n+1} < R_n < p_{n+1} \qquad \text{or} \qquad |R_n| < p_{n+1}.$$

Example 7.   The sum of the first n terms of the convergent alternating series

$$\frac{1}{10} - \frac{1}{100} + \frac{1}{1000} - \cdots + \frac{(-1)^{n+1}}{10^n} + \cdots$$

differs from the actual sum of the series by less than $1/10^{n+1}$. If $n = 5$, the sum of the first five terms of the series differs from the actual sum by less than $1/10^6 = 0.000001$.

PROBLEM LIST 112

1.   Show that the following series converge absolutely:

(a) $\sum\limits_{i=1}^{\infty} \dfrac{(-1)^{i+1}}{i^3}$.

(b) $\sum\limits_{i=1}^{\infty} \dfrac{(-1)^{i+1}}{2^i}$.

(c) $\sum\limits_{i=1}^{\infty} \dfrac{(-1)^{i+1}}{1 + i^2}$.

(d) $\sum\limits_{i=1}^{\infty} \dfrac{\cos i}{i^4}$.

(e) $\sum\limits_{i=1}^{\infty} \dfrac{\sin (\pi i/6)}{i^2}$.

(f) $\sum\limits_{i=1}^{\infty} (-1)^{i+1} i e^{-i}$.

2.   Show that the following series converge:

(a) $\sum\limits_{i=1}^{\infty} \dfrac{(-1)^{i+1}}{i^3}$.

(b) $\sum\limits_{i=1}^{\infty} \dfrac{\sin i}{i^2}$.

(c) $\sum\limits_{i=1}^{\infty} \dfrac{(-1)^{i+1} i}{\pi^i}$.

(d) $\sum\limits_{i=1}^{\infty} \dfrac{(-1)^{i+1}}{i^{2i}}$.

3.   Show that the following series converge conditionally:

(a) $\sum\limits_{i=1}^{\infty} \dfrac{(-1)^{i+1}}{2i - 1}$.

(b) $\sum\limits_{i=2}^{\infty} \dfrac{(-1)^{i+1}}{\log i}$.

(c) $\sum\limits_{i=1}^{\infty} \dfrac{(-1)^{i+1} i}{4 + i^2}$.

(d) $\sum\limits_{i=2}^{\infty} \dfrac{(-1)^{i+1}}{\log \log i}$.

4. Determine whether each of the following series is divergent, absolutely convergent, or conditionally convergent:

(a) $\sum\limits_{i=1}^{\infty} \dfrac{(-1)^{i+1}}{\sqrt{i}}$.

(f) $\sum\limits_{i=2}^{\infty} \dfrac{(-1)^{i+1} \log i}{2i}$.

(b) $\sum\limits_{i=1}^{\infty} \dfrac{\sin i}{i^2}$.

(g) $\sum\limits_{i=1}^{\infty} \dfrac{(-1)^{i+1}}{3i+1}$.

(c) $\sum\limits_{i=1}^{\infty} \dfrac{(-1)^{i+1}(i+1)}{3^i}$.

(h) $\sum\limits_{i=1}^{\infty} \dfrac{(-1)^{i+1} i^3}{3^{2i}}$.

(d) $\sum\limits_{i=1}^{\infty} \dfrac{(-1)^{i+1}}{2^i+1}$.

(i) $\sum\limits_{i=2}^{\infty} \dfrac{(-1)^{i+1}}{\log i}$.

(e) $\sum\limits_{i=1}^{\infty} \dfrac{(-1)^{i+1}}{\sqrt[3]{i}}$.

(j) $\sum\limits_{i=2}^{\infty} \dfrac{(-1)^{i+1} \log^2 i}{i}$.

5. Plot on the x-axis the elements of the sequence $\{S_n\}$ of partial sums of the alternating harmonic series

$$\sum_{i=1}^{\infty} \frac{(-1)^{i+1}}{i} \qquad \text{for } n = 1, 2, 3, \cdots, 10.$$

Estimate the sum of the series.

6. Plot on the x-axis the elements of the sequence $\{S_n\}$ of partial sums of the alternating series

$$\sum_{i=1}^{\infty} \frac{(-1)^{i+1}(i+1)}{i} \qquad \text{for } n = 1, 2, 3, \cdots, 10,$$

of Example 4.

7. Prove that the sequence $\{S_{2n}\}$ of even partial sums of the series

$$\sum_{i=1}^{\infty} \frac{(-1)^{i+1}}{2i+1}$$

is monotone-increasing and bounded above.

8. Prove that the series in illustrative Example 5 diverges.

9. Prove that if a mixed series is absolutely convergent, then the series obtained by deleting its negative terms is convergent and the series obtained by deleting its positive terms is convergent.

10. Prove that if a series is conditionally convergent, then the series obtained by deleting its negative terms is divergent and the series obtained by deleting its positive terms is divergent.

11. Given

$$S = \sum_{i=1}^{\infty} \frac{(-1)^{i+1}}{i^2} = S_n + R_n,$$

write an inequality satisfied by R_n when $n = 24$.

12. Find the sum of the series

$$\sum_{i=1}^{\infty} \frac{(-1)^{i+1}}{(2i-1)!}$$

correct to two decimal places.

13. Find the sum of the series

$$\sum_{i=1}^{\infty} \frac{(-1)^{i+1}}{i^3}$$

correct to two decimal places.

19.5   Power Series

If $\{c_n\}$ is a sequence of real numbers,

$$\sum_{i=0}^{\infty} c_i x^i = c_0 + c_1 x + c_2 x^2 + \cdots + c_{n-1} x^{n-1} + \cdots \qquad (19.8)$$

is called a power series in x. If a real number is substituted for x, a series of constants of the type already studied is obtained. It is natural to ask for what values of x series (19.8) converges. Obviously every power series converges for $x = 0$ and has sum c_0. The following theorem is proved in Ref. 19.4.

Theorem 19-XII.   One of the three following possibilities holds for every power series:

(i) it converges for all values of x;
(ii) it converges for $x = 0$ and diverges for $x \neq 0$;
(iii) there exists a positive number R such that it converges for $|x| < R$ and diverges for $|x| > R$.

The number R in (iii) is called the radius of convergence of the series. The series may converge for $x = R$ and $x = -R$, or may converge for only one of these two values of x, or may diverge for both $x = R$ and $x = -R$. The set of values of x for which the series converges is called the interval of convergence of the series.

In case (ii), $R = 0$ and the interval of convergence consists of the single number $x = 0$. Case (i), in which the interval of convergence is the set of all real numbers, is designated by writing $R = \infty$.

It is often possible to determine the interval of convergence by applying the ratio test.

Example 1.   Determine the interval of convergence of the power series

$$\sum_{i=0}^{\infty} \frac{x^i}{i!} = 1 + x + \frac{x^2}{2!} + \frac{x^3}{3!} + \cdots + \frac{x^{n-1}}{(n-1)!} + \cdots.$$

Solution.   Applying the ratio test, we obtain

$$\lim_{n \to \infty} \left| \frac{a_{n+1}}{a_n} \right| = \lim_{n \to \infty} \left| \frac{x^n}{n!} \cdot \frac{(n-1)!}{x^{n-1}} \right|$$

$$= \lim_{n \to \infty} \left| \frac{x}{n} \right| = 0$$

for all x. Hence the series converges absolutely for all x. Thus the series converges for all x by Theorem 19-IX and we write $R = \infty$.

Example 2. Determine the interval of convergence of the power series

$$\sum_{i=0}^{\infty} i!x^i = 1 + x + 2!x^2 + 3!x^3 + \cdots + (n-1)!x^{n-1} + \cdots.$$

Solution. Since

$$\lim_{n\to\infty} \left| \frac{a_{n+1}}{a_n} \right| = \lim_{n\to\infty} \left| \frac{n!x^n}{(n-1)!x^{n-1}} \right|$$
$$= \lim_{n\to\infty} |nx| = \infty$$

for $x \neq 0$ and $= 0$ for $x = 0$, the series converges only for $x = 0$ and hence $R = 0$.

Example 3. Find the interval of convergence of the power series

$$\sum_{i=0}^{\infty} \frac{x^i}{(i+1)2^i} = 1 + \frac{x}{2\cdot 2} + \frac{x^2}{3\cdot 2^2} + \frac{x^3}{4\cdot 2^3} + \cdots + \frac{x^{n-1}}{n\cdot 2^{n-1}} + \cdots.$$

Solution. Since

$$\lim_{n\to\infty} \left| \frac{a_{n+1}}{a_n} \right| = \lim_{n\to\infty} \left| \frac{x^n}{(n+1)2^n} \cdot \frac{n2^{n-1}}{x^{n-1}} \right|$$
$$= \lim_{n\to\infty} \left| \frac{nx}{2n+2} \right| = \frac{|x|}{2},$$

the series converges absolutely and hence converges when

$$\frac{|x|}{2} < 1 \qquad \text{or} \qquad |x| < 2$$

and diverges when

$$\frac{|x|}{2} > 1 \qquad \text{or} \qquad |x| > 2.$$

When $x = 2$, the power series reduces to the harmonic series $1 + (1/2) + (1/3) + \cdots$ which is known to diverge.

When $x = -2$, the power series reduces to the alternating harmonic series $1 - (1/2) + (1/3) - \cdots$ which is known to converge. Thus the power series has radius of convergence $R = 2$ and interval of convergence $-2 \leqslant x < 2$.

It is interesting to note that since the ratio test was employed in determining the interval of convergence, it follows that the power series converges absolutely for $-2 < x < 2$. The convergence is conditional at $x = -2$.

A series of the form

$$\sum_{i=0}^{\infty} c_i(x-a)^i = c_0 + c_1(x-a) + c_2(x-a)^2 + \cdots$$
$$+ c_{n-1}(x-a)^{n-1} + \cdots$$

(19.9)

is called a power series in $x - a$. The interval of convergence is centered at $x = a$ rather than at $x = 0$.

Example 4. Find the interval of convergence of the series

$$\sum_{i=0}^{\infty} \frac{(x-3)^i}{(i+1)2^i}.$$

Solution. Since

$$\lim_{n \to \infty} \left| \frac{(x-3)^n}{(n+1)2^n} \cdot \frac{n2^{n-1}}{(x-3)^{n-1}} \right| = \lim_{n \to \infty} \left| \frac{n(x-3)}{2n+2} \right| = \frac{|x-3|}{2},$$

the series converges when

$$\frac{|x-3|}{2} < 1 \qquad \text{or} \qquad |x-3| < 2$$

and diverges when

$$\frac{|x-3|}{2} > 1 \qquad \text{or} \qquad |x-3| > 2.$$

As in Example 3, the series converges when $x - 3 = -2$ (or $x = 1$) and diverges when $x - 3 = 2$ (or $x = 5$). The series has interval of convergence $1 \leqslant x < 5$. The radius of convergence $R = 2$ is the same as that of the series in Example 3, but the interval of convergence has been shifted $a = 3$ units to the right.

PROBLEM LIST 113

1. Find the radius of convergence and the interval of convergence of each of the following power series:

(a) $\sum_{i=0}^{\infty} \frac{x^{i+1}}{i+1}$.

(g) $\sum_{i=1}^{\infty} \frac{(-1)^{i+1}x^{2i-2}}{(2i-2)!}$.

(b) $\sum_{i=0}^{\infty} \frac{(-1)^i x^{2i+1}}{(2i+1)!}$.

(h) $\sum_{i=1}^{\infty} \frac{x^i}{(2i-1)^2 2^i}$.

(c) $\sum_{i=1}^{\infty} \frac{x^i}{i(i+1)}$.

(i) $\sum_{i=1}^{\infty} \frac{x^i}{i^2+1}$.

(d) $\sum_{i=0}^{\infty} \frac{x^{2i}}{i!}$.

(j) $\sum_{i=1}^{\infty} \frac{(-1)^{i+1}(x-1)^i}{i}$.

(e) $\sum_{i=0}^{\infty} \frac{(-1)^i x^{i+2}}{(i+1)^2 2^{2i}}$.

(k) $\sum_{i=1}^{\infty} (-1)^{i+1} i(x-2)^{i-1}$.

(f) $\sum_{i=0}^{\infty} 2^i x^i$.

2. For what values of x does the series

$$\sum_{i=1}^{\infty} \frac{(-1)^i}{ix^i}$$

converge?

3. For what values of x does the series

$$\sum_{i=1}^{\infty} \frac{(-1)^{i+1}x^i}{2i}$$

converge (a) absolutely, (b) conditionally?

4. Construct a power series for which $R = \infty$.

5. Construct a power series for which $R = 0$.

6. Construct a power series for which $R = 3$.

7. Given that the power series

$$\sum_{i=1}^{\infty} \frac{(-1)^i x^i}{i 2^i}$$

has interval of convergence $-2 \leqslant x \leqslant +2$, state the interval of convergence of the power series

$$\sum_{i=1}^{\infty} \frac{(-1)^i (x + 5)^i}{i 2^i}.$$

8. Prove that if a power series in x converges for $x = k_1$ and if $|k_2| < |k_1|$, then the series converges absolutely for $x = k_2$.

9. Let R be the radius of convergence of the power series

$$\sum_{i=0}^{\infty} c_i (x - a)^i.$$

Show that

$$R = \lim_{n \to \infty} \left| \frac{c_n}{c_{n+1}} \right|,$$

provided this limit exists. Also show that if

$$\lim_{n \to \infty} \left| \frac{c_n}{c_{n+1}} \right| = \infty,$$

then $R = \infty$.

19.6   *Maclaurin's and Taylor's Series*

A power series in x defines a function f whose domain is the interval of convergence of the series. If x_1 is in the interval of convergence, then $f(x_1)$ is the sum of the series obtained by substituting x_1 for x.

The following theorem concerning power series is proved in Ref. 19.4.

Theorem 19-XIII.   If the power series

$$\sum_{i=0}^{\infty} c_i x^i$$

defines a function f given by $f(x) = \sum_{i=0}^{\infty} c_i x^i$ in an interval of convergence of radius $R > 0$, then the power series $\sum_{i=1}^{\infty} i c_i x^{i-1}$ also has radius of convergence R and converges to $f'(x)$ for $-R < x < R$.

The theorem states that if a power series in x is differentiated term by term, the resulting series has the same radius of convergence R as the original series.

Also, if $-R < x_1 < R$, the new series has sum $f'(x_1)$. That is, the new series converges to the derivative of f inside the interval of convergence. The theorem makes no statement concerning the convergence of the new series at $x = R$ or at $x = -R$.

Instead of starting with a power series in x, let us assume that a function f is given. It is natural to ask whether or not there exists a power series in x which converges to $f(x)$, if not for all values of x in the domain D of f, then possibly for some values of x contained in D.

Assume that f possesses derivatives of all orders (can be differentiated any number of times) in some open interval centered at $x = 0$. Assume also that f can be represented by a power series in x in its interval of convergence of radius $R > 0$. Then

$$f(x) = \sum_{i=0}^{\infty} c_i x^i = c_0 + c_1 x + c_2 x^2 + c_3 x^3 + \cdots + c_{n-1} x^{n-1} + \cdots. \quad (19.10)$$

By repeated application of Theorem 19-XIII,

$$f'(x) = c_1 + 2c_2 x + 3c_3 x^2 + \cdots$$
$$f''(x) = \qquad 2c_2 + 3 \cdot 2c_3 x + \cdots$$
$$f'''(x) = \qquad\qquad 3 \cdot 2c_3 + 4 \cdot 3 \cdot 2c_4 x + \cdots$$

$$\vdots$$

$$f^{(n)}x = n!c_n + (n+1)!c_{n+1}x + \cdots$$

for $-R < x < R$.

It follows that if f can be represented by series (19.10), the coefficients must be given by

$$c_0 = f^{(0)}(0), \quad c_1 = \frac{f'(0)}{1!}, \quad c_2 = \frac{f''(0)}{2!}, \quad c_3 = \frac{f'''(0)}{3!}, \cdots,$$

$$c_{n-1} = \frac{f^{(n-1)}(0)}{(n-1)!}, \cdots,$$

where $f^{(0)}(0)$ denotes $f(0)$.

The series

$$f(x) = \sum_{i=0}^{\infty} \frac{f^{(i)}(0)}{i!} x^i \qquad (19.11)$$

is called Maclaurin's series for f, after the Scottish mathematician Colin Maclaurin (1698–1746), who published formula (19.11) in 1742. We will now obtain Maclaurin's expansions for two specific functions. We have not shown that the Maclaurin's series for a function actually converges to the function. That is, if $-R < k < R$ and we substitute $x = k$ in the right member of (19.11), we have no assurance that the resulting series will have sum $f(k)$. However, the Maclaurin's series for most of the simple functions with which we are familiar do converge to these functions. For an exception, see Problem 18 of Problem List 115. In Section 19.7 we will consider the question of whether or not the Maclaurin's series for a function actually represents the function.

Example 1.   Find the Maclaurin's series for e^x.

   Solution.   From

$$f(x) = e^x \qquad f(0) = 1,$$
$$f'(x) = e^x \qquad f'(0) = 1,$$
$$\vdots \qquad\qquad \vdots$$
$$f^{(n-1)}(x) = e^x \qquad f^{(n-1)}(0) = 1,$$

we obtain, from formula (19.11),

$$e^x = \sum_{i=0}^{\infty} \frac{x^i}{i!} = 1 + \frac{x}{1!} + \frac{x^2}{2!} + \frac{x^3}{3!} + \cdots + \frac{x^{n-1}}{(n-1)!} + \cdots. \qquad \textbf{(19.12)}$$

In Example 1 of Sec. 19.5 it was shown that series (19.12) converges for all values of x. In Sec. 19.7 we will show that the series represents e^x for all values of x. That is, the right member of (19.12) is merely another way of writing the value at x of the function f defined by $f(x) = e^x$.

Example 2.   Find the Maclaurin's series for $\sin x$.

   Solution.   Since

$$f(x) = \sin x \qquad\qquad f(0) = 0,$$
$$f'(x) = \cos x \qquad\qquad f'(0) = 1,$$
$$f''(x) = -\sin x \qquad\qquad f''(0) = 0,$$
$$f'''(x) = -\cos x \qquad\qquad f'''(0) = -1,$$
$$f^{(\mathrm{iv})}(x) = \sin x = f(x) \qquad f^{(\mathrm{iv})}(0) = f(0) = 0,$$

we obtain from formula (19.11),

$$\sin x = \sum_{i=1}^{\infty} \frac{(-1)^{i-1}x^{2i-1}}{(2i-1)!}$$
$$= x - \frac{x^3}{3!} + \frac{x^5}{5!} - \cdots + \frac{(-1)^{n-1}x^{2n-1}}{(2n-1)!} + \cdots. \qquad \textbf{(19.13)}$$

This series is known to converge to $\sin x$ for all values of x.

———————

Functions defined by expressions such as $\log x$ or $\sqrt{x}$ do not have Maclaurin's expansions. The first is not defined at $x = 0$ and the second is not differentiable at $x = 0$. Such functions can often be represented by series of the form

$$f(x) = \sum_{i=0}^{\infty} \frac{f^{(i)}(a)}{i!}(x-a)^i$$
$$= f(a) + f'(a)(x-a) + \frac{f''(a)}{2!}(x-a)^2$$
$$+ \cdots + \frac{f^{(n-1)}(a)}{(n-1)!}(x-a)^{n-1} + \cdots. \qquad \textbf{(19.14)}$$

Series of the form (19.14) are derived in the same manner as Maclaurin's series with a playing the role played by 0 in the Maclaurin case. These generalized Maclaurin's series are called Taylor's series after Brook Taylor (1685–1731), the English mathematician who published formula (19.14) in 1715.

Example 3.   Find the Taylor's series for $\log x$ in powers of $x - 1$.

Solution.   From

$$f(x) = \log x \qquad\qquad\qquad f(1) = 0$$
$$f'(x) = x^{-1} \qquad\qquad\qquad f'(1) = 1$$
$$f''(x) = (-1)x^{-2} \qquad\qquad f''(1) = -1$$
$$f'''(x) = (-2)(-1)x^{-3} \qquad\quad f'''(1) = 2!$$
$$f^{(iv)}(x) = (-3)(-2)(-1)x^{-4} \qquad f^{(iv)}(1) = -3!$$
$$\vdots \qquad\qquad\qquad\qquad\qquad \vdots$$
$$f^{(n-1)}(x) = (-1)^n(n-2)!x^{-(n-1)} \qquad f^{(n-1)}(1) = (-1)^n(n-2)!$$

and formula (19.14) we obtain

$$\log x = \sum_{i=1}^{\infty} \frac{(-1)^{i+1}}{i}(x-1)^i$$
$$= \frac{(x-1)}{1} - \frac{(x-1)^2}{2} + \frac{(x-1)^3}{3} - \cdots$$
$$+ \frac{(-1)^{n+1}}{n}(x-1)^n + \cdots. \qquad \textbf{(19.15)}$$

Series (19.15) is known to converge to $\log x$ in the interval $0 < x \leqslant 2$.

PROBLEM LIST 114

Assume that the Maclaurin's (or Taylor's) series for the function defined by each of the following expressions represents that function for all x in the interval of convergence.

1.   Find the Maclaurin's series for the function defined by each of the following expressions:

(a) e^{2x}.

(b) $\cos x$.

(c) $\log(1 + x)$.

(d) $x^2 - 5x + 7$.

(e) $1/(1 + x)$.

(f) $1/(1 + x)^2$.

(g) $\log(1 - x)$.

(h) $1/(1 - x)^2$.

(i) $\sin 3x$.

(j) $(1 + x)^m$.

2. Find the first three nonzero terms of the Maclaurin's series for

(a) $\tan x$.   (c) $e^x \cos x$.

(b) $\sec x$.   (d) e^{-x^2}.

3. Find the Taylor's series for

(a) e^x in powers of $x - 1$;

(b) $\log x$ in powers of $x - 2$;

(c) $\sqrt{x}$ in powers of $x - 1$;

(d) $\sin x$ in powers of $x - (\pi/4)$;

(e) $1/x$ in powers of $x - 3$;

(f) $\sec x$ in powers of $x - \pi/6$ (four terms).

4. Compute e^{-1} to three decimal places, using the Maclaurin's series for e^x.

5. Compute $\sin 46$ deg to three decimal places.

6. Compute $\log 1.2$ to three decimal places.

7. Apply Theorem 19-XIII to the Maclaurin's series for (a) e^x, (b) $\sin x$.

8. If $P(x)$ is a polynomial of degree m, show that

$$P(x) = P(a) + P'(a)(x - a) + \frac{P''(a)}{2!}(x - a)^2 + \cdots + \frac{P^{(m)}(a)}{m!}(x - a)^m.$$

9. Expand $x^4 - 3x^3 + 2x - 7$ in powers of $x - 2$.

10. Use the result of Problem 9 to find

$$\int \frac{x^4 - 3x^3 + 2x - 7}{(x - 2)^2} dx.$$

11. Find $\sin 0.1$ radian correct to three decimal places.

12. Use the Maclaurin's series for $\sin x$ to evaluate

$$\lim_{x \to 0} \frac{\sin x}{x}.$$

19.7   The Remainder in Taylor's Series

The question of whether or not the value $f(x)$ of a function f can be approximated by the first n terms of its Taylor's series can often be resolved by applying the following theorem.

Theorem 19-XIV.   If f and its first $n - 1$ derivatives are continuous in the closed interval from a to x, and if $f^{(n)}(x)$ exists on the open interval from a to x, then

$$f(x) = f(a) + f'(a)(x - a)$$
$$+ \cdots + \frac{f^{(n-1)}(a)}{(n - 1)!}(x - a)^{n-1}$$
$$+ \frac{f^{(n)}(\xi)}{n!}(x - a)^n \tag{19.16}$$

for at least one ξ in the open interval from a to x. (The number a may be greater than or less than x.)

Theorem 19-XIV is called the extended law of the mean, since it reduces to Theorem 4-IV (mean-value theorem) when $n = 1$. Equation (19.16) is called Taylor's formula with remainder. If Taylor's series (19.14) is written in the form

$$f(x) = S_n(x) + R_n(x),$$

where $S_n(x)$ denotes the nth partial sum of the series and $R_n(x)$ the remainder after n terms, comparison with (19.16) indicates that the Taylor's series for $f(x)$ converges to $f(x)$ for all values of x for which

$$R_n(x) = \frac{f^{(n)}(\xi)}{n!}(x - a)^n$$

approaches zero as $n \longrightarrow \infty$.

Example 1.   Find the values of x for which the Maclaurin's series for e^x converges to e^x.

Solution.   In Example 1 of Sec. 19.6 it was shown that the series

$$e^x = 1 + x + \frac{x^2}{2!} + \frac{x^3}{3!} + \cdots + \frac{x^{n-1}}{(n-1)!} + \cdots \qquad (19.17)$$

converges for all values of x. Since $a = 0$,

$$R_n(x) = \frac{f^{(n)}(\xi)}{n!} x^n = e^{\xi} \left(\frac{x^n}{n!} \right).$$

As $n \longrightarrow \infty$, ξ takes on different values, but $e^{\xi} < e^x$ if $x > 0$, while $e^{\xi} < 1$ if $x < 0$. The quantity $x^n/n!$ approaches 0 as $n \longrightarrow \infty$, since it is the $(n+1)$st term of a convergent series. Thus $\lim_{n\to\infty} R_n(x) = 0$ for all x and hence series (19.17) represents e^x for all values of x.

19.8   Operations on Power Series

Power series can be regarded as infinite polynomials. Many of the operations which can be performed upon polynomials can also be performed upon power series. For example, Theorem 19-XIII states that, inside the interval of convergence of f (endpoints excluded), the derivative of the sum of an infinite number of terms is the sum of the derivatives of the infinite number of terms. The following theorem is the generalization of the theorem stating that the integral of a sum is the sum of the integrals.

Theorem 19-XV.   A power series may be integrated term by term in any closed interval lying entirely inside (endpoints excluded) the interval of convergence of the power series.

Example 1.   The Maclaurin's series

$$\frac{1}{1+x^2} = 1 - x^2 + x^4 - \cdots + (-1)^{n-1}x^{2n-2} + \cdots$$

is known to converge to $1/(1 + x^2)$ for $-1 < x < 1$.
By Theorem 19-XV,

$$\int_0^x \frac{dt}{1+t^2} = \int_0^x dt - \int_0^x t^2 \, dt + \int_0^x t^4 \, dt - \cdots + (-1)^{n-1} \int_0^x t^{2n-2} \, dt + \cdots,$$

or

$$\operatorname{Tan}^{-1} x = x - \frac{x^3}{3} + \frac{x^5}{5} - \cdots + (-1)^{n-1}\frac{x^{2n-1}}{2n-1} + \cdots \qquad (19.18)$$

for $-1 < x < 1$. For example,

$$\operatorname{Tan}^{-1}(0.1) = 0.1 - \frac{0.001}{3} + \frac{0.00001}{5} - \cdots + (-1)^{n-1}\frac{(0.1)^{2n-1}}{2n-1} + \cdots.$$

It is interesting to note that (19.18) also holds when $x = 1$, although this result does not follow from Theorem 19-XV, since $x = 1$ is not inside the interval of convergence of the series for $1/(1 + x^2)$. Setting $x = 1$ in (19.18) yields the following well-known series for $\pi/4$:

$$\frac{\pi}{4} = 1 - \frac{1}{3} + \frac{1}{5} - \cdots + \frac{(-1)^{n-1}}{2n-1} + \cdots.$$

The following theorem is easily proved by resorting to the definition of convergence of an infinite series.

Theorem 19-XVI.   Let

$$f_1(x) = \sum_{i=0}^{\infty} a_i x^i \qquad \text{and} \qquad f_2(x) = \sum_{i=0}^{\infty} b_i x^i.$$

Then the two series

$$\sum_{i=0}^{\infty} (a_i \pm b_i)x^i,$$

obtained from the given series by term-by-term addition or subtraction, converge to $f_1(x) \pm f_2(x)$ at least in the common interval of convergence of the two series.

Example 2.   Since

$$\cos x = 1 - \frac{x^2}{2!} + \frac{x^4}{4!} - \frac{x^6}{6!} + \cdots$$

and

$$\sin x = x - \frac{x^3}{3!} + \frac{x^5}{5!} - \frac{x^7}{7!} + \cdots,$$

we obtain, from Theorem 19-XVI,

$$\sin x + \cos x = 1 + x - \frac{x^2}{2!} - \frac{x^3}{3!} + \frac{x^4}{4!} + \frac{x^5}{5!} - \frac{x^6}{6!} - \frac{x^7}{7!} + \cdots,$$

true for all values of x.

Reference 19.3, in addition to giving proofs of Theorems 19-XIV and 19-XV, also states conditions under which multiplication and division of power series is permissible.

Remark. The student should not gain the impression that the only series of functions are power series. See Ref. 19.3 for a discussion of other important series of functions.

PROBLEM LIST 115

1. Set $n = 1$ in (19.16) to obtain the mean-value theorem.

2. Find the values of x for which the Maclaurin's series for $\sin x$ converges to $\sin x$.

3. Find the values of x for which the Maclaurin's series for $\cos x$ converges to $\cos x$.

4. Obtain the Maclaurin's series for
$$f(x) = \frac{e^x + e^{-x}}{2}.$$
For what values of x does the series converge to $f(x)$?

5. Employ the series for $1/(1 - x)$ to obtain the series for $-\log(1 - x)$.

6. Employ the series for $1/(1 + x)$ to obtain the series for $\log(1 + x)$.

7. Use the results of Problems 5 and 6 to obtain a series for $\log[(1 + x)/(1 - x)]$. Set $x = 1/3$ in this series to obtain a series for $\log 2$.

8. Evaluate $\int_0^1 \sin x^2 \, dx$ correct to three decimal places.

9. Evaluate $\int_0^{0.3} e^{-x^2} \, dx$ correct to three decimal places.

10. Find the area under $y = (\sin x)/x$ from $x = 0$ to $x = 1$ correct to three decimal places. Assume that $y = 1$ when $x = 0$. (The integral $\int_0^x [(\sin u)/u] \, du$, known as the sine integral, has many important applications, particularly in electrical and radio engineering.)

11. Use the formula $\pi/4 = \mathrm{Tan}^{-1}(1/7) - 2\,\mathrm{Tan}^{-1}(1/3)$, due to Machin, and the series for $\mathrm{Tan}^{-1} x$ to find the value of π correct to two decimal places.

12. Write Taylor's formula for $f(x) = 1/(1 + x)$ with $a = 1$ and $n = 2$.

13. Write Taylor's formula for $f(x) = \log x$ with $a = 2$ and $n = 2$.

14. Find the first three nonzero terms of the Maclaurin's series for $\sec^2 x$ from the Maclaurin's series for $\tan x$.

15. Evaluate $\sin 0.2$ radian correct to three decimal places.

16. Evaluate $\cos 3$ deg correct to three decimal places.

17. Evaluate $\sin 44$ deg correct to three decimal places.

18. Let $f(x) = e^{-1/x^2}$ for $x \neq 0$ and let $f(0) = 0$. Show that $f^{(n)}(0) = 0$ for $n = 1, 2, 3, \cdots$ and that the Maclaurin's series for f does not converge to $f(x)$ in any open interval centered at the origin. (This example is due to Cauchy.)

REFERENCES

19.1 T. M. APOSTOL, *Mathematical Analysis*, Addison-Wesley, Reading, Mass., 1960.

19.2 G. H. HARDY, *Divergent Series*, Oxford University Press, New York, 1949.

19.3 K. KNOPP, *Theory and Application of Infinite Series*, translated by R. C. Young, Hafner, New York, 1951.

19.4 A. E. TAYLOR, *Advanced Calculus*, Ginn, Boston, 1955.

Chapter

20___

Differential equations

20.1   Introduction

A differential equation is an equation involving unknown functions and their derivatives. If these functions are functions of one variable, the derivatives occurring are ordinary derivatives and the equation is called an ordinary differential equation. Some simple equations of this type were considered in Sec. 7.6. If the unknown functions are functions of more than one variable, the derivatives occurring are partial derivatives and the equation is called a partial differential equation. Equations of this type were mentioned briefly in Sec. 16.4.

In this chapter we will consider ordinary differential equations involving one unknown function.

By a solution of the differential equation

$$F(x, y, y', y'', \cdots, y^{(n)}) = 0 \tag{20.1}$$

we mean a function f denoted by $y = f(x)$, defined on an interval $a < x < b$, such that

$$F(x, f(x), f'(x), f''(x), \cdots, f^{(n)}(x)) = 0$$

for all x satisfying $a < x < b$.

[A solution is sometimes given in the implicit form $g(x, y) = 0$.]

Example 1.   The function defined by $y = e^{2x}$ is a solution of the differential equation $(dy/dx) - 2y = 0$ for all values of x, since

$$2e^{2x} - 2[e^{2x}] = 0$$

for all x.

Example 2.   The function defined by $y = \sqrt{1 - x^2}$ is a solution of the differential equation $y(dy/dx) + x = 0$ on the interval $-1 < x < 1$, since

$$\sqrt{1-x^2}\left(\frac{-2x}{2\sqrt{1-x^2}}\right)+x=0$$

for $-1 < x < 1$.

Example 3.   The differential equation $(dy/dx)^2 + x^2y^2 + 1 = 0$ has no solution, since the left member is positive for all differentiable real functions of a real variable.

———————

The order of a differential equation is the order of the highest derivative appearing in the equation. The differential equations of Examples 1, 2, and 3 are first-order equations.

The differential equation

$$\frac{d^2y}{dx^2} + x\frac{dy}{dx} + y = 0$$

is a second-order equation, while the differential equation

$$\frac{d^3y}{dx^3} - x^2 = 0$$

is a third-order equation.

Let y denote an element of the range of the unknown function. An equation which is linear (of the first degree) in y and its derivatives is called a linear differential equation. All other differential equations are called nonlinear.

Example 4.   The differential equation

$$y'' + xy' + x^2y - e^x = 0$$

is linear, since it is linear in y, y', and y''.

Example 5.   The differential equation

$$y'' + \cos y = 0$$

is nonlinear, since it is not linear in y.

Example 6.   The differential equation

$$y'' + yy' + x = 0$$

is nonlinear, since the term yy' is of degree 2.

———————

The first-order equation

$$\frac{dy}{dx} = \cos x$$

has a solution given by $y = \sin x$, valid for all x. It also has the solution $y = \sin x + C$, where C is an arbitrary constant.

The second-order equation

$$\frac{d^2y}{dx^2} = 6x$$

has the solution given by $y = x^3 + C_1 x + C_2$, valid for all x, where C_1 and C_2 are arbitrary constants. The solution is obtained by integrating twice.

In general, the solution of an nth-order differential equation contains n arbitrary constants. The n constants are said to be independent if it is not possible to write the solution in a form involving fewer than n constants. For example, the function given by Ae^{B+x} appears to contain two independent arbitrary constants, but in fact contains only one. This is readily seen by writing

$$Ae^{B+x} = Ae^B e^x = Ce^x$$

where Ae^B is replaced by the single arbitrary constant C. For a more complete discussion of the independence of arbitrary constants, see Ref. 20.1. We will assume that any constants appearing in a solution are independent unless we state otherwise.

By the general solution of an nth-order differential equation we mean a solution containing n independent arbitrary constants. If *every* solution of the equation can be obtained by assigning particular values to the n arbitrary constants in the general solution, the general solution is then said to be the complete solution. A solution of the differential equation which cannot be obtained from the general solution by assigning particular values to the arbitrary constants is called a singular solution.

Example 7.   The solution given by $y = \sin x + C$ is the general solution of the equation $y' = \cos x$. This solution is also the complete solution, since two functions having derivative given by $\cos x$ can differ by at most a constant.

Example 8.   The function given by $y = Cx - C^2$, where C is an arbitrary constant, is the general solution of the first-order equation $(dy/dx)^2 - x(dy/dx) + y = 0$. This is not the complete solution, since the equation also has the singular solution given by $y = x^2/4$. The singular solution cannot be obtained from the general solution by assigning a particular value to C.

———————

Any solution of a differential equation which can be obtained from the general solution by assigning values to the independent arbitrary constants is called a partciular solution. For example, by setting $C = 0$ in Example 7, we obtain the particular solution given by $y = \sin x$ of the equation $y' = \cos x$.

———————

The solutions of many important problems in applied mathematics involve differential equations. This is due to the fact that physical laws are usually stated as differential equations.

Example 9.   The motion of a particle of mass m moving on the x-axis is governed by Newton's second law, which states that the force f acting on the particle is equal to the mass m times the acceleration a of the particle. Since $a = d^2x/dt^2$, Newton's second law is expressed as a second-order differential equation. When we say that the motion is governed by the differential equation, we mean that the displacement function, denoted by $x = h(t)$, is a solution of the differential equation. If the force f depends upon the time t, the velocity dx/dt, the displacement x, or some combination of these three quantities, the differential equation will have the form

$$F\left(t, x, \frac{dx}{dt}, \frac{d^2x}{dt^2}\right) = 0, \tag{20.2}$$

which is of the type (20.1) with t replacing x and x replacing y.

The general solution of (20.2) would contain two independent arbitrary constants. These constants could be determined from initial conditions of the form

$$t = 0, x = x_0; \qquad t = 0, \frac{dx}{dt} = v_0.$$

The resulting particular solution would be given by the displacement function denoted by $x = h(t)$. In summary, if we know the initial displacement and velocity of the particle, and also the differential equation governing the motion, a solution of the problem consists of the displacement function, which gives the position of the particle at variable time t. The differential equation and the initial conditions funish a mathematical model for the physical situation.

Example 10.   The current i in amperes at time t in an electric circuit satisfies Kirchoff's law, a first-order linear differential equation of the form

$$L\frac{di}{dt} + Ri - E = 0,$$

where L, R, and E are constants. The procedure for finding the current function, denoted by $i - f(t)$, is to find the general solution of the differential equation and then to determine the arbitrary constant in the solution from an initial condition of the form

$$t = 0, \qquad i = i_0.$$

An important problem in the theory of differential equations consists of proving that, under certain conditions, solutions of a differential equation of a particular type exist. Theorems of this nature are termed existence theorems. Another important problem consists of proving that a particular solution (satisfying certain initial conditions) of a differential equation is unique. Theorems of this nature are termed uniqueness theorems. Finally, the theory involves methods of finding actual solutions of differential equations. In this brief introduction we will restrict ourselves to this problem of finding solutions to a few simple differential equations. However, the student should not gain the false impression that most differential equations which arise in applications can be solved in simple form, that is, in terms of simple, known functions. Although it is not an easy matter to solve many of the differential equations which arise, it is often possible to determine many of the properties of the solutions by studying the equations. It is also possible in many cases, once a unique solution is known to exist, to approximate the solution to any required degree of accuracy. Computing machines are very useful in this type of attack.

It is also interesting to note that differential equations often give rise to new functions. For example, the equation

$$x^2\frac{d^2y}{dx^2} + x\frac{dy}{dx} + (x^2 - k^2) = 0, \tag{20.3}$$

where k is constant, is known as Bessel's equation, after the German astronomer Friedrich Wilhelm Bessel (1784–1846), who encountered the equation in a problem on planetary motion. The same equation arises in problems involving heat flow in cylinders, propagation of electric currents in cylindrical conductors, vibration of membranes, vibration of chains, and in many other important investigations. This is one of the many instances in which the same mathematical model is appropriate for describing several different physical situations. The solutions of (20.3) have been investigated in detail, have been extensively tabulated, and are termed Bessel functions.

PROBLEM LIST 116

1. Find the general solution of each of the following equations:
   (a) $y' - e^x = 0$.
   (b) $y'' - e^x = 0$.
   (c) $y'' - \cos x = 0$.
   (d) $y''' - x + 1 = 0$.
   (e) $y' - x \log x = 0$.

2. Find the particular solution in each of the following cases:
   (a) $y' - \sec^2 x = 0$; $x = 0$, $y = 1$.
   (b) $y' + e^x = 0$; $x = 1$, $y = 1$.
   (c) $y'' - 1 = 0$; $x = 0$, $y = 1$, $y' = 2$.
   (d) $y'' = 0$; $x = 1$, $y = 2$, $y' = -1$.

3. For what values of x does $y = \sqrt{x^2 - 1}$ define a solution of $x - y(dy/dx) = 0$?

4. Verify that the following expressions define functions which are solutions of the given differential equations.
   (a) $y = \sin x$; $y'' + y = 0$.
   (b) $y = e^{3x}$; $y'' - 9y = 0$.
   (c) $y = \dfrac{x^3}{2} + 5x$; $xy' - x^3 - y = 0$.
   (d) $y = \tan x$; $y' - y^2 - 1 = 0$.

5. Show that the function defined by $y = A \sin 2x + B \cos 2x$ is a solution of $y'' + 4y = 0$, where A and B are arbitrary constants.

6. Show that the function defined by $y = x \int_0^x e^{-t^2} dt$ is a solution of $xy' - y - x^2 e^{-x^2} = 0$.

7. Give the order of each of the following equations and state whether it is linear or nonlinear:
   (a) $\dfrac{d^2y}{dx^2} + xy = 0$.
   (b) $\dfrac{dy}{dt} + t^2y = 0$.

(c) $\dfrac{d^3x}{dy^3} + \cos y = 0.$ (e) $\dfrac{d^2r}{d\theta^2} + r\dfrac{dr}{d\theta} = 0.$

(d) $\dfrac{d^3y}{dx^3} + \cos y = 0.$ (f) $x^2y'' + xy' + x^2 - 1 = 0.$

8. Show that $x = 2te^{t-1}$ defines a particular solution of $x'' - 2x' + x = 0$ satisfying the conditions $t = 0, x = 0; t = 1, x = 2.$

9. Find by inspection a particular solution of $d^2y/dx^2 + 2(dy/dx) - 8y = 16.$

10. For what values of m does $y = e^{mx}$ define a solution of $y'' + y' - 12y = 0$?

11. Find a differential equation having the function defined by $y = e^t + e^{-t}$ as a solution.

12. Given that $y = f(x)$ and $y = g(x)$ define solutions of $y'' + y = 0$, show that $y = Af(x) + Bg(x)$, where A and B are arbitrary constants, also defines a solution.

13. Show that the arbitrary constants A, B, and C in the expression $y = A \sin^2 x + B \cos^2 x + C \cos 2x$ are not independent.

14. The equation

$$\left(\frac{dy}{dx}\right)^2 - 4x\frac{dy}{dx} + 4y = 0$$

has the general solution defined by $y = cx - (c^2/4)$. Employ the function given by $y = x^2$ to show that the general solution is not the complete solution.

15. A particle of unit mass $(m = 1)$ moves on the x-axis with acceleration $a = d^2x/dt^2 = 6t - 4$, t denoting time in seconds and x being measured in feet. Find x when $t = 3$ if $x = 0$ and $dx/dt = 2$ when $t = 0$.

16. A particle of unit mass $(m = 1)$ moves on the x-axis with acceleration $a = d^2x/dt^2 = te^{-t}$, t denoting time in seconds and x being measured in feet. Find x and dx/dt when $t = 1$ if $x = 2$ and $dx/dt - 5$ when $t = 0$. Also find

$$\lim_{t\to\infty} x \quad \text{and} \quad \lim_{t\to\infty} \frac{dx}{dt}.$$

17. A differential equation of the form

$$y = x\left(\frac{dy}{dx}\right) + f\left(\frac{dy}{dx}\right)$$

is known as Clairaut's equation. Show that $y = Cx + f(C)$ defines a solution of the equation.

18. Write a differential equation for which the function given by $y = |x|$ is a solution: (a) on $-2 < x < -1$, (b) on $1 < x < 2$.

20.2   Exact Equations

We consider the first-order differential equation of the form

$$M(x, y) + N(x, y)\frac{dy}{dx} = 0, \tag{20.4}$$

where M and N denote continuous functions of x and y possessing continuous first partial derivatives in a region R of the xy-plane.

Equation (20.4) is often written in the differential form

$$M(x, y)dx + N(x, y)dy = 0. \tag{20.5}$$

An advantage of form (20.5) is that it enables us to regard either y or x as an element of the range of the unknown function.

Definition.   Equation (20.5) is said to be exact in a region R if and only if there exists a function, denoted by $u(x, y)$, such that

$$\frac{\partial u}{\partial x} = M; \qquad \frac{\partial u}{\partial y} = N$$

at every point of R.

Since

$$du = \frac{\partial u}{\partial x}dx + \frac{\partial u}{\partial y}dy,$$

equation (20.5) is exact if and only if the left member denotes the exact differential of a function given by $u = u(x, y)$. This is the reason the term "exact" is used.

Example 1.   The equation

$$y \, dx + x \, dy = 0$$

is exact, since the left member is the differential of the function given by $u = xy$.

The following theorem states a necessary condition for an equation to be exact.

Theorem 20-I.   If $M(x, y) \, dx + N(x, y)dy = 0$ is exact in R, then $\partial M/\partial y = \partial N/\partial x$ in R.

Proof.   Since the equation is exact in R, there exists a function given by $u(x, y)$ such that $\partial u/\partial x = M$ and $\partial u/\partial y = N$ in R. Therefore,

$$\frac{\partial M}{\partial y} = \frac{\partial^2 u}{\partial y \, \partial x} \qquad \text{and} \qquad \frac{\partial N}{\partial x} = \frac{\partial^2 u}{\partial x \, \partial y}.$$

Hence $\partial M/\partial y = \partial N/\partial x$. (See Sec. 16.4.)

———————

Now let $y = f(x)$ denote any differentiable function of x defined implicitly by the equation

$$u(x, y) = c, \tag{20.6}$$

where c is an arbitrary constant. Then, by the chain rule,

$$\frac{\partial u}{\partial x} + \frac{\partial u}{\partial y}\frac{dy}{dx} = 0,$$

$$\frac{\partial u}{\partial x}dx + \frac{\partial u}{\partial y}dy = M(x, y)dx + N(x, y)dy = 0,$$

and hence $y = f(x)$ defines a solution of equation (20.4) or (20.5).

Example 2.   The function defined by $y = c/x$, obtained by solving $xy = c$ for y in Example 1, is a solution of $y\,dx + x\,dy = 0$ on any interval not containing $x = 0$.

All equations of the form (20.5) are not exact. If certain restrictions are placed on the region R, the converse of Theorem 20-I states sufficient conditions for an equation to be exact. For simplicity we assume R to be the interior of a rectangle.

Theorem 20-II.   If $\partial M/\partial y = \partial N/\partial x$ in the interior of a rectangle, then the equation $M(x, y)\,dx + N(x, y)dy = 0$ is exact in the interior of the rectangle.

A proof of Theorem 20-II is given in Ref. 20.1.

Example 3.   The equation

$$(2xy + 3y^3)dx + (x^2 + 9xy^2)dy = 0$$

is exact since

$$\frac{\partial}{\partial y}(2xy + 3y^3) = 2x + 9y^2$$

$$= \frac{\partial}{\partial x}(x^2 + 9xy^2).$$

If Theorem 20-II is applied and it is determined that equation (20.5) is exact, the problem of obtaining equation (20.6) still remains. There exist various methods of finding (20.6), but we will restrict ourselves to cases in which $u(x, y)$ can be obtained by inspection.

Example 4.   The equation

$$2xy\,dx + x^2\,dy = 0$$

is exact since

$$\frac{\partial}{\partial y}(2xy) = 2x = \frac{\partial}{\partial x}(x^2).$$

By inspection the equation has solution $x^2y = C$.

If equation (20.5) is not exact, it is still plausible that there may exist a function given by $\mu = \mu(x, y)$, such that

$$\mu(x, y)M(x, y)\,dx + \mu(x, y)N(x, y)dy = 0$$

is exact. Such a function μ is called an integrating factor of equation (20.5). In Ref. 20.3 it is shown that equation (20.5) always possesses an integrating factor.

Example 5.   The equation

$$-y\,dx + x\,dy = 0 \tag{20.7}$$

is not exact since

$$\frac{\partial}{\partial y}(-y) \neq \frac{\partial}{\partial x}(x).$$

By recalling the formula

$$d\left(\frac{y}{x}\right) = \frac{x\,dy - y\,dx}{x^2}$$

we note that $\mu(x, y) = 1/x^2$ is an integrating factor of (20.7). Hence, $y/x = C$ or $y = Cx$ defines the general solution of (20.7).

PROBLEM LIST 117

1. Use the contrapositive of Theorem 20-I to show that the following equations are not exact:

    (a) $x^2y\,dx + x^3y^2\,dy = 0$.

    (b) $x^2\,dx + y^2x\,dy = 0$.

    (c) $x \cos y\,dx + y \cos x\,dy = 0$.

    (d) $(x^2 + 2xy)\,dx + (y^2 - 2xy)\,dy = 0$.

2. Use Theorem 20-II to show that the following equations are exact:

    (a) $y^2\,dx + 2xy\,dy = 0$.

    (b) $\log y\,dx + \dfrac{x}{y}\,dy = 0$.

    (c) $3x^2 \sin y\,dx + x^3 \cos y\,dy = 0$.

    (d) $2xye^{x^2}\,dx + e^{x^2}\,dy = 0$.

3. Solve the following equations:

    (a) $4xy\,dx + 2x^2\,dy = 0$.   (e) $\dfrac{y}{x}\,dx + \log x\,dy = 0$.

    (b) $y^2\,dx + 2xy\,dy = 0$.   (f) $ye^x\,dx + e^x\,dy = 0$.

    (c) $y \cos x\,dx + \sin x\,dy = 0$.   (g) $(y + 2x)\,dx + x\,dy = 0$.

    (d) $2xy\,dx + (x^2 + 2y)\,dy = 0$.   (h) $e^x \sin y\,dx - e^x \cos y\,dy = 0$.

4. Solve by finding an integrating factor.

    (a) $y\,dx - x\,dy = 0$.

    (b) $2y\,dx + 3x\,dy = 0$.

5. Show that $\exp\left(\int P(x)\,dx\right)$ is an integrating factor of

    $$[yP(x) - Q(x)]\,dx + dy = 0,$$

    where P and Q denote functions of x.

6. Employ the formula for the differential of $\mathrm{Tan}^{-1}(y/x)$ to solve the equation

    $$(x^2 + y^2)dx + x\,dy - y\,dx = 0.$$

20.3 Separation of Variables

If equation (20.5) can be written in the form

$$M(x)dx + N(y)dy = 0, \tag{20.8}$$

where M denotes a function of x alone and N denotes a function of y alone, the variables x and y in (20.8) are said to be separable. Equation (20.8) is exact, since

$$\frac{\partial}{\partial y} M(x) \equiv 0 \equiv \frac{\partial N(y)}{\partial x}.$$

If

$$\frac{dG(x)}{dx} = M(x) \quad \text{and} \quad \frac{dH(y)}{dy} = N(y),$$

the general solution of (20.8) is given implicitly by

$$G(x) + H(y) = c. \tag{20.9}$$

If $y = f(x)$ denotes any differentiable function defined by (20.9), it follows from the chain rule that $y = f(x)$ defines a solution of (20.8).

Example 1. The solution of

$$x \, dx + y^2 dy = 0$$

is given implicitly by

$$\frac{x^2}{2} + \frac{y^3}{3} = c.$$

Example 2. To solve

$$2xy \, dx + dy = 0, \tag{20.10}$$

we divide by y to obtain

$$2x \, dx + \frac{dy}{y} = 0, \quad (y \neq 0). \tag{20.11}$$

The variables are now separated and the general solution of (20.11) is given by

$$x^2 + \log |y| = c.$$

Solving for y we obtain

$$\log |y| = c - x^2,$$
$$|y| = e^{c-x^2} = e^c e^{-x^2},$$

or

$$y = \pm e^c e^{-x^2}.$$

Replacing $\pm e^c$ by k, the solution becomes $y = ke^{-x^2}$. Note that although (20.11) is meaningless when $y = 0$, the function given by $y \equiv 0$, obtained by setting $k = 0$, is easily shown to be a solution of (20.10).

PROBLEM LIST 118

1. Find the general solution in implicit or explicit form.

(a) $dx - 2xy \, dy = 0$.

(b) $x \, dx - 3dy = 0$.

(c) $\dfrac{dx}{y(1 + x^2)} - 2dy = 0$.

(d) $\dfrac{dy}{dx} = e^{y-x}$.

(e) $2x(1 + y^2) \, dx + dy = 0$.

(f) $\sqrt{1 - y^2} \, dx - x \sqrt{x^2 - 1} \, dy = 0$.

(g) $\dfrac{dy}{dx} = \dfrac{y}{x^2}$.

(h) $\dfrac{dy}{dx} = \dfrac{2x + xy^2}{3y + x^2y}$.

2. Find the particular solution satisfying the given condition.

  (a) $(2xy + 2x)\, dx - dy = 0$; $y = 0$ when $x = 0$.

  (b) $dx = 4\sqrt[3]{y(x - 1)}\, dy$; $y = 0$ when $x = 1$.

  (c) $\dfrac{dy}{dx} = 3y$; $y = 1$ when $x = 0$.

  (d) $\dfrac{dy}{dx} = \dfrac{3y - xy}{x}$; $y = 3e^{-1}$ when $x = 1$.

  (e) $\dfrac{dy}{dx} = (3 + y) \cot x$; $y = 4$ when $x = \dfrac{\pi}{2}$.

  (f) $(y^2 + 4)\, dx - (x^2 + 4)\, dy = 0$; $y = 1$ when $x = 2$.

3. Find the particular solution of $x\, dy + y\, dx = 0$ satisfying the condition $y = 4$ when $x = 1$,

  (a) by separating the variables;

  (b) by treating the equation as exact.

20.4   *Homogeneous First-Order Equations*

A function denoted by $f(x, y)$ is called a homogeneous function of x and y of degree n if and only if $f(\lambda x, \lambda y) = \lambda^n f(x, y)$. The equation (20.5),

$$M(x, y)\, dx + N(x, y)\, dy = 0,$$

is called a homogeneous first-order differential equation if M and N are homogeneous functions of the same degree. In this case (20.5) becomes

$$\lambda^{-n} M(\lambda x, \lambda y)\, dx + \lambda^{-n} N(\lambda x, \lambda y)\, dy = 0.$$

Multiplying by λ^n and letting $\lambda = 1/x$, we obtain

$$M\left(1, \frac{y}{x}\right) dx + N\left(1, \frac{y}{x}\right) dy = 0. \qquad (20.12)$$

If we now let $y = vx$, dy becomes $v\, dx + x\, dv$, and equation (20.12) takes the form

$$M(1, v)\, dx + N(1, v)[v\, dx + x\, dv] = 0$$

or

$$\frac{dx}{x} + \frac{N(1, v)\, dv}{M(1, v) + vN(1, v)} = 0. \qquad (20.13)$$

Equation (20.13), in which the variables x and v are separated, is solved to find $v = v(x)$ in terms of x, whereupon (20.5) has the solution defined by $y = xv(x)$.

Example 1.   Solve the equation $(y^2 - xy)dx + x^2\, dy = 0$.

Solution.   Since M and N are homogeneous functions of degree 2, we let $y = vx$. Replacing dy by $v\, dx + x\, dv$, we obtain

$$(v^2x^2 - vx^2)\, dx + x^2(v\, dx + x\, dv) = 0,$$

or

$$v^2\, dx + x\, dv = 0.$$

Separating the variables and simplifying yields

$$\frac{dx}{x} + v^{-2}\, dv = 0,$$

from which we obtain

$$\log|x| - v^{-1} = c.$$

Replacing v by y/x and simplifying yields the required solution defined by

$$y = \frac{x}{\log|x| - c}.$$

The effect of the substitution $y = vx$ is to replace the variable y by a new variable v. The introduction of a new variable by a substitution often simplifies the solution of a differential equation.

Example 2.   Solve the equation $dy/dx = (x + y)^2$.

    Solution.   Letting $v = x + y$ and replacing dy by $dv - dx$, we obtain

$$dv - dx = v^2\, dx$$

or

$$(1 + v^2)dx - dv = 0.$$

Separating the variables yields

$$dx - \frac{dv}{1 + v^2} = 0.$$

This equation has the solution defined by

$$x - \mathrm{Tan}^{-1} v = c.$$

Replacing v by $x + y$ and solving for y, we obtain the required solution defined by

$$y = \tan(x - c) - x.$$

PROBLEM LIST 119

1. Show that each of the following expressions defines a homogeneous function and find the degree:

    (a) $x^2y + 3xy^2$.

    (b) $4x - 3y$.

    (c) $x^3 + y^3 - 3x^2y$.

    (d) $\log y - \log x$.

    (e) $\dfrac{x^2 e^{x/y}}{y^2}$.

2. Find the general solution of each of the following equations:

    (a) $(x + y)\, dx - x\, dy = 0$.

    (b) $(x^2 + y^2)\, dx - xy\, dy = 0$.

    (c) $\dfrac{dy}{dx} = \dfrac{x}{y} + \dfrac{y}{x} + 2$.

(d) $\dfrac{dy}{dx} = \dfrac{y + x}{y - x}$.

(e) $(y^2 + xy)\, dx - x^2\, dy = 0$.

(f) $y\, dx - (x + 2y)\, dy = 0$.

(g) $(y - \sqrt{x^2 - y^2})\, dx - x\, dy = 0$.

3. Find the particular solution of $(x + y)\, dx - x\, dy = 0$ satisfying the condition $y = 0$ when $x = 2$.

4. Find the particular solution of

$$\frac{dy}{dx} + \frac{3x^2 y}{x^3 + y^3} = 0$$

satisfying the condition $y = 1$ when $x = 1$.

5. Show that if the equation $M(x, y)\, dx + N(x, y)\, dy = 0$ is homogeneous, the substitution $x = vy$ separates the variables.

6. Show that the substitution $v = ax + by + c$ separates the variables in the equation

$$\frac{dy}{dx} = f(ax + by + c).$$

7. Solve the equation $dy/dx = x + y - 1$.

8. Solve the equation $dy/dx = (x - y)^2$.

9. Show that the substitution $v = y/x^n$ separates the variables in the equation

$$\frac{dy}{dx} = x^{1-n} f\left(\frac{y}{x^n}\right).$$

20.5   First-Order Linear Equations

The general form of a first-order linear differential equation is

$$A(x)\frac{dy}{dx} + B(x)y + C(x) = 0, \tag{20.14}$$

where the coefficients A, B, and C denote continuous functions of x on some interval I. It is customary to assume that $A(x)$ is not identically zero on I, to divide (20.14) by $A(x)$, and to obtain the form

$$\frac{dy}{dx} + P(x)y = Q(x). \tag{20.15}$$

Linear equations of this type play a significant role in both pure and applied mathematics.

The appearance of the left member of (20.15) resembles the derivative of the product of y by some expression involving x. This suggests that we seek an integrating factor $\mu = \mu(x)$ which will make the left member of (20.15) the derivative of a product.

In order that the equation

$$\mu(Py - Q)\, dx + \mu\, dy = 0$$

be exact, we must have

$$\frac{\partial}{\partial y}[\mu(Py - Q)] = \mu P = \frac{\partial \mu}{\partial x} = \frac{d\mu}{dx},$$

or

$$\frac{d\mu}{\mu} = P\, dx,$$

from which we obtain

$$\log|\mu| = \int P\, dx \qquad \text{or} \qquad \mu = ce^{\int P\, dx}.$$

Taking $c = 1$, we observe that

$$e^{\int P\, dx}\frac{dy}{dx} + e^{\int P\, dx}P(x)y$$

can be written in the form

$$\frac{d}{dx}(ye^{\int P\, dx}).$$

Thus the general solution of (20.15) is given by

$$ye^{\int P\, dx} = \int Q(x)e^{\int P\, dx}. \qquad\qquad \textbf{(20.16)}$$

Example 1.   Solve the equation

$$\frac{dy}{dx} + \frac{2y}{x} = 4x.$$

Solution.   The integrating factor

$$\mu(x) = \exp\left(\int P\, dx\right) = \exp\left(\int \frac{2dx}{x}\right)$$
$$= \exp\left(2 \log|x|\right)$$
$$= \exp\left(\log x^2\right) = x^2.$$

Hence, from (20.16), the equation has general solution given by

$$yx^2 = \int (4x)x^2\, dx = x^4 + c,$$

or

$$y = x^2 + \frac{c}{x^2}.$$

Example 2.   Solve the equation

$$\frac{dy}{dx} + \frac{y}{x} = 3x.$$

Solution.   Since $\mu(x) = \exp\left(\int \frac{dx}{x}\right) = \exp\left(\log|x|\right) = |x|$, we have, from (20.16),

$$y|x| = \int 3x|x|\, dx.$$

On any interval I_1 where $x > 0$, $|x| = x$ and the equation has the solution given by

$$yx = \int 3x^2 \, dx = x^3 + c$$

or

$$y = x^2 + \frac{c}{x}.$$

On any interval I_2 where $x < 0$, $|x| = -x$ and (20.16) yields

$$-yx = \int 3x(-x) \, dx = -x^3 + k$$

or

$$y = x^2 - \frac{k}{x}.$$

If we set $k = -c$, we note that the solutions on I_1 and I_2 agree.

PROBLEM LIST 120

1. Solve

   (a) $\dfrac{dy}{dx} + \dfrac{2y}{x} = x^2 + 1$;

   (b) $\dfrac{dy}{dx} + 2xy = 2x$;

   (c) $\dfrac{dy}{dx} + \dfrac{y}{x} = x^2$;

   (d) $\dfrac{dy}{dx} + y \tan x = \cos x$;

   (e) $\dfrac{dr}{d\theta} + \dfrac{4r}{\theta} = \theta$;

   (f) $\dfrac{dy}{dx} + e^x y = e^x$;

   (g) $\dfrac{dy}{dx} - \dfrac{2y}{x+1} = 3(x+1)^2$;

   (h) $\dfrac{dy}{dx} + y \cot x = \csc^2 x$.

2. Solve

   (a) $\dfrac{dx}{dy} + 2xy = y$;

   (b) $dx + (2x - y^2) \, dy = 0$.

3. Find the particular solution satisfying the given condition in each of the following cases:

   (a) $\dfrac{dy}{dx} + y = e^{-x}$; $y = 5$ when $x = 0$.

   (b) $\dfrac{dy}{dx} + \dfrac{2y}{x} = \dfrac{4}{x}$; $y = 6$ when $x = 1$.

(c) $\dfrac{dy}{dx} + \dfrac{y}{x} = e^x$; $y = e^{-1}$ when $x = -1$.

(d) $\dfrac{dy}{dx} + y \cot x = 2 \cos x$; $y = 3$ when $x = \dfrac{\pi}{2}$.

4. Show that no greater generality is obtained by adding a constant of integration to the integrating factor $\mu(x) = e^{\int P\,dx}$ of equation (20.15).

5. Show that if $f(x)$ denotes the general solution of $y' + P(x)\, y = 0$, and $g(x)$ denotes any particular solution of $y' + P(x)y = Q(x)$, then $y = f(x) + g(x)$ gives the general solution of $y' + P(x)y = Q(x)$.

6. The nonlinear equation $(dy/dx) + P(x)y = Q(x)y^n$ is known as Bernoulli's equation, named after the Swiss mathematician James Bernoulli (1654–1705). Show that the substitution $z = y^{1-n}$ reduces Bernoulli's equation to a linear equation.

7. Use the results of Problem 6 to solve

(a) $\dfrac{dy}{dx} + \dfrac{2y}{x} = xy^2$;

(b) $\dfrac{dy}{dx} + \dfrac{y}{x} = \dfrac{1}{x^3 y^3}$.

8. Find the particular solution of

$$\frac{d^2y}{dx^2} + \frac{2}{x}\frac{dy}{dx} = \frac{6}{x}$$

satisfying the conditions $y = 5$ and $dy/dx = 2$ when $x = 1$.

20.6   Applications of First-Order Differential Equations

Growth and Decay

Nature abounds in quantities whose time rate of change at any instant is proportional (or approximately proportional) to the amount of the quantity present at that instant. If y denotes the amount of the quantity present at time t, the function denoted by $y = f(t)$ satisfies the differential equation

$$\frac{dy}{dt} = ky, \tag{20.17}$$

known as the differential equation of growth and decay. When $k > 0$, the amount y increases (grows) with t; when $k < 0$, y decreases (decays) with t.

Example 1.   Bacteria in a certain culture increase at a rate proportional to the number present. If the number doubles in 1 hr, how long does it take for the number to triple?

Solution.   Let y denote the number present at time t. Then the function denoted by $y = f(t)$ satisfies the differential equation

$$\frac{dy}{dt} = ky$$

and the conditions

$$\begin{cases} t = 0 \\ y = y_0 \end{cases}; \qquad \begin{cases} t = 1 \\ y = 2y_0 \end{cases}.$$

Writing the differential equation in the linear form

$$\frac{dy}{dt} - ky = 0,$$

we see that $e^{\int -k\,dt} = e^{-kt}$ is an integrating factor. Hence the equation has solution

$$ye^{-kt} = \int 0\,dt = c \qquad \text{or} \qquad y = ce^{kt}.$$

From the condition $t = 0$, $y = y_0$ we find that $y_0 = c$. The additional condition $t = 1$, $y = 2y_0$ is now employed to find the constant of proportionality k. From $2y_0 = y_0 e^{k(1)}$ we obtain $k = \log 2$.

Hence the function denoted by $y = f(t)$ is given by

$$y = y_0 e^{t \log 2}.$$

Substituting $y = 3y_0$ and solving for t yields

$$3y_0 = y_0\, e^{t \log 2} \qquad \text{or} \qquad \log 3 = t \log 2.$$

Hence the number will triple in

$$t = \frac{\log 3}{\log 2} \cong 1.6 \text{ hr.}$$

Example 2.   Radium disintegrates at a rate proportional to the amount of radium present at any instant. It takes 1600 years, known as the half-life of the radium, for half of the original radium to disintegrate. What percentage of the original amount will remain in 1200 years?

Solution.   Let $y = f(t)$ denote the amount of radium present at time t and y_0 the amount present at $t = 0$. The function denoted by $y = f(t)$ satisfies the differential equation

$$\frac{dy}{dt} = ky,$$

having general solution defined by $y = ce^{kt}$. From the condition $t = 0$, $y = y_0$, we find that $c = y_0$ and hence $y = y_0 e^{kt}$.

From the condition $t = 1600$, $y = y_0/2$, we find that

$$\frac{y_0}{2} = y_0\, e^{1600k} \qquad \text{or} \qquad k = \frac{-\log 2}{1600}.$$

Thus, at time t,

$$y = y_0 \exp\left(\frac{-t \log 2}{1600}\right) = f(t),$$

and when $t = 1200$,

$$y = y_0 \exp\left(\frac{-3 \log 2}{4}\right) \cong y_0\, e^{-0.52} \cong 0.59 y_0.$$

Thus, approximately 59% of the original radium remains after 1200 years.

Temperature Rate of Change

Under certain conditions the temperature rate of change of a body is proportional to the difference between the temperature of the body and the temperature of the surrounding medium. (It is assumed that the temperature of the surrounding medium remains constant.) This is known as Newton's law of cooling. If $T = f(t)$ denotes the temperature at time t, and τ the temperature of the surrounding medium, then f satisfies the differential equation

$$\frac{dT}{dt} = -k(T - \tau), \tag{20.18}$$

where $k > 0$ is the constant of proportionality.

Example 3.   A body whose temperature T is initially 200 deg is immersed in a liquid whose temperature τ is constantly 100 deg. If the temperature of the body is 150 deg at $t = 1$ minute, find its temperature at $t = 2$ minutes.

Solution.   Separating the variables in (20.18) and assuming that $T > \tau$, we obtain

$$\frac{dT}{T - 100} = -k \, dt.$$

Hence

$$\log (T - 100) = -kt + c. \tag{20.19}$$

From the initial condition $t = 0$, $T = 200$, we find that $c = \log 100$.
From the condition $t = 1$, $T = 150$, we find that

$$\log 50 = -k(1) + \log 100 \qquad \text{or} \qquad k = \log 2.$$

Substituting these values of c and k into (20.19) and simplifying, we obtain

$$T = f(t) = 100[1 + 2^{-t}].$$

When $t = 2$ minutes, $T = 125$ deg. Note that as $t \to \infty$, $T \to 100$ deg $= \tau$.

Rectilinear Motion

When Newton's second law is applied to the motion of a particle moving in a straight line, the resulting differential equation is generally of the form

$$\frac{d^2x}{dt^2} = f\left(x, \frac{dx}{dt}, t\right),$$

where x denotes the displacement at time t.

Example 4.   The motion of a body moving in a straight line in a resisting medium is governed by the differential equation

$$\frac{d^2x}{dt^2} = -\frac{1}{2} \frac{dx}{dt}.$$

If $dx/dt = 50$ fps and $x = 0$ ft when $t = 0$ sec, find the displacement x in terms of t, $\lim\limits_{t \to \infty} x$, and $\lim\limits_{t \to \infty} v$.

Solution. Setting

$$\frac{d^2x}{dt^2} = \frac{dv}{dt} \quad \text{and} \quad \frac{dx}{dt} = v$$

and separating the variables, we obtain

$$\frac{dv}{v} = \frac{-dt}{2}.$$

This equation has the general solution given by $v = ce^{-t/2}$ and the particular solution given by $v = 50e^{-t/2}$ satisfying $v = 50$ when $t = 0$. Integrating, we obtain $x = -100e^{-t/2} + k$. Since $x = 0$ when $t = 0$, it follows that $k = 100$ and hence $x = 100(1 - e^{-t/2})$. As $t \to \infty$, $x \to 100$ ft and $v \to 0$ fps.

Electric Circuits

The current i in an electric circuit is the time rate of change of the quantity of electricity flowing from one element of the circuit to another. At time t seconds the current has value i amperes. In a simple circuit containing no capacitor, it is a consequence of Kirchhoff's second law that the function f defined by $i = f(t)$ satisfies the differential equation

$$L\frac{di}{dt} + Ri = E(t), \tag{20.20}$$

where L (the coefficient of inductance, in henrys) and R (the resistance, in ohms) are constant, and $E(t)$ is the electromotive force in volts at time t.

Example 5. In a circuit with no capacitor, the inductance is 4 henrys, the resistance is 20 ohms, and E is constantly equal to 100 volts. Given that $i = 0$ when $t = 0$, find the relationship between i and t.

Solution. Equation (20.20) becomes

$$4\frac{di}{dt} + 20i = 100 \quad \text{or} \quad \frac{di}{dt} + 5i = 25.$$

This equation has general solution given by

$$ie^{5t} = \int 25e^{5t}\, dt = 5e^{5t} + c.$$

Setting $i = 0$ and $t = 0$ we determine that $c = -5$ and hence

$$i = 5 - 5e^{-5t}.$$

Example 6. Solve Example 5 with $E(t) = 20 \sin 5t$.

Solution. The differential equation now becomes

$$4\frac{di}{dt} + 20i = 20 \sin 5t,$$

or

$$\frac{di}{dt} + 5i = 5 \sin 5t.$$

The general solution is given by

$$ie^{5t} = \int 5e^{5t} \sin 5t \, dt$$

$$= e^{5t}\frac{\sin 5t - \cos 5t}{2} + c.$$

Setting $i = 0$ and $t = 0$, we find that $c = 1/2$ and hence

$$i = \frac{\sin 5t - \cos 5t}{2} + \frac{e^{-5t}}{2}.$$

The term $e^{-5t}/2$ becomes negligible as $t \to \infty$, and is called the transient current, while the remaining terms $(\sin 5t - \cos 5t)/2$ are called the steady-state current.

PROBLEM LIST 121

1. Bacteria in a certain culture increase at a rate proportional to the number present. If the number doubles in 2 hr, what percentage of the original number will be present at the end of 3 hr?

2. A certain chemical substance decomposes at a rate proportional to the amount of the substance present. If 60 of an original 100 grams remain after 1 hr, find an expression for the amount remaining at time t.

3. The amount of active ferment in a culture of yeast increases at a rate proportional to the amount present. If the amount doubles in 1 hr, how long will it take for the amount to quadruple?

4. The angular velocity ω of a certain rotating wheel decreases at a rate proportional to ω. If $\omega = 200$ rps at $t = 0$, and $\omega = 150$ rps at $t = 10$ sec, find how fast the wheel is rotating at $t = 20$ sec.

5. Assume that radium decomposes at a rate proportional to the amount present. If 100 mg reduces to 90 mg in 200 years, how many milligrams will remain at the end of 1000 years? Determine the half-life of the radium.

6. Uranium disintegrates at a rate proportional (approximately) to the amount present at any instant. If N_0 grams are present at $t = 0$ and N_1 grams are present at $t = t_1$ years, find a formula for the half-life of uranium.

7. If 25% of a radioactive substance disappears in 10 years, how many years does it take for 60% of the substance to disappear?

8. A body of temperature 160 deg is immersed in a liquid of constant temperature

100 deg. If it takes 2 minutes for the body to cool to 140 deg, how long does it take for it to cool to 110 deg?

9. The motion of a body falling vertically from rest in a resisting medium is governed by the differential equation $dv/dt = 32 - (v/5)$, where v denotes the velocity in feet per second and t is in seconds. Find v when $t = 5$ sec, $\lim_{t\to\infty} v$, and the distance the body falls in the first 10 sec.

10. The motion of a particle moving on the x-axis with acceleration d^2x/dt^2 directed toward the origin and proportional to x is governed by the equation $d^2x/dt^2 = -k^2x$, known as the differential equation of a simple harmonic motion. If $x = 1$ and $v = dx/dt = 0$ at $t = 0$, find v and x in terms of t when $k = 4$. *Hint.* Write $d^2x/dt^2 = dv/dt$ in the form

$$\frac{dv}{dx} \cdot \frac{dx}{dt} = v\frac{dv}{dx}.$$

11. A body moves in a straight line with constant acceleration $a = d^2x/dt^2$. If $v = v_0$ and $x = 0$ when $t = 0$, find
    (a) v in terms of x,
    (b) x in terms of t,
    (c) v in terms of t.

12. The amount a, in dollars, obtained from p dollars invested at r percent per year with interest compounded n times per year for t years is given by

$$a = p\left(1 + \frac{r}{n}\right)^{nt}.$$

Find $A = \lim_{n\to\infty} a$ and show that A, called the amount when interest is compounded continuously, satisfies the differential equation $dA/dt = rA$. This accounts for the fact that equation (20.17) is often called the compound interest law.

13. Find the amount A at the end of 1 year if \$1.00 is invested at 4% compounded continuously.

14. How long does it take for a given amount of money to double at 5% compounded continuously?

15. The rate of change of atmospheric pressure p with respect to altitude h is (approximately) proportional to p. If $p = 14.7$ psi at $h = 0$, and $p = 7.35$ psi at $h = 18,000$ ft, find p at $h = 1000$ ft.

16. An electric circuit consists of an inductance L of 2 henrys, a resistance R of 20 ohms, and a constant voltage E of 100 volts. If the current $i = 0$ amp when $t = 0$ sec, find an equation satisfied by i and t and draw its graph.

17. In Problem 16, replace the constant voltage $E = 100$ by the variable voltage $E = E(t) = 100 \cos 10t$.

18. The population of a city grows at a rate equal (approximately) to the population at any instant. If the population increases 25% in 10 years, how long will it take for the population to double?

19. The rate of change of population in a certain region is governed (approximately) by the differential equation

$$\frac{dy}{dt} = ay - by^2,$$

where $y = f(t)$ denotes the number of people alive at time t, and a and b are positive constants.

(a) Show that $\lim\limits_{t \to \infty} y = a/b$.

(b) If $y = a/(2b)$ when $t = 0$, find $y = f(t)$ and draw the graph of f.

20.7   Geometrical Interpretation of Differential Equations

A first-order linear differential equation can be written in the form

$$\frac{dy}{dx} = F(x, y). \tag{20.21}$$

In Ref. 20.3 it is shown that if F and $\partial F/\partial y$ are continuous in a closed rectangle, then through each interior point (a, b) of the rectangle there passes a unique curve $y = f(x)$, called an integral curve of (20.21), such that $f'(a) = F(a, b)$. We say that (20.21) determines a direction field, since it defines at a point (a, b) the slope or direction of the particular integral curve of (20.21) passing through (a, b). A direction field is illustrated graphically by drawing short line segments at several points, each line segment (or line element) having slope $F(a, b)$ at (a, b). The appearance of

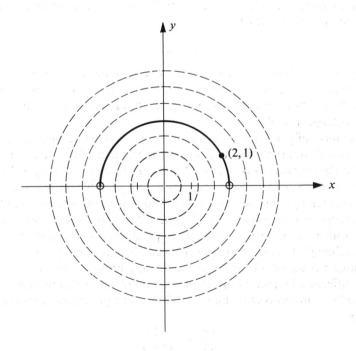

Figure 20.1

a direction field gives a good indication of the nature of the integral curves of the associated differential equation. The direction field determined by $dy/dx = -x/y$ is illustrated in Fig. 20.1. The general solution is given by $x^2 + y^2 = c^2$, an equation of the family of circles with centers at the origin. Figure 20.1 also illustrates the integral curve through $(2, 1)$, having equation $y = \sqrt{5 - x^2}$, where $-\sqrt{5} < x < \sqrt{5}$. Note that the direction field is not defined on the x-axis.

Now let us assume that we are given a family of curves

$$y = F(x, c), \tag{20.22}$$

where c is an arbitrary constant. For each member of family (20.22),

$$\frac{dy}{dx} = \frac{\partial}{\partial x} F(x, c). \tag{20.23}$$

If it is possible to eliminate c from (20.22) and (20.23), the result will be a differential equation of the form

$$G\left(y, \frac{dy}{dx}, x\right) = 0. \tag{20.24}$$

Equation (20.24) will be satisfied by every member of family (20.22); it is called a differential equation of the family.

Example 1. Find a differential equation of the family having equation $y = cx^2$.

Solution. Eliminating c from $y = cx^2$ and $dy/dx = 2cx$, we obtain the differential equation $x(dy/dx) - 2y = 0$. We say that the family is characterized by the differential equation.

Let us assume that the equation $y = F(x, c)$ defines a family of curves in a domain D in the xy-plane. We assume also that if $P(x, y)$ is a point of D, then one and only one member of the family passes through P and that this curve has a well-defined tangent at P.

If a second family of curves in D has the property that one and only one member passes through P and that this curve meets the member of the first family at right angles, then the members of the second family are called the orthogonal trajectories of the first family. The members of the first family are also orthogonal trajectories of the second family and the two families are said to be orthogonal. Orthogonal trajectories play an important role in applied mathematics. For example, the family of isotherms, or curves of equal temperature, on a weather map is orthogonal to the family of curves representing the direction of heat flow.

To find an equation of the orthogonal trajectories of the family $y = F(x, c)$, we find a differential equation of the family and from it determine the slope $m = m(x, y)$ at $P(x, y)$ in terms of x and y. A differential equation of the required family is given by

$$\frac{dy}{dx} = \frac{-1}{m(x, y)}.$$

The general solution of this differential equation yields an equation of the required family.

Example 2.   Find the family orthogonal to the family $y = cx$.

Solution.   Eliminating c from $y = cx$ and $dy/dx = c$, we obtain $dy/dx = y/x$, a differential equation of the family. Hence, a differential equation of the required family is

$$\frac{dy}{dx} = \frac{-1}{y/x} = \frac{-x}{y}.$$

The general solution given by $x^2 + y^2 = k^2$ of this equation yields an equation of the required family. The two families are illustrated in Fig. 20.2. The domain D must not include the origin, since infinitely many members of $y = cx$ pass through that point.

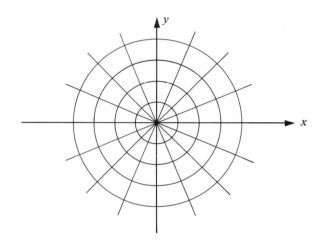

Figure 20.2

Example 3.   Find the family orthogonal to the family $y = ce^{-x}$ of exponential curves.

Solution.   From $y' = -ce^{-x}$ we obtain $y' = -y$, a differential equation of the family. Solving $dy/dx = 1/y$ or $y\, dy = dx$, we obtain the general solution given by $y^2 = 2(x + k)$, a family of parabolas. The parabolas are orthogonal to the exponential curves.

PROBLEM LIST 122

1. Depict graphically the direction field defined by each of the following differential equations:

    (a) $y' = y$.   (e) $y' = 2x$.

    (b) $y' = -y/x$.   (f) $y' = x + y$.

    (c) $y' = 1/x$.   (g) $y' = x - y$.

    (d) $y' = xy$.   (h) $y' = \dfrac{-2y}{1 + x^2}$.

2. Depict graphically the direction field determined by the differential equation $y' = x/2$. Find the integral curve passing through $(3, 4)$.

3. Find a differential equation of the family having equation

   (a) $y = cx^3$;   (e) $x^2 - y^2 = c^2$;

   (b) $x^2 + y^2 = c^2$;   (f) $y^2 = cx$;

   (c) $y = ce^x$;   (g) $xy = c$.

   (d) $y = x + ce^x$;

4. Find a differential equation of the family

   (a) of circles of radius 3 with centers on the x-axis;

   (b) of parabolas with vertices at the origin and foci on the x-axis.

5. Find a differential equation of each of the following two-parameter families: (a) $y = ae^x + be^{-x}$; (b) $y = a \sin x + b \cos x$; (c) $y = x^2 + ax + b$.

6. Find an equation of the family of curves whose tangent line at (x, y) passes through $(-x, 0)$.

7. Find a differential equation of all nonvertical straight lines in the xy-plane.

8. Find a differential equation of all circles whose centers lie on the line $y = x$.

9. Show that the family $xy = c$ is orthogonal to the family $x^2 - y^2 = k$.

10. Find an equation of the family orthogonal to

   (a) $y = \dfrac{a}{x^2}$;   (f) $x^2 + y^2 + cy = 0$;

   (b) $y = mx + 4$;   (g) $\dfrac{x^2}{4c^2} + \dfrac{y^2}{c^2} = 1$;

   (c) $y = 2x + b$;   (h) $2y^2 + x^2 = c^2$;

   (d) $y = cx^2$;   (i) $x^2 = 4cy$;

   (e) $y^2 = cx^3$;   (j) $x^2 + y^2 = c^2$.

11. Find an equation of the family orthogonal to the family of circles through the origin with centers on the y-axis.

12. Find an equation of the family orthogonal to the family of ellipses with vertices at $(\pm 5, 0)$ and centers at the origin.

13. Find the orthogonal trajectories of the family of parabolas $y^2 = cx$ and determine the member of each family which passes through $(1, 2)$.

14. Find an equation of the family orthogonal to the family $y = cx^4$ and depict the two families graphically.

15. A family whose orthogonal trajectories are the members of the same family is said to be "self-orthogonal." Show that the family $y^2 = 4cx + 4c^2$ is self-orthogonal.

16. Find an equation of the family whose members intersect the members of the family $xy = c$ at an angle of $\pi/4$.

20.8 Second-Order Linear Equations

The general form of a second-order linear differential equation is

$$A(x)\frac{d^2y}{dx^2} + B(x)\frac{dy}{dx} + C(x)y + D(x) = 0, \tag{20.25}$$

where the coefficients A, B, C, and D denote continuous functions of x on some interval I. Assuming that $A(x)$ is not identically zero on I, we divide (20.25) by $A(x)$ and obtain the form

$$y'' + P(x)y' + Q(x)y = R(x). \qquad (20.26)$$

The mathematical theory required for a detailed discussion of (20.26) is quite extensive. We restrict ourselves to a simple introduction to this theory.

Since each term on the left of (20.26) contains y, or one of its derivatives, while the right member $R(x)$ depends upon x alone, equation (20.26) is said to be non-homogeneous. If $R(x) \equiv 0$, equation (20.26) reduces to the homogeneous equation (or reduced equation)

$$y'' + P(x)y' + Q(x)y = 0. \qquad (20.27)$$

The following theorem, proved in Ref. 20.4, states sufficient conditions for the existence of a unique solution of equation (20.26) satisfying a set of initial conditions.

Theorem 20-III.   If P, Q, and R are continuous functions of x for $a \leqslant x \leqslant b$, then there exists one and only one solution denoted by $y = f(x)$ of (20.26) on $a \leqslant x \leqslant b$ which satisfies the initial conditions

$$f(x_0) = y_0; \qquad f'(x_0) = y_0',$$

where $a \leqslant x_0 \leqslant b$ and y_0 and y_0' are given constants.

We will apply Theorem 20-III by finding the complete solution of (20.26) and then determining from it the particular solution which we seek and which is guaranteed by Theorem 20-III.

The following theorem, often referred to as the principle of superposition, states that a linear combination of solutions of a second-order linear differential equation is also a solution. Although the theorem is stated for two functions, it is easily extended to any finite number of functions. A similar theorem holds for higher-order linear differential equations.

Theorem 20-IV.   If y_1 and y_2 are any two solutions of (20.27), then $y_3 = c_1 y_1 + c_2 y_2$, where c_1 and c_2 are arbitrary constants, is also a solution.

Proof.   We note that

$$\begin{aligned}
y_3'' + Py_3' + Qy_3 &= (c_1 y_1'' + c_2 y_2'') + P(c_1 y_1' + c_2 y_2') \\
&\quad + Q(c_1 y_1 + c_2 y_2) \\
&= c_1(y_1'' + Py_1' + Qy_1) + c_2(y_2'' + Py_2' + Qy_2) \\
&= 0,
\end{aligned}$$

the coefficients of c_1 and c_2 being zero because y_1 and y_2 are solutions of (20.27).

_____

Two functions y_1 and y_2 are said to be linearly independent on an interval $a \leqslant x \leqslant b$ if and only if neither function is a constant multiple of the other for

$a \leqslant x \leqslant b$. In other words, the ratio of the two functions is not constant on the given interval.

Example 1.   The functions defined by $y_1 = \sin^2 x$ and $y_2 = 2 - 2\cos^2 x$ are not linearly independent on any interval I, since $y_2 \equiv 2y_1$ for every x in I.

Two functions which are not linearly independent on any interval I are said to be linearly dependent on I.

The following theorem is proved in Ref. 20.1.

Theorem 20-V.   Let y_1 and y_2 be solutions of equation (20.27). Then y_1 and y_2 are linearly independent on an interval I if and only if

$$W(y_1, y_2) = y_1 y_2' - y_2 y_1' \neq 0 \qquad (20.28)$$

for any x in I.

The quantity $W(y_1, y_2)$ is called the Wronskian of the functions y_1 and y_2 after the Polish mathematician H. Wronsky (1778–1853).

Example 2.   The functions defined by $y_1 = \sin x$ and $y_2 = \cos x$ satisfy the differential equation $y'' + y = 0$ on any interval I. They are linearly independent on I, since

$$W(y_1, y_2) = \sin x(-\sin x) - \cos x(\cos x)$$
$$= -(\sin^2 x + \cos^2 x) \equiv -1$$

is not zero for any x in I.

———————

The following theorems are also proved in Ref. 20.1.

Theorem 20-VI.   If y_1 and y_2 are two linearly independent solutions of (20.27), then every solution of (20.27) can be expressed in the form $y_3 = c_1 y_1 + c_2 y_2$.

Theorem 20-VII.   If $y_3 = c_1 y_1 + c_2 y_2$ defines the complete solution of (20.27) and $Y = Y(x)$ defines *any* particular solution of (20.26), then *every* solution of (20.26) can be expressed in the form

$$y = c_1 y_1 + c_2 y_2 + Y(x).$$

Theorem 20-VI is more complex than Theorem 20-IV. Theorem 20-IV merely states that a linear combination of any two solutions of (20.27) is also a solution, whereas Theorem 20-VI states that a linear combination of any two *linearly independent* solutions of (20.27) yields the *complete* solution.

It is easy to show that the complete solution given by $y_3 = c_1 y_1 + c_2 y_2$ of (20.27) plus a particular solution given by $Y = Y(x)$ of (20.26) is a solution of (20.26). (See Problem 10.) Theorem 20-VII states the less obvious fact that $y = y_3 + Y$ defines the *complete* solution of (20.26).

In summary, to find the complete solution of (20.26), first find two linearly independent solutions y_1 and y_2 of (20.27), the reduced equation of (20.26). Then add to $c_1 y_1 + c_2 y_2$ any particular solution $Y = Y(x)$ of (20.26). In the following section we will carry out this program in the special case in which the coefficients $P(x)$ and $Q(x)$ in (20.26) are constant.

PROBLEM LIST 123

1. Given that $y_1 = e^x$ and $y_2 = e^{-2x}$ define solutions of $y'' + y' - 2y = 0$, show that $y_3 = c_1 e^x + c_2 e^{-2x}$, where c_1 and c_2 are arbitrary constants, also defines a solution.

2. Find the solution of, $y'' = 6x$ satisfying $y(0) = 5$ and $y'(0) = 2$.

3. Let $y_1, y_2, \cdots, y_n$ denote solutions of an nth-order linear differential equation. Show that the linear combination $y = c_1 y_1 + c_2 y_2 + \cdots + c_n y_n$ also defines a solution.

4. The functions given by $y_1 = 5x$ and $y_2 \equiv 1$ define solutions of the equation $y'' = 0$. Show that y_1 and y_2 are linearly independent.

5. The functions given by $y_1 = \sin 2x$ and $y_2 = \cos 2x$ are solutions of the equation $y'' + 4y = 0$. Show that y_1 and y_2 are linearly independent on any interval I. Write the complete solution of $y'' + 4y = 0$.

6. The functions given by $y_1 = e^{3x}$ and $y_2 = e^{-3x}$ are solutions of the equation $y'' - 9y = 0$. Show that the solutions are linearly independent on any interval I. Write the complete solution of $y'' - 9y = 0$.

7. The functions given by $y_1 = x$ and $y_2 = x^{-1}$ are solutions of $y'' + x^{-1} y' - x^{-2} y = 0$ on any interval I not including $x = 0$. Find $W(y_1, y_2)$ and write the complete solution of the differential equation on I.

8. Evaluate $W(y_1, y_2)$ where $y_1 = x^2$ and $y_2 = x^{-2}$.

9. Given $y_1 = 1 - 2 \sin^2 x$ and $y_2 = 3 \cos 2x$, find $W(y_1, y_2)$.

10. Given that $y_3 = c_1 y_1 + c_2 y_2$ defines the complete solution of (20.27) and that $Y = Y(x)$ defines a particular solution of (20.26), show that $y = y_3 + Y$ defines a solution of (20.26).

11. Find by inspection a particular solution of $y'' + 2y = 6x$.

12. Find by inspection a particular solution of $y'' + 3y = 6$.

13. Given that $y_1 = e^{4x}$ and $y_2 = x e^{4x}$ define solutions of $y'' - 8y' + 16y = 0$, show that y_1 and y_2 are linearly independent on any interval I. Write the complete solution of $y'' - 8y' + 16y = 0$.

14. Construct a second-order differential equation for which $y = e^{3x}$ defines a solution.

15. Given that $y_3 = c_1 + c_2 e^{-x}$ defines the complete solution of $y'' + y' = 0$ and that $Y = c^x$ defines a particular solution of $y'' + y' = 2e^x$, find the complete solution of $y'' + y' = 2e^x$.

16. The equation $y'' + 4y = 0$ has complete solution given by $y_3 = c_1 \sin 2t + c_2 \cos 2t$. If $Y = \cos 3t$ denotes a particular solution of $y'' + 4y = -5 \cos 3t$, find the solution denoted by $y = y(x)$ of $y'' + 4y = -5 \cos 3t$ satisfying $y(0) = 2$ and $y'(0) = 4$.

17. Show that $y_1 = x + 1$ defines a solution of $y'' - 4y' + y = x - 3$. Show also that

$y_2 = 3(x + 1)$ does not define a solution of the same differential equation. Does this result contradict Theorem 20-IV?

18. Show that $y_1 \equiv 4$ and $y_2 = \sqrt{x}$ define solutions of the equation $yy'' + (y')^2 = 0$ on $x > 0$. Show also that every linear combination $c_1 y_1 + c_2 y_2$ does not define a solution of the same equation on the same interval. Does this result contradict Theorem 20-IV?

19. Show that if the Wronskian of two functions is different from zero at every point of an interval I, then there is no point of I at which both functions are simultaneously zero.

20. Show that the Wronskian of the functions given by $y_1 = x^3$ and $y_2 = |x|^3$ is identically zero on $-1 \leqslant x \leqslant 1$ but that y_1 and y_2 are not linearly dependent on $-1 \leqslant x \leqslant 1$. Does this result contradict Theorem 20-V?

21. Let $y_1(x)$ and $y_2(x)$ denote two solutions of (20.27) on an interval I. Employ Theorem 20-V to show that if $y_1(x) = 0$ and $y_2(x) = 0$ have a common root in I, then y_1 and y_2 are linearly dependent on I. Show also that if $y_1 = y_1(x)$ and $y_2 = y_2(x)$ have maxima or minima at the same point x_0 of I, then y_1 and y_2 are linearly dependent on I.

22. Let $P(x)$ and $Q(x)$ in equation (20.27) be continuous on an interval $I(a < x < b)$. Let x_0 be a point of I and let $y_1(x)$ and $y_2(x)$ denote two solutions of (20.27). Show that $(dW/dx) + PW = 0$ has solution on I given by

$$W = W(x) = W(x_0) \exp \left(-\int_{x_0}^{x} P(t) \, dt \right)$$

where $W(x) = y_1 y_2' - y_2 y_1'$. This proves that on I the Wronskian of y_1 and y_2 is everywhere positive, everywhere negative, or identically zero.

23. Let $y_1 = y_1(x)$ and $y_2 = y_2(x)$ define two linearly independent solutions of $y'' + P(x)y' + Q(x)y = 0$ on an interval I. Show that if $y_1(a) = y_1(b) = 0$ are two consecutive zeros of $y_1(x)$ on I, then there is one and only one number c such that $a < c < b$ and $y_2(c) = 0$. This is Sturm's (1803–1855) separation theorem and is illustrated by $y_1 = \sin x$ and $y_2 = \cos x$, which define linearly independent solutions of $y'' + y = 0$. *Hints.* (i) Employ Theorem 20-V. (ii) Apply Rolle's theorem to

$$\phi(x) = \frac{y_1(x)}{y_2(x)} \qquad \text{on } a \leqslant x \leqslant b.$$

20.9   Homogeneous Second-Order Linear Equations with Constant Coefficients

We now consider the equation

$$y'' + ay' + by = 0, \tag{20.29}$$

which is the special case of (20.27) in which $P(x) \equiv a$ and $Q(x) \equiv b$.

Let us see if (20.29) has a solution given by the form $y = e^{rx}$, where r is constant. This trial solution is suggested by the fact that a first-order linear equation of the form $y' + ky = 0$ has a solution given by the form $y = e^{rx}$. Furthermore, the left member of (20.29) is a linear combination of y'', y', and y, so it is conceivable that a function whose derivatives are multiples of the function may satisfy (20.29).

Substituting $y = e^{rx}$ into (20.29), we obtain

$$r^2 e^{rx} + are^{rx} + be^{rx} = 0$$

or

$$e^{rx}(r^2 + ar + b) = 0.$$

Since e^{rx} is never zero, we conclude that $y = e^{rx}$ defines a solution of (20.29) if and only if r is a root of the equation

$$r^2 + ar + b = 0. \tag{20.30}$$

The quadratic equation (20.30) is termed the characteristic equation of equation (20.29). Now let us assume that the characteristic equation has two distinct real roots r_1 and r_2. Then $y_1 = e^{r_1 x}$ and $y_2 = e^{r_2 x}$ define solutions of (20.29). These solutions are linearly independent, since

$$W(y_1, y_2) = e^{r_1 x}(r_2 e^{r_2 x}) - e^{r_2 x}(r_1 e^{r_1 x})$$
$$= e^{(r_1 + r_2)x}(r_2 - r_1) \neq 0.$$

Hence, by Theorem 20-VI,

$$y = c_1 e^{r_1 x} + c_2 e^{r_2 x}$$

defines the complete solution of (20.29).

Example 1.   Find the complete solution of $y'' + 2y' - 15y = 0$.

Solution.   The characteristic equation $r^2 + 2r - 15 = 0$ has roots $r_1 = 3$ and $r_2 = -5$, and hence the differential equation has complete solution given by

$$y = c_1 e^{3x} + c_2 e^{-5x}.$$

Example 2.   Find the complete solution of $y'' - 2y' = 0$.

Solution.   The characteristic equation $r^2 - 2r = 0$ has roots $r_1 = 0$ and $r_2 = 2$, and hence the differential equation has complete solution given by

$$y = c_1 e^{0x} + c_2 e^{2x} \quad \text{or} \quad y = c_1 + c_2 e^{2x}.$$

If the roots r_1 and r_2 of the characteristic equation are real and equal, $y_1 = e^{r_1 x}$ defines a solution of (20.29), but we lack a second solution y_2 such that y_1 and y_2 are linearly independent. However, we note that the equation $y'' = 0$ is of this type, since it has characteristic equation $r^2 = 0$ with roots $r_1 = r_2 = 0$. But $y'' = 0$ is easily solved by integrating twice to obtain the solution given by

$$y = c_1 x + c_2(1).$$

This is the complete solution of $y'' = 0$, since the functions defined by $y_1 = x$ and $y_2 \equiv 1$ are linearly independent. (See Problem 5.)

Since $y_1 = xy_2$ in this particular example, it is natural to test to see if $y_2 = xe^{r_1 x}$ defines a solution of (20.29) when $r_1 = r_2$. It is easily verified that $y_2 = xe^{r_1 x}$ does define a solution of (20.29) and that $y_1 = e^{r_1 x}$ and $y_2 = xe^{r_1 x}$ are linearly independent. (See Problem 6.) Hence, when $r_1 = r_2$, equation (20.29) has complete solution given by

$$y = c_1 e^{r_1 x} + c_2 x e^{r_1 x}.$$

Example 3. Find the complete solution of $y'' - 8y' + 16y = 0$.

Solution. The characteristic equation $r^2 - 8r + 16 = 0$ has $r = 4$ as a repeated root. Hence the differential equation has complete solution given by

$$y = c_1 e^{4x} + c_2 x e^{4x}.$$

If the roots of the characteristic equation $r^2 + ar + b = 0$ are not real, then they must be complex conjugates, since a and b are real numbers. Let these complex roots be denoted by $r_1 = \alpha + i\beta$ and $r_2 = \alpha - i\beta$, where $i = \sqrt{-1}$ is the complex imaginary unit having the property that $i^2 = -1$.

Since $a = -(r_1 + r_2) = -2\alpha$ and $b = r_1 r_2 = \alpha^2 + \beta^2$, the characteristic equation can be written in the form

$$r^2 - 2\alpha r + (\alpha^2 + \beta^2) = 0.$$

If $\beta = 0$, $r = \alpha$ is a double root of the characteristic equation $r^2 - 2\alpha r + \alpha^2 = 0$, the differential equation being $y'' - 2\alpha y' + \alpha^2 y = 0$. We know that this equation has one solution given by $y = e^{\alpha x}$.

If $\alpha = 0$, $r^2 + \beta^2 = 0$ is the characteristic equation, the differential equation being $y'' + \beta^2 y = 0$. But it is seen by inspection that this equation has solutions given by $y_1 = \sin \beta x$ and $y_2 = \cos \beta x$.

These two special differential equations suggest that when α and β are both different from zero, we try f_1 and f_2, defined by $y_1 = f_1(x) = e^{\alpha x} \sin \beta x$ and $y_2 = f_2(x) = e^{\alpha x} \cos \beta x$ as solutions of (20.29). (See Problem 9.)

It is left as an exercise to show that the functions f_1 and f_2 are indeed solutions of (20.29) and that they are linearly independent functions. (See Problem 7.)

Hence, when $\beta \neq 0$, it follows from Theorem 20-VI that

$$y = c_1 e^{\alpha x} \sin \beta x + c_2 e^{\alpha x} \cos \beta x$$

or

$$y = e^{\alpha x}(c_1 \sin \beta x + c_2 \cos \beta x) \tag{20.31}$$

defines the complete solution of (20.29).

Example 4. Find the complete solution of $y'' - 4y' + 13y = 0$.

Solution. By the quadratic formula, the characteristic equation $r^2 - 4r + 13 = 0$ has roots $r_1 = 2 + 3i$ and $r_2 = 2 - 3i$. Hence the differential equation has complete solution given by

$$y = e^{2x}(c_1 \sin 3x + c_2 \cos 3x).$$

Example 5.   Find the solution of $y'' + 4y = 0$ for which $y = 0$ and $y' = 6$ when $x = 0$.

   Solution.   The characteristic equation $r^2 + 4 = 0$ has roots $r_1 = 0 + 2i$ and $r_2 = 0 - 2i$. The complete solution of $y'' + 4y = 0$ is given by

$$y = e^{0x}(c_1 \sin 2x + c_2 \cos 2x)$$

or

$$y = c_1 \sin 2x + c_2 \cos 2x.$$

Substituting $x = 0$ and $y = 0$, we find that $c_2 = 0$. Hence

$$y = c_1 \sin 2x \quad \text{and} \quad y' = 2c_1 \cos 2x.$$

Substituting $x = 0$ and $y' = 6$, we find that $c_1 = 3$. Hence the required particular solution is given by

$$y = 3 \sin 2x.$$

PROBLEM LIST 124

1. Find the complete solution of each of the following differential equations:

   (a) $y'' - 7y' + 12y = 0$.   (h) $16y'' - 8y' - 3y = 0$.

   (b) $y'' + y' - 6y = 0$.   (i) $y'' - 6y' + 9y = 0$.

   (c) $y'' + 7y' + 6y = 0$.   (j) $y'' + 4y' + 4y = 0$.

   (d) $y'' - 4y = 0$.   (k) $y'' + 25y = 0$.

   (e) $y'' - 9y' = 0$.   (l) $y'' - 6y' + 25y = 0$.

   (f) $y'' + 5y' = 0$.   (m) $y'' + 10y' + 29y = 0$.

   (g) $y'' - 4y' + y = 0$.   (n) $y'' + 2y' + 2y = 0$.

2. For each of the following differential equations find the particular solution which satisfies the given conditions.

   (a) $y'' = 0$; $y = 4$ and $y' = 3$ when $x = 0$.

   (b) $y'' - y = 0$; $y = 1$ and $y' = 3$ when $x = 0$.

   (c) $y'' + y' = 0$; $y = 5$ and $y' = 2$ when $x = 0$.

   (d) $y'' - 4y' + 4y = 0$; $y = 1$ when $x = 0$ and $y = 3e^2$ when $x = 1$.

   (e) $y'' - y' - 2y = 0$; $y = 1$ and $y' = 8$ when $x = 0$.

   (f) $y'' + 9y = 0$; $y = 5$ and $y' = 6$ when $x = 0$.

   (g) $y'' + 2y' + 2y = 0$; $y = 3$ and $y' = -3$ when $x = 0$.

3. Solve the equation $y' + 3y = 0$ by considering the characteristic equation $r + 3 = 0$.

4. Solve the equation $y' - 5y = 0$ by considering the characteristic equation $r - 5 = 0$.

5. Show that the solutions of $y'' = 0$ given by $y_1 = x$ and $y_2 = 1$ are linearly independent.

6. Show that if r_1 is a double root of $r^2 + ar + b = 0$, then $y_1 = e^{r_1 x}$ and $y_2 = xe^{r_1 x}$

both define solutions of $y'' + ay' + by = 0$. Show also that the solutions y_1 and y_2 are linearly independent.

7. Show that if $\alpha \pm i\beta$ are complex conjugate roots of $r^2 + ar + b = 0$, then $y_1 = e^{\alpha x}$ sin βx and $y_2 = e^{\alpha x}$ cos βx both define solutions of $y'' + ay' + by = 0$. Show also that y_1 and y_2 are linearly independent.

8. Solve the equation $y'' + \omega^2 y = 0$ by letting $v = y'$ and writing

$$y'' = \frac{d^2y}{dx^2} = \frac{dv}{dx}$$

in the form $v(dv/dy)$.

9. Evaluate

    (a) $\lim\limits_{\alpha \to 0} e^{\alpha x}(c_1 \sin \beta x + c_2 \cos \beta x)$;

    (b) $\lim\limits_{\beta \to 0} e^{\alpha x}(c_1 \sin \beta x + c_2 \cos \beta x)$.

10. Show that the complete solution of $y'' + \omega^2 y = 0$ can be denoted by $y = A$ sin $(\omega x + \alpha)$ or by $y = B \cos (\omega x + \theta)$, where A, B, α, and θ denote arbitrary constants.

11. The functions defined by $y_1 = e^{r_1 x}$ and $y_2 = e^{r_2 x}$ are solutions of the equation $y'' - (r_1 + r_2)y' + r_1 r_2 y = 0$. Show that the function defined by

$$y_3 = \lim_{r_1 \to r_2} \frac{e^{r_2 x} - e^{r_1 x}}{r_2 - r_1}$$

is a solution of the equation $y'' - 2r_2 y' + r_2^2 y = 0$.

12. Let y_1 and y_2 define linearly independent solutions of the constant coefficient equation $y'' + ay' + by = 0$. Show that the Wronskian W of y_1 and y_2 is constant if and only if $a = 0$. *Hint*. Consider dW/dx.

20.10   *Nonhomogeneous Second-Order Equations*

Equation (20.29) is the reduced equation associated with equation

$$y'' + ay' + by = R(x), \tag{20.32}$$

which is the special case of equation (20.26) with $P(x) \equiv a$ and $Q(x) \equiv b$.

It is shown in Ref. 20.4 that a particular solution given by $Y = Y(x)$ of (20.32) can always be found whenever the general solution of the reduced equation (20.29) is known. In many simple cases a particular solution of (20.32) can be found by the method of undetermined coefficients. In this method we assume $Y = Y(x)$ to be a linear combination of $R(x)$ and its independent derivatives. The method will be illustrated by examples.

Example 1.   Find a particular solution of $y'' - y' - 2y = 8e^{3x}$.

Solution.   Since all derivatives of $8e^{3x}$ are of the form Ae^{3x}, we try $Y = Ae^{3x}$.

Substitution into the differential equation yields

$$9Ae^{3x} - 3Ae^{3x} - 2Ae^{3x} = 8e^{3x}.$$

Dividing by e^{3x} we obtain $4A = 8$ or $A = 2$. It is easily shown that $Y = 2e^{3x}$ defines a particular solution of $y'' - y' - 2y = 8e^{3x}$.

Example 2.   Find a particular solution of

$$y'' - 7y' + 12y = 12x^2 + 10x - 11.$$

Solution.   Trying $Y = Ax^2 + Bx + C$ yields

$$(2A) - 7(2Ax + B) + 12(Ax^2 + Bx + C) = 12x^2 + 10x - 11.$$

Equating the coefficients of like powers of x, we obtain the equations

$$2A - 7B + 12C = -11$$
$$-14A + 12B \qquad = 10$$
$$12A \qquad\qquad = 12 \ .$$

From these equations we find that $A = 1$, $B = 2$, and $C = 1/12$. It is easily shown that $Y = x^2 + 2x + (1/12)$ defines a particular solution.

Example 3.   Find a particular solution of $y'' + 2y' = 80 \sin 4x$.

Solution.   Trying $Y = A \sin 4x + B \cos 4x$ yields

$$(-16A \sin 4x - 16B \cos 4x)$$
$$+ 2(4A \cos 4x - 4B \sin 4x) = 80 \sin 4x.$$

Setting $4x = 0$ and then $4x = \pi/2$ yields the equations

$$-16B + 8A = 0,$$
$$-16A - 8B = 80,$$

from which we obtain $A = -4$ and $B = -2$.

It is easily shown that $Y = -4 \sin 4x - 2 \cos 4x$ defines a particular solution of the given equation.

If the suggested trial solution is part of the complete solution of the reduced equation, the usual trial solution will not yield a particular solution of (20.32), since it will produce zero rather than $R(x)$ when substituted into the left member. In this case we try the usual trial solution multiplied by x.

Example 4.   Find a particular solution of $y'' - 3y' = 2e^{3x}$.

Solution.   Since $Y = Ae^{3x}$ is part of the complete solution

$$y = c_1 + c_2e^{3x} \qquad \text{of} \qquad y'' - 3y' = 0,$$

the given equation cannot have a solution of the form $Y = Ae^{3x}$. Hence we try $Y = Axe^{3x}$. Then

$$Y' = 3Axe^{3x} + Ae^{3x}$$

and $$Y'' = 9Axe^{3x} + 3Ae^{3x} + 3Ae^{3x}.$$

Substituting into $y'' - 3y' = 2e^{3x}$, we obtain

$$(9Axe^{3x} + 6Ae^{3x}) - 3(3Axe^{3x} + Ae^{3x}) = 2e^{3x},$$

and upon setting $x = 0$, we find that $A = 2/3$. We then verify that $Y = (2/3)xe^{3x}$ defines a particular solution of $y'' - 3y' = 2e^{3x}$.

Example 5.   Find the complete solution of $y'' - y' - 2y = 8e^{3x}$.

Solution.   From $r^2 - r - 2 = 0$, we obtain $r_1 = 2$ and $r_2 = -1$. Hence the complete solution of the reduced equation is given by $y_c = c_1e^{2x} + c_2e^{-x}$, often termed the complementary function. In Example 1 the given equation was found to possess the particular solution given by $Y = 2e^{3x}$. Hence, by Theorem 20-VII, $y = c_1e^{2x} + c_2e^{-x} + 2e^{3x}$ defines the required complete solution.

———

Example 6.   Find the solution of $y'' - 3y' = 2e^{3x}$ satisfying the conditions $y = 1$ and $y' = 3$ when $x = 0$.

Solution.   It follows from Example 4 that the given equation has complete solution given by

$$y = c_1 + c_2e^{3x} + \frac{2}{3}xe^{3x}.$$

Differentiating,

$$y' = 3c_2e^{3x} + 2xe^{3x} + \frac{2}{3}e^{3x}.$$

Employing the given conditions, we obtain the equations

$$1 = c_1 + c_2; \qquad 3 = 3c_2 + \frac{2}{3},$$

and hence $c_2 = 7/9$ and $c_1 = 2/9$. Thus the required solution is given by

$$y = \frac{2}{9} + \frac{7}{9}e^{3x} + \frac{2}{3}xe^{3x}.$$

PROBLEM LIST 125

1. Find a particular solution of
   (a) $y'' + 5y' - 4y = 6e^x$;
   (b) $y'' + 4y' + 2y = 5e^{-x}$;
   (c) $y'' - y' + 3y = 8e^{2x}$;
   (d) $y'' + 3y' + 4y = 12x^2 - 6x - 8$;

(e) $y'' - y' + 2y = 8x^2 - 10$;

(f) $y'' - 6y' + y = 24 \sin x$;

(g) $y'' + 2y' + 10y = 2 \sin 2x + 10 \cos 2x$;

(h) $y'' + y' + 4y = 12e^x + 4x^2 + 2x + 2$;

(i) $y'' - 2y' = 5e^{2x}$;

(j) $y'' + y = 3 \sin x$.

2. Find the complete solution of

(a) $y'' - y' - 2y = 8e^x$;

(b) $y'' + 4y = 26e^{3x}$;

(c) $y'' - 9y = 6x^2 + 4x$;

(d) $y'' + y = 9 \sin 2x$;

(e) $y'' + 4y' + 13y = -3 \sin 4x + 16 \cos 4x$;

(f) $y'' - y = e^{-x}$;

(g) $y'' - y = 6e^x$;

(h) $y'' + y = 4 \sin x$.

3. For each equation find the solution satisfying the given conditions.

(a) $y'' - 2y' = e^{3x}$; $y = 4/3$ and $y' = 5$ when $x = 0$.

(b) $y'' + y = 20e^{-3x}$; $y = 2$ and $y' = -2$ when $x = 0$.

(c) $y'' + y' = x^2 + 2x + 1$; $y = 1$ when $x = 0$ and $y = 12 + e^{-3}$ when $x = 3$.

(d) $y'' - 4y' + 3y = e^{2x}$; $y = 0$ and $y' = 0$ when $x = 0$.

(e) $y'' + y = 2x$; $y = 1$ and $y' = 2$ when $x = 0$.

(f) $y'' + 16y = 32 \sin 4x$; $y = 0$ and $y' = 0$ when $x = 0$.

4. Show that $y = xe^{kx}$ defines a solution of $y'' - 2ky' + k^2y = 0$.

5. Find a second-order differential equation having solution defined by $y = c_1e^x + c_2e^{-2x}$.

6. Find a second-order differential equation having solution defined by $y = c_1 \sin x + c_2 \cos x + e^x$.

7. The number k is a repeated root of the characteristic equation of $y'' - 2ky' + k^2y = 0$, and hence $y = e^{kx}$ defines a solution. Find a second solution given by the form $y = \phi(x)e^{kx}$.

8. Find three solutions y_1, y_2, and y_3 of $y''' - 6y'' + 11y' - 6y = 0$ by considering the characteristic equation $r^3 - 6r^2 + 11r - 6 = 0$. The complete solution is given by a linear combination of y_1, y_2, and y_3.

9. Solve the equation $xy'' - 4y' = x^6$ by letting $u = y'$.

10. The equation

$$a_0x^ny^{(n)} + a_1x^{n-1}y^{(n-1)} + \cdots + a_{n-1}xy' + a_ny = 0$$

is known as Euler's equation. Show that the substitution $x = e^u$ transforms Euler's equation into a linear equation with constant coefficients. Solve the equation $x^2y'' + xy' + y = 0$.

20.11 Applications of Second-Order Equations

Rectilinear Motion

In Fig. 20.3, a small block of mass m is attached to the end of a spring. The block is pulled to the right, stretching the spring x_0 inches, and is then released from rest (with initial velocity zero).

According to Hooke's law, named after the English experimental scientist Robert Hooke (1635–1703), the force that stretches or compresses the spring is proportional to the change in length of the spring. If f denotes the force in pounds exerted by the spring on the block when the block is x feet from the origin, then $f = kx$, $k > 0$ being known as the spring constant. The force of f pounds is called a restoring force, since it always acts toward the origin and tends to restore the block to its original (or equilibrium) position. Note that $kx > 0$ when $x > 0$, $kx = 0$ when $x = 0$, and $kx < 0$ for $x < 0$.

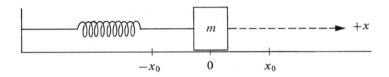

Figure 20.3

By Newton's second law, the unbalanced force acting on the block in the x direction equals the mass of the block times its acceleration in the x direction. Since the unbalanced force in the x direction has value $-kx$ (regardless of whether x is positive, negative, or zero),

$$m\frac{d^2x}{dt^2} = -kx.$$

The mass m is measured in slugs and is obtained by dividing the weight W of the block in pounds by g, the acceleration of gravity in feet per second per second. That is, $m = W/g$. In numerical work we will use the approximation $g \cong 32$ ft/sec².

The differential equation governing the motion of the block can now be written in the form

$$\frac{d^2x}{dt^2} + \frac{kg}{W}x = 0. \tag{20.33}$$

This is a linear equation with constant coefficients. The characteristic equation $r^2 + (kg/W) = 0$ has roots $\pm i\sqrt{kg/W}$ and equation (20.33) has complete solution given by

$$x = c_1 \sin\sqrt{\frac{kg}{W}}\,t + c_2 \cos\sqrt{\frac{kg}{W}}\,t. \tag{20.34}$$

Substituting $t = 0$ and $x = x_0$, we obtain $c_2 = x_0$.

Differentiation of (20.34) with respect to t yields

$$v = \frac{dx}{dt} = c_1 \sqrt{\frac{kg}{W}} \cos \sqrt{\frac{kg}{W}} t$$

$$- c_2 \sqrt{\frac{kg}{W}} \sin \sqrt{\frac{kg}{W}} t. \tag{20.35}$$

Substituting $v = 0$ and $t = 0$, we obtain $c_1 = 0$. Hence the particular solution of (20.33) satisfying the initial conditions we have set is given by

$$x = x_0 \cos \sqrt{\frac{kg}{W}} t. \tag{20.36}$$

Equation (20.36) reveals that the block moves forever back and forth between the points $x = x_0$ and $x = -x_0$. The motion is said to be simply harmonic, and (20.33) is termed the differential equation of a simple harmonic motion. The maximum distance x_0 of the block from the origin is called the amplitude of the motion. The time required for the block to go from $x = x_0$ to $x = -x_0$ and back again is called the period of the motion. It is equal to the period of the periodic function given by

$$f(t) = \cos \sqrt{\frac{kg}{W}} t$$

and has value

$$T = \frac{2\pi}{\sqrt{kg/W}} = 2\pi \sqrt{\frac{W}{kg}} \qquad \text{seconds.} \tag{20.37}$$

The reciprocal of T denotes the number of complete oscillations of the block per second and is called the frequency of the motion.

Example 1.   Assume that the spring of Fig. 20.3 is stretched 1 in. by a force of 12 lb. If the block weighs 2 lb and is released from rest at $x = 3$ in., find the amplitude and period of the resulting motion.

Solution.   Letting $f = 12$ and $s = 1/12$ in $f = ks$, we find that $k = 144$. The differential equation (20.33) becomes

$$\frac{d^2 x}{dt^2} + \frac{(144)(32)}{2} x = 0.$$

Since $x = 1/4$ ft and $v = 0$ when $t = 0$, the solution is given by (20.36), which reduces to

$$x = \frac{1}{4} \cos 48t.$$

The motion has amplitude 1/4 ft and period $2\pi/48 \doteq 0.13$ scc. The graph in Fig. 20.4 shows how the displacement x varies with the time t during one period of the motion.

We next assume that the block of Fig. 20.3 is acted upon by a force of friction which opposes the motion. In many applications, sufficiently accurate results are obtained by assuming that the magnitude of the resisting force is proportional to

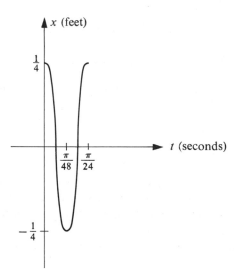

Figure 20.4

the speed. That is, the resistance is given by $-c(dx/dt)$, where $c > 0$. Note that when the block moves to the right ($dx/dt > 0$), the resistance acts to the left, and when the block moves to the left ($dx/dt < 0$), the resistance acts to the right.

Applying Newton's second law we now obtain

$$m\frac{d^2x}{dt^2} = -kx - c\frac{dx}{dt},$$

or

$$\frac{d^2x}{dt^2} + \frac{cg}{W}\frac{dx}{dt} + \frac{kg}{W}x = 0 \qquad (20.38)$$

as the differential equation governing the motion. The character of the motion is determined by the nature of the roots of the characteristic equation of (20.38). If these roots are real and unequal the motion is said to be overdamped. The resistance is sufficient to prevent the block from oscillating. If the roots are real and equal the motion is said to be critically damped. Again no oscillation takes place. Finally, if the roots are conjugate complex numbers the motion is said to be underdamped. In this case the block oscillates, but the motion tends to die out as $t \rightarrow \infty$. The different possibilities will be illustrated by examples.

Example 2.   The block in Fig. 20.3 weighs 32 lb, the spring constant $k = 36$ lb/ft, and the resistance coefficient $c = 13$. Determine the resulting motion if $x = 1/2$ ft and $v = 0$ fps when $t = 0$.

Solution.   Equation (20.38) becomes

$$\frac{d^2x}{dt^2} + 13\frac{dx}{dt} + 36x = 0.$$

The characteristic equation $r^2 + 13r + 36 = 0$ has roots -4 and -9, and hence the differential equation has complete solution

$$x = c_1 e^{-4t} + c_2 e^{-9t}. \tag{20.39}$$

The velocity $v = dx/dt$ is given by

$$v = -4c_1 e^{-4t} - 9c_2 e^{-9t}. \tag{20.40}$$

Substituting $x = 1/2$ and $t = 0$ into (20.39) and $v = 0$ and $t = 0$ into (20.40), we find that $c_1 = 9/10$ and $c_2 = -(4/10)$. Thus the displacement x is given by

$$x = \frac{9e^{-4t} - 4e^{-9t}}{10}$$

$$= \frac{e^{-4t}}{10}(9 - 4e^{-5t}).$$

It is easily seen that x is never zero and that $x \to 0$ as $t \to \infty$. The motion is overdamped and the displacement-time curve is shown in Fig. 20.5.

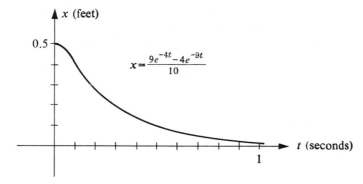

Figure 20.5

Example 3.   Solve Example 2 if $c = 12$ instead of 13.

Solution.   The characteristic equation $r^2 + 12r + 36 = 0$ has a repeated root $r = -6$. The differential equation has complete solution given by

$$x = e^{-6t}(c_1 + c_2 t).$$

Setting $x = 1/2$ and $t = 0$, we find that $c_1 = 1/2$.
Substituting $v = 0$ and $t = 0$ into $v = e^{-6t}(c_2 - 3 - 6c_2 t)$, we find that $c_2 = 3$. The displacement x is given by

$$x = e^{-6t}\left(\frac{1}{2} + 3t\right)$$

and the displacement-time curve is similar to that of Fig. 20.5. The motion is critically damped.

Example 4.   Solve Example 2 if $c = 8$ instead of 13.

Solution.   The characteristic equation $r^2 + 8r + 36 = 0$ has roots $-4 \pm$

$2\sqrt{5}\ i$. The differential equation has complete solution given by

$$x = e^{-4t}(c_1 \sin 2\sqrt{5}\,t + c_2 \cos 2\sqrt{5}\,t).$$

Setting $x = 1/2$ and $t = 0$ we find that $c_2 = 1/2$.
Substituting $v = 0$ and $t = 0$ into

$$v = e^{-4t}(2\sqrt{5}\,c_1 \cos 2\sqrt{5}\,t - \sqrt{5}\,\sin 2\sqrt{5}\,t)$$

$$-4e^{-4t}\left(c_1 \sin 2\sqrt{5}\,t + \frac{1}{2}\cos 2\sqrt{5}\,t\right)$$

we find that $c_1 = 1/\sqrt{5}$. The displacement x is given by

$$x = e^{-4t}\left(\frac{1}{\sqrt{5}}\sin 2\sqrt{5}\,t + \frac{1}{2}\cos 2\sqrt{5}\,t\right).$$

The motion is underdamped; the factor e^{-4t} is termed the damping factor and the factor

$$\frac{1}{\sqrt{5}}\sin 2\sqrt{5}\,t + \frac{1}{2}\cos 2\sqrt{5}\,t$$

is termed the harmonic factor. Figure 20.6 shows the displacement-time curve, which is drawn by first sketching the dotted curves $f(t) = \pm e^{-4t}$, observing that the height of the displacement curve is numerically equal to the value of the damping factor when the harmonic factor is numerically

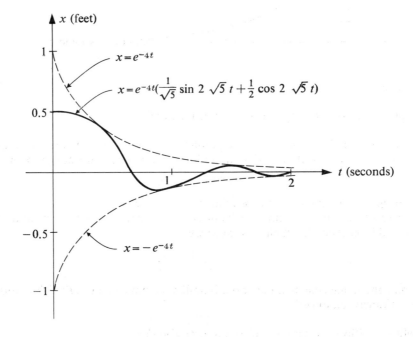

Figure 20.6

equal to 1, and is zero when the harmonic factor has value zero. It is also helpful to write

$$x = e^{-4t}\left(\frac{1}{\sqrt{5}} \sin 2\sqrt{5}\,t + \frac{1}{2} \cos 2\sqrt{5}\,t\right)$$

in the form

$$x = 0.3\sqrt{5}\,e^{-4t} \sin (2\sqrt{5}\,t + \phi),$$

where $\cos \phi = 2/3$ and $\sin \phi = \sqrt{5}/3$.

We now assume that the block of Fig. 20.3 is acted upon by an external force in the x-direction, which we denote by $F(t)$. In many applications $F(t)$ is periodic in nature and has the form $F_0 \sin \omega t$ or $F_0 \cos \omega t$, where F_0 and ω are constant. The function F is called the forcing function and $F(t)$ is called the driving, or impressed, force. The differential equation governing the motion becomes

$$\frac{W}{g}\frac{d^2x}{dt^2} + c\frac{dx}{dt} + kx = F(t). \tag{20.41}$$

Example 5.   Solve Example 4 if an impressed force $F(t) = 72 \cos 6t$ acts upon the block.

Solution.   The motion is governed by the differential equation

$$\frac{d^2x}{dt^2} + 8\frac{dx}{dt} + 36x = 72 \cos 6t.$$

We try a particular solution given by the form $x_p = A \sin 6t + B \cos 6t$ and find by the method of undetermined coefficients that $B = 0$ and $A = 3/2$. The displacement x is given by

$$x = e^{-4t}(C_1 \sin 2\sqrt{5}\,t + C_2 \cos 2\sqrt{5}\,t) + \frac{3}{2} \sin 6t.$$

Differentiating to find v, and then employing the initial conditions, we find that $C_1 = -7/(2\sqrt{5})$ and $C_2 = 1/2$.

The terms in the solution which involve e^{-4t} have appreciable effect upon the motion only for small values of t, since they contribute very little to the value of x when t is large. These terms are called the transient solution. The remaining term $(3/2) \sin 6t$ is called the steady-state solution because it gives the displacement (approximately) for large values of t. The steady-state solution is periodic and has the same period as the impressed external force. The motion is approximately a simple harmonic motion of period $\pi/3$ and amplitude $3/2$.

Example 6.   The block in Fig. 20.7 weighs W pounds. When it is held at rest by the spring its position is termed the equilibrium position. Find its displacement in terms of the time t if it is pulled x_0 feet below the equilibrium position and released from rest.

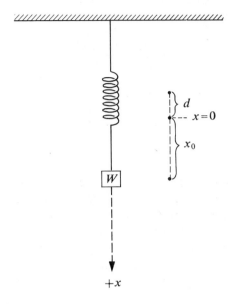

Figure 20.7

Solution.   Let x denote the displacement of the block, measured positive downward from the equilibrium position. If d denotes the stretch in the spring when the block is in the equilibrium position ($x = 0$), and k denotes the spring constant, then from Hooke's law,

$$W = kd.$$

When the block is x feet from the equilibrium position, the spring exerts a force of $-k(d + x) = -kd - kx = -W - kx$ pounds in the x direction. Since the earth pulls on the block with a force of W pounds, from Newton's second law we have

$$\frac{W}{g} \frac{d^2x}{dt^2} = W + (-W - kx)$$

or

$$\frac{d^2x}{dt^2} + \frac{kg}{W}x = 0.$$

Making use of the initial conditions $x = x_0$ and $dx/dt = 0$ when $t = 0$, we find that the displacement x is given by

$$x = x_0 \cos \sqrt{\frac{kg}{W}} t.$$

The block undergoes a simple harmonic motion about the point $x = 0$. The simplicity of the differential equation is due to the fact that the displacement is measured from the equilibrium position.

Electric Circuits

By applying Kirchhoff's laws to electric circuits it is shown (see Ref. 20.6) that the charge q in coulombs and the current i in amperes satisfy the differential equations

$$L\frac{d^2q}{dt^2} + R\frac{dq}{dt} + \frac{1}{C}q = E(t) \tag{20.42}$$

and

$$L\frac{d^2i}{dt^2} + R\frac{di}{dt} + \frac{1}{C}i = \frac{d}{dt}E(t). \tag{20.43}$$

Such a circuit is depicted in Fig. 20.8, in which L denotes the inductance in henrys, R the resistance in ohms, C the capacitance in farads, and $E(t)$ the impressed voltage in volts. It is assumed that L, R, and C are constants and that t it measured in seconds. The current i is given by

$$i(t) = \frac{dq(t)}{dt}.$$

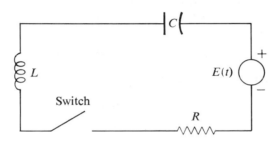

Figure 20.8

Comparing equation (20.42) with equation (20.41) we note the correspondences

$$\text{Mass } m = \frac{W}{g} \longleftrightarrow \text{inductance } L,$$

$$\text{Friction constant } c \longleftrightarrow \text{resistance } R,$$

$$\text{Spring constant } k \longleftrightarrow \text{inverse capacitance } \frac{1}{C},$$

$$\text{Impressed force } F \longleftrightarrow \text{impressed voltage } E,$$

$$\text{Displacement } x \longleftrightarrow \text{charge } q,$$

$$\text{Velocity } v = \frac{dx}{dt} \longleftrightarrow \text{current } i = \frac{dq}{dt}.$$

This analogy also prevails in more complicated circuits, and consequently makes it possible to study certain mechanical systems by building and studying their electrical analogs. It is another of the many instances in which the same mathematical model or theory can be employed to describe more than one concrete application. This illustrates one of the advantages of the tendency of modern mathematics toward abstraction; an abstract mathematical theory often unifies the study of several diverse phenomena whose underlying similarities are not always readily apparent.

Example 7. A circuit of the type shown in Fig. 20.8 consists of an inductor of 1 henry, a resistor of 12 ohms, a capacitor of 0.01 farad, and a generator having voltage given by $E(t) = 24 \sin 10t$. Find the charge q and the current i at time t if $q = 0$ and $i = 0$ when $t = 0$.

Solution.   Equation (20.42) becomes

$$\frac{d^2q}{dt^2} + 12\frac{dq}{dt} + 100q = 24 \sin 10t. \qquad (20.44)$$

The characteristic equation $r^2 + 12r + 100 = 0$ has roots $-6 \pm 8i$ and hence the complementary function (solution of the reduced equation) is given by

$$q_c = e^{-6t}(c_1 \cos 8t + c_2 \sin 8t).$$

Trying a particular solution given by the form $q_p = A \cos 10t + B \sin 10t$ in (20.44), we determine that $A = -1/5$ and $B = 0$. The complete solution of (20.44) is given by

$$q = e^{-6t}(c_1 \cos 8t + c_2 \sin 8t) - \frac{1}{5} \cos 10t.$$

Differentiation with respect to t yields

$$\frac{dq}{dt} = i = e^{-6t}(-8c_1 \sin 8t + 8c_2 \cos 8t)$$
$$- 6e^{-6t}(c_1 \cos 8t + c_2 \sin 8t) + 2 \sin 10t.$$

Substituting $t = 0$ and $q = 0$ in the first equation and $t = 0$ and $i = 0$ in the second equation, we find that $c_1 = 1/5$ and $c_2 = 3/20$. Hence the charge q is given by

$$q(t) = \frac{e^{-6t}}{20}(4 \cos 8t + 3 \sin 8t) - \frac{1}{5} \cos 10t,$$

and the current $i = dq/dt$ by

$$i(t) = \frac{-5e^{-6t}}{2} \sin 8t + 2 \sin 10t.$$

The transient current, given by $i_t = (-5/2)e^{-6t} \sin 8t$, is determined by the initial conditions and becomes negligible soon after $t = 0$. The steady-state current, given by $i_s = 2 \sin 10t$, approximates the actual current when the transient current becomes negligible.

The Simple Pendulum

A simple pendulum consists of a particle of weight W supported by a straight rod or piece of string of length l. The particle is free to oscillate in a vertical plane, the mass of the particle is assumed to be concentrated at a point, and the weight of the rod is assumed to be negligible. See Fig. 20.9.

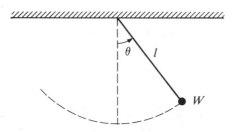

Figure 20.9

By applying Newton's second law it is shown (see Ref. 20.5) that the angular displacement θ satisfies the differential equation

$$\frac{d^2\theta}{dt^2} + \frac{g}{l} \sin \theta = 0. \tag{20.45}$$

Equation (20.45) is nonlinear and cannot be solved by the methods at our disposal. However, we know that for small values of θ (say, in the interval $-\pi/36 \leqslant \theta \leqslant \pi/36$), θ and $\sin \theta$ have approximately the same value. This suggests that we replace $\sin \theta$ by θ in (20.45) to obtain

$$\frac{d^2\theta}{dt^2} + \frac{g}{l}\theta = 0. \tag{20.46}$$

We assume that θ is measured in radians, t in seconds, g in feet per second per second, and l in feet. If the pendulum is displaced so that the rod makes an angle of θ_0 radians with the vertical when released from rest, initial conditions are

$$\theta = \theta_0 \quad \text{and} \quad \frac{d\theta}{dt} = 0 \quad \text{when } t = 0.$$

Now let θ_1, defined by $\theta_1(t) = f_1(t)$, denote the solution of (20.45) which satisfies the given initial conditions. We state without proof that such a unique solution exists. Also let θ_2, defined by $\theta_2(t) = f_2(t)$, denote the unique solution of (20.46) which satisfies the same initial conditions. It is far from obvious that $\theta_2(t)$ yields an approximation to $\theta_1(t)$ even though θ_0 is small. For a discussion of the truth of this statement see Ref. 20.1. Equation (20.46) is called a linearization of equation (20.45).

Since (20.46) is the differential equation of a simple harmonic motion, it is clear that θ_2 is given by

$$\theta_2(t) = \theta_0 \cos \sqrt{\frac{g}{l}}\, t.$$

The period T of the motion is the time in seconds required for θ to change from θ_0 to $-\theta_0$ and back to θ_0, and is given by

$$T = 2\pi \sqrt{\frac{l}{g}}.$$

This formula is approximately true for small oscillations and is frequently employed in elementary physics. It is interesting to note that the period is independent of the initial conditions.

PROBLEM LIST 126

Note. Use $g = 32$.

Figure 20.10

1. The block in Fig. 20.10 weighs 3 lb and the spring constant $k = 150$ lb/ft. The block is pulled 4 in. to the right of the equilibrium position ($x = 0$) and released from rest. Find the acceleration, velocity, and displacement at time t and determine the period and amplitude of the motion. Neglect friction.

2. The block in Fig. 20.10 weighs 2 lb and the spring constant $k = 16$ lb/ft. The block is given an initial velocity of 48 fps at the equilibrium position ($x = 0$). Find the displacement and velocity at time t, the velocity at $t = \pi/48$ seconds, and the amplitude and frequency of the motion. Neglect friction.

3. The block in Fig. 20.10 weighs 2 lb and the spring constant $k = 144$ lb/ft. After being pulled 6 in. to the right the block is given an initial velocity of -12 fps. Find the displacement and velocity at time t, the maximum speed, and the period and amplitude of the motion. Neglect friction.

4. The block in Fig. 20.10 will be stretched 6 in. by a force of 81 lb. If the block weighs 1 lb and is given an initial velocity of 12 fps at $x = 0$, determine how far to the right the block will move. Neglect friction.

5. A particle moves around a circle at constant speed. Prove that the projection of the particle onto a diameter of the circle undergoes a simple harmonic motion.

6. The block in Fig. 20.10 weighs 16 lb, the spring constant $k = 36$ lb/ft, and the resistance coefficient $c = 9$. If the block is pulled 4 in. to the right and released from rest, find the displacement and velocity at time t. Draw the displacement-time curve for the motion.

7. Solve Problem 6 if $k = 32$ and $c = 8$.

8. The motion of a particle is governed by equation (20.38). Show that if the motion is either overdamped or critically damped, the particle will not be located at the origin ($x = 0$) for more than one value of t.

9. Solve Problem 6 if $c = 6$.

10. The block in Fig. 20.10 weighs 32 lb, the spring constant $k = 16$ lb/ft, the resistance coefficient $c = 2$, and the block is acted upon by an external impressed force given by $F(t) = 96 \cos 4t$. If $x = 1/2$ ft and $v = 0$ fps when $t = 0$ sec, find the displacement and velocity at time t.

11. A particle moves along the x-axis. At time $t = 0$ sec the particle is at the origin and
     has velocity $dx/dt = 3$ fps. Find the displacement and velocity at $t = \pi/6$ seconds
     if its motion is governed by the differential equation

$$\frac{d^2x}{dt^2} + 2\frac{dx}{dt} + 4x = 0.$$

12. The block in Fig. 20.11 weighs 32 lb and the spring constant $k = 25$ lb/ft. The block
     is pulled down 3 in. below the equilibrium position ($x = 0$) and released from rest.
     Find the displacement and velocity at time t and determine the period of the motion.
     Neglect friction.

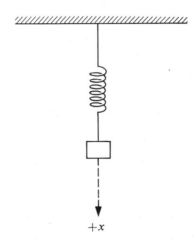

$+x$

Figure 20.11

13. Solve Problem 12 if the block is given an initial velocity of -5 fps instead of being
     released from rest. Find the amplitude of the motion and the maximum speed of
     the block.

14. If friction is neglected, the vertical motion of a certain buoy is governed by the
     differential equation

$$\frac{d^2y}{dt^2} + 400y = 0.$$

     Find the period of the motion.

15. The circuit in Fig. 20.8 consists of an inductor of L henrys, a resistor of R ohms,
     a capacitor of C farads, and a generator whose voltage at time t seconds is given by
     $E(t)$. Find the charge q (in coulombs) and the current i (in amperes) at time t seconds.
     In each case assume that $q = 0$ and $i = 0$ at $t = 0$.

     (a) $L = 1$, $R = 6$, $C = 0.01$, $E(t) = 100$.
     (b) $L = 0.5$, $R = 5$, $C = 0.005$, $E(t) = 100 \sin 20t$.
     (c) $L = 2$, $R = 8$, $C = 1/1250$, $E(t) = 200 \cos 25t$.

16. Show that the charge q and the current i satisfying equations (20.42) and (20.43)
     will be oscillatory if $R < 2\sqrt{L/C}$.

17. Given that the charge q satisfies

$$L\frac{d^2q}{dt^2} + R\frac{dq}{dt} + \frac{1}{C}q = 0$$

and that $q = q_0$ and $i = dq/dt = 0$ at $t = 0$, find q and i at time t.

18. Solve the equation

$$\frac{d^2x}{dt^2} + \omega^2 x = k \sin \omega t.$$

Observe that the impressed force has the same period $2\pi/\omega$ as the natural motion (motion with no impressed force). Note also that the amplitude of the term in the solution corresponding to the impressed force becomes infinite with t. This phenomenon is called resonance and can be both useful and harmful in mechanical and electrical systems.

19. Find the period of a simple pendulum whose rod has length (a) $l = 4$ in., (b) $l = 16$ in. Assume that the oscillations are small.

20. A simple pendulum undergoing small oscillations has a period T of (a) 1 sec, (b) 2 sec. Find the length l of the pendulum rod in each case.

21. Given that the angular displacement θ of a simple pendulum satisfies the equation

$$\frac{d^2\theta}{dt^2} + \frac{g}{l}\sin\theta = 0,$$

show that if $\theta = \theta_0$ and $\omega = d\theta/dt = 0$ at time $t = 0$, then

$$\omega = \frac{d\theta}{dt} = \pm\left[\frac{2g}{l}(\cos\theta - \cos\theta_0)\right]^{1/2}. \qquad (20.47)$$

Equation (20.47) is called a first integral of the given differential equation.

22. A simple pendulum whose rod has length $l = 2$ ft is released from rest with initial angular displacement $\theta_0 = \pi/3$ radians. Find the speed of the pendulum when it passes its lowest position ($\theta = 0$).

23. A substance is produced inside a spherical living cell of radius r at a rate proportional to the concentration c of the dissolved substance. In a mathematical model describing this situation, the function f given by $c = f(r)$ satisfies the differential equation

$$D\left(\frac{d^2c}{dr^2} + \frac{2}{r}\frac{dc}{dr}\right) + kc = 0,$$

where $k > 0$ is the constant of proportionality and D is a positive constant known as the coefficient of diffusion. The concentration c is measured in grams per cubic centimeter and r is measured in centimeters. Show that

$$c = \frac{A\sin(\sqrt{k/D})r}{r} + \frac{B\cos(\sqrt{k/D})r}{r}$$

where A and B are arbitrary constants. *Hint.* Let $c = x/r$.

REFERENCES

20.1 R. P. AGNEW, *Differential Equations*, McGraw-Hill, New York, 1942.

20.2 R. E. GASKELL, *Engineering Mathematics*, The Dryden Press, New York, 1958.

20.3 M. GOLOMB and M. SHANKS, *Elements of Ordinary Differential Equations*, McGraw-Hill, New York, 1965.

20.4 W. KAPLAN, *Ordinary Differential Equations*, Addison-Wesley, Reading, Mass., 1958.

20.5 M. R. SPIEGEL, *Applied Differential Equations*, Prentice-Hall, Englewood Cliffs, N. J., 1961.

20.6 C. R. WYLIE, JR., *Advanced Engineering Mathematics*, McGraw-Hill, New York, 1960.

Appendix

A

Formulas from geometry and trigonometry

In Formulas 1–10, r (or r') denotes a radius, C the circumference of a circle, s the length of a circular arc, b (or b') a base, h a height, l the slant height of a cone or frustrum, A an area, S a lateral area, V a volume, and θ a central angle in radians.

(1) *Circle:*

$$C = 2\pi r, \qquad A = \pi r^2.$$

(2) *Circular arc:*

$$s = r\theta \qquad (\theta \text{ in radians}).$$

(3) *Circular sector:*

$$A = \frac{1}{2}r^2\theta \qquad (\theta \text{ in radians}).$$

(4) *Parallelogram:*

$$A = bh.$$

(5) *Triangle:*

$$A = \frac{1}{2}bh = \frac{ab}{2}\sin C. \qquad (\text{angle } C \text{ opposite side } c)$$

(6) *Trapezoid:*

$$A = \frac{h}{2}(b + b').$$

(7) *Sphere:*

$$V = \frac{4}{3}\pi r^3, \qquad A = 4\pi r^2.$$

(8)   *Right-circular cylinder:*
$$V = \pi r^2 h, \qquad S = 2\pi rh.$$

(9)   *Right-circular cone:*
$$V = \frac{\pi}{3} r^2 h, \qquad S = \pi rl.$$

(10)   *Frustrum of right-circular cone:*
$$V = \frac{\pi h}{3}(r^2 + r'^2 + rr'),$$
$$S = \pi(r + r')l.$$

(11)   *Law of cosines:*
$$c^2 = a^2 + b^2 - 2ab \cos C.$$

(12)   *Law of sines:*
$$\frac{a}{\sin A} = \frac{b}{\sin B} = \frac{c}{\sin C}.$$

(13)   *Pythagorean identities:*
$$\sin^2 \theta + \cos^2 \theta = 1.$$
$$1 + \tan^2 \theta = \sec^2 \theta,$$
$$1 + \cot^2 \theta = \csc^2 \theta.$$

(14)   *Addition formulas:*
$$\sin(\theta \pm \phi) = \sin \theta \cos \phi \pm \cos \theta \sin \phi,$$
$$\cos(\theta \perp \phi) - \cos \theta \cos \phi \mp \sin \theta \sin \phi,$$
$$\tan(\theta \pm \phi) = \frac{\tan \theta \pm \tan \phi}{1 \mp \tan \theta \tan \phi}.$$

(15)   *Double-angle formulas:*
$$\sin 2\theta = 2 \sin \theta \cos \theta,$$
$$\cos 2\theta = \cos^2 \theta - \sin^2 \theta$$
$$= 2 \cos^2 \theta - 1$$
$$= 1 - 2 \sin^2 \theta.$$

(16)   *Half-angle formulas:*
$$\sin^2 \theta = \frac{1}{2}(1 - \cos 2\theta),$$
$$\cos^2 \theta = \frac{1}{2}(1 + \cos 2\theta).$$

Appendix

B

Table of integrals

(1) $\displaystyle\int u^n \, du = \frac{u^{n+1}}{n+1} + C \qquad (n \neq -1).$

(2) $\displaystyle\int \frac{du}{u} = \log |u| + C.$

(3) $\displaystyle\int u \, dv = uv - \int v \, du.$

(4) $\displaystyle\int e^u \, du = e^u + C.$

(5) $\displaystyle\int a^u \, du = \int e^{u \log a} \, du = \frac{a^u}{\log a} + C \qquad (a > 0, \, a \neq 1).$

(6) $\displaystyle\int \sin u \, du = -\cos u + C.$

(7) $\displaystyle\int \cos u \, du = \sin u + C.$

(8) $\displaystyle\int \tan u \, du = -\log |\cos u| + C.$

(9) $\displaystyle\int \cot u \, du = \log |\sin u| + C.$

(10) $\displaystyle\int \sec u \, du = \log |\sec u + \tan u| + C.$

(11) $\displaystyle\int \csc u \, du = \log |\csc u - \cot u| + C.$

(12) $\displaystyle\int \sec^2 u \, du = \tan u + C.$

(13) $\displaystyle\int \csc^2 u \, du = -\cot u + C.$

(14) $\displaystyle\int \sec u \tan u \, du = \sec u + C.$

(15) $\int \csc u \cot u \, du = -\csc u + C.$

(16) $\int \dfrac{du}{a^2 + u^2} = \dfrac{1}{a} \operatorname{Tan}^{-1} \dfrac{u}{a} + C.$

(17) $\int \dfrac{du}{\sqrt{a^2 - u^2}} = \operatorname{Sin}^{-1} \dfrac{u}{a} + C.$

(18) $\int \sin^2 u \, du = \dfrac{u}{2} - \dfrac{\sin 2u}{4} + C.$

(19) $\int \cos^2 u \, du = \dfrac{u}{2} + \dfrac{\sin 2u}{4} + C.$

(20) $\int \sin^3 u \, du = \dfrac{\cos^3 u}{3} - \cos u + C.$

(21) $\int \cos^3 u \, du = \sin u - \dfrac{\sin^3 u}{3} + C.$

(22) $\int \sin^2 au \cos^2 au \, du = \dfrac{u}{8} - \dfrac{1}{32a} \sin 4au + C.$

(23) $\int \tan^2 u \, du = \tan u - u + C.$

(24) $\int \cot^2 u \, du = -\cot u - u + C.$

(25) $\int \sec^3 u \, du = \dfrac{1}{2} \sec u \tan u + \dfrac{1}{2} \log|\sec u + \tan u| + C.$

(26) $\int \csc^3 u \, du = \dfrac{-1}{2} \csc u \cot u + \dfrac{1}{2} \log|\csc u - \cot u| + C.$

(27) $\int u \sin u \, du = \sin u - u \cos u + C.$

(28) $\int u \cos u \, du = \cos u + u \sin u + C.$

(29) $\int u^2 \sin u \, du = 2u \sin u - (u^2 - 2) \cos u + C.$

(30) $\int u^2 \cos u \, du = 2u \cos u + (u^2 - 2) \sin u + C.$

(31) $\int \sin^m u \cos^n u \, du = \dfrac{-\sin^{m-1} u \cos^{n+1} u}{m+n} + \dfrac{m-1}{m+n} \int \sin^{m-2} u \cos^n u \, du.$
$$(m + n \ne 0).$$

(32) $\int \sin^m u \cos^n u \, du = \dfrac{\sin^{m+1} u \cos^{n-1} u}{m+n} + \dfrac{n-1}{m+n} \int \sin^m u \cos^{n-2} u \, du.$
$$(m + n \ne 0).$$

(33) $\int u e^{au} \, du = \dfrac{e^{au}}{a^2} (au - 1) + C.$

(34) $\int u^2 e^{au} \, du = \dfrac{e^{au}}{a^3} (a^2 u^2 - 2au + 2) + C.$

(35) $\displaystyle\int u^n e^u du = u^n e^u - n \int u^{n-1} e^u\, du.$

(36) $\displaystyle\int \frac{e^u du}{u^n} = \frac{-e^u}{(n-1)u^{n-1}} + \frac{1}{n-1} \int \frac{e^u du}{u^{n-1}}. \qquad (n \neq 1).$

(37) $\displaystyle\int e^{au} \sin bu\, du = \frac{e^{au}}{a^2 + b^2}(a \sin bu - b \cos bu) + C.$

(38) $\displaystyle\int e^{au} \cos bu\, du = \frac{e^{au}}{a^2 + b^2}(a \cos bu + b \sin bu) + C.$

(39) $\displaystyle\int \log u\, du = u(\log u - 1) + C.$

(40) $\displaystyle\int u^n \log|u|\, du = u^{n+1}\left[\frac{\log|u|}{n+1} - \frac{1}{(n+1)^2}\right] + C. \qquad (n \neq -1).$

(41) $\displaystyle\int \mathrm{Sin}^{-1} u\, du = u\, \mathrm{Sin}^{-1} u + \sqrt{1 - u^2} + C.$

(42) $\displaystyle\int \mathrm{Tan}^{-1} u\, du = u\, \mathrm{Tan}^{-1} u - \log\sqrt{1 + u^2} + C.$

Forms Involving $a + bu$

(43) $\displaystyle\int \frac{u\, du}{a + bu} = \frac{1}{b^2}\left[a + bu - a \log|a + bu|\right] + C.$

(44) $\displaystyle\int \frac{u^2\, du}{a + bu} = \frac{1}{b^3}\left[\frac{1}{2}(a + bu)^2 - 2a(a + bu) + a^2 \log|a + bu|\right] + C.$

(45) $\displaystyle\int \frac{u\, du}{(a + bu)^2} = \frac{1}{b^2}\left[\frac{a}{a + bu} + \log|a + bu|\right] + C.$

(46) $\displaystyle\int \frac{u^2\, du}{(a + bu)^2} = \frac{1}{b^3}\left[a + bu - \frac{a^2}{a + bu} - 2a \log|a + bu|\right] + C.$

(47) $\displaystyle\int \frac{du}{u(a + bu)} = \frac{-1}{a} \log\left|\frac{a + bu}{u}\right| + C.$

(48) $\displaystyle\int \frac{du}{u^2(a + bu)} = \frac{-1}{au} + \frac{b}{a^2} \log\left|\frac{a + bu}{u}\right| + C.$

(49) $\displaystyle\int \frac{du}{u(a + bu)^2} = \frac{1}{a(a + bu)} - \frac{1}{a^2} \log\left|\frac{a + bu}{u}\right| + C.$

(50) $\displaystyle\int u\sqrt{a + bu}\, du = \frac{2(3bu - 2a)}{15b^2}(a + bu)^{3/2} + C.$

(51) $\displaystyle\int u^2\sqrt{a + bu}\, du = \frac{2(15b^2u^2 - 12abu + 8a^2)}{105b^3}(a + bu)^{3/2} + C.$

(52) $\displaystyle\int \frac{u\, du}{\sqrt{a + bu}} = \frac{2(bu - 2a)}{3b^2}\sqrt{a + bu} + C.$

(53) $\displaystyle\int \frac{u^2\, du}{\sqrt{a + bu}} = \frac{2(3b^2u^2 - 4abu + 8a^2)}{15b^3}\sqrt{a + bu} + C.$

Forms Involving $u^2 \pm a^2$ $(a > 0)$

(54) $\quad \displaystyle\int \frac{du}{u^2 - a^2} = \frac{1}{2a} \log \left| \frac{u - a}{u + a} \right| + C.$

(55) $\quad \displaystyle\int \frac{u^2\, du}{u^2 - a^2} = u + \frac{a}{2} \log \left| \frac{u - a}{u + a} \right| + C.$

(56) $\quad \displaystyle\int \frac{u^2\, du}{u^2 + a^2} = u - a \operatorname{Tan}^{-1} \frac{u}{a} + C.$

(57) $\quad \displaystyle\int \frac{du}{u(u^2 \pm a^2)} = \frac{\pm 1}{2a^2} \log \left| \frac{u^2}{u^2 \pm a^2} \right| + C.$

(58) $\quad \displaystyle\int \frac{du}{\sqrt{u^2 \pm a^2}} = \log \left| u + \sqrt{u^2 \pm a^2} \right| + C.$

(59) $\quad \displaystyle\int \frac{u^2\, du}{\sqrt{u^2 \pm a^2}} = \frac{u}{2} \sqrt{u^2 \pm a^2} \mp \frac{a^2}{2} \log |u + \sqrt{u^2 \pm a^2}| + C.$

(60) $\quad \displaystyle\int \frac{du}{u\sqrt{u^2 + a^2}} = \frac{1}{a} \log \left| \frac{u}{a + \sqrt{u^2 + a^2}} \right| + C.$

(61) $\quad \displaystyle\int \frac{du}{u\sqrt{u^2 - a^2}} = \frac{1}{a} \operatorname{Sec}^{-1} \frac{u}{a} + C.$

(62) $\quad \displaystyle\int \sqrt{u^2 \pm a^2}\, du = \frac{u}{2}\sqrt{u^2 \pm a^2} \pm \frac{a^2}{2} \log |u + \sqrt{u^2 \pm a^2}| + C.$

(63) $\quad \displaystyle\int u^2\sqrt{u^2 \pm a^2}\, du = \frac{u}{4}(u^2 \pm a^2)^{3/2} \mp \frac{a^2 u}{8}\sqrt{u^2 \pm a^2}$
$$- \frac{a^4}{8} \log |u + \sqrt{u^2 \pm a^2}| + C.$$

(64) $\quad \displaystyle\int \frac{\sqrt{u^2 + a^2}\, du}{u} = \sqrt{u^2 + a^2} - a \log \left| \frac{a + \sqrt{u^2 + a^2}}{u} \right| + C.$

(65) $\quad \displaystyle\int \frac{\sqrt{u^2 - a^2}\, du}{u} = \sqrt{u^2 - a^2} - a \operatorname{Sec}^{-1} \frac{u}{a} + C.$

Forms Involving $\sqrt{a^2 - u^2}$ $(a > 0)$

(66) $\quad \displaystyle\int \sqrt{a^2 - u^2}\, du = \frac{u}{2}\sqrt{a^2 - u^2} + \frac{a^2}{2} \operatorname{Sin}^{-1}\frac{u}{a} + C.$

(67) $\quad \displaystyle\int u^2\sqrt{a^2 - u^2}\, du = \frac{-u}{4}(a^2 - u^2)^{3/2} + \frac{a^2 u}{8}\sqrt{a^2 - u^2}$
$$+ \frac{a^4}{8} \operatorname{Sin}^{-1}\frac{u}{a} + C.$$

(68) $\quad \displaystyle\int \frac{\sqrt{a^2 - u^2}\, du}{u} = \sqrt{a^2 - u^2} - a \log \left| \frac{a + \sqrt{a^2 - u^2}}{u} \right| + C.$

(69) $\quad \displaystyle\int \frac{\sqrt{a^2 - u^2}\, du}{u^2} = \frac{-\sqrt{a^2 - u^2}}{u} - \operatorname{Sin}^{-1}\frac{u}{a} + C.$

(70) $\displaystyle\int \frac{u^2\,du}{\sqrt{a^2-u^2}} = \frac{-u}{2}\sqrt{a^2-u^2} + \frac{a^2}{2}\mathrm{Sin}^{-1}\frac{u}{a} + C.$

Wallis's Formulas

(71) $\displaystyle\int_0^{\pi/2} \sin^m x\,dx = \int_0^{\pi/2} \cos^m x\,dx$

$$= \frac{(m-1)(m-3)\cdots(2\text{ or }1)}{m(m-2)\cdots(3\text{ or }2)}k,$$

where $k = 1$ if m is odd, and $k = \pi/2$ if m is even.

(72) $\displaystyle\int_0^{\pi/2} \sin^m x\cos^n x\,dx =$

$$\frac{(m-1)(m-3)\cdots(2\text{ or }1)\times(n-1)(n-3)\cdots(2\text{ or }1)}{(m+n)(m+n-2)\cdots(2\text{ or }1)}k,$$

where $k = 1$ unless both m and n are even, and $k = \pi/2$ if both m and n are even.

Appendix

C

Tables

TABLE C.1. Trigonometric Functions

Degrees	Radians	Sin	Tan	Cot	Cos		
0	0	0	0	——	1.0000	1.5708	90
1	.0175	.0175	.0175	57.290	.9998	1.5533	89
2	.0349	.0349	.0349	28.636	.9994	1.5359	88
3	.0524	.0523	.0524	19.081	.9986	1.5184	87
4	.0698	.0698	.0699	14.301	.9976	1.5010	86
5	.0873	.0872	.0875	11.430	.9962	1.4835	85
6	.1047	.1045	.1051	9.5144	.9945	1.4661	84
7	.1222	.1219	.1228	8.1443	.9925	1.4486	83
8	.1396	.1392	.1405	7.1154	.9903	1.4312	82
9	.1571	.1564	.1584	6.3138	.9877	1.4137	81
10	.1745	.1736	.1763	5.6713	.9848	1.3963	80
11	.1920	.1908	.1944	5.1446	.9816	1.3788	79
12	.2094	.2079	.2126	4.7046	.9781	1.3614	78
13	.2269	.2250	.2309	4.3315	.9744	1.3439	77
14	.2443	.2419	.2493	4.0108	.9703	1.3265	76
15	.2618	.2588	.2679	3.7321	.9659	1.3090	75
16	.2793	.2756	.2867	3.4874	.9613	1.2915	74
17	.2967	.2924	.3057	3.2709	.9563	1.2741	73
18	.3142	.3090	.3249	3.0777	.9511	1.2566	72
19	.3316	.3256	.3443	2.9042	.9455	1.2392	71
20	.3491	.3420	.3640	2.7475	.9397	1.2217	70
21	.3665	.3584	.3839	2.6051	.9336	1.2043	69
22	.3840	.3746	.4040	2.4751	.9272	1.1868	68
23	.4014	.3907	.4245	2.3559	.9205	1.1694	67
24	.4189	.4067	.4452	2.2460	.9135	1.1519	66
25	.4363	.4226	.4663	2.1445	.9063	1.1345	65
26	.4538	.4384	.4877	2.0503	.8988	1.1170	64
27	.4712	.4540	.5095	1.9626	.8910	1.0996	63
28	.4887	.4695	.5317	1.8807	.8829	1.0821	62
29	.5061	.4848	.5543	1.8040	.8746	1.0647	61
30	.5236	.5000	.5774	1.7321	.8660	1.0472	60
31	.5411	.5150	.6009	1.6643	.8572	1.0297	59
32	.5585	.5299	.6249	1.6003	.8480	1.0123	58
33	.5760	.5446	.6494	1.5399	.8387	.9948	57
34	.5934	.5592	.6745	1.4826	.8290	.9774	56
35	.6109	.5736	.7002	1.4281	.8192	.9599	55
36	.6283	.5878	.7265	1.3764	.8090	.9425	54
37	.6458	.6018	.7536	1.3270	.7986	.9250	53
38	.6632	.6157	.7813	1.2799	.7880	.9076	52
39	.6807	.6293	.8098	1.2349	.7771	.8901	51
40	.6981	.6428	.8391	1.1918	.7660	.8727	50
41	.7156	.6561	.8693	1.1504	.7547	.8552	49
42	.7330	.6691	.9004	1.1106	.7431	.8378	48
43	.7505	.6820	.9325	1.0724	.7314	.8203	47
44	.7679	.6947	.9657	1.0355	.7193	.8029	46
45	.7854	.7071	1.0000	1.0000	.7071	.7854	45
		Cos	Cot	Tan	Sin	Radians	Degrees

TABLE C.2. Natural Logarithms

N	.0	.1	.2	.3	.4	.5	.6	.7	.8	.9
1	0.0000	0.0953	0.1823	0.2624	0.3365	0.4055	0.4700	0.5306	0.5878	0.6419
2	0.6931	0.7419	0.7885	0.8329	0.8755	0.9163	0.9555	0.9933	1.0296	1.0647
3	1.0986	1.1314	1.1632	1.1939	1.2238	1.2528	1.2809	1.3083	1.3350	1.3610
4	1.3863	1.4110	1.4351	1.4586	1.4816	1.5041	1.5261	1.5476	1.5686	1.5892
5	1.6094	1.6292	1.6487	1.6677	1.6864	1.7047	1.7228	1.7405	1.7579	1.7750
6	1.7918	1.8083	1.8245	1.8405	1.8563	1.8718	1.8871	1.9021	1.9169	1.9315
7	1.9459	1.9601	1.9741	1.9879	2.0015	2.0149	2.0281	2.0412	2.0541	2.0669
8	2.0794	2.0919	2.1041	2.1163	2.1282	2.1401	2.1518	2.1633	2.1748	2.1861
9	2.1972	2.2083	2.2192	2.2300	2.2407	2.2513	2.2618	2.2721	2.2824	2.2925

TABLE C.3. Exponential Functions

x	e^x	e^{-x}	x	e^x	e^{-x}	x	e^x	e^{-x}	x	e^x	e^{-x}
.00	1.0000	1.0000	.85	2.3396	.4274	2.4	11.023	.0907	4.0	54.598	.0183
.05	1.0513	.9512	.90	2.4596	.4066	2.5	12.182	.0821	4.1	60.340	.0166
.10	1.1052	.9048	.95	2.5857	.3867	2.6	13.464	.0743	4.2	66.686	.0150
.15	1.1618	.8607	1.0	2.7183	.3679	2.7	14.880	.0672	4.3	73.700	.0136
.20	1.2214	.8187	1.1	3.0042	.3329	2.8	16.445	.0608	4.4	81.451	0.123
.25	1.2840	.7788	1.2	3.3201	.3012	2.9	18.174	.0550	4.5	90.017	.0111
.30	1.3499	.7408	1.3	3.6693	.2725	3.0	20.086	.0498	4.6	99.484	.0101
.35	1.4191	.7047	1.4	4.0552	.2466	3.1	22.198	.0450	4.7	109.95	.0091
.40	1.4918	.6703	1.5	4.4817	.2231	3.2	24.533	.0408	4.8	121.51	.0082
.45	1.5683	.6376	1.6	4.9530	.2019	3.3	27.113	.0369	4.9	134.29	.0074
.50	1.6487	.6065	1.7	5.4739	.1827	3.4	29.964	.0334	5.0	148.41	.0067
.55	1.7333	.5769	1.8	6.0496	.1653	3.5	33.115	.0302	6.0	403.43	.0025
.60	1.8221	.5488	1.9	6.6859	.1496	3.6	36.598	.0273	7.0	1096.6	.0009
.65	1.9155	.5220	2.0	7.3891	.1353	3.7	40.447	.0247	8.0	2981.0	.0003
.70	2.0138	.4966	2.1	8.1662	.1225	3.8	44.701	.0224	9.0	8103.1	.0001
.75	2.1170	.4724	2.2	9.0250	.1108	3.9	49.402	.0202	10.0	22026.	.0000
.80	2.2255	.4493	2.3	9.9742	.1003						

Answers to odd-numbered problems

Chapter 1

List 1 — Page 4

5. Yes, provided $c/d \neq 0$.

List 2 — Page

1. $+3$ or -3; $+3$ **3.** Roots are 7 and -1.

7. (a) 0 (b) 0 (c) undefined (d) 0 (e) undefined

9. (a) 3 (b) undefined (c) 5 (d) 6 (e) 0

List 3 — Page 11

1. (a) $1, 4, 9, 16$ (b) $-1, 4, -9, 16$ (c) $0, 1/2, 2/3, 3/4$ (d) $2, 3^{1/2}, 4^{1/3}, 5^{1/4}$
    (e) π, π, π, π (f) $-1, 1/2, -1/3, 1/4$ (g) $1, 1, 4/3, 2$ (h) $0, -1/2, 0, 1/4$

3. (a) d, ∞ (b) d (c) $c, 3$ (d) d (e) $c, 0$ (f) $c, 2$ (g) $c, 2$ (h) $c, 0$ (i) d (j) $c, 1/3$

5. (a) 5 (b) 7 (c) 9

List 4 — Page 15

1. (a) 1 (b) 2 (c) $a^2 + 1$ (d) $b^2 + 1$ (e) $(a + b)^2 + 1$ (f) $a^2 b^2 + 1$ (g) 10
    (h) $(x + h)^2 + 1$ (i) $2hx + h^2$ (j) $4x^2 + 1$ (k) $x + 1$ (l) $t^4 + 2t^2 + 2$

3.

	D	R
(a)	$-\infty < x < \infty$	$1 \leqslant y$
(b)	$1 \leqslant x$	$0 \leqslant y$
(c)	$-\infty < x < \infty$	$y = 5$
(d)	$x \neq 0$	$y \neq 0$
(e)	$x \neq 0$	$y = 2$
(f)	$n = 1, 2, 3, \cdots$	$n^2 = 1, 4, 9, \cdots$
(g)	$-\infty < x < \infty$	$-1 \leqslant y \leqslant 1$
(h)	$-1 \leqslant x \leqslant 1$	$0 \leqslant y \leqslant 1$
(i)	$0 \leqslant x$	$0 \leqslant y$
(j)	$-\infty < x < \infty$	$y \leqslant 4$
(k)	$-\infty < x < \infty$	$0 \leqslant y \leqslant 1$
(l)	$n = 1, 2, 3, \cdots$	$1/n = 1, 1/2, 1/3, \cdots$

7. 25

9. Yes, D consists of $x = 0$, R consists of $y = 0$.

11. $D: -\infty < x < \infty$; $R: -1 \leqslant y$

Chapter 2

List 5 — Page 21

9.   (a) 5 (b) 8 (c) $2\sqrt{13}$ (d) -9 (e) 0 (f) -8 (g) -8 (h) $8\sqrt{2}$

11. (a) 5 (b) -8 (c) $2\sqrt{13}$ (d) 9 (e) 0 (f) 8 (g) 8 (h) $8\sqrt{2}$

13. $P = \sqrt{146} + 2\sqrt{73}$, $A = 73/2$ 15. $x = 1 \pm 2\sqrt{5}$, $y = 0$

19. $P = \sqrt{29} + \sqrt{73} + \sqrt{34}$, $A = 15.5$

List 7 — Page 37

1.   (a) $0°$ (b) $90°$ (c) $45°$ (d) $30°$ (e) $120°$ (f) $135°$

3.   (a) -2 (b) $2/3$ (c) 0 (d) undefined (e) $2/9$ (f) $-5/2$ (g) $5/3$ (h) $1/(\pi + 3)$

5. a, c 7. (i) d and g (ii) a and g, b and h

11. $y = -7/3$ 13. $x = 2$

17. $x = (3 \pm \sqrt{73})/2$, or $x = -24/7$, or $x = 50/7$

19. (a) $A = \text{Tan}^{-1}(9/2)$, $B = \text{Tan}^{-1}(9/83)$, $C = \pi - \text{Tan}^{-1}9$

     (b) $A = \pi - \text{Tan}^{-1}21$, $B = \text{Tan}^{-1}(7/6)$, $C = \text{Tan}^{-1}(7/9)$

     (c) $A = \text{Tan}^{-1}(19/33)$, $B = \pi - \text{Tan}^{-1}(19/8)$, $C = \text{Tan}^{-1}(19/25)$

     (d) $A = \text{Tan}^{-1}(37/41)$, $B = \text{Tan}^{-1}(37/9)$, $C = \text{Tan}^{-1}(37/20)$

21. (a) $\phi + \psi = \text{Tan}^{-1}3$ (b) $x = 2$ (c) $x = 10/3$ (d) $x = 4\sqrt{10} - 10$

     (e) $\phi = \text{Tan}^{-1}(3/5)$, $\psi = \text{Tan}^{-1}(6/7)$

List 8 — Page 41

1.   (a) $(3/2, 1/2)$ (b) $(-3/2, -5/2)$ (c) $(-7/2, -3/2)$ (d) $(-1, 2)$

3. $x = 8$; $y = -8$ 5. $(7/2, 2)$; $r = \sqrt{65}/2$

7. $\sqrt{85}, \sqrt{34}, \sqrt{85}$ 11. $(0, 3)$

13. (a) $(0, 1/3)$ (b) $(8, -13)$

List 9 — Page 45

1.   (a) $y = 0$ (b) $x = 0$ (c) $y = x$ (d) $x = -4$ (e) $y = -1$

3.   (a) $6x - y + 37 = 0$ (b) $5x + y + 11 = 0$ (c) $2x - y - 13 = 0$

     (d) $y = 2$ (e) $x - 5y - 6 = 0$ (f) $10x - y + 33 = 0$ (g) $x + 3y - 21 = 0$

     (h) $4x + y - 27 = 0$

5.   (a) $x + 3y - 7 = 0$ (b) $10x - 16y + 29 = 0$ (c) $x = 3/2$ (d) $x + y = 0$

     (e) $y = 2$ (f) $3x - 5y - 35 = 0$ 9. $4x + 3y + 7 = 0$

11. sides: $5x - 3y + 2 = 0$, $x + 2y - 10 = 0$, $4x - 5y - 14 = 0$

     altitudes: $3x + 5y - 28 = 0$, $5x + 4y - 26 = 0$, $2x - y + 2 = 0$

     medians: $3x - 7y - 4 = 0$, $6x - y - 8 = 0$, $9x - 8y - 12 = 0$

13. no

List 10 — Page 48

1.   (a) $-3/2$ (b) $4/3$ (c) $1/2$ (d) undefined (e) 0 (f) -1 (g) $9/11$ (h) $-4/3$ (i) $6/5$

     (j) $-5/6$ (k) $-2/3$ (l) $-4/9$

3.   (a) $(-1/14, 9/7)$ (b) $(-11/26, 19/13)$ (c) $(12, -9)$ (d) $(5, -12), (-5, 12)$

     (e) $(\sqrt{10}/10, 3\sqrt{10}/10), (-\sqrt{10}/10, -3\sqrt{10}/10)$ (f) $(0, 0), (1, 1)$

     (g) $(2/3, 3/2), (-1, -1)$ (h) no intersections (i) no intersections (j) $(1, 2)$

(k) $(5/2, 5/2), (-5/3, 5/3)$ **5.** $\sqrt{62}$

7. $8x + 51y - 35 = 0$

9. altitudes: $x = 8, 2x - 3y = 0, 4x + 3y - 48 = 0; (8, 16/3)$
medians: $3x - 10y = 0, 3x + 8y - 36 = 0, 3x - y - 18 = 0; (20/3, 2)$
perpendicular bisectors: $x = 6, 4x + 3y - 25 = 0, 2x - 3y - 11 = 0; (6, 1/3)$

List 11 — Page 51

1. (a) $y = 3x + b$ (b) $y - 3 = m(x + 2)$ (c) $x = k$ (d) $y = -x/\sqrt{2} + b$
(e) $2x - 4y = k$ (f) $4x - 3y = k$

5. $y + 2 = m(x - 3)$ (a) $y + 2 = 2(x - 3)$ (b) $y + 2 = -3(x - 3)$
(c) $y + 2 = -2(x - 3)/3$ (d) $y + 2 = -2(x - 3)$

7. $y = 2|x|$ **9.** $y = x \pm \sqrt{2}$

11. $80x + 8y - 5 = 0, 216x + 162y - 859 = 0, 104x - 130y + 839 = 0$

List 12 — Page 55

1. (a) $\sqrt{3}\,(x/2) + (y/2) - 3 = 0$ (b) $-(x/\sqrt{2}) + (y/\sqrt{2}) - 5 = 0$
(c) $(x/\sqrt{2}) - (y/\sqrt{2}) - 1 = 0$ (d) $-(x/2) + \sqrt{3}\,(y/2) - 7 = 0$
(e) $y - 2 = 0$ (f) $-x - 10 = 0$ (g) $-(x/2) - \sqrt{3}\,(y/2) - 6 = 0$
(h) $(\sqrt{6} - \sqrt{2})\,x/4 + (\sqrt{6} + \sqrt{2})\,y/4 - 3 = 0$

3. (a) $-x - 3 = 0$ (b) $x - 3 = 0$ (c) $\sqrt{3}\,(x/2) + (y/2) - 7 = 0$
(d) $-\sqrt{3}\,(x/2) - (y/2) - 4 = 0$ (e) $\sqrt{2}\,(x/2) - \sqrt{2}\,(y/2) - 5 = 0$
(f) $-\sqrt{3}\,(x/2) + (y/2) - 3 = 0$ (g) $-\sqrt{2}\,(x/2) + \sqrt{2}\,(y/2) = 0$
(h) $(\sqrt{6} + \sqrt{2})\,x/4 + (\sqrt{6} - \sqrt{2})\,y/4 - 7 = 0$

5. (a) $(3x/5) + (4y/5) - 5 = 0; 3/5, 4/5, 5$
(b) $-(5x/13) + (12y/13) - 2 = 0; -(5/13), 12/13, 2$
(c) $(2x/\sqrt{13}) + (3y/\sqrt{13}) - (1/\sqrt{13}) = 0; 2/\sqrt{13}, 3/\sqrt{13}, 1/\sqrt{13}$
(d) $(7x/25) + (24y/25) - 25 = 0; 7/25, 24/25, 25$
(e) $(5x/\sqrt{29}) + (2y/\sqrt{29}) - (4/\sqrt{29}) = 0; 5/\sqrt{29}, 2/\sqrt{29}, 4/\sqrt{29}$
(f) $(x/\sqrt{2}) + (y/\sqrt{2}) - (1/\sqrt{2}) = 0; 1/\sqrt{2}, 1/\sqrt{2}, 1/\sqrt{2}$
(g) $(12x/13) + (5y/13) = 0; 12/13, 5/13, 0$ (h) $-(4x/5) + (3y/5) = 0; -4/5, 3/5, 0$

7. (a) $(4x/5) + (3y/5) - 1 = 0; 4/5, 3/5, 1$
(b) $(5x/13) + (12y/13) - 3 = 0; 5/13, 12/13, 3$
(c) $(x/\sqrt{10}) + (3y/\sqrt{10}) - (\sqrt{10}/2) = 0; 1/\sqrt{10}, 3/\sqrt{10}, \sqrt{10}/2$
(d) $(2x/\sqrt{5}) - (y/\sqrt{5}) - (3/\sqrt{5}) = 0; 2/\sqrt{5}, -(1/\sqrt{5}), 3/\sqrt{5}$
(e) $(8x/17) - (15y/17) - 2 = 0; 8/17, -15/17, 2$ (f) $x - 5 = 0; 1, 0, 5$
(g) $-x - 5 = 0; -1, 0, 5$ (h) $-y - 2 = 0; 0, -1, 2$

9. 6   **11.** $3x + 4y \pm 15 = 0$

13. $7x + 24y - 275 = 0; 3x + 4y - 55 = 0$

List 13 — Page 57

1. (a) $-58/5$ (b) $-16/17$ (c) $-17/13$ (d) $2/\sqrt{5}$ (e) -7 (f) $-6/5$ (g) $-(11/\sqrt{10})$
(h) 8   **3.** (a) $3/10$ (b) $13/5$ (c) $\sqrt{2}/4$
(d) $4/\sqrt{13}$ **5.** opposite

7. $115/4, 13/4$ **11.** (a) $118/\sqrt{197}, 118/\sqrt{145}, 59/5$
(b) 59   **13.** $y = -15/16; x = 25/12$

15. $(8 + \sqrt{13})x + (1 + 2\sqrt{13})y - 8 - 16\sqrt{13} = 0,$
$(16 + \sqrt{130})x + (2 - \sqrt{130})y - 16 - \sqrt{130} = 0,$
$(2 - \sqrt{10})x + (4 + \sqrt{10})y - 32 + \sqrt{10} = 0$

Chapter 3

List 15 — Page 72

5. (a) 0 (b) 1 (c) -1 (d) 0 (e) does not exist (f) 2 (g) 1 (h) ∞ (i) ∞ (j) $-\infty$
(k) does not exist (l) 0

List 16 — Page 79

1. (a) 3 (b) 4 (c) $2x - 3$ (d) $4x + 5$ (e) $-2/x^2$ (f) $-3/(x - 1)^2$
(g) $3x^2 + 3$ (h) $4x^3 - 1$
3. (a) $1 - 1/(2\sqrt{x})$ (b) $(-x^{-3/2})/2$ (c) $1/(2\sqrt{x + 1})$ (d) $-3/(x + 1)^2$
7. 16, 8, 33, 0
11. $(x^{-2/3})/3$, all real numbers, all nonzero real numbers

List 17 — Page 85

1. (a) -2 (b) $-3/2$ (c) -1 (d) $-1/2$ (e) 0 (f) 1/2 (g) 1 (h) 3/2 (i) 2
3. (a) $y = -3x, y = x/3$ (b) $y = 3x, y = -x/3$
(c) $y - 10 = -7(x + 2), y - 10 = (x + 2)/7$
5. (3/2, 3/4)
7. m
9. $\text{Tan}^{-1}(6/7)$
11. $(1/2, -3/4)$
13. 10
15. $(-3/8, -9/64), 151/80$
17. $a = -3, b = 2$
19. (a) $\text{Tan}^{-1} 1/2$ (b) $\text{Tan}^{-1} 1/2$
(c) $\pi/2$

List 18 — Page 90

1. (a) 0 (b) 0 (c) $6x^5$ (d) $15x^4$ (e) $3x^2 - 2x$ (f) $x^{-1/2}/2 + 3x^{-1/4}/4 - 2x^{-2/3}/3$
(g) $-6x^{-3} - (x^{-3/2})/2$ (h) $2x(2x - 3)(4x - 3)$(i) $4x^3$
(j) $30x^4 - 8x^3 + 15x^2 - 14x + 3$ (k) $\sqrt{5}\,(7x^{5/2} + x^{-1/2})/2$ (l) $3x^2$
(m) $2/(x + 1)^2$ (n) $6x(x^2 + 1)^{-2}$ (o) $-10x/(x^2 - 1)^2$ (p) $-(2\sqrt{x})^{-1}(\sqrt{x} - 1)^{-2}$
(q) $3x^2 + 6x^{-4}$ (r) $(-x^4 + 6x^2 + 2x)(1 + x^3)^{-2}$ (s) $-2x/(x^2 - 1)^2$
(t) $(-2x^2 + 2)(x^2 - x + 1)^{-2}$
(3) 18/121 (5) $-1/320$ lb/ft (7) $6x^5 - 5x^4 + 8x^3 - 3x^2 + 2x$

List 19 — Page 93

1. (a) $3(2u - 1)$ (b) $(3u^2 + 5)(2x - 2)$ (c) $-(3x^2 - 2)/u^2$ (d) $1/(4\sqrt{ux})$
(e) $3(u^2 - 2u + 1)^2(2u - 2)(-4x + 3)$
3. (a) $2(x^3 - x + 1)(3x^2 - 1)$ (b) $18x(x^2 - 1)^8$
(c) $2x(x^2 - 1)(x^2 + 3)/(x^2 + 1)^2$ (d) $(x^2 - 1)(5x - 1)(x + 1)$
(e) $4(1 + x)/(1 - x)^3$ (f) $3x^2/(2\sqrt{x^3 - 1})$ (g) $2x(x^2 - 1)^{-2/3}/3$
(h) $(1 + x)(3 - x)/(1 - x)^2$ (i) $(1 - 3x^2)/[2\sqrt{x}\,(1 + x^2)^2]$
(j) $-(1 + x)^{-2}\sqrt{(1 + x)/(1 - x)}$ (k) $2(3x^2 - x + 1)^{-1/3}(6x - 1)/3$
5. 2
7. 30 units/sec

9. $(3\pi^2/16) \cos(\pi^3/64)$, $3/(2\sqrt{2})$ **11.**   12,996 π cu ft/sec
13.   0

List 20 — Page 96

1. (a) $4x^3 + 6x$, $12x^2 + 6$ (b) $12x^5 - 6x - 1$, $60x^4 - 6$
   (c) $1 + x^{-2}$, $-2x^{-3}$ (d) $3 + x^{-1/2}/2$, $(-x^{-3/2})/4$
   (e) $(2x^{-2/3})/3 - 2x^{-5/3}$, $(-4x^{-5/3})/9 + (10x^{-8/3})/3$
   (f) $2(x^2 - 3x)(2x - 3)$, $12x^2 - 36x + 18$ (g) $-(x + 1)^{-2}$, $2(x + 1)^{-3}$
   (h) $(1 - x)^{-2}$, $2(1 - x)^{-3}$
3. $f(2) = 2/5$, $f'(2) = -3/25$, $f''(2) = 4/125$
5. (a) $y^{(n)} = (-1)^n\, n!\,(x + 1)^{-n-1}$ (b) $(-1)^n\,(n + 1)!\,(x - 1)^{-n-2}$
   (c) $1/2(-1)^n\,(n + 2)!\,x^{-n-3}$ (d) $(-1)^{n+1}\,(2n - 2)!\,x^{-(2n-1)/2}/2^{2n-1}\,(n - 1)!$
   (e) $(-1)^n\, n!\, x^{-n-1}$ (f) $(-1)^{n+1}\, n!\,(x - 1)^{-n-1}\,[n \geqslant 2]$
7. (a) 8 (b) 4   **11.**   5

List 21 — Page 100

1. (a) $-3/4$ (b) $8x$ (c) $-x/y$ (d) $3(2y)^{-1}$ (e) x/y (f) $1/(2y + 2)$ (g) $3x^2(2y)^{-1}$
   (h) $(-2x - y)/(x + 2y)$
3. (a) $-y/x$, $2x^{-2}y$ (b) $(2y)^{-1}$, $-(4y^3)^{-1}$ (c) $-x/y$, $-4y^{-3}$ (d) x/y, $3y^{-3}$
   (e) $-x^2y^{-2}$, $-16xy^{-5}$ (f) $10xy^{-2}/3$, $-10y^{-2}/9$ (g) $3/(y - 2)$, $-9(y - 2)^{-3}$
   (h) $-\sqrt{y/x}$, $3x^{-3/2}/2$
5. $y - 2 = 17(x - 1)/4$, $y - 2 = -4(x - 1)/17$
7. (a) $(3y^2 - 8y)^{-1}$ (b) $5(6y + 2)^{-1}$
9. (a) $x(2 + 3x)/[2y(1 - x)]$ (b) $xy^{-2}/(3 - 2y)$ (c) $(9 - 2xy)/(x^2 + 4)$
   (d) $(-2x^3 - xy^2 + 3x^2 + y^2 + 3x)/[y(x - 1)^2]$ (e) $(x - xy^2)/(x^2y - 16y)$
   (f) $(-2x^3 - 2xy^2 + 3x^2 + y^2)/(2y^3 + 2x^2y - 2xy - y)$
11. (a) $3(2^{1/3})/5$ (b) 0

List 22 — Page 105

1. (a) $2x\,dx$ (b) dx (c) $(4x^3 - 6x)\,dx$ (d) $[2 + 1/(2\sqrt{x})]\,dx$ (e) $-x(1 - x^2)^{-1/2}\,dx$
   (f) $(2x^{-1/3}/3 - x^{-3/2}/2)\,dx$ (g) $32t\,dt$ (h) $2s\,ds$ (i) $4\pi\,r^2\,dr$ (j) $2\pi\,r\,dr$
   (k) $3s^2\,ds$ (l) $\pi\,dl/(8\sqrt{2l})$
3. $3x^2\,dx$, $3x^2(\Delta x) + 3x(\Delta x)^2 + (\Delta x)^3$, 0.12, 0.120601
5. $-x^{-2}dx$ **7.** -0.4
9. (a) $dy/dx = (3t - 1)/2$, $dx/dy = 2/(3t - 1)$
   (b) $dy/dx = (4t - 4)/(4t + 1)$, $dx/dy = (4t + 1)/(4t - 4)$
   (c) $dy/dx = t^{-1/2}/(4x + 6)$, $dx/dy = (4x + 6)\sqrt{t}$

Chapter 4

List 23 — Page 112

1. (a) incr (b) incr (c) decr (d) neither (e) neither (f) incr (g) neither (h) decr
   (i) neither (j) decr (k) incr (l) decr (m) neither (n) incr
3. (a) $M = 6$ (b) $m = 0$ (c) $m = 2$, $M = 5$ (d) $M = 1$ (e) $m = -1$, $M = 2^{1/3}$
   (f) f assumes neither m nor M (g) $M = \sqrt{2}$ (h) f assumes neither m nor M

(i) $m = -2$, $M = 2$ (j) $m = -2$

List 24 — Page 118

1. (a) $1/2$ (b) 3 (c) $(4 + \sqrt{7})/3$ (d) 0

List 25 — Page 125

3. no   5. a, b, d, e, f, g, i, j, k, and l

7. (a) 0 (e) 2 (f) 0 (g) $1/2$ (i) 3 (j) 0 (k) 0 (l) 1

9. Yes, $-5 < L < 5$

11. (a) $\sum_{i=1}^{n} i^4$ (b) $\sum_{i=1}^{5} i^2$ (c) $\sum_{i=0}^{n-1} 2^{2i}$ (d) $\sum_{i=1}^{n} f(x_i)$

List 26 — Page 132

1. 80 5. 7

7. $r^3/3$ 9. 4

11. $(2a + 3b + 6c)/6$

List 27 — Page 137

5. $23/12$

List 28 — Page 140

1. $2\pi r^3/3$ 3. $\pi h(r^2 + r'^2 + rr')/3$

List 29 — Page 143

1. 26

3. (a) 0 (b) $x^2/2$ (c) $9/2$ (d) $(9 - x^2)/2$ (e) $y^2/2$ (f) x (g) 5 (h) 1

7. They are inverse processes.

List 30 — Page 148

1. (a) $2x^3/3 + C$ (b) $x^6/6 - x^3 + C$ (c) $x - x^4/4 + C$ (d) $6x + C$ (e) C

   (f) $x^3/3 - 2x^2 + 5x + C$ (g) $x^4/4 + x^2 - 7x + C$ (h) $x^k/k + C$

   (i) $x^3/3 + 2x^{3/2}/3 + C$ (j) $x^2/2 - 2x^{3/2}/3 + C$ (k) $2x^{3/2}/3 - 3x^{5/3}/5 + 4x^{1/4} + C$

   (l) $x^5/5 - 2x^3/3 + 9x^{4/3}/2 + C$

3. (a) $x^3/3 + 2x + C$ (b) $x^4/4 - 3x^2/2 + 4x + C$ (c) $7x + C$ (d) C

   (e) $\pi(r^3x - x^4/4) + C$ (f) $4x^2$ (g) $f(x)$ (h) $f(x) + C$

5. $76/3$ 7. $28/3$, (a) $80/3$ (b) 36

11. $\pi h(r^2 + r'^2 + rr')/3$ 13. $128\pi/7$

Chapter 5

List 31 — Page 155

1. (a) -8; 6 (b) 3, -2; -6 (c) -4, $3/2$; -12 (d) -2, 3; 18 (e) ± 2; 2

   (f) 6; 2, -3 (g) 1, -2, 3; 6 (h) 5, -1; -1

3. (a) incr $x \geqslant 0$; decr $x \leqslant 0$ (b) incr $x \leqslant 0$; decr $x \geqslant 0$

   (c) incr $x \geqslant -3/2$; decr $x \leqslant -3/2$ (d) incr $x \leqslant 1$; decr $x \geqslant 1$ (e) incr $x \geqslant 0$

   (f) incr $-\infty < x < \infty$ (g) decr $-\infty < x < \infty$ (h) incr $x \geqslant 5/6$; decr $x \leqslant 5/6$

(i) incr $x \geqslant 2/\sqrt{3}$, $x \leqslant -2/\sqrt{3}$; decr $-2/\sqrt{3} \leqslant x \leqslant 2/\sqrt{3}$
(j) incr $x \leqslant -4/3$, $x \geqslant 0$; decr $-4/3 \leqslant x \leqslant 0$
(k) incr $x \leqslant -1$, $x \geqslant 1$; decr $-1 \leqslant x \leqslant 1$ (l) incr $x \geqslant 0$; decr $x \leqslant 0$
(m) incr $-\infty < x < \infty$ (n) incr $-\infty < x < \infty$
(o) incr $x \leqslant 1$, $x \geqslant 4$; decr $1 \leqslant x \leqslant 4$ (p) decr $x \geqslant 0$ (q) incr $x \geqslant 0$
(r) incr $x \geqslant 0$; decr $x \leqslant 0$ (s) incr $x \geqslant 1$; decr $x \leqslant 1$
(t) incr $-2 \leqslant x \leqslant 0$; decr $0 \leqslant x \leqslant 2$
(u) incr $-1 \leqslant x \leqslant -1/2$, $x \geqslant 0$; decr $x \leqslant -1$, $-1/2 \leqslant x \leqslant 0$

5. 2, 1, 0 depending upon whether $b^2 - 3ac$ is positive, zero, or negative.

List 32 — Page 159

1. (a) abs min at $(2/3, 11/3)$ (b) abs min at $(3/5, 1/5)$
   (c) rel min at $(3, -78)$, rel max at $(-2, 47)$
   (d) rel min at $(-1, 3)$, rel max at $(1, 7)$
   (e) abs min at $(\pm 3, 0)$, abs max at $(0, 3/2)$ (f) abs min at $(3, -27)$

List 33 — Page 162

1. (a) concave upward on $-\infty < x < \infty$ (b) concave downward on $-\infty < x < \infty$
   (c) concave upward on $x > 0$, concave downward on $x < 0$
3. (a) $x > 0$, $(0, 0)$ (b) $x < 0$, $(0, 0)$ (c) nowhere concave upward
   (d) concave upward on $x > 1$, $(1, -3)$
   (e) concave upward on $x > -3/2$, $(-3/2, -15/2)$
   (f) concave upward on $x < 5/2$, $(5/2, -45/2)$
   (g) concave upward on $x < -1$ and $x > 1$, $(\pm 1, 1/4)$
   (h) concave upward on $x < -2$ and $x > 2$, $(\pm 2, 1/16)$

List 34 — Page 165

1. (a) y-axis (b) x-axis (c) origin (d) origin (e) x-axis, y-axis, origin, $y = x$
   (f) origin (g) origin, $y = x$ (h) x-axis (i) y-axis (j) y-axis (k) origin (l) origin
3. $f(-y, -x) = 0$

List 35 — Page 168

1. (a) vertical $x = 0$; horizontal $y = 0$ (b) vertical $x = 3$; horizontal $y = -2$
   (c) vertical $x = -2$, $x = 3$; horizontal $y = 0$
   (d) vertical $x = 1$, $x = -2$; horizontal $y = 2$ (e) horizontal $y = 0$
   (f) vertical $x = 5$; horizontal $y = -3$ (g) vertical $x = 0$, $x = 3$; horizontal $y = 0$
   (h) horizontal $y = 1$ (i) vertical $x = -2$, $x = 1$; horizontal $y = 4$
   (j) vertical $x = \pm 2$; horizontal $y = 1$

Chapter 6

List 39 — Page 178

1. (a) $(x - 4)^2 + (y + 5)^2 = 36$ (b) $(x - 2)^2 + (y - 6)^2 = 4$
   (c) $(x - 2)^2 + (y - 6)^2 = 36$ (d) $(x - 5)^2 + (y + 2)^2 = 29$
   (e) $(x - 4)^2 + (y + 3)^2 = 34$ (f) $(x - 8)^2 + (y - 2)^2 = 40$
   (g) $(x - 2)^2 + (y - 1)^2 = 100$ (h) $(x + 3)^2 + (y - 2)^2 = 36$

    (i) $(x - 5)^2 + (y - 5)^2 = 25$, $(x - 5)^2 + (y + 5)^2 = 25$,

      $(x + 5)^2 + (y - 5)^2 = 25$, $(x + 5)^2 + (y + 5)^2 = 25$

    (j) $(x + 7/4)^2 + y^2 = 1025/16$ (k) $(x - 4)^2 + (y + 5)^2 = 45$

    (l) $(x - 4/3)^2 + (y + 4/3)^2 = 16/9$, $(x - 4)^2 + (y - 4)^2 = 16$

3. (a) $(2, -3)$, $r = 4$ (b) $(4, 2)$, $r = 5$ (c) $(6, 1)$, $r = 7$ (d) imaginary circle

    (e) $(5, -3)$, point circle (f) $(1/6, -1/3)$, $r = \sqrt{5}/6$

5. (a) $x^2 + y^2 + 4x - 6y - 12 = 0$ (b) $x^2 + y^2 - 2x + 4y - 20 = 0$

    (c) $x^2 + y^2 - 6x - 8y = 0$ (d) $71x^2 + 71y^2 - 143x - 245y - 2794 = 0$

7. $(-a/2, -b/2)$ **9.** $3x + 4y - 25 = 0$

11. $(h - x)/(y - k)$ **13.** $4\sqrt{2}$

15. outside   **17.** $(x - 3)^2 + (y - 1)^2 = 13$

19. $x^2 + y^2 - 2x - 124 = 0$

List 40 — Page 182

1. (a) $uv - 2 = 0$ (b) $uv - 5 = 0$ (c) $uv + 1 = 0$ (d) $uv - 32 = 0$

3. (a) $u^2 + v^2 = 1$ (b) $u^2 + v^2 = 25$ (c) $4u^2 + 4v^2 = 9$ (d) $4u^2 + 4v^2 = 5$

5. $v^2 = 4u$

List 41 — Page 187

1. (a) $V(0, 0)$, $F(5/2, 0)$, $x = -5/2$ (b) $V(0, 0)$, $F(0, -2)$, $y = 2$

    (c) $V(0, 0)$, $F(-7/2, 0)$, $x = 7/2$ (d) $V(0, 0)$, $F(0, -1)$, $y = 1$

    (e) $V(0, 0)$, $F(-3/2, 0)$, $x = 3/2$ (f) $V(0, 0)$, $F(0, 15/4)$, $y = -15/4$

    (g) $V(0, 0)$, $F(-5/8, 0)$, $x = 5/8$ (h) $V(0, 0)$, $F(0, -7/12)$, $y = 7/12$

3. (a) $V(2, -4)$, $F(2, -3/2)$, $y = -13/2$ (b) $V(1, -4)$, $F(-1/2, -4)$, $x = 5/2$

    (c) $V(-5, -2)$, $F(-5, -4)$, $y = 0$ (d) $V(1, -3)$, $F(9/2, -3)$, $x = -5/2$

    (e) $V(0, 0)$, $F(k/4, 0)$, $x = -k/4$ (f) $V(-5/4, 55/32)$, $F(-5/4, 71/32)$, $y = 39/32$

    (g) $V(19/6, -2/3)$, $\varGamma(3, -2/3)$, $x = 10/3$

5. (a) Each member has vertex at $(0, 0)$ and opens to the left.

    (b) Each member has vertex at $(2, -4)$ and opens upward.

    (c) Each member has vertex at $(h, -1)$ and opens to the left.

    (d) Each member has vertex at $(0, k)$ and opens upward.

9. (a) $(-3, 2)$ (b) $(4, -2)$ (c) $(-a/2, [a^2 - 4c]/4b)$

    (d) $([a^2 - 4c]/4b, -a/2)$

11. $b = 1$, $(1, 2)$ **13.** $y = x^2/1000$, 10 ft

15. $(4/3, 0)$

List 42 — Page 193

1. (a) $(0, \pm 4)$, $(\pm 3, 0)$, $\sqrt{7}/4$ (b) $(\pm 5, 0)$, $(0, \pm 2)$, $\sqrt{21}/5$

    (c) $(0, \pm 6)$, $(\pm 1, 0)$, $\sqrt{35}/6$ (d) $(0, \pm 7)$, $(\pm 2, 0)$, $3\sqrt{5}/7$

    (e) $(\pm 10, 0)$, $(0, \pm 8)$, $3/5$ (f) $(0, \pm\sqrt{3})$, $(\pm 1, 0)$, $\sqrt{6}/3$

    (g) $(\pm 1, 0)$, $(0, \pm\sqrt{2}/2)$, $\sqrt{2}/2$ **9.** $(7/5, 4)$, $(4/5, 5)$

13. $x^2 + 4y^2 - 2x - 24y - 63 = 0$ **15.** $c = 172$ ft

List 43 — Page 200

1. (a) vertices $(\pm 3, 0)$, foci $(\pm 5, 0)$ (b) vertices $(0, \pm 5)$, foci $(0, \pm\sqrt{26})$

    (c) vertices $(\pm 6, 0)$, foci $(\pm 2\sqrt{10}, 0)$ (d) vertices $(0, \pm 3)$, foci $(0, \pm 5)$

(e) vertices $(\pm 1, 0)$, foci $(\pm\sqrt{17}, 0)$ (f) vertices $(0, \pm 1)$, foci $(0, \pm\sqrt{6}/2)$
(g) vertices $(0, \pm\sqrt{10}$, foci $(0, \pm 2\sqrt{5})$ (h) vertices $(\pm 2\sqrt{7}, 0)$, foci $(\pm\sqrt{35}, 0)$

7. $x^2/64 - y^2/36 = 1$

11. (a) $2\sqrt{3}\, b/(3a)$ (b) $3\sqrt{2}\, b/(4a)$ (c) $4\sqrt{15}\, b/(15a)$ (d) $10\sqrt{11}\, b/(33a)$

19. $x \cong 15, y \cong 11$

List 45 — Page 206

1. (a) $4x + 2y - 5 = 0$ (b) $x^2 + y^2 + 20x + 64 = 0$
   (c) $160x^2 + 153y^2 - 864x - 1152y - 24xy - 20{,}736 = 0$ (d) $xy = 8$
   (e) $x^2 + 4y^2 = 16$ (f) $x^2 + y^2 = 36$
   (g) $16x^2 + 9y^2 - 24xy + 360x + 480y - 3600 = 0$ (h) $y^2 - x^2 = 0$
   (i) $x^2 = 4ry, (x \neq 0)$ (j) $x^2 - 2ay + a^2 = 0$

3. $y^2 = 4x^2(x^2 + y^2), (y \neq 0)$ 7. $C(168/13, 48/13), r = 24/13$

Chapter 7

List 46 — Page 210

1. (a) 6 (b) 5.5 (c) 5.01 (d) 5.001 (e) 5.00001, $v_2 = 5$

3. $v_0 = 192$ fps, rises for 6 sec, rises 576 ft, $y_{10} = 320$ ft, $v_{10} = -128$ fps,
   $a_{10} = -32$ ft/sec^2

5. $\Delta s = -3$ ft, total distance traveled $= 5$ ft, $v_{av.} = -1$ fps, av speed $= 5/3$ fps

7. When $t = 3$, first particle has $v = 10$ fps and $a = 2$ ft/sec^2, second particle has
   $v = -2$ fps and $a = 2$ ft/sec^2.

9. $y_2 = 164$ ft, $v_4 = -64$ fps, $v_{y=0} = -16\sqrt{41}$ fps

11. 6 ft/sec^3

List 47 — Page 214

1. 6, 2   3. 20 ft by 30 ft

5. (a) highest $(1, 10/9)$, lowest $(3, 2/3)$
   (b) highest $(6, 5/6)$, lowest $(4, 25/36)$

7. $b = 2h$ and $h = P/(\pi + 4)$, where b and h denote the base and height of the rectangle, and P the perimeter of the window

9. $(88/25, -9/25)$ 11. 14 in. by 21 in.

13. rectangle has dimensions 6 by 18   15. $P(9, 0)$

17. $P(2\sqrt{15}/5, 0)$ 19. 250

21. $h = 4a$ 25. $k = 156/49$

27. (a) $(4, 8)$ (b) $(0, 0)$ (c) $(0, 0)$

List 48 — Page 220

1. 30 sq in./sec   3. $5\sqrt{3}$ ipm

5. 25/3 sq ft/sec   7. 3 fps

9. $8/(225\pi)$ fpm   11. $14\sqrt{5}$ knots

13. $(110/29, 0), (0, 275/29)$ 15. 8/3 mph

17. $dV/dt = r/2\, dS/dt$ 19. $5/(16\pi)$ fpm

21. 125 units/sec

List 49 — Page 223

1. 3.004
3. 26.25 sq in.
5. 17.28π cu in.
7. one inch thick
11. (a) 163/18 (b) 122/11 (c) 0.009998 (d) 499/7500 (e) 159/80 (f) 97/6
    (g) 9 plus 1/243 (h) 3 plus 255/256 (i) 1.9
13. (a) 9% (b) 6%
15. 1%
17. 2π ft
19. -4.12

List 50 — Page 227

1. (a) 3.73, 0.27 (b) 4.41, 1.59 (c) 1.71, 0.29 (d) 0.18, -1.85
3. 2.09
5. $-0.7, -3.2, 1.9$
7. $-1.53, -0.35, 1.88$
9. 2.520 in.
11. 2.25 in.
13. 1.8

List 51 — Page 231

1. (a) $y = x^3/3 - x^2 + C$ (b) $y = x^4/4 + x^2/2 - 2x + C$
    (c) $y = 3x^5/5 - 4x^3/3 + C$ (d) $y = x^4/2 - x^3/3 + x^2/2 - 4x + C$
3. (a) $y = x^3/2 + 2x + 5$ (b) $y = x^3 + 4x^2 - x + 2$ (c) $y = x^3 + 5x^2 + 2$
    (d) $y = x^4 - 3x - 5$ (e) $y = x^4 + x^3 + x^2 + 1$ (f) $y = x^5 + 9x^2 + 3x + 2$
5. (a) $y = x^2 + c$ (b) $y = 4x + c$ (c) $y = c$ (d) $y = -3x^2 + c$
    (e) $y = -x^2 + 3x + c$ (f) $y = x^3/3 + c$ (g) $y = -x^3 + c$
    (h) $y = 2\sqrt{x} + c$
7. $y = x^3 - x^2 + 5x$
9. $x_2 = 6$ ft, $v_2 = 7$ fps
11. $x_3 = 68/3$ ft, $v_3 = 12$ fps
13. $x_5 = 125/6$ ft
15. 960 ft
17. $s_{20} = 6400$ ft, $v_{40} = -640$ fps
19. $20\sqrt{6}$ fps

Chapter 8

List 52 — Page 237

1. (a) 64/3 (b) 52/3 (c) 5/192 (d) 36 (e) 3 (f) 5/12 (g) 9.6 (h) 4.5 (i) 18 (j) 1/10
    (k) 1/10 (l) 877/192 (m) 4.5 (n) 4/3 (o) 32 (p) 512/5 (q) 25/4 (r) 50/3
3. (a) $p^2/12$ (b) $4\sqrt{2p}\,k^{3/2}/3$ (c) $p\,2^{-5/3}$
7. 9

List 53 — Page 243

1. (a) 64/5 (b) 32/5 (c) 32/5 (d) 1/20
3. $a^2h/3$
5. (a) 50π (b) $3093\pi/5$ (c) $12{,}383\pi/7$ (d) $1824\pi/5$ (e) 64π (f) $27\pi/2$
7. $135\pi/2$
9. 144π
11. $4\pi a^3/3$
13. $\pi r^2 h/3$
15. $4\pi a^2 b/3$
17. 384
19. $16a^3/3$

List 54 — Page 249

1. (a) $99\pi/2$ (b) $124\pi/5$ (c) 216π (d) $\pi/6$ (e) $45\pi/2$ (f) $8\pi/15$ (g) 54π
3. (a) $3\pi/10$ (b) $9\pi/2$
5. $\pi r^2 h/3$

7. $2\pi^2 a^3$

List 55 — Page 254

1. (a) $\sqrt{1 + 4x^2}$ (b) $\sqrt{1 + 9x/4}$ (c) $\sqrt{16x^2 - 8x + 2}$ (d) $\sqrt{x^4 + 2x^2 + 1}$
5. (a) $(x - 3)^3/3 + C$ (b) $(2x + 1)^5/10 + C$ (c) $[-(1 - 6x)^{3/2}]/9 + C$
   (d) $[3(1 + 8x/9)^{3/2}]/4 + C$ (e) $[(x^2 - 9)^{3/2}]/3 + C$ (f) $[-3(4 - x^2)^{5/3}]/10 + C$
7. $(31\sqrt{31} - 13\sqrt{13})/27$ **9.** $2(82\sqrt{82} - 10\sqrt{10})/27$
11. $1917/128$ **13.** $(17 + \sqrt{265})/12$
15. $(6\sqrt{3} - 4)/3$
17. (a) $\displaystyle\int_0^3 \sqrt{1 + 4x^2}\, dx$ (b) $\displaystyle\int_{-1}^2 \sqrt{1 + 9x^4}\, dx$ (c) $\displaystyle\int_1^4 (\sqrt{x^4 + 1}/x^2)\, dx$

List 56 — Page 259

1. (a) 156π (b) $50\sqrt{5}\,\pi$ (c) 25π (d) $4\sqrt{2}\,\pi$ (e) $\pi[(145)^{3/2} - 1]/27$
   (f) $\pi[(17)^{3/2} - 1]/6$ (g) $16{,}911\pi/1024$ (h) $1{,}057{,}967\pi/25{,}600$ (i) 88π
3. $\pi r\sqrt{r^2 + h^2}$ **5.** $2(2\sqrt{2} - 1)\pi p^{2/3}$

List 57 — Page 263

1. (a) $4/3$ (b) 2 (c) $5/6$ (d) 8 (e) 0 (f) $13/6$ (g) $(5\sqrt{10} - \sqrt{2})/3$
3. (a) 3 (b) 3 (c) 3 (d) 3 **5.** $2b^2/3$
7. $a^2/3$ **9.** (a) $4/3$ (b) $3/2$

Chapter 9

List 58 — Page 269

3. 2π for sin, cos, sec, and csc; π for tan and cot
5. π, 3

List 59 — Page 273

1. (a) $3 \cos 3x$ (b) $1 - 4 \sin 4x$ (c) $(\sec^2 x/5)/5$ (d) $3 \sec 3x \tan 3x - 2x$
   (e) $-2 \csc^2 x \cot x$ (f) $-2x \csc^2 (1 + x^2)$ (g) $-2 \sin (2 - x) \cos (2 - x)$
   (h) $2(x - 2) \cos (2 - x)^2$ (i) $-6 \cos^2 2x \sin 2x$ (j) $-3 \cos (x/2) \sin (x/2)$
   (k) $-2 \sin^4 x + 6 \sin^2 x \cos^2 x$ (l) $[2(1 + \tan x) \cos 2x - \sin 2x \sec^2 x]/(1 + \tan x)^2$
   (m) $-6 \sin^4 2x \cos 3x \sin 3x + 8 \cos^2 3x \sin^3 2x \cos 2x$
   (n) $3 \csc^3 x \cot x/(2\sqrt{1 - \csc^3 x})$
   (o) $[(3 + \sin x) 2 \sec 2x \tan 2x - \sec 2x \cos x]/(3 + \sin x)^2$
   (p) $-12 \sin x \cos x (1 - 2 \sin^2 x)^2$ (q) $1 - 3 \sin^2 x \cos x/(2\sqrt{1 - \sin^3 x})$
9. (a) $(2 \cos 2x - 1)/\sin y$ (b) $[1 - 2 \cos (x + y)]/[2 \cos (x + y)]$
13. 125 sq ft/sec   **15.** $r = \sqrt{2}\, a/2, h = \sqrt{2}\, a$
17. 1.02 **19.** $M = 5, m = -5$
21. $r = a\sqrt{6}/3, h = 2a\sqrt{3}/3$ **23.** $h = 4a, r = \sqrt{2}\, a$
25. $400a$ fps toward A

List 60 — Page 278

5. (a) $\mathrm{Tan}^{-1} (2\sqrt{2})$ (b) $\mathrm{Tan}^{-1} (4/3)$ (c) $\mathrm{Tan}^{-1} [(6 + 2\pi\sqrt{3})/(4\pi - 3\sqrt{3})]$

List 61 — Page 284

1. (a) $\pi/6$ (b) $5\pi/6$ (c) $-\pi/3$ (d) $2\pi/3$ (e) 0 (f) π (g) $\pi/4$ (h) $\pi/2$
3. (a) $5/\sqrt{1-25x^2}$ (b) $-1/\sqrt{2x-x^2}$ (c) $6x/(1+9x^4)$ (d) $-1/[2\sqrt{x}\,(1+x)]$
   (e) $3/\sqrt{x-x^2}$ (f) $2x^2/\sqrt{1-4x^2}+2x\,\text{Sin}^{-1}(2x)$ (g) $6/(x\sqrt{x^6-4})$
   (h) $4x/(5-2x^2+x^4)$ (i) $-\sqrt{9-x^2}/x^2$ (j) $-2x\,\text{Tan}^{-1}x$ (k) $\sqrt{a^2-x^2}$
   (l) $[(1+x^2)\,\text{Tan}^{-1}x - x]/[(1+x^2)(\text{Tan}^{-1}x)^2]$
   (m) $-\sin^2 x/\sqrt{1-x^2}+2\sin x\cos x\,\text{Cos}^{-1}x$ (n) $[(1-x)\sqrt{1-2x}]^{-1}$
   (o) $-x^2/(x^2+1)+2x\,\text{Tan}^{-1}[(x+1)/(x-1)]$ (p) $[2x\sqrt{-1-x}]^{-1}$
13. $3/(8\sqrt{39})$ rad/sec   15. $2\sqrt{2}/3$ rad/sec
17. $P(20,0)$

Chapter 10

List 62 — Page 291

9. (a) x^{-1} (b) $x/(x^2-1)$ (c) $-6x/[(x^2-1)(x^2-4)]$
   (d) $(x^2-4x+1)/[3(x^2-1)(x-2)]$
   (e) $x(3x^2+8x+1)/[(x^2-1)(x+2)]+\log[(x^2-1)^2/(x+2)]$ (f) $\sec x$
   (g) $(2ax+b)/[2(ax^2+bx+c)]$ (h) $4/[x(x^2-4)]$ (i) $(3x^2+1)/[x(1-x^4)]$
   (j) $-2/\sqrt{x^2+1}$ (k) $-6x/[(x^3-1)(x+1)]$ (l) $\text{Tan}^{-1}x$
11. $1/2$, $1/8$ 13. 0.02

List 63 — Page 295

3. (a) $1/3$ (b) 243 (c) $1/2$
5. (a) $5e^{5x}$, $25e^{5x}$ (b) e^x+e^{-x}, e^x-e^{-x} (c) xe^x+e^x, xe^x+2e^x
   (d) $2xe^{-2x}(1-x)$, $2e^{-2x}(2x^2-4x+1)$ (e) $e^{1/x}(x-1)/x$, $e^{1/x}x^{-3}$.
   (f) $e^{-3x}(-3x^2+14x-10)$, $e^{-3x}(9x^2-48x+44)$
7. $x=\log 5$, $\log 2$ 13. $(\mu, 1/[\sqrt{2\pi}\sigma])$, $(\mu\pm\sigma, e^{-1/2}/[\sqrt{2\pi}\sigma])$
17. 1.002

List 64 — Page 299

1. (a) $e^{\log 3}$ (b) $e^{\log \pi}$ (c) $e^{(\log 2)/2}$ (d) $e^{-\log 2}$ (e) e^1
11. $y=e^{x^2\log 2}$ 15. (a) $2x/[(x^2-4)\log 2]$
   (b) $\cot x/\log 10$ 21. (a) e^{-2} (b) $\sqrt{e}$ (c) e^x (d) $\log a$

List 65 — Page 302

1. (a) $(x-3)(3x-1)$ (b) $e^{-2x}(1-2x)$ (c) $3x^2+6x-4$
   (d) $-e^{-x}x^{-4}\cos x(x+x\tan x+3)$ 7. 2%

Chapter 11

List 66 — Page 308

1. $(x^2+2)^2/4+C$ 3. $1/2\log|x^2-1|+C$
5. $3\log|\csc(x/3)-\cot(x/3)|+C$ 7. $(-2\cos^3 x)/3+C$
9. $e^{4x^2}/8+C$ 11. $(\sec^2 2x)/4+C$

13. $x + \log|x + 1| + C$

15. $(-\csc^2 2x)/4 + C$

17. $e^{2x}/2 - 2x - e^{-2x}/2 + C$

19. $x - \text{Tan}^{-1} x + C$

21. $3(1 + \log x)^{4/3}/4 + C$

23. $-3 \csc (x/3) + C$

25. $-2(1 + x^{-1})^{1/2} + C$

27. $\text{Tan}^{-1} e^x + C$

29. $2\sqrt{e^x - 2} + C$

31. $2 \log (1 + \sqrt{x}) + C$

33. $x + \text{Tan}^{-1} x + C$

35. $(\text{Tan}^{-1} x)^2/2 + C$

37. $\text{Tan}^{-1}\sqrt{e^{2x} - 1} + C$

39. $(\sin 4x)/4 + C$

41. $-\log (1 + e^{-x}) + C$

43. $x^2/2 + 2x^5/5 + x^8/8 + C$

45. $2, 2/\pi$

47. $\pi(e^4 - 1)/2$

49. $\pi/3$

51. $\log (2 + \sqrt{3})$

List 67 — Page 312

1. $-\cos x + (\cos^3 x)/3 + C$

3. $(-\cos^3 x)/3 + (\cos^5 x)/5 + C$

5. $2(\sin x)^{3/2}/3 - 2(\sin x)^{7/2}/7 + C$

7. $\sec x + C$

9. $(4 \sin^3 x)/3 - (4 \sin^5 x)/5 + C$

11. $(-\cos 3x)/3 + (2 \cos^3 3x)/9 - (\cos^5 3x)/15 + C$

13. $5x/2 + 2 \sin 2x + (3 \sin 4x)/8 - (\sin^3 2x)/6 + C$

15. $(-\sin 2x)/2 + (\sin^3 2x)/6 + C$

17. $(\cos^4 x)/4 - (\cos^2 x)/2 + C$

19. $(\tan^4 x)/4 - (\tan^2 x)/2 - \log|\cos x| + C$

21. $(-\cot^2 2x)/4 - (1/2) \log|\sin 2x| + C$

23. $-(1/2) \cot 2x - (\cot^3 2x)/6 + C$

25. $x/2 + (\sin 4x)/8 + C$

27. $x/16 - (\sin 4x)/64 - (\sin^3 2x)/48 + C$

29. $(-\cot^3 x)/3 + C$

31. $-3x/2 + \tan x + (\sin 2x)/4 + C$

33. $-19/80$

35. $(3 \sin^4 x)/2 - (4 \sin^6 x)/3 + C$

37. $-(1/2) \cos x - (\cos 7x)/14 + C$

39. $(\sin x)/2 + (\sin 5x)/10 + C$

41. $\pi^2/2$

List 68 — Page 316

1. $-x \cos x + \sin x + C$

3. $(x \sin 2x)/2 + (\cos 2x)/4 + C$

5. $x^2 e^x - 2xe^x + 2e^x + C$

7. $x \tan x + \log|\cos x| - x + C$

9. $x \text{Tan}^{-1} x - 1/2 \log (1 + x^2) + C$

11. $2^{-1}[(x^2 + 1) \text{Tan}^{-1} x - x] + C$

13. $2^{-1} \sin^2 x + C$

15. $x \log (1 + x^2) - 2x + 2 \text{Tan}^{-1}x + C$

17. $[\cos x \sin 3x - 3 \cos 3x \sin x]/8 + C$

19. $x^2 \sin x + 2x \cos x - 2 \sin x + C$

21. $(2x^{3/2} \log x)/3 - 4x^{3/2}/9 + C$

23. $2(x + 1)^{3/2}(3x - 2)/15 + C$

25. $2^{-1} \log^2 x + C$

27. $-x \cos x + (x \cos^3 x)/3 + (2 \sin x)/3 + (\sin^3 x)/9 + C$

29. $-x^2 \cos x + 2x \sin x + 2 \cos x + C$

31. $(x \sin^3 x)/3 + (\cos x)/3 - (\cos^3 x)/9 + C$

33. $xe^{3x}/3 - e^{3x}/9 + C$

35. $e^{ax}(a \sin bx - b \cos bx)/(a^2 + b^2) + C$

37. $\pi/4$

39. $\text{Tan}^{-1} 3 - (\log 10)/6$

47. $5\pi/32$

49. $2\pi^2$

53. $(x + 3) \log (x + 3) - x + C$

List 69 — Page 321

1. $\sqrt{x} - 2^{-1} \log (1 + 2\sqrt{x}) + C$

3. $3(1 + x)^{4/3} (14x^2 - 12x + 9)/140 + C$

5. $2\sqrt{x} - 3x^{1/3} + 6x^{1/6} - 6 \log (x^{1/6} + 1) + C$

7. $2(1 - x^{1/3})^{5/2}(-8 - 20x^{1/3} - 35x^{2/3})/105 + C$

9. $2\sqrt{x+2}\,(x+5)/3 + C$ 11. $2(x+1)^{3/2}/3 + 2x^{3/2}/3 + C$
13. $4(1+\sqrt{x})^{3/2}\,(3\sqrt{x}-2)/15 + C$ 15. $9088/45$
17. $2 - \pi/2$
21. $-(1-x)^{n+1}/(n+1) + (1-x)^{n+2}/(n+2) + C$
27. $256/15$

List 70 — Page   325

1. $\log(x + \sqrt{x^2+9}) + C$ 3. $\log|x + \sqrt{x^2-4}| + C$
5. $[\mathrm{Tan}^{-1}(x/a)]/a + C$
7. $2^{-1}[x\sqrt{x^2-a^2} - a^2\log|x+\sqrt{x^2-a^2}|] + C$
9. $-\sqrt{x^2-a^2}/x + \log|x+\sqrt{x^2-a^2}| + C$
11. $(1/3)\log|(\sqrt{4x^2+9}-3)/x| + C$ 13. $\mathrm{Sin}^{-1} x$
15. $\sqrt{3} - 2^{-1}\log(2+\sqrt{3})$ 17. $2\sqrt{2} + 2\log(\sqrt{2}+1)$
19. πab 21. $2^{-1}[4\sqrt{17} + \log(\sqrt{17}+4)]$
23. $\pi/8$ 25. $2a^2(1 - \pi/4)$

List 71 — Page 329

1. $\log|(x-1)^{7/5}\,(x+4)^{18/5}| + C$ 3. $\log|(x+2)^3\,(x-2)^4| + C$
5. $\log|(x-8)^2/(x-1)^5| + C$ 7. $\log(x-2)^2 + 3/(x-2) + C$
9. $x^3/3 + \log|(x+1)^5/(x-2)^4| + C$ 11. $\log|(x+1)^2\,(x-1)(x+2)^3| + C$
13. $[\log|(a+x)/(a-x)|]/(2a) + C$ 15. $\log|x-1| - 3/(x-2) + C$
17. $3x^2/2 - 4/(x-1) + C$ 19. $\log|x-1| + 3\,\mathrm{Tan}^{-1} x + C$
21. $\log|(x-1)^2(x^3-1)| + C$ 23. $(15\log 1.2)/11$
25. $5\pi/12 - 2\log 2$ 27. $\log[(1+3e^{-x})^{1/3}/(1+2e^{-x})^{1/2}] + C$
29. $\{\log|[\tan(\theta/2)+2]/[\tan(\theta/2)-2]|\}/4 + C$
31. $(\pi^2 + 2\pi)/4$

List 72 — Page 331

1. $\{\mathrm{Tan}^{-1}[(x+2)/3]\}/3 + C$ 3. $\mathrm{Sin}^{-1}[(x+1)/3] + C$
5. $2^{-1}\log(1+x^2) + \mathrm{Tan}^{-1} x + C$
7. $-\log(x^2-2x+5) + \mathrm{Tan}^{-1}[(x-1)/2] + C$
9. $18\,\mathrm{Sin}^{-1}[(2x-9)/9] - 4\sqrt{9x-x^2} + C$
11. $\log|x| + \mathrm{Tan}^{-1}(x+1) + C$
13. $\{\mathrm{Sin}^{-1}[(2x+1)/\sqrt{11}]\}/4 - 3(10-4x-4x^2)^{1/2}/4 + C$
15. $\log(x^2+2x+2) + \mathrm{Tan}^{-1}(x+1) - (x^2+2x+2)^{-1} + C$

List 73 — Page 334

1. $8/15$ 3. $5\pi/32$
5. $5\pi/256$ 7. $2/63$
9. $1/5$ 11. $256/315$
13. 0 15. 0
17. 0 19. $4/9$
21. $3\pi/512$ 23. $21\pi/128$
25. $\pi/4$ 27. 3π
31. $16/15$ 33. $17,496/35$

List 74 — Page 335

1. $x/2 - (3\log|2x+3|)/4 + C$
3. $(x+1)\sqrt{2x-1}/3 + C$
5. $x/16 + (1/128)\log|(4x-1)/(4x+1)| + C$
7. $(x\sqrt{x^2+4})/2 + 2\log|x+\sqrt{x^2+4}| + C$
9. $(-\sqrt{4-9x^2})/(9x) - 3\,\mathrm{Sin}^{-1}(3x/2) + C$
11. $x/2 - (\sin 10x)/20 + C$
13. $e^{6x}(6x-1)/36 + C$
15. $e^{2x}(2\cos 3x + 3\sin 3x)/13 + C$
17. $x(\log|4x|-1) + C$

List 75 — Page 339

1. $1/8$
3. diverges
5. diverges
7. $3/2$
9. $1/2$
11. $1/2$
13. diverges
15. $\pi/2$
17. diverges
19. diverges
21. 1
23. 2π
25. $\pi a/2$
27. $3\pi a^2$
29. $4\sqrt{3}$
31. $3\pi a^2/2$
33. (a) $1 - e^{-6}$ (c) e^{-1}

List 76 — Page 343

1. Exact answers are: (a) 168 (b) log 10 (c) 1 (d) 1 (e) $e^2 - e$.
3. (a) (i) 0.82 (ii) 0.84 (b) (i) 0.88 (ii) 0.88 (c) (i) 1.90 (ii) 2.00 (d) (i) 99.78 (ii) 98.63
   (e) (i) 96.09 (ii) 95.98 (f) (i) 1.78 (ii) 1.85
5. 1.11

Chapter 12

List 77 — Page 351

3. $(0,0); r = \sqrt{a^2+b^2}$
7. $x = 2a\cot\theta; y = 2a\sin^2\theta$
9. πab
11. $64\pi a^2/3$
13. $V = 32\pi a^3/105,\ S = 12\pi a^2/5$

Chapter 13

List 78 — Page 361

5. (a) $x^2 + y^2 = 9$ (b) $(x-1)^2 + y^2 = 1$ (c) $(x^2+y^2)^3 = 16(x^2-y^2)^2$
   (d) $y^2 = -4a(x-a)$ (e) $(x^2+y^2)^2 = 2a^2xy$ (f) $y = x$
   (g) $a^2(x^2+y^2) = (x^2+y^2+ax)^2$ (h) $4(x^2+y^2) = (x^2+y^2+x)^2$
   (i) $x(x^2+y^2) = 2ay^2$ (j) $3x^2 + 4y^2 - 16x - 64 = 0$
9. $r = -2\sin\alpha$

List 79 — Page 370

3. $2a = 2ep/(1-e^2),\ 2b = 2ep/\sqrt{1-e^2}$

5. $y \longrightarrow + \infty$ as $\theta \longrightarrow 0^+$ and $y \longrightarrow - \infty$ as $\theta \longrightarrow 0^-$

9. $2\sqrt{2}\, a$ **11.** $\sqrt{2}\, (e^\pi - 1)$

13. 2   **15.** $2\sqrt{2}\, \pi a^2$

17. $4\pi a^2$ **19.** (a) πa^2 (b) πa^2 (c) $a^2/2$ (d) $33\pi/2$

(e) $\pi/2$ (f) 3π (g) $3\pi a^2/2$ (h) $(e^{4\pi} - e^{2\pi})/4$ (i) $a^2(\pi - 2)/2$ (j) $7\pi/8 - 1$

(k) $a^2(9\sqrt{3} - 2\pi)/2$ (l) $\mathbf{a}^2(\pi + 2)/2$ (m) $2p^2/3$ (n) $3\sqrt{3}\, a^2$ (o) $(2\pi - 3\sqrt{3})/2$

(p) $3a^2/2$ (q) $8\sqrt{3}\, \pi$

Chapter 14

List 80 — Page 376

11. (a) $2^{-1} \cosh 2x + C$ (b) $2^{-1} \sinh x^2 + C$ (c) $(\tanh 3x)/3 + C$

(d) $\coth (1 - x) + C$ (e) $(-\operatorname{sech}^2 2x)/4 + C$ (f) $(2 \cosh^3 x)/3 + C$

(g) $x/2 + (\sinh 6x)/12 + C$

(h) $(\sinh^3 x \cosh x)/4 + 3x/8 - (3 \sinh 2x)/16 + C$

(i) $9/16$ (j) $(e^2 + 1)/4$

13. $\pi(-2 + \sinh 2)/4$ **15.** 225.52, 308.62

List 81 — Page 381

11. (a) $\sinh^{-1} (x/2) + C$ (b) $2^{-1} \cosh^{-1} 2x + C$ (c) $[\tanh^{-1} (2x/3)]/6 + C$

(d) $[2x \sqrt{9 + 4x^2} + 9 \sinh^{-1} (2x/3)]/4 + C$

(e) $[5x \sqrt{25x^2 - 4} - 4 \cosh^{-1} (5x/2)]/10 + C$

(f) $\cosh^{-1} [(x - 2)/\sqrt{3}] + C$

(g) $(3x - 2) \sqrt{9x^2 - 12x + 8}/6 + \{2 \sinh^{-1}[(3x - 2)/2]\}/3 + C$

(h) $-\sqrt{x^2 + 1}/x + C$ (i) $-x/\sqrt{a^2 + x^2} + \sinh^{-1} (x/a) + C$

(j) $-x\sqrt{a^2 - x^2}/2 + [a^2 \operatorname{Sin}^{-1} (x/a)]/2 + C$ (k) $x \cosh^{-1} x - \sqrt{x^2 - 1} + C$

(l) $x \tanh^{-1} x + 2^{-1} \log (1 - x^2) + C$

(m) $[2x^3 \tanh^{-1} x + x^2 + \log (1 - x^2)]/6 + C$ (n) $\tanh^{-1} (1/2)$

13. $40/3 - 6 \cosh^{-1} (5/3)$

Chapter 15

List 82 — Page 386

3. (a) $\sqrt{29}$ (b) -7 (c) -9 (d) $\sqrt{17}$ (e) $\sqrt{34}$ (f) $\sqrt{77}$ (g) $\sqrt{11}$ (h) $\sqrt{189}$

5. $\sqrt{41}$ to x-axis, $\sqrt{29}$ to y-axis, $2\sqrt{5}$ to z-axis

List 83 — Page 391

3. $\pm 2\sqrt{41}/15$

5. (a) $(-1, 4, 6)$ (b) $(5, -6, 2)$ (c) $(4, -2, 8)$ (d) $(-9, 15, 6)$ (e) $(-2, 1, -4)$

(f) $(9, -15, -6)$ (g) $(-5, 13, 14)$ (h) $(-18, 23, -4)$

7. $(-2, -5, 5)$ **9.** $11(2/11, -6/11, 9/11)$

15. $(6, -3, 9)$

List 84 — Page 396

1. (a) 28 (b) 8 (c) 1 (d) 12
11. $12/77$, $109/(11\sqrt{146})$, $37/(7\sqrt{146})$

9. $\theta = \mathrm{Cos}^{-1}(2/3)$

List 85 — Page 399

1. (a) $7\mathbf{i} - 14\mathbf{j} - 14\mathbf{k}$ (b) $-16\mathbf{i} - 13\mathbf{j} - 14\mathbf{k}$ (c) $-2\mathbf{i} + 10\mathbf{j} + 4\mathbf{k}$
    (d) $38\mathbf{i} - 31\mathbf{j} - 36\mathbf{k}$
21. $4/\sqrt{170}$

9. $(-5\mathbf{i} - \mathbf{j} + 7\mathbf{k})/(5\sqrt{3})$

List 86 — Page 403

5. $(36/169, 144/169, -48/169)$
9. $\theta = \mathrm{Cos}^{-1}(7/9)$

7. $10/3$
11. $6/7, 3/7, 2/7$

List 87 — Page 405

1. (a) $x = 4 + 5t; y = 3 - 3t; z = -6 + 2t$
    (b) $x = 3 + 3t; y = -4 + 5t; z = 2 - 4t$
    (c) $x = 4; z = 1$ (d) $x = -3 - 2t; y = 2 + 3t; z = 1 + 8t$
    (e) $x = -6 + 14t; y = 4 - 7t; z = 2 - 2t$
    (f) $x = 5 + 18t; y = 4 + 7t; z = -2 - 8t$
3. (a) $(x - 9/35)/-2 = (y - 2/35)/19 = z/35$
    (b) $(x - 13/11)/14 - (y - 1/22)/-2 = z/22$
5. $\sqrt{1239/19}$
11. $(2, 3, -4)$

9. $(-74/49, 212/49, 1/49)$

List 88 — Page 412

1. (a) $x^2 + y^2 + z^2 = 25$ (b) $(x - 2)^2 + (y + 3)^2 + (z - 6)^2 = 4$
    (c) $(x + 3)^2 + (y - 2)^2 + (z - 1)^2 = 121$
    (d) $(x - 11/2)^2 + (y - 11/2)^2 + (z + 4)^2 = 50/4$
    (e) $(x - 6)^2 + (y - 4)^2 + (z \pm 5)^2 = 25$ (f) $(x - 4)^2 + (y - 3)^2 + (z - 6)^2 = 25$
3. (a) $x^4 = 16(y^2 + z^2)$ (b) $\sqrt{y^2 + z^2} = \sqrt{4 - x^2}$ (c) $x^2/a^2 + y^2/b^2 + z^2/b^2 = 1$
    (d) $y^2 = 25(x^2 + z^2)$ (e) $z = 4 - x^2 - y^2$ (f) $x^2/a^2 - y^2/b^2 - z^2/b^2 = 1$
9. $x^2 + y^2 = z^2$
11. $2(x - 4) + 4(y - 4) + 4(z + 5) = 0$ 13. $4\pi abc/3$
15. $(x - 9)^2 + y^2 + z^2 = 9$; sphere

List 89 — Page 415

3. $18\mathbf{i} - 135\mathbf{j} - 6\mathbf{k}, 6\mathbf{i} - 90\mathbf{j}$

5. $(-4/5, -3/5, 0)$

List 90 — Page 426

5. $t = (2v_0 \sin \alpha)/g$, $x = (v_0^2 \sin 2\alpha)/g$, $y(\max) = (v_0^2 \sin^2 \alpha)/(2g)$
7. $a_t = 4/\sqrt{5}$, $a_n = 2/\sqrt{5}$, $v = \sqrt{5}$, $\kappa = 2/(5\sqrt{5})$
9. $a_t = 0, a_n = 2$ 11. $2/(5\sqrt{5})$
13. $(\max) \kappa = 2\sqrt{3}/9$ at $(\log 2, 2)$ 17. $x = \pm\sqrt{y - y^2}, y = y, z = y$
19. $2(x - 1) + 6(y - 3) + 5(z - 2) = 0$ 21. $\pi\sqrt{a^2\omega^2 + b^2}/\omega$

Chapter 16

List 91 — Page 431

1.   (a) $D: -\infty < x < \infty, -\infty < y < \infty; R: z \geqslant 0$
    (b) $D: -2 \leqslant x \leqslant 2, -\infty < y < \infty; R: 0 \leqslant z \leqslant 2$
    (c) $D: -\infty < x < \infty, -\infty < y < \infty; R: z \leqslant 4$
    (d) $D: xy \geqslant 0; R: z \geqslant 0$ (e) $D: x + y > 0; R: -\infty < z < \infty$
    (f) $D: -\infty < x < \infty, -\infty < y < \infty; R: -1 \leqslant z \leqslant 1$
    (g) $D: x^2 + y^2 + z^2 \leqslant 1; R: 0 \leqslant u \leqslant 1$
    (h) $D: -\infty < x < \infty, y^2 + z^2 \leqslant 4; R: -\infty < u < \infty$

List 92 — Page 435

1.   (a) $z_x = 2x - 6x^2y^4, z_y = -8x^3y^3$ (b) $z_x = 3y^2 + 4y^3, z_y = 6xy + 12xy^2$
    (c) $z_x = xy^2e^{xy} (xy + 2), z_y = x^2ye^{xy} (xy + 2)$
    (d) $z_x = x^2y \cos xy + 2x \sin xy, z_y = x^3 \cos xy$
    (e) $z_x = -\sin x \cos y - \cos x \sin y, z_y = -\cos x \sin y - \sin x \cos y$
    (f) $z_x = 8x(x^2 + 2y^3)^3, z_y = 24y^2(x^2 + 2y^3)^3$
3.   (a) $u_x = 4xy + 3z^2, u_y = 2x^2, u_z = 6xz$
    (b) $u_x = y/(2\sqrt{xy}), u_y = x/(2\sqrt{xy}) + z^3, u_z = 3yz^2$
    (c) $u_x = 2x^2y^2z \cos (x^2z) + y^2 \sin (x^2z), u_y = 2xy \sin (x^2z), u_z = x^3y^2 \cos (x^2z)$
    (d) $u_x = ye^{xy} \sin (2y^2z), u_y = 4e^{xy}yz \cos (2y^2z) + xe^{xy} \sin (2y^2z), u_z = 2y^2e^{xy} \cos (2y^2z)$
5.   (a) $z_{xx} = 18xy^2 - 8y^4$ (b) $z_{yy} = 6x^3 - 48x^2y^2$ (c) $z_{xy} = 18x^2y - 32xy^3$
    (d) $z_{xxx} = 18y^2$
7. $x_r = \cos \theta, y_r = \sin \theta, x_\theta = -r \sin \theta, y_\theta = r \cos \theta$
13.   (a) $z_x = -x/z, z_y = -y/z$ (b) $z_x = -x/z, z_y = -9y/(4z)$
    (c) $z_x = x/(4z), z_y = y/(9z)$ (d) $z_x = 2x, z_y = 8y$
    (e) $z_x = (yz - x^2)/(z^2 - xy), z_y = (xz - y^2)/(z^2 - xy)$
    (f) $z_x = x(x^2 + y^2 + z^2)^2/\{z[9 - (x^2 + y^2 + z^2)^2]\},$
      $z_y = y(x^2 + y^2 + z^2)^2/\{z[9 - (x^2 + y^2 + z^2)^2]\}$

List 93 — Page 438

1.   (a) $(6x + 3x^2) dx$ (b) $(3x^2 - 3y) dx + (-3x + 3y^2) dy$ (c) $(8x^3 + y^2) dx + 2xy \, dy$
    (d) $3 \cos x \, dx + 4 \sin y \, dy$
    (e) $(\cos y + 2y^2 \sin 2x) dx + (-x \sin y - 2y \cos 2x) dy$
    (f) $(-e^{xy} \sin x + ye^{xy} \cos x) dx + xe^{xy} \cos x \, dy$
    (g) $-4y \sin xy \cos xy \, dx - 4x \sin xy \cos xy \, dy$
    (h) $(-2 \cos x \sin x + 2xy) dx + x^2 dy$ (i) $-x^{-1} dx + (2y - y^{-1}) dy$
    (j) $[2x^2y^2/(1 + x^4y^4) + \text{Tan}^{-1} (x^2y^2)] dx + [2x^3y/(1 + x^4y^4)] dy$
3. -0.9
5. $dz = 0.27, \Delta z = 0.278525, \Delta z - dz = 0.008525$
7.   83/8 cu in.   9.   10,145.925
11.   (a) 17.50 (b) 7.10

List 94 — Page 442

1. (a) $2(x - 1) + 4(y - 2) - (z - 5) = 0$; $(x - 1)/2 = (y - 2)/4 = (z - 5)/-1$
   (b) $16(x - 2) - 18(y + 1) - (z - 25) = 0$;
   $(x - 2)/16 = (y + 1)/-18 = (z - 25)/-1$
   (c) $6(x - 3) - (z - 9) = 0$; $(x - 3)/6 = (z - 9)/-1$, $y = 0$
   (d) $2(x - 1) + 2(y - 1) + (z - 2) = 0$; $(x - 1)/2 = (y - 1)/2 = (z - 2)/1$
   (e) $4(x - 3) + 3(y - 4) - (z - 12) = 0$; $(x - 3)/4 = (y - 4)/3 = (z - 12)/-1$
   (f) $(\pi\sqrt{3}/12)(x - 1) + (\sqrt{3}/2)(y - \pi/6) - (z - 1/2) = 0$;
   $(x - 1)/(\pi\sqrt{3})/12) = (y - \pi/6)/(\sqrt{3}/2) = (z - 1/2)/-1$
   (g) $z = 1$; $x = 1$, $y = 1$
   (h) $2e(x - 1) + e(y - 2) - (z - 2e) = 0$,
   $(x - 1)/(2e) = (y - 2)/e = (z - 2e)/-1$

5. $25/\sqrt{101}$ 7.   7.16, 7.1613
11. $1(x - 1/3) + 2(y - 2/3) - 2(z - 4/3) = 0$

List 95 — Page 446

1. (a) $\partial u/\partial t = 4x + 10y + 3sz^2$, $\partial u/\partial s = 6x - 4y + 3tz^2$
   (b) $\partial u/\partial t = 4xy^3 + 6x^2y^2st - 2zs^2$, $\partial u/\partial s = 2xy^3 + 3x^2y^2t^2 - 4zst$
   (c) $\partial u/\partial t = y \cos z - x \cos z - 2xyst \sin z$,
   $\partial u/\partial s = y \cos z + 2x \cos z - xyt^2 \sin z$
   (d) $\partial u/\partial t = -2xs \sin t + 2ys \cos t$, $\partial u/\partial s = 2x \cos t + 2y \sin t$

3. (a) 0   (b) 10   (c) 10   9.   (a) $2\sqrt{u}$ (b) $\sqrt{y^2 + x^2 + 144z^6}$
11. $6\mathbf{i} + 9\mathbf{j} + 12\mathbf{k}$, $3\sqrt{29}$ 13. $13/(5\sqrt{3})$, $\sqrt{21}$, $-\sqrt{21}$
15. hottest direction: that of $\mathbf{grad}\ \tau = 8\mathbf{i} + 16\mathbf{j} + 18\mathbf{k}$,
   coldest direction: that of $-\mathbf{grad}\ \tau = -8\mathbf{i} - 16\mathbf{j} - 18\mathbf{k}$

List 96 — Page 451

5. (a) $4\mathbf{i} - 216\mathbf{j}$ (b) $15\mathbf{i} + 8\mathbf{j}$ 9. $4\sqrt{5}$
11. $(8\sqrt{3} + 11)/2$, $\sqrt{185}$ in direction $\text{Tan}^{-1} (11/8)$

List 97 — Page 454

1. (a) $-x/(2y)$ (b) $4x/(9y)$ (c) $(2x^3 + 1)/(3y)$
   (d) $(-e^x \sin y - e^y \cos x)/(e^x \cos y + e^y \sin x)$

3. $1/4$, -1

7. (a) $2(x - 1) - 6(x + 3) + 4(z - 2) = 0$
   (b) $8(x - 2) + 6(y - 1) + 2(z - 1) = 0$

9. (a) $u_x = (-x - vy)/(u + v)$, $v_x = (x - uy)/(u + v)$,
   $u_y = -vx/(u + v)$, $v_y = -ux/(u + v)$
   (b) $u_x = (2v + uy)/(-2v^2 - 2u^2)$, $v_x = (2u - vy)/(-2v^2 - 2u^2)$,
   $u_y = (2v + ux)/(-2v^2 - 2u^2)$, $v_y = (-vx + 2u)/(-2v^2 - 2u^2)$
   (c) $u_x = \cos v$, $v_x = (-\sin v)/u$, $u_y = \sin v$, $v_y = (\cos v)/u$
   (d) $u_x = e^{-u} \sin v$, $v_x = e^{-u} \cos v$, $u_y = e^{-u} \cos v$, $v_y = -e^{-u} \sin v$

11. $(x - 1)/8 = (y + 1)/10 = (z - 2)/7$

List 98 — Page 459

1. (a) 3 (b) $2\sqrt{14}/7$ (c) $4\sqrt{3}/3$ (d) $\sqrt{3}$ 3. 32
7. 8 by 8 by 12   9. $2x + 4y + z = 12$
11. $a = 11/10, b = -1/5$ 13. (a) $M = 11, m = 2$
    (b) $M = 4, m = 2$
15. (a) $M = 1, m = e^{-1}$ (b) $M = 1, m = e^{-4}$

Chapter 17

List 99 — Page 466

3. (a) 4 (b) 6 (c) $\sqrt{34}$ 5. 84

List 100 — Page 470

1. (a) 15/8 (b) 621/20 (c) $-17/12$ (d) 196 (e) $37/3 + \cos 4 - \cos 3$
    (f) $e(e^3 - 2e - 1)/2$ (g) $\pi/8$ (h) 1/20 (i) $-41/60$
3. 56/3   5. 12
7. 3π 9. $abc/6$
11. (a) 8/3 (b) 1/4 (c) $1 - \sqrt{3}/2$ (d) $4 \log 2 - 1.5$ (e) $ab/2$ (f) 4.5 (g) 32/3
    (h) 4.5   13. $4\pi a^3/3$

List 101 — Page 476

1. $15\pi/8$ 3. $3\pi/2$
5. $8\pi/3$ 7. 32/5
9. (a) 25π (b) $25 \operatorname{Cos}^{-1}(2/5) - 2\sqrt{21}$ (c) $\pi/8$ (d) $2 + \pi/4$ (e) $\sqrt{3}/4 - \pi/12$
    (f) $3\pi/2$ (g) $13\pi/96 - [7 \operatorname{Sin}^{-1}(1/4)]/16 + (\sqrt{15}/32) - (\sqrt{3}/8)$
11. $a^2\alpha - [a^2 \sin(2\alpha)]/2$ 13. $2a^3(3\pi - 4)/9$

List 102 — Page 483

1. (a) $2k/3$ (b) $64k/5$ (c) $k(e^2 - 1)/4$ (d) $130k/3$ (e) $32k/9$
3. 40/3
5. (a) (8/5, 16/7) (b) (147/50, 27/20) (c) (1/2, 8/5) (d) $(\pi/2, \pi/8)$ (e) (9/20, 9/20)
    (f) (5a/6, 0) (g) $([16 - 5\pi]/[6\pi - 16], 2/[9\pi - 24])$ (h) (17/72, 0) (i) $(\sqrt{2}\pi/8, 0)$
7. $(2a \sin \alpha)/(3\alpha)$ from center of circle   9. $(4a/[3\pi], 4b/[3\pi])$
11. (0, 164/55)   13. $2\pi^2 a^2 b^2$

List 103 — Page 489

1. (a) $2187k/14$ (b) $128k/3$ (c) $256k$ (d) $k\pi a^5/5$
3. (a) 1/20 (b) 1/28 (c) 1/20 (d) 61/140 (e) 1/120
5. $bh^3/3, h/\sqrt{3}$ 7. $21\pi a^4/32$
9. 124,988   11. $a^4/12$

List 104 — Page 492

1. (a) $3\sqrt{17} + (3/4) \log (4 + \sqrt{17})$ (b) $(5\sqrt{5} - 1)/12$ (c) $\sqrt{14}/6$
    (d) $(2 - \sqrt{3})\pi a^2$ (e) $(5\sqrt{5} - 1)/24$ (f) $12[\operatorname{Sin}^{-1}(2/3) - \operatorname{Sin}^{-1}(1/3)]$

3. $\pi[(4a^2 + 1)^{3/2} - 1]/6$

7. $4a^2(\pi - 2)$

9. $\pi a^2(5\sqrt{5} - 1)/6$

11. $6\sqrt{37} + \log(6 + \sqrt{37})$

List 105 — Page 502

1. (a) 6 (b) 4779/40 (c) 1376/21 (d) $\pi/8$ (e) 0 (f) $\pi a^4/4$

3. 128π

5. $\pi/2$

7. $4\pi abc/3$

9. 18

11. $\pi(8\sqrt{2} - 7)/6$

13. $16(3\pi - 4)/9$

15. $k\pi a^4 h/2$

17. $\bar{z} = 3a/8$

19. $(a/4, b/4, c/4)$

21. $\bar{z} = (10h^2 - 6a^2)/(20h - 15a)$

23. $[r_1^2 + r_2^2 - 2r_1 r_2 \cos(\theta_2 - \theta_1) + (z_2 - z_1)^2]^{1/2}$ **25.** $28ka^7/45$

27. (a) $I_{x=0} = 84/5$, $I_{y=0} = 20/3$, $I_{z=0} = 134/3$ (b) $I_{\substack{y=0 \\ z=0}} = 154/3$, $I_{\substack{x=0 \\ z=0}} = 922/15$,

$I_{\substack{x=0 \\ y=0}} = 352/15$

29. $m(a^2 + b^2)/3$

31. (a) $3ma^2/10$ (b) $m(3a^2/20 + h^2/10)$

List 106 — Page 506

1. $4\pi a^3/3$

3. $8\pi a^5/15 = 2ma^2/5$

5. 8π

Chapter 18

List 107 — Page 513

1. 6

3. 1

5. 1/6

7. 2

9. 6

11. 1/2

13. 3/2

15. $-1/2$

17. $\log(2/3)$

19. 1

21. na

23. 0

25. 1

27. $-\pi$

29. na^{n-1}

31. 0

33. 3/4

35. ∞

37. 0

39. 0

41. 1

43. 8

45. 3/4

47. 1/4

49. 0

53. (a) -1 (b) $-1/4$ (c) ∞ (d) $\log 2$

List 108 — Page 517

1. e

3. 1

5. e^{-1}

7. 1

9. 1

11. e

13. e^4

15. e^a

17. 1

19. 1

21. $e^{1/\pi}$

23. ∞

25. $-e/2$

Chapter 19

List 109 — Page 523

1. (a) 1/8 (b) 31/32 (c) 0 (d) 1

3. (a) 1/3 (b) 4/3 (c) 1/8 (d) 0 (e) 2/3 (f) $-5/6$

9. 25/99

15. $-1/[n(n - 1)]$

21. 3/2

List 110 — Page 529

1. (a) C (b) C (c) D (d) D (e) C (f) D (g) C (h) C (i) C (j) D (k) D (l) C
    (m) D (n) C (o) D (p) C 5. $0.0001 < R_n < 0.00010001$
7. (a) 7 (b) 20 (c) 54   9. no conclusion

List 111 — Page 532

1. (a) C (b) C (c) D (d) C (e) C (f) D (g) C (h) C (i) D (j) C (k) C (l) D
    (m) C (n) C (o) C (p) C (q) D (r) C (s) C (t) C (u) D

List 112 — Page 538

5. approximately 0.7   11. $|R_{24}| < 1/625$
13. 0.90

List 113 — Page 542

1. (a) $-1 \leqslant x < 1$, $R = 1$ (b) $R = \infty$ (c) $-1 \leqslant x \leqslant 1$, $R = 1$ (d) $R = \infty$
    (e) $-4 \leqslant x \leqslant 4$, $R = 4$ (f) $-1/2 < x < 1/2$, $R = 1/2$ (g) $R = \infty$
    (h) $-2 \leqslant x \leqslant 2$, $R = 2$ (i) $-1 \leqslant x \leqslant 1$, $R = 1$ (j) $0 < x \leqslant 2$, $R = 1$
    (k) $1 < x < 3$, $R = 1$ 3. (a) $-1 < x < 1$ (b) $x = 1$
7. $-7 < x \leqslant -3$

List 114 — Page 546

1. (a) $\sum\limits_{i=0}^{\infty} (2^i/i!)x^i$ (b) $\sum\limits_{i=0}^{\infty} (-1)^i x^{2i}/(2i)!$ (c) $\sum\limits_{i=1}^{\infty} (-1)^{i+1} x^i/i$ (d) $x^2 - 5x + 7$

    (e) $\sum\limits_{i=0}^{\infty} (-1)^i x^i$ (f) $\sum\limits_{i=0}^{\infty} (-1)^i x^{2i}$ (g) $\sum\limits_{i=1}^{\infty} -x^i/i$ (h) $\sum\limits_{i=0}^{\infty} (i + 1)x^i$

    (i) $\sum\limits_{i=1}^{\infty} (-1)^{i+1} (3x)^{2i-1}/(2i - 1)!$ (j) $\sum\limits_{i=0}^{\infty} m!x^i/[i!(m - i)!]$

3. (a) $e \sum\limits_{i=0}^{\infty} (x - 1)^i/i!$ (b) $\log 2 + \sum\limits_{i=1}^{\infty} (-1)^{i+1} (x - 2)^i/(i2^i)$

    (c) $1 + (x - 1)/2 + \sum\limits_{i=2}^{\infty} (-1)^{i+1} (2i - 3)(2i - 5) \cdots (1)(x - 1)^i/(2^i i!)$
    (d) $[1 + (x - \pi/4) - (x - \pi/4)^2/2! - (x - \pi/4)^3/3! + \cdots]/\sqrt{2}$
    (e) $\sum\limits_{i=0}^{\infty} (-1)^i (x - 3)^i/3^{i+1}$
    (f) $2/\sqrt{3} + 2(x - \pi/6)/3 + 5\sqrt{3}(x - \pi/6)^2/9 + 7(x - \pi/6)^3/9 + \cdots$
5. 0.719
9. $-11 - 2(x - 2) + 6(x - 2)^2 + 5(x - 2)^3 + (x - 2)^4$
11. 0.100

List 115 — Page 550

3. all x 5. $\sum\limits_{i=1}^{\infty} x^i/i$

7. $2 \sum\limits_{i=1}^{\infty} x^{2i-1}/(2i - 1)$, $\log 2 = 2 \sum\limits_{i=1}^{\infty} 1/[3^{2i-1}(2i - 1)]$
9. 0.291   11. 3.14
13. $\log x = \log 2 + (x - 2)/2 - (x - 2)^2/(2\xi^2)$
15. 0.199   17. 0.695

Chapter 20

List 116 — Page 556

1. (a) $y = e^x + C$ (b) $y = e^x + C_1 x + C_2$ (c) $y = -\cos x + C$
(d) $y = x^4/24 - (x^3/6) + (C_1 x^2/2) + C_2 x + C_3$ (e) $y = (x^2 \log x)/2 - (x^2/4) + C$
3. $|x| > 1$
7. (a) 2, L (b) 1, L (c) 3, L (d) 3, NL (e) 2, NL (f) 2, L
9. $y = -2$ 11. $y' = e^t - e^{-t}$
15. 15 ft

List 117 — Page 560

3. (a) $2x^2 y = C$ (b) $xy^2 = C$ (c) $y \sin x = C$ (d) $x^2 y + y^2 = C$ (e) $y \log x = C$
(f) $ye^x = C$ (g) $xy + x^2 = C$ (h) $e^x \sin y = C$

List 118 — Page 561

1. (a) $y = \pm [C + \log x]^{1/2}$ (b) $y = x^2/6 + C$ (c) $y = \pm [C + \mathrm{Tan}^{-1} x]^{1/2}$
(d) $e^{-y} = e^{-x} + C$ (e) $x^2 + \mathrm{Tan}^{-1} y = C$ (f) $\mathrm{Cos}^{-1}(1/x) - \mathrm{Sin}^{-1} y = C$
(g) $\log y = -x^{-1} + C$ (h) $2 + y^2 = C(3 + x^2)$
3. $y = 4/x$

List 119 — Page 563

1. (a) 3 (b) 1 (c) 3 (d) 0 (e) 0 3. $y = x \log |x| - x \log 2$
7. $y = Ce^x - x$

List 120 — Page 566

1. (a) $y = (x^3/5) + (x/3) + Cx^{-2}$ (b) $y = 1 + Ce^{-x^2}$ (c) $y = (x^3/4) + Cx^{-1}$
(d) $y = (x + C) \cos x$ (e) $r = (\theta^2/6) + C\theta^{-4}$ (f) $y = 1 + Ce^{-e^x}$
(g) $y = 3x(x + 1)^2 + C(x + 1)^{-2}$ (h) $y = \csc x \log |\csc x - \cot x| + C \csc x$
3. (a) $y = e^{-x}(x + 5)$ (b) $y = 2 + 4x^{-2}$ (c) $y = e^x - x^{-1}e^x + (ex)^{-1}$
(d) $y = \sin x + 2 \csc x$
7. (a) $y = [x^2 \log |Cx^{-1}|]^{-1}$ (b) $y^4 x^4 = 2x^2 + C$

List 121 — Page 571

1. 283% 3. 2 hr
5. 59 mg, 1308 years 7. 31.9 years
9. $v_5 = 160(1 - e^{-1})$, $\lim\limits_{t \to \infty} v = 160$, $x_{10} = 800(1 + e^{-2})$
11. (a) $v^2 = v_0^2 + 2ax$ (b) $x = at^2/2 + v_0 t$ (c) $v = at + v_0$
13. $1.0408 15. 14.1
17. $i = 5(\cos 10t + \sin 10t)/2 - (5e^{-10t})/2$ 19. $y = a[1 + e^{-at}]^{-1}/b$

List 122 — Page 575

3. (a) $y' = 3y/x$ (b) $y' = -x/y$ (c) $y' = y$ (d) $y' = 1 + y - x$ (e) $y' = x/y$
(f) $y' = y/(2x)$ (g) $y' = -y/x$
5. (a) $y'' - y = 0$ (b) $y'' + y = 0$ (c) $y'' = 2$

7. $y'' = 0$ 11. $x^2 + y^2 = cx$
13. $2x^2 + y^2 = C$, $2x^2 + y^2 = 6$, $y^2 = 4x$

List 123 — Page 579

5. $y = c_1 \sin 2x + c_2 \cos 2x$ 7. $W = -2x^{-1}$, $y = c_1 x + c_2 x^{-1}$
9. $W = 0$ 11. $y = 3x$
13. $y = c_1 e^{4x} + c_2 x e^{4x}$ 15. $y = c_1 + c_2 e^{-x} + e^x$
17. no

List 124 — Page 583

1. (a) $y = c_1 e^{4x} + c_2 e^{3x}$ (b) $y = c_1 e^{-3x} + c_2 e^{2x}$ (c) $y = c_1 e^{-x} + c_2 e^{-6x}$
    (d) $y = c_1 e^{2x} + c_2 e^{-2x}$ (e) $y = c_1 + c_2 e^{9x}$ (f) $y = c_1 + c_2 e^{-5x}$
    (g) $y = c_1 e^{(2+\sqrt{3})x} + c_2 e^{(2-\sqrt{3})x}$ (h) $y = c_1 e^{3x/4} + c_2 e^{-x/4}$ (i) $y = c_1 e^{3x} + c_2 x e^{3x}$
    (j) $y = c_1 e^{-2x} + c_2 x e^{-2x}$ (k) $y = c_1 \sin 5x + c_2 \cos 5x$
    (l) $y = e^{3x}(c_1 \sin 4x + c_2 \cos 4x)$ (m) $y = e^{-5x}(c_1 \sin 2x + c_2 \cos 2x)$
    (n) $y = e^{-x}(c_1 \sin x + c_2 \cos x)$ 3. $y = c_1 e^{-3x}$
9. (a) $c_1 \sin \beta x + c_2 \cos \beta x$ (b) $e^{\alpha x}$

List 125 — Page 586

1. (a) $Y = 3e^x$ (b) $Y = -5e^{-x}$ (c) $Y = 8e^{2x}/5$ (d) $Y = 3x^2 - 6x + 1$
    (e) $Y = 4x^2 + 4x - 7$ (f) $Y = 4 \cos x$ (g) $Y = \sin 2x + \cos 2x$
    (h) $Y = 2e^x + x^2$ (i) $Y = 5xe^{2x}/2$ (j) $Y = (-3x \cos x)/2$
3. (a) $y = -1 + 2e^{2x} + e^{3x}/3$ (b) $y = 4 \sin x + 2e^{-3x}$ (c) $y = e^{-x} + x + x^3/3$
    (d) $y = (e^x + e^{3x} - 2e^{2x})/2$ (e) $y = 2x + \cos x$ (f) $y = \sin 4x - 4x \cos 4x$
5. $y'' + y' - 2y = 0$ 7. $y = (c_1 x + c_2)e^{kx}$
9. $y = x^7/14 + c_1 x^5/5 + c_2$

List 126 — Page 598

1. $x = (\cos 40t)/3$, $v = (-40 \sin 40t)/3$, $a = (-1600 \cos 40t)/3$,
    $T = \pi/20$ sec, amp $= 1/3$ ft
3. $x = (\cos 48t)/2 - (\sin 48t)/4$, $v = -24 \sin 48t - 12 \cos 48t$,
    $\max |v| = 12\sqrt{5}$ ft/sec, amp $= \sqrt{5}/4$ ft, $T = \pi/24$ sec
7. $x = e^{-8t}(1 + 8t)/3$, $v = -64te^{-8t}/3$
9. $x = e^{-6t}(\sin 6t + \cos 6t)/3$, $v = -4e^{-6t} \sin 6t$
11. When $t = \pi/6$, $x = e^{-\pi/6}$ ft and $v = -e^{-\pi/6}$ fps
13. $x = -\sin 5t + (\cos 5t)/4$, $v = -5 \cos 5t - (5 \sin 5t)/4$,
    $T = 2\pi/5$ sec, amp $= \sqrt{17}/4$, $\max |v| = 5\sqrt{17}/4$
15. (a) $q = 1 + e^{-3t}[-\cos \sqrt{91}t - (3 \sin \sqrt{91}t)/\sqrt{91}]$, $i = (100e^{-3t} \sin \sqrt{91}t)/\sqrt{91}$
    (b) $q = (-\cos 20t)/2 + e^{-5t}(\sqrt{15} \cos 5\sqrt{15}t + \sin 5\sqrt{15}t)/(2\sqrt{15})$,
        $i = 10 \sin 20t - (8\sqrt{15} \sin 5\sqrt{15}t)/3$
    (c) $q = (\sqrt{621} \sin 25t - 25e^{-2t} \sin \sqrt{621}t)/(2\sqrt{621})$,
        $i = [25\sqrt{621} \cos 25t - e^{-2t}(25\sqrt{621} \cos \sqrt{621}\, t + 50 \sin \sqrt{621}t)]/(2\sqrt{621})$
17. $q = q_0 e^{-Rt/(2L)}[R^2 + 4\omega^2 L^2]^{1/2} \sin (\omega t + \phi)/(2\omega L)$,
    $i = -q_0(R^2 + 4\omega^2 L^2)e^{-Rt/(2L)} \sin \omega t/(4\omega L^2)$,
    where $\omega = [L^{-1}C^{-1} - R^2/(4L^2)]^{1/2}$; $\phi = \text{Tan}^{-1} (2\omega LR^{-1})$
19. (a) $\pi\sqrt{6}/12$ sec (b) $\pi\sqrt{6}/6$ sec

Index

QA303 .T54   CU-Main
c.1
Tierney, John A., 1/Calculus and analytic geometry

3 9371 00021 4940